REVIEWS IN
ECONOMIC GEOLOGY
(ISSN 0741-0123) Volume 10

TECHNIQUES IN HYDROTHERMAL ORE DEPOSITS GEOLOGY

ISBN 1-887483-54-3

Volume Editors

JEREMY P. RICHARDS
Department of Earth and Atmospheric Sciences
University of Alberta
Edmonton, Alberta, Canada T6G 2E3

PETER B. LARSON
Department of Geology
Washington State University
Pullman, Washington 99164

SOCIETY OF ECONOMIC GEOLOGISTS, INC.

The Authors:

Greg M. Anderson
Department of Geology
University of Toronto
22 Russell Street
Toronto, Ontario M5S 3B1
Canada
Tel.+1.416.978.4852
Fax: +1.416.978.3938
email:
greg@quartz.geology.utoronto.ca

Philip E. Brown
Department of Geology & Geophysics
Univ. of Wisconsin-Madison
1215 W. Dayton
Madison, Wisconsin 53706
USA
Tel. +1.608.262.5954
Fax: +1.608.262.0693
email: pbrown@geology.wisc.edu

Philip A. Candela
Department of Geology
University of Maryland
College Park, Maryland 20742
USA
Tel. +1.301.405.2783
Fax: +1.301.314.9661
email: candela@geol.umd.edu

Andrew R. Campbell
Department of Earth &
Environmental Sciences
New Mexico Tech
Socorro, New Mexico 87801
USA
Tel. +1.505.835.5327
Fax: +1.505.835.6436
email: campbell@mailhost.nmt.edu

Jeffrey W. Hedenquist
Mineral Resources Department
Geological Survey of Japan
1-1-3 Higashi, Tsukuba 305
Japan
Tel. +011.81.298.54.3649
Fax: +011.81.298.54.3633
email: jeffrey@gsj.go.jp

Peter B. Larson
Department of Geology
Washington State University
Pullman, Washington 99164-2812
USA
Tel. +1.509.335.3095
Fax: +1.509.335.7816
email: plarson@wsu.edu

Steve R. Noble
NIGL
Kingsley Dunham Centre
Keyworth, Nottingham NG12 5GG
United Kingdom
Tel.+011.5.936.3555
Fax: +011.5.936.3302
email: SRN@wpo.nerc.ac.uk

Philip Piccoli
Department of Geology
University of Maryland
College Park, Maryland 20742-4211
USA
Tel. +1.301.405.6966
Fax: +1.301.314.9661
email: piccoli@geol.umd.edu

Andrew H. Rankin
School of Geological Sciences
Kingston University
Penrhyn Road
Kingston Upon Thames,
Surrey KT1 2E
United Kingdom
Tel. +011.0181.547.7245
Fax: +011.0181.547.7419
email: a.rankin@kingston.ac.uk

Mark H. Reed
Department of Geological Sciences
Unversity of Oregon
Eugene, Oregon 97403-1272
USA
Tel: +1.541.346.5587
Fax: +1.541.346.4692
email: mhreed@oregon.uoregon.edu

Jeremy P. Richards
Department of Earth &
Atmospheric Sciences
University of Alberta
Edmonton, Alberta T6G 2E3
Canada
Tel: +1.403.492.3430
Fax: +1.403.492.2030
email: Jeremy.Richards@ualberta.ca

Iain M. Samson
Earth Sciences
University of Windsor
Windsor, Ontario N9B 3P4
Canada
Tel. +1.519.253.4232
Fax: +1.519.973.7081
email: ims@uwindsor.ca

Tom J. Shepherd
British Geological Survey
Keyworth, Nottingham NG12 5GG
United Kingdom
Tel. +011.5.936.3100
Fax: +011.5.936.3302
email: TJS@wpo.nerc.ac.uk

Scott A. Wood
Department of Geology &
Geological Engineering
University of Idaho
Moscow, Idaho 83844-3022
USA
Tel.+1.208.885.5966
Fax: +1.208.885.5724
email: swood@uidaho.edu

PREFACE

One of the best things about being an "economic geologist" is the fact that the term almost defies definition. The only requirements are that one should be a geologist (preferably a good one!), and have an interest in the economic applications of that science to the minerals industry. Consequently, we can be mineralogists, geochemists, geophysicists, exploration geologists, mine geologists, paleontologists, geochronologists, geomorphologists, sedimentologists, structural geologists—the list could go on, but we are all unified by that interest in mineral deposits. To be fully conversant with this broad science, however, it is not sufficient for us to operate exclusively within our own specialization: the isotope geochemist cannot afford to ignore the paragenetic information available from petrography and mineralogy; the fluid inclusionist can eke far more information out of microthermometric or analytical data by fitting them to thermodynamic models. This requirement can be both a blessing and a curse, however. On the one hand, it encourages us to be geologists in the broadest sense, with a full appreciation of the mechanics of our planet and how they affect ore formation. On the other hand, we cannot possibly hope to be experts in all of these fields in the space of one lifetime.

The solution, therefore, must be interdisciplinary collaboration, combined with more effective communication, so that, although we may not become experts, we at least have a working knowledge of the full range of disciplines at our disposal.

The impetus for this volume arises from the editors' own feelings of inadequacy when confronted with certain aspects of our science, and also our experiences in trying to communicate this subject to our students and colleagues. We all know that the easiest lectures to give are those based on our own specializations and research; however, these are not necessarily the easiest lectures to give *well*, particularly if the target audience is non-expert in our field. Likewise in our writings: as professionals we are expected to write succinct papers focusing solely on our new results and interpretations, with no room for background explanations, and lots of unspoken pressure to impress our peers. However, such writings are opaque to a broader readership, and do little to help expose our science to other scientists, let alone the general public.

In an attempt to address these problems, at least within the broader circle of economic geologists, we have sought contributions from user-friendly expert authors on specific aspects of geochemical data collection and modeling as applied to hydrothermal ore deposits. Our intention was not to compete with Hubert Barnes' milestone volumes (Geochemistry of Hydrothermal Ore Deposits). Rather, we wished to insert a stepping stone in front of these volumes, to enable a wider audience to access and appreciate their wealth of information. Thus, our target audience is very broad, and includes everyone from final-year undergraduate students to industry geologists and academics with specializations in other fields.

Each chapter is self-contained, but the reader may find that he or she needs to read an earlier chapter to brush up on some background theory. However, a specialist's knowledge is not required at any point. The chapters aim to provide the basic principles of the topic, and then to explore the practical applications of the techniques in the study of ore deposits. The volume is thus both a reference book and a handbook, with practical information ranging from the construction and interpretation of commonly used geochemical diagrams, to the size and type of samples required for geochronological analyses.

The volume editors would like to thank all of the authors for their efforts in taming their science, the reviewers for providing an excellent test of our successes and failures and thereby significantly improving the volume, and Mike Lesher, who as former Series Editor provided the lift and encouragement required to turn an idea into a reality.

Finally, we remember and thank Werner Giggenbach, who was preparing a manuscript for this volume at the time of his death in November 1997.

Jeremy P. Richards
Peter B. Larson

LIST OF REVIEWERS

Antonio Arribas, Jr.
Mark D. Barton
William L. Bourcier
Douglas E. Crowe
John H. Dilles
Christopher H. Gammons
Thomas H. Giordano
Larry M. Heaman
Gaham D. Layne
Jacob B. Lowenstern
Jon A. Naden
David I. Norman
David A. Polya
W. Ian Ridley
Edward M. Ripley
Edward T.C. Spooner
Holly J. Stein
James A. Whitney
Anthony E. Williams-Jones
Thomas J. Wolery

BIOGRAPHIES

GREG M. ANDERSON began his career as a mining engineer and exploration geologist before he discovered the joy of geochemistry. After completing his Ph.D. at Toronto with F.G. Smith, he spent five years at Pennsylvania State University in Wayne Burnham's lab, doing experimental work on mineral solubilities. Afterward he returned to Toronto, where he has divided his time between studies of mineral solubilities, MVT deposits, and theoretical geochemistry. He is the author of two textbooks on thermodynamics — Thermodynamics in Geochemistry, with D.A. Crerar (Oxford), and Thermodynamics of Natural Systems (Wiley).

PHILIP E. BROWN received a B.A. degree in geology from Carleton College in 1974, and M.S. (1976) and Ph.D. (1980) degrees from the University of Michigan, where he specialized in economic geology, in general, and the Pine Creek, California, tungsten skarn, in particular. After a one-year post-doctoral appointment at the U.S. Geological Survey in Reston, Virginia, he accepted a position at the University of Wisconsin-Madison in 1981 and has been there since. His research interests center around fluids in the Earth's crust and Archean gold deposits, metamorphic and metamorphosed orebodies, fluid inclusions, skarns and the Proterozoic massive sulfide deposits of Wisconsin. A six-month sabbatical in Western Australia in 1991 began a collaborative research program with the then 'Key Centre' at the University of Western Australia — this continues today, with Dr. Brown holding an Adjunct Faculty position in Perth. Recently his interests include exploring the role that computer visualization technology can play in geological education.

ANDREW R. CAMPBELL received a B.S. in geology from Indiana University in 1977 and a Ph.D. in geology from Harvard University in 1983. Since then, he has been teaching at New Mexico Tech in Socorro, N.M., where he is currently Professor of Geology. He has served the Society as an Associate Editor for Economic Geology and as Editor of the Newsletter. Dr. Campbell's research interests include fluid inclusion and stable isotope studies of ore deposits as well as application of stable isotope geochemistry to other topics. He pioneered the use of infrared microscopy to study fluid inclusions in opaque ore minerals.

PHILIP A. CANDELA received his Ph.D. from Harvard University in 1982. Since then he has been at the University of Maryland, where he is now Professor of Geology and co-director of the Laboratory for Mineral Deposits Research. He has also been a Visiting Fellow at the Department of Geology at the Australian National University, and is a Fellow of the Geological Society of America, the Mineralogical Society of America, and the Society of Economic Geologists. His research involves: the study of element partitioning in melt-vapor-brine-crystal systems, with special reference to the behavior of ore metals, including Au and Cu; field and theoretical studies of the mass transfer dynamics in devolatilizing magma chambers; textural studies in igneous rocks; experimental studies of wall-rock alteration in ore deposits and geothermal systems; experimental studies of sulfides in magmatic-hydrothermal environments; and ore deposits and tectonics of the Appalachian Orogen. At the University of Maryland, he teaches graduate level classes in thermodynamics, advanced economic geology, and igneous petrology; he is also the director the undergraduate senior thesis program in Geology.

JEFFREY W. HEDENQUIST is a geologist with the Geological Survey of Japan, in the Department of Mineral and Fuel Resources. He began graduate studies on an Archean gold deposit, and at the same time worked for the U.S. Geological Survey on coastal sedimentology, granites, and lunar petrology. He completed his graduate study on gold mineralization of an active geothermal system while at the University of Auckland, New Zealand, on a Fulbright fellowship. He joined Chemistry Division, DSIR New Zealand, in 1982, and while based at Wairakei was involved in geothermal energy development and epithermal gold exploration in the western Pacific. He moved to Japan in 1989 to expand his epithermal research to the porphyry environment, and also to study metals in volcanic discharges.

PETER B. LARSON is Chair of the Geology Department at Washington State University, where he has served on the faculty since earning his Ph.D. from Caltech in 1983. His primary research interests are water-rock interaction in hydrothermal environments, and igneous petrogenesis, to which he applies stable isotope analyses. He was born and raised in the midst of the Michigan native copper district, and received his B.Sc. in geology from Michigan Tech in 1973.

STEPHEN R. NOBLE received a B.Sc. (geological engineering) in 1980 and an M.Sc. (geology) in 1992 from the University of Toronto. During this time he was involved in research associated with porphyry Mo-W and related skarn deposits in the Yukon and Northwest Territories. Noble received a Ph.D. in geochemistry in 1989 from the University of Toronto, where his work involved investigating the U-Pb geochronology, and geochemical and Sm-Nd isotope characteristics of Archean granite-greenstone terranes in northwest Ontario. Since then he has been a research geologist, responsible for establishing the U-Pb geochronology laboratory at the Natural Environment Research Council Isotope Geosciences Laboratory, now part of the British Geological Survey. Current research focuses on high precision U-Pb geochronology in the Himalayas and Scottish Highlands, Lu-Hf isotope systematics, and the development of ICP-MS and laser ablation geochronology techniques.

PHILIP M. PICCOLI is a Research Scientist at the Laboratory for Mineral Deposits Research, University of Maryland. His interests include field studies of silicic volcanic and plutonic rocks; the use of accessory phases in the determination of magmatic, hydrothermal, and ore-forming processes; chemical modeling of ore-forming processes; microanalysis of minerals; and experimental simulation of magmatic-ore systems involving Au, Cu, etc. Piccoli employs a multidimensional approach involving field observations, modeling, and experimentation to solve problems in ore-genesis.

ANDY H. RANKIN received his B.Sc. in chemistry and his Ph.D. in geology from the University of Leicester, UK. Prior to his current appointment in 1991 as Professor of Applied Geology and Head of the School of Geological Sciences at Kingston University, UK, he held various faculty positions in the Royal School of Mines, Imperial College, London, over the period 1974-1991, first as lecturer in Mining Geology, then as Reader in Applied Mineralogy and Head of the Fluid Process Research Group. His main research interests are in hydrothermal and magmatic processes in ore genesis and in the development and application of fluid inclusion methods to a range of problems in the Geosciences. He has published widely on these topics and has organized and participated in a number of successful short courses in fluid inclusion in the UK, USA, and South America. Until recently he was president of the Mineralogical Society of Great Britain and Ireland.

MARK H. REED received B.A. degrees in chemistry and geology from Carleton College in 1971, followed by an M.S. in 1974 and a Ph.D. in 1977 from University of California, Berkeley. His Ph.D. research focused on the origin of massive sulfide mineralization in seafloor settings, for which studies he developed original forms of two computer programs for multicomponent, multiphase chemical equilibrium calculations. Reed worked as a staff geologist and project geologist for the Anaconda Company in Butte, Montana, from 1977 through 1979. During that period, he mapped underground exploration crosscuts and underground and surface drill core, focusing on describing the hydrothermal alteration and mineralization in the large porphyry copper-molybdenum system at Butte. From 1980 to the present, Reed has been on the faculty of the Department of Geological Sciences, University of Oregon, specializing in studies of ore deposits and in modeling geochemical processes in geothermal systems, hydrothermal ore systems, volcanic gas fumaroles, and sediment diagenesis.

JEREMY P. RICHARDS received his B.A. (1983) in geology from the University of Cambridge, UK, his M.Sc. (1986) in economic geology from the University of Toronto, Canada, and a Ph.D. (1990) in economic geology from the Australian National University. After a two-year post-doctoral position at the University of Saskatchewan, Canada, he joined the faculty at the University of Leicester, UK, in 1992. He has since recently moved back to Canada, where he is currently an Associate Professor in economic geology at the University of Alberta. His research focuses on the genesis of hydrothermal ore deposits, and previous and ongoing investigations include studies of the Keweenawan basalt-hosted copper deposits in Michigan and Ontario, sediment-hosted stratiform copper deposits in the Democratic Republic of Congo (formerly Zaère), porphyry copper deposits in Chile and Ecuador, and alkalic intrusive-related gold deposits in Papua New Guinea.

IAIN M. SAMSON received a B.Sc. in applied geology in 1979 and Ph.D. in economic geology in 1983 from the University of Strathclyde. From 1983 until 1986 he was a Research Associate with the Mineral Exploration Research Institute (IREM-MERI) at McGill University. In 1986 he joined the faculty of the University of Windsor where he is currently an Associate Professor in the Department of Earth Sciences. His research interests are in the genesis of hydrothermal mineral deposits and the geochemistry of hydrothermal systems. He has published papers on a variety of types of mineral deposits, including SEDEX Pb-Zn, granite-related W, Mo, Sn, and Cu deposits and Precambrian Au-Ag deposits. His current research is focused on the genesis of REE and other rare-element deposits, particularly those associated with alkalic igneous rocks, and on the microbeam analysis of fluid inclusions.

TOM J. SHEPHERD received his B.Sc. and Ph.D. in geology from the University of Durham, UK. Following a two-year period as an exploration geologist working from Cominco's European office he joined the Geochemical Division of the British Geological Survey (Institute of Geological Sciences), where his initial brief was to develop methods for fluid inclusion analysis. He has maintained his current interest in the development and application of fluid inclusion methods, especially in relation to mineral and petroleum exploration and ore genesis, since joining the survey in 1971. He currently holds a Cabinet Office Individual Merit Position at the BGS, Nottingham, UK, which permits him to further develop his research interests in these fields. He has published widely in these and related fields, including a textbook on fluid inclusions, coauthored with Andy Rankin and Dave Alderton.

SCOTT A. WOOD received a B.A. degree in both geology and chemistry from Hamilton College in Clinton, New York, in May 1980. He then went on to obtain an M.A. (1982) and a Ph.D. (1985) in Geochemistry from Princeton University under the supervision of Dr. David Crerar. From January 1985 until December 1991 he was first an Assistant and then Associate Professor at McGill University in Montreal. Since then he has been at the University of Idaho where he is currently Professor of Geochemistry. Starting with his Ph.D., he has been involved in experimental and theoretical research into the solubility of ore minerals and the speciation of ore metals in hydrothermal solutions, and has had particular interests in the platinum-group elements, the rare earth elements, tungsten, gold, beryllium, and zirconium. He has also been involved in field-based geochemical studies of the origin of ore deposits, including hydrothermal REE, epithermal Ag-Au and porphyry Cu mineralization. In recent years he has devoted a significant proportion of his research effort to environmental geochemistry. Since 1989, Dr. Wood has been an Associate Editor of the journal Geochimica et Cosmochimica Acta.

CONTENTS

Chapter 9—Application of Radiogenic Isotope Systems to the Timing and Origin of Hydrothermal Processes

Chapter 10—The Influence of Geochemical Techniques on the Development of Genetic Models for Porphyry Copper Deposits

Chapter 1

The Thermodynamics of Hydrothermal Systems

G.M. Anderson

Department of Geology, University of Toronto, Toronto, Ontario, Canada M5S 3B1

The basic problem of thermodynamics is the determination of the equilibrium state that eventually results after the removal of internal constraints in a closed composite system.

Callen (1960), p. 24.

Introduction

Anyone studying an ore deposit winds up with a lot of data: field observations in the form of maps, sections and drill logs, chemical analyses, isotope analyses, fluid inclusion data, paragenetic relations, and so on. In addition, there is a vast amount experimental data in the literature on systems relevant to the deposit being studied, in the form of data on the chemical and physical properties of solids and fluids. The investigator then tries to come up with a model of ore formation that is consistent with all these data. Naturally, the model must also be consistent with accepted principles of chemistry and physics, and one of the subjects most useful, in fact essential, in assembling all these data into consistent models is thermodynamics.

The purpose of this chapter is to introduce the concepts and terms of chemical thermodynamics that are useful in constructing models of hydrothermal systems. These will be used extensively in the chapters to follow. The concepts covered in this chapter normally occupy a complete book; the coverage is therefore necessarily brief. We can save considerable space, for example, by assuming that we are all familiar with the concepts of energy, work, heat, and temperature. These are in fact quite difficult subjects, but an intuitive understanding is usually sufficient for us.

Some Basic Definitions

In this chapter we will not describe any natural system, and only one model of a simple natural system (H_2–N_2). Most of the discussion will be about a model of energy relationships, called thermodynamics. Although natural systems and thermodynamic models of natural systems are described using many of the same terms, there are some subtle differences. To begin with, a *natural system* is any part of the universe we choose to consider, such as the contents of a beaker, a crystal of quartz, the solar system, or a bacterium. *Thermodynamic systems*, on the other hand, are not real but conceptual and mathematical, and are of three types. The three types are used to distinguish between the ways that changes in composition and energy content can be effected, and therefore they are defined basically by the nature of their boundaries.

Thermodynamic Systems

Isolated systems can exchange neither matter nor energy with their surroundings. They are therefore described as having walls that are rigid (preventing any change in volume and hence any energy change due to work), and impermeable to matter and energy. No such systems exist in nature, of course, emphasizing the difference between thermodynamic and natural systems. Nevertheless, isolated systems are a vital part of thermodynamic theory, as we will see.

Closed systems can exchange energy but not matter with their surroundings. They are therefore described as having walls that can be deformed, permitting transfer of mechanical energy, and that can conduct heat, permitting transfer of thermal energy. They are, however, impermeable to matter. Both isolated and closed systems have constant compositions.

Open systems can exchange both energy and matter with their surroundings. They can therefore change composition, as well as energy content.

In practice, isolated systems are used only in the development of the thermodynamic model. Both closed and open systems are also used in models of natural systems.

Equilibrium, Constraints, and State Variables

A system is said to be at *equilibrium* when none of its properties is changing. However, we know that many systems can reach more than one state of equilibrium under identical conditions: for example, a system composed of pure $CaCO_3$ can exist at equilibrium as either calcite or aragonite. These different equilibrium states have different energy contents (excluding those in isolated systems), and those having higher energy contents are *constrained* from spontaneously proceeding to a lower energy state. Equilibrium states can in fact be characterized by their number of *constraints,* defined as state variables associated with the ways a closed system can change its energy content. The minimum number of constraints required to define an equilibrium state is two [e.g., temperature (T) and pressure (P)]. Equilibrium states having only two constraints have the lowest energy for given conditions and are *stable* equilibrium states. Equilibrium states having more than two constraints are *metastable* equilibrium states. Calcite, for example, has stable equilibrium states at chosen values of T and P within certain ranges. These are the two constraints. At these T and P values, aragonite has a third constraint, an energy barrier, which prevents it from recrystallizing to calcite. A system consisting of a beaker of water and a gram of solid salt also has three constraints—T, P, and the separation of water and salt. When the third constraint is released by adding the salt to the water, the system reaches stable equilibrium as a salt solution with only two constraints. Whatever the nature of the third (or higher) constraint, the state variable used to describe it is the *progress variable* (later in this chapter). The nature of constraints and their relationship to other terms such as *degrees of freedom* will be discussed in more detail in this chapter.

Many definitions of the term metastable include cases in which systems are changing, but imperceptibly slowly. It is indeed difficult to distinguish slowly changing unstable states from metastable equilibrium states. However, these definitions and difficulties always refer to real systems; in our model systems, we have complete control over our variables, and there is no need for such confusion. If we model a natural system that is unstable as being in a metastable equilibrium state, we are in error, but it is only one of many possible errors we might make, and probably not one of the more serious ones.

Systems, when at equilibrium, have many different measurable properties (volume, density, refractive indices, etc.). Most of these properties depend on what equilibrium state the system is in, and not on how the system achieved that state (i.e., its previous history). These properties are therefore called *state variables.* Those whose values depend on the mass of the system (e.g., total volume, total energy content) are called *extensive* properties or variables; those that are independent of the mass of system considered (e.g., density, all molar properties) are called *intensive* properties or variables.

Local Equilibrium

The application of thermodynamics to natural systems presents us with a fundamental paradox, and that is that thermodynamics applies *only* to equilibrium states, whereas natural systems are usually not (and in the strictest sense, never) in equilibrium. Given the T, P, and composition of a natural system, even one far from equilibrium, thermodynamics can in principle tell us what the equilibrium state of the system is—the phases that should exist, and their compositions, and this is very useful. But often we want to know more. For example, we want to know what will happen to that system if we change the conditions. At what point will it boil, and what will be the composition of the gas phase, and what will that gas phase do if it cools down, and so on. Thermodynamics will be completely useless if all these things happen far from equilibrium.

The natural systems of interest to geologists (magmatic-hydrothermal systems, sedimentaty basins, etc.) are generally large, and have gradients in temperature, and/or pressure, and/or composition. They are in states of flux, and are not in overall equilibrium. The only way that thermodynamics can be useful in such cases is if these large systems have volumes within them (sub-systems) that are at or are close to equilibrium. These sub-systems are called areas of *local equilibrium.* Thermodynamics can be applied to each of these smaller areas, and hence to the whole system, assuming that it does have these states of local equilibrium. In studies of geological systems, the assumption of local equilibrium may or may not be referred to, but it is always implicit.

It is difficult to determine whether a given natural system has areas of local equilibrium, and if so, what their dimensions are. This is an important question, because it determines, or should determine, the size of the finite element or finite difference grids used to model fluid or heat flow processes. It involves quite a number of factors, many of which are poorly known, such as rate constants and reactive surface areas. Knapp (1989) discusses this problem in the context of fluid flow problems, and shows that at elevated temperatures the assumption of local equilibrium is generally speaking quite reasonable.

Processes

In geological systems, we are interested in many kinds of processes—igneous, metamorphic, diagenetic, ore-forming, and so on. In thermodynamic systems, a process is what happens between equilibrium states, and there are only two kinds of such processes that are of any great interest:

Irreversible processes are themselves of two types. Those of greatest interest are those that occur when a constraint on a metastable state is released, allowing it to proceed toward a more stable state (this is the process referred to in the Callen quotation at the beginning of this chapter). Aragonite recrystallizing to calcite within the stability field of calcite is an example, as is salt dissolving in water, or in fact, any chemical reaction proceeding from reactants to products. Because the metastable state has more energy than the stable state (again excluding isolated systems), this change occurs *spontaneously,* by dissipating energy (doing work). Therefore, another term for irreversible processes of this type is *spontaneous process.* The reverse process, from stable to metastable, can never occur spontaneously, but can be made to occur by adding energy to the system without changing the two constraints that define the stable system, just as a ball can be made to roll uphill by pushing it. In nature this actually happens in some cases, such as photosynthesis, where the added energy is supplied by sunlight.

Irreversible processes can also occur in systems initially at stable equilibrium when one or both of the two constraints defining the system are changed. This happens, for example, when a gas at P_1, V_1 expands to P_2, V_2 by a sudden decrease in the system pressure, or when a calcite crystal is heated suddenly from T_1 to T_2.

Reversible processes are those in which a system in a state of equilibrium (either stable or metastable) changes to another equilibrium state, *without ever becoming out of equilibrium.* Constraints are not released but changed infinitesimally, and third or higher constraints are not released at all (release of a third constraint always results in an irreversible process). For example, calcite or aragonite could be heated from T_1 to T_2 infinitely slowly, without ever having internal temperature gradients. This cannot happen in natural systems, but is quite simple in our thermodynamic model systems, because temperature, volume, and all other properties of the system are just points on mathematical surfaces in the model, and there is nothing to prevent the point representing the temperature, for example, from moving around on a surface representing the equilibrium values of various properties of the system. Reversible processes are therefore often used to *calculate* property differences between equilibrium states, no matter what the system actually does between these states.

Conventions

Delta notation. The Δ symbol refers to a finite change in some property, by convention the final state minus the initial state, or in the case of a chemical reaction, products minus reactants. For example, ΔZ means $Z_{final} - Z_{initial}$, or $\sum Z_{products} - \sum Z_{reactants}$, where Z is some property, as explained below.

Total and molar quantities. We will use Roman letters for *total* (or extensive) properties (e.g., total energy, U; total volume, V), and Italic letters for *molar* (or intensive) properties (e.g., molar energy, U; molar volume, V). Molar quantities are simply the total quantities divided by the number of moles involved. A few terms such as pressure (P) and temperature (T) do not have the total vs. molar distinction, and are denoted by Italic symbols. In engineering thermodynamics, *specific* properties (the property per gram, rather than per mole) are commonly used, but we have no special symbol for these quantities.

The sign of energy changes. Energy added to systems, in whatever form, will be considered a positive quantity. Energy subtracted from systems, or expended by systems, will be considered a negative quantity. The most noticeable result of this convention is that work terms tend to have a negative sign.

The Three Laws of Thermodynamics

Thermodynamics is quite elegant, in the sense that a large number of useful relationships spring from a very small number of basic principles, called the Laws of Thermodynamics. In most treatments there are actually four Laws, but we have passed over one already by assuming we understand the concepts of heat and temperature.

The First Law

The First Law of thermodynamics is basically the Law of Conservation of Energy. Therefore, having defined a system, and taking into account our convention about the sign of energy changes, it follows from the Law of Energy Conservation that the algebraic sum of energy added to and subtracted from the system must equal the change in the energy content of the system. Apart from radiation, there are only two ways of transferring energy to a closed system—heat and work. So, if the total energy content of a closed system is U, a quantity of heat energy is q, and a quantity of work energy is w (both of which may be positive or negative quantities), the First Law is therefore expressed as

$$\Delta \mathrm{U} = q + w \tag{1.1}$$

Note that we have defined only the energy *change* of the system, not the energy itself. Further development of the subject depends on introducing ways of defining the heat and work terms. However, there are many kinds of work. Development of the theory is greatly simplified by considering only one kind of work (pressure-volume work) to start with, and later, to introduce other kinds of work (work associated with magnetic fields, surface tension, electrochemical cells, and so on) as they are required. In the majority of cases in geochemical modeling, they are not required at all except in the form of *constraints*, to be discussed later.

Any time a system changes volume, work is done, except in the special case of a system enclosed by a vacuum. To calculate this work, we must know the pressure acting on the system, P_{ext}, and how it varies during the process considered. If pressure-volume work is the only kind considered, then

$$-w \leq \int_{\mathrm{V}_1}^{\mathrm{V}_2} P_{ext}\, d\mathrm{V} \tag{1.2}$$

where the minus sign is made necessary by our conventions. The minimum amount of work for an expansion from V_1 to V_2 is zero (when $P_{ext} = 0$), and the maximum is obtained when the system pressure (P) is never more than infinitesimally different from the external pressure (a reversible process), in which case we need make no distinction between the system pressure and the external pressure, and the work equation becomes

$$-w_{max} = -w_{rev} = \int_{\mathrm{V}_1}^{\mathrm{V}_2} P\, d\mathrm{V} \tag{1.3}$$

where P is the equilibrium system pressure. In the special case of a reversible, constant pressure process, integration of (1.3) gives

$$-w_{rev} = P\,\Delta\mathrm{V} \tag{1.4}$$

Enthalpy: For isobaric processes, not necessarily reversible, P_{ext} is a fixed quantity. Integration of equation (1.2) with P_{ext} constant gives

$$\begin{aligned} -w &= P_{ext}(\mathrm{V}_2 - \mathrm{V}_1) \\ &= P_{ext}\Delta\mathrm{V} \end{aligned} \tag{1.5}$$

Combining this with equation (1.1) gives

$$\begin{aligned} \Delta\mathrm{U} &= q_P - P_{ext}\Delta\mathrm{V} \\ \mathrm{U}_2 - \mathrm{U}_1 &= q_P - P_{ext}(\mathrm{V}_2 - \mathrm{V}_1) \\ q_P &= (\mathrm{U}_2 + P_{ext}\mathrm{V}_2) - (\mathrm{U}_1 + P_{ext}\mathrm{V}_1) \end{aligned} \tag{1.6}$$

where q_P is the heat transferred in any isobaric process. It involves only a constant (P_{ext}) and state variables (U and V), and so q_P depends only on the equilibrium states 1 and 2, and not on the nature of the process between them. If we define a new variable, enthalpy, H, as

$$\mathrm{H} = \mathrm{U} + P\mathrm{V} \tag{1.7}$$

it is evident from (1.6) that

$$\begin{aligned} q_P &= \mathrm{H}_2 - \mathrm{H}_1 \\ &= \Delta\mathrm{H} \end{aligned} \tag{1.8}$$

The derivation could just as easily be carried out using the molar internal energy and molar volume, U and V, leading to the molar enthalpy, H, and the change in molar enthalpy, ΔH.

Being a state variable, enthalpy is a well-defined quantity between any two equilibrium states. It is when those two states are at the same pressure that it is most useful, though, because then it is equal to the heat exchanged in the process involved in changing from one state to the other. If the process is a chemical reaction, it is called the *heat of reaction.* We have said nothing about the temperature of the two states, but most commonly it is the same in both states as well.

Enthalpy of formation from the elements: A major problem arises from the definition of enthalpy, equation (1.7). The problem is that we cannot measure it. This arises from the nature of energy itself, because we can only measure energy changes, not absolute energies. Therefore we can only measure enthalpy changes, and changes in any other property that includes the energy U (or U).

The problem this creates is that we do not want to have to tabulate an enthalpy change for every process or chemical reaction that might become of interest to us—there are too many. We would like to be able to associate an enthalpy with every substance—solids, liquids, gases, and solutes—for some standard conditions, so that having tabulated these, we could then easily calculate an enthalpy change between any such substances under those standard conditions. After that, we could deal with the changes introduced by impurities and other non-standard conditions. The method developed to allow this is to determine, for every pure compound, the difference between the enthalpy of the compound and the sum of the enthalpies of the elements, each in its most stable state, that make up the compound. This quantity is called $\Delta_f H^\circ$, the standard molar enthalpy of formation from the elements. For aqueous ions, the quantity determined is a little more complicated (later in this chapter), but the principle is the same.

For example, the standard enthalpy of formation of anhydrite is

$$\Delta_f H^\circ_{\mathrm{CaSO_4}(s)} = H^\circ_{\mathrm{CaSO_4}(s)} - H^\circ_{\mathrm{Ca}(s)} - H^\circ_{\mathrm{S}(s)} - 2\,H^\circ_{\mathrm{O_2}(g)} \quad (1.9)$$

where the superscript $^\circ$ refers to the standard conditions (see below). None of the individual H° quantities is determinable, but the difference is determinable by calorimetry. Now if we want to know the heat liberated or absorbed in a chemical reaction, we need only look up these $\Delta_f H^\circ$, values for each reactant and product. For example, for the formation of gypsum from anhydrite, we write

$$\mathrm{CaSO_4}(s) + 2\,\mathrm{H_2O}(l) = \mathrm{CaSO_4} \cdot 2\,\mathrm{H_2O}(s) \quad (1.10)$$

for which the "standard molar heat of reaction," $\Delta_r H^\circ$, is

$$\Delta_r H^\circ = \Delta_f H^\circ_{\mathrm{CaSO_4 \cdot 2H_2O}} - \Delta_f H^\circ_{\mathrm{CaSO_4}} - 2\Delta_f H^\circ_{\mathrm{H_2O}(l)} \quad (1.11)$$

$$= H^\circ_{\mathrm{CaSO_4 \cdot 2H_2O}} - H^\circ_{\mathrm{CaSO_4}} - 2\,H^\circ_{\mathrm{H_2O}(l)} \quad (1.12)$$

Note that in balanced reactions the H° terms for all the elements cancel out, and we are left with the "real" enthalpy difference between products and reactants, with no contribution from arbitrary conventions or assumptions. It is, however, a heat of reaction for standard conditions only.

Standard states: It is often assumed that the "standard conditions" are 25°C, 1 bar. Actually, it is a bit more complicated in two respects. First, knowing the T and P of the state is not sufficient—we must also specify the physical state of the substance. For solids and liquids, it is simply the pure substance, but for gases it is the gas acting ideally at one bar (or 10^5 Pa), and for solutes it is the solute acting ideally at a concentration of one molal. The reasons for these choices will be discussed later. Secondly, although the temperature and pressure of the standard conditions are indeed 25°C and one bar for purposes of tabulating data, we can and often do have standard conditions at any T and P. These more complete definitions of our "standard conditions" define our standard states, which will be seen to become particularly useful when we later define the concept of *activity.*

Heat capacity. It takes less heat to raise the temperature of some materials than others. If the heat absorbed is q and the rise in temperature is ΔT, the ratio $q/\Delta T$ is in many cases approximately a constant characteristic of each material, called the *heat capacity.* The heat capacity is itself a function of T, and it can be determined either holding P constant or holding V constant, so the strict definition is

$$\frac{\partial q_P}{\partial T} = C_p \quad (1.13)$$

$$= \left(\frac{\partial H}{\partial T}\right)_P \quad (1.14)$$

and

$$\frac{\partial q_V}{\partial T} = C_v \quad (1.15)$$

$$= \left(\frac{\partial U}{\partial T}\right)_V \quad (1.16)$$

[with V constant, $w = 0$, $\Delta H = \Delta U$, and $(\partial H/\partial T)_V$ becomes the same as $(\partial U/\partial T)_V$]. For a difference between two equilibrium states ΔH or ΔU

$$\left(\frac{\partial \Delta H}{\partial T}\right)_P = \Delta C_p \quad (1.17)$$

and

$$\left(\frac{\partial \Delta U}{\partial T}\right)_V = \Delta C_v \quad (1.18)$$

Both the enthalpy change and the heat capacity are determined by calorimetry.

Temperature dependence of the heat capacity: It is evident from equations (1.14) and (1.17) that to calculate a ΔH

at some elevated temperature, we need to know C_p as a function of temperature. We will soon see that the same statement can be made about many of the major thermodynamic parameters, including entropy and Gibbs energy. Therefore, knowing how C_p for solids, liquids, gases, and solutes varies with T is of fundamental importance. For pure substances (solids, liquids, and gases), this quantity is well understood and measurements are available for most. For aqueous solutes the problem is more difficult and will be described later.

Many different equations have been suggested to represent the variation of C_p with temperature, and several are in current use. No differences in principle are involved, so we will consider only one of these equations. It was suggested by Maier and Kelley (1932), and is used in the program SUPCRT92 (Johnson et al., 1992) (except for a different sign for the c term) for minerals and gases, to be described later. It is

$$C_p = a + bT - cT^{-2} \tag{1.19}$$

Thus to know how C_p for a substance varies with T we need only look up the values of a, b, and c for that substance.

For chemical reactions in which solutes are not involved, the change in each coefficient between products and reactants is evaluated in the usual way. For example, for reaction (1.10),

$$\Delta_r a = a_{CaSO_4 \cdot 2H_2O} - a_{CaSO_4} - 2a_{H_2O(l)}$$
$$\Delta_r b = b_{CaSO_4 \cdot 2H_2O} - b_{CaSO_4} - 2b_{H_2O(l)}$$
$$\Delta_r c = c_{CaSO_4 \cdot 2H_2O} - c_{CaSO_4} - 2c_{H_2O(l)}$$

and so

$$\Delta_r C_p^\circ = \Delta_r a + \Delta_r b\, T - \Delta_r c\, T^{-2} \tag{1.20}$$

Temperature dependence of the enthalpy: Equation (1.17) for our more explicit situation now becomes

$$\left(\frac{\partial \Delta_r H^\circ}{\partial T}\right)_P = \Delta_r C_p^\circ \tag{1.21}$$

which, using (1.20), can now be integrated to give the standard enthalpy of reaction at any elevated temperature T at one bar pressure:

$$\int_{T_r}^{T} d\Delta_r H^\circ = \int_{T_r}^{T} \Delta_r C_p^\circ\, dT$$

$$\Delta_r H_T^\circ - \Delta_r H_{T_r}^\circ = \int_{T_r}^{T} (\Delta_r a + \Delta_r bT - \Delta_r cT^{-2})dT$$

$$= \Delta_r a(T - T_r) + \frac{\Delta_r b}{2}(T^2 - T_r^2) + \Delta_r c\left(\frac{1}{T} - \frac{1}{T_r}\right) \tag{1.22}$$

where $\Delta_r H_T^\circ$ is the standard enthalpy of reaction at temperature T, and $\Delta_r H_{T_r}^\circ$ is the standard enthalpy of reaction at the reference temperature, T_r, normally 298.15 K. This is determined by calorimetry, and is available for most compounds. The effect of pressure on enthalpy will be considered later.

Note that we have not introduced several kinds of enthalpy, we have just made subdivisions of the general concept. Thus ΔH means the difference in H between any two equilibrium states; $\Delta_r H$ means that the two equilibrium states are the products and reactants in a chemical reaction (heat of reaction); $\Delta_r H^\circ$ means that reaction takes place under some defined standard conditions; and $\Delta_f H^\circ$ refers to a specific reaction, in which a compound is formed from its elements.

Entropy (I): Equation (1.3) shows a simple relationship between the work done ($-w$) in reversible processes, and two state variables. One way to introduce the concept of entropy is simply to say that heat (q) has an analogous relationship, which is

$$q_{rev} = \int_{S_1}^{S_2} T\, dS \tag{1.23}$$

where S is a new state variable (entropy). To actually derive this relationship requires consideration of Carnot Cycles, mercifully omitted here. Combining the First Law (1.1), with (1.3) and (1.23) unleashes virtually all the power of chemical thermodynamics.

The Second Law

Equation (1.23) is given only as an analogy. To actually introduce the concept of entropy is the business of the Second Law. The problem addressed by the Second Law is our common experience of irreversibility. Processes that are spontaneous in one direction (perfume evaporating into a room when the bottle is opened) are never observed to proceed spontaneously in the opposite direction (perfume going back into the bottle). The First Law, Newton's Laws of motion, and indeed all of the equations of classical physics say nothing about why this should be so.

The most direct approach to resolving this difficulty is simply to define a quantity (a state variable) that will always increase (or decrease) in spontaneous processes. This is known in mechanics as a *potential quantity*. Potential energy is an example; mechanical systems always adjust themselves so as to lower their potential energy to a minimum. We need a potential quantity for thermodynamic systems (those that can transfer energy by heat as well as by work). We need to define a new state variable (potential quantity; or in thermodynamics a *thermodynamic potential*), and we should define it for processes in which it can operate with no influence from outside energy sources, i.e., when no work or heat is involved. We have defined a type of system, the Isolated System, in which things can happen with no exchange of work or heat, and so we use it here.

Entropy (II): We resolve one of the most profound problems in physics with the following definition, paraphrased after Callen (1960). It is one way of stating the Second Law:

> There exists a state variable, entropy (S), which for isolated systems achieves a maximum when

the system is at stable equilibrium. Entropy is a smoothly varying function of the other state variables and is an increasing function of the internal energy U.

We insert the postulate that entropy increases with U to ensure that other directionality parameters to be derived decrease to a minimum (have minima) rather than increase to a maximum. This is simple to demonstrate, but we will not bother here. We will also not demonstrate that the entropy defined in this way is identical to the entropy in equation (1.23). However, it follows from our definition that S, U, and V are functionally related, and that for spontaneous processes,

$$\Delta S_{U,V} > 0 \tag{1.24}$$

or, switching to molar units, and differential notation,

$$dS_{U,V} > 0 \tag{1.25}$$

and, at equilibrium,

$$dS_{U,V} = 0 \tag{1.26}$$

or in general,

$$dS_{U,V} \geq 0 \tag{1.27}$$

Thermodynamic potentials: S, U, and G. Equation (1.27) is a concise statement of the Second Law. It refers to a functional relationship between *S*, *U*, and *V*. To determine what this function is, we substitute $w_{rev} = -P\Delta V$ [equation (1.4)] and $q_{rev} = T\,\Delta S$ [integration of equation (1.23) at constant *T*] into equation (1.1), giving

$$\Delta U_{T,P} = T\,\Delta S - P\,\Delta V \tag{1.28}$$

This can also be written in differential notation as

$$dU = T\,dS - P\,dV \tag{1.29}$$

which, because of its importance, is called a *Fundamental Equation*. It can also be written using the molar terms *U*, *S*, and *V*.

We should note several things about this equation:

1. Differentials (e.g., *d*U) are not necessarily infinitesimals. Remembering this often helps in visualizing such differential equations. In this case, there is a surface in U–S–V space, representing equilibrium states of some system (Figure 1). At any point on this surface, equation (1.29) represents a tangent plane to the surface if the differential terms are macroscopic. However, to move along the equilibrium surface (to calculate ΔU between *A* and *B*, say), we must allow the differential terms to become infinitesimal, and then integrate.

2. Although we derived this equation for the reversible case (by substituting w_{rev} and q_{rev}), the equation involves only state variables and is not restricted to reversible processes. However, it *is* restricted to processes that do not involve a decrease in the number of constraints on the system. It does not apply to metastable → stable processes [equation (1.36) does].

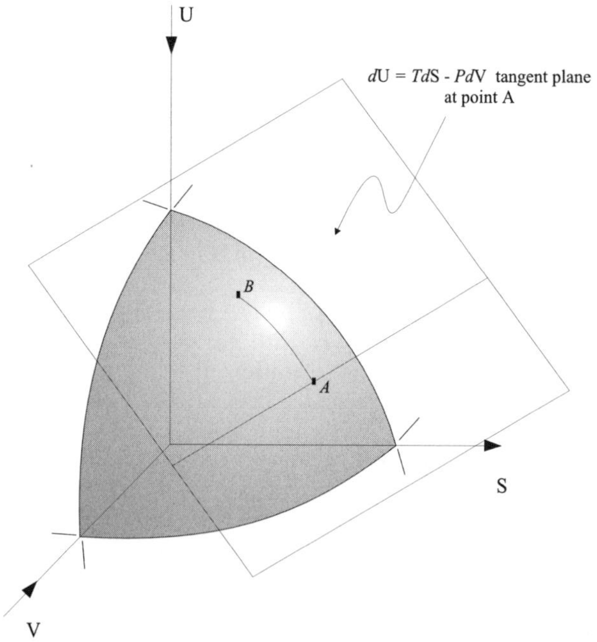

FIG. 1. Equilibrium states of any system can be represented by a surface in U–S–V space. Equation (1.29) can refer to a tangent plane to the surface (if the differentials are macroscopic), or it can be used to calculate ΔU between points on the surface (e.g., A and B) by integration of the equation. Note that for ease of representation, U increases downward in this figure.

3. It is also, of course, restricted to closed (constant composition) systems, because we have not yet considered compositional changes.

Equation (1.29) can also be written in the form of a total differential as

$$dU = \left(\frac{\partial U}{\partial S}\right)_V dS + \left(\frac{\partial U}{\partial V}\right)_S dV \tag{1.30}$$

showing that [comparing with (1.29)]

$$\left(\frac{\partial U}{\partial S}\right)_V = T \tag{1.31}$$

and

$$\left(\frac{\partial U}{\partial V}\right)_S = -P \tag{1.32}$$

which are the slopes of the U–S–V surface in the V and S directions.

The U–S–V surface defined by this equation has an energy U defined for given values of the two constraint variables S and V. It refers to changes in energy between stable equilibrium states of a system (which may take place reversibly or irreversibly). On this surface, $dU_{S,V} = 0$ At given values of S and V, a metastable state of the system will have a greater U than that represented by this surface.

Therefore an irreversible change in U resulting from the release of a third constraint will always be negative, $dU_{S,V}$ <0, or in general, for systems with three constraints,

$$dU = T\,dS - P\,dV + [\textbf{a negative quantity}] \quad (1.33)$$

We can expand the total differential in equation (1.30) to include this "negative quantity" as

$$dU = \left(\frac{\partial U}{\partial S}\right)_{V,\xi} dS + \left(\frac{\partial U}{\partial V}\right)_{S,\xi} dV + \left(\frac{\partial U}{\partial \xi}\right)_{S,V} d\xi \quad (1.34)$$

where we introduce a new state variable, ξ, to represent the third constraint. In real systems ξ might represent degree of disorder, activation energy, or some other property, but in any case, $d\xi$ represents increments in this constraint, as the system *progresses* from its metastable state towards a stable state. ξ is therefore called the *progress variable.* The derivative $-(\partial U/\partial \xi)_{S,V}$ is one definition of the *affinity*, A, so that (1.34) can be written

$$dU = T\,dS - P\,dV - A\,d\xi \quad (1.35)$$

These relationships are illustrated in Figure 2A for the system $CaSO_4-H_2O$, which will be used later as an example of the usefulness of the affinity.

If this third term on the right side is not included, we can only write, for the irreversible process resulting from the release of a third constraint,

$$dU < T\,dS - P\,dV \quad (1.36)$$

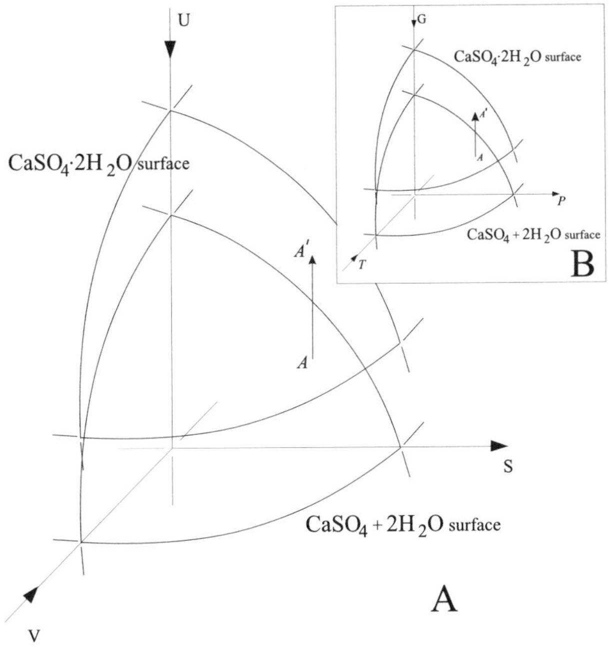

FIG. 2. Two equilibrium states of the system $CaSO_4-H_2O$ in U–S–V space: metastable anhydrite plus water, and stable gypsum. The process $A \rightarrow A'$ is reaction (1.10). Changes in U along either surface can be described by equation (1.29). Changes in U, along either surface, or between the surfaces ($A \rightarrow A'$) is described by equation (1.35). B. Inset: The same system in *G–T–P* space. Note that U and G increase downward.

and, combining (1.36) and (1.29), a general Fundamental Equation for all types of processes is

$$dU \leq T\,dS - P\,dV \quad (1.37)$$

It follows from (1.37) that

$$dU_{S,V} \leq 0 \quad (1.38)$$

which is analogous to (1.27), and shows that the Second Law provides another criterion for spontaneous processes, this time that U is minimized at equilibrium in systems having constant values of S and V. It is another Thermodynamic Potential. More usefully, we can also write, from equation (1.37),

$$dU - T\,dS + P\,dV \leq 0 \quad (1.39)$$

If we define a function

$$G = U - TS + PV \quad (1.40)$$

called the Gibbs Free Energy, the differential of which is

$$dG = dU - T\,dS - S\,dT + P\,dV + V\,dP \quad (1.41)$$

or

$$dG_{T,P} = dU - T\,dS + P\,dV \quad (1.42)$$

we find by comparing (1.42) and (1.39) that

$$dG_{T,P} \leq 0 \quad (1.43)$$

Thus our definition of the Second Law has led to a function, G, that will always decrease to a minimum in spontaneous processes in systems having specified values of T and P. It is an extremely useful Thermodynamic Potential. All we have to do is to find a way to get measurable values of this function for all pure compounds and solutes, and to find how they change with T, P, and concentration, and we will then be able to predict the equilibrium configuration of any system.

But what exactly *is* G? It is not just a useful but abstract concept: ΔG represents the maximum useful work that can be obtained from a process. For example, consider a battery, which does electrical work as reactants change to products in a chemical reaction within the battery. The ΔG between the products and reactants at any moment is the maximum work remaining to be given by the battery. When ΔG the battery is at equilibrium—that is, dead. The analogy with the simple mechanical system of a ball in a valley is fairly close: if the ball is not at the bottom of the (lowest) valley (stable equilibrium), it can do work (ΔG) as it rolls down, or work must be done to push it up. If it is stuck in some valley above the lowest one (metastable equilibrium), a constraint must be released before it can roll down (do work).

To see how G changes with T and P is fairly simple. To see how it changes with composition is a little more difficult. Combining (1.29) and (1.41), we find another Fundamental Equation,

$$dG = -S\,dT + V\,dP \tag{1.44}$$

Because (1.44) could also be written as a total differential, we see from (1.44) that

$$(\partial G/\partial T)_P = -S \tag{1.45}$$

and

$$(\partial G/\partial P)_T = V \tag{1.46}$$

which are the slopes of the G–*T*–*P* surface in the *T* and *P* directions (Figure 2B). We will see how to integrate these expressions shortly.

Combining (1.35) and (1.41), we get

$$dG = -S\,dT + V\,dP - A\,d\xi \tag{1.47}$$

which is analogous to (1.35). We have much more to say about this relationship in this chapter.

Gibbs Energy of formation from the elements: Measuring the Gibbs energy presents a now familiar problem: because it contains the internal energy, *U*, we cannot get values of *G* itself for any substance. We get around this problem just as we did for enthalpy, by finding, for all substances in their standard states, the *difference* between *G* for the substance, and the sum of the *G* values of its constituent elements. Of course, we don't know those either, but we can still determine the difference. For example, for hematite,

$$\Delta_f G^\circ_{Fe_2O_3} = G^\circ_{Fe_2O_3} - 2G^\circ_{Fe} - \tfrac{3}{2}\,G^\circ{}_{O_2(g)} \tag{1.48}$$

where $\Delta_f G^\circ$ can be determined by calorimetry (see below). Then, having determined $\Delta_f G^\circ$ values for all substances of interest, the difference in *G* between any two equilibrium states of the same system (both in their standard states) is determined, as for enthalpy, by calculating the standard molar Gibbs energy of reaction, $\Delta_r G^\circ$. For example, for the formation of hematite from magnetite, we write

$$3\,Fe_2O_3(s) = 2\,Fe_3O_4(s) + \tfrac{1}{2}O_2(g) \tag{1.49}$$

for which

$$\Delta_r G^\circ = 2\,\Delta_f G^\circ_{Fe_3O_4} + \tfrac{1}{2}\Delta_f G^\circ_{O_2} - 3\Delta_f G^\circ_{Fe_2O_3} \tag{1.50}$$

And now we know, thanks to our G minimization principle, that for whatever conditions the superscript $^\circ$ refers to, if $\Delta_r G^\circ$ for (1.50) is negative, then magnetite is more stable than hematite; if it is positive, hematite is more stable. For the standard states mentioned earlier, this means that for pure hematite and magnetite, and pure O_2 gas acting ideally at 1 bar, 25°C, $\Delta_r G^\circ$ in (1.50) is a large positive number, and hematite is stable.

The next question is, how do we measure $\Delta_f G^\circ$ for substances? From equation (1.7), we see that

$$dH = dU + P\,dV + V\,dP \tag{1.51}$$

or

$$dH_P = dU + P\,dV \tag{1.52}$$

Combining this with the intensive form of (1.42) we get

$$dG_{T,P} = dH - T\,dS \tag{1.53}$$

or, integrating between any two equilibrium states,

$$\Delta G_{T,P} = \Delta H - T\,\Delta S \tag{1.54}$$

from which we see that we can calculate ΔG for any process (including formation from the elements) if we know ΔH and ΔS for that process. These quantities can be determined by calorimetry, and therefore ΔG values, including $\Delta_f G^\circ$ values, can be determined by calorimetry. Equation (1.54) also shows that if ΔH and ΔS are assumed to be constants (independent of *T*), then ΔG is a linear function of *T* at a given *P*. We have already seen [equation (1.22)] that ΔH *is* a function of *T*, as is ΔS (next section), but over small temperature ranges the assumption that they are constants is often useful.

In an equilibrium state where $dG_{T,P} = 0$, (1.53) shows that

$$dH = T\,dS \tag{1.55}$$

or

$$d\Delta H = T\,d\Delta S \tag{1.56}$$

and, integrating at constant *T*,

$$\Delta H = T\,\Delta S \tag{1.57}$$

which is particularly useful when the equilibrium state is a two-phase equilibrium, because the enthalpy and entropy of phase transition are then very simply related.

Dependence of S, H, and G on temperature and pressure: Temperature. From (1.55) and (1.14) we see that

$$dS = \frac{dH}{T} = \frac{C_P}{T}dT \tag{1.58}$$

from which

$$S_{T_2} - S_{T_1} = \int_{T_1}^{T_2} \frac{C_P}{T}dT \tag{1.59}$$

or, considering a difference between two equilibrium states,

$$d\Delta S = \frac{d\Delta H}{T} = \frac{\Delta C_P}{T}dT \tag{1.60}$$

$$\Delta S_{T_2} - \Delta S_{T_1} = \int_{T_1}^{T_2} \frac{\Delta C_P}{T}dT \tag{1.61}$$

This is a very general relationship between *S* and *T* at constant *P*. At constant *V*, C_p is replaced by C_v.

In the special case of an ideal gas, a simpler relationship is found. Rearranging equation (1.29), and introducing (1.16) and the ideal gas equation $PV = RT$ (where R is the ideal gas constant, 8.31451JK^{-1}mol^{-1}),

$$\begin{aligned} dS &= dU/T + P\,dV/T \\ &= \frac{C_v\,dT}{T} + \frac{RT\,dV}{V\;T} \\ &= \frac{C_v}{T}dT + R\,d\ln V \end{aligned} \tag{1.62}$$

For a change of an ideal gas from state 1 to state 2 at constant T, this becomes

$$dS = R\,d\ln V$$

$$\Delta S = R\ \ln\frac{V_2}{V_1} \tag{1.63}$$

$$= R\ \ln\frac{P_1}{P_2} \tag{1.64}$$

It appears from (1.59) that to determine the entropy of any substance above the reference temperature 298.15° K (referred to as T_r in the equations below), we need values of C_p over the temperature range of interest. This is exactly what was needed to evaluate high temperature enthalpies. Therefore we can proceed in the same way, substituting our Maier-Kelley heat capacity expression (1.20) into equation (1.60), and integrating from 298.15° K to T. The result is

$$\begin{aligned} \int_{T_r}^{T} d\Delta_r S^\circ &= \int_{T_r}^{T} \frac{\Delta_r C_P^\circ}{T} dT \\ \Delta_r S_T^\circ - \Delta_r S_{T_r}^\circ &= \int_{T_r}^{T} \left(\frac{\Delta_r a}{T} + \Delta_r b - \frac{\Delta_r c}{T^3}\right) dT \\ &= \Delta_r a\ \ln\left(\frac{T}{T_r}\right) + \Delta_r b(T - T_r) \\ &\quad + \frac{\Delta_r c}{2}\left(\frac{1}{T^2} - \frac{1}{T_r^2}\right) \end{aligned} \tag{1.65}$$

The temperature dependence of the enthalpy was discussed previously.

Knowing $\Delta_r S^\circ$ as a function of T [equation(1.65)] means we also know $\Delta_r G^\circ$ as a function of T, because we can now integrate equation (1.45). This results in

$$\begin{aligned} \Delta_r G_T^\circ &= \Delta_r G_{T_r}^\circ - \Delta_r S_{T_r}^\circ(T - T_r) \\ &\quad + \Delta_r a\left[T - T_r - T\ \ln\left(\frac{T}{T_r}\right)\right] \\ &\quad + \frac{\Delta_r b}{2}\left(2TT_r - T^2 - T_r^2\right) \\ &\quad + \frac{\Delta_r c\,(T^2 + T_r^2 - 2TT_r)}{2TT_r^2} \end{aligned} \tag{1.66}$$

for reactions not involving solutes (for which use of Maier-Kelley coefficients is inappropriate). Equations (1.22), (1.65) and (1.66) may look a little intimidating, but they simply relate the enthalpy, entropy, and free energy changes of a chemical reaction ($\Delta_r H^\circ$, $\Delta_r S^\circ$, and $\Delta_r G^\circ$) at the reference temperature T_r, usually 25°C , to the values at some other temperature T, using three constants a, b, and c [defined in equation (1.19)]. These constants are measured for each product and reactant using calorimetry and are widely available, for example in the databases in the SUPCRT92 package.

Pressure. One of the many simple relationships between the derivatives of thermodynamic parameters (not derived here) is

$$\left(\frac{\partial S}{\partial P}\right)_T = -\left(\frac{\partial V}{\partial T}\right) \tag{1.67}$$

showing that the effect of pressure on entropy can be obtained by measuring the effect of temperature on volume (or density), which is usually a much simpler task. Fairly simple manipulations then show the effect of pressure on enthalpy to be

$$\left(\frac{\partial H}{\partial P}\right)_T = V - T\left(\frac{\partial V}{\partial T}\right) \tag{1.68}$$

so that

$$H_{T,P} - H_{T,P_r} = \int_{P_r}^{P}\left[V - T\left(\frac{\partial V}{\partial T}\right)_P\right] dP \tag{1.69}$$

showing that enthalpy change with pressure can also be evaluated from volume data. This can be quite useful in calculating the heat effects during boiling.

These are very general relationships. Sometimes reasonable assumptions lead to simpler approaches. To find the effect of P on G for solids, for example, we can take advantage of equation (1.46), plus the fact that solids are quite incompressible. Expanding (1.46), we write

$$(\partial\Delta_r G^\circ/\partial P)_T = \Delta_r V^\circ \tag{1.70}$$

so that

$$\Delta_r G_P^\circ = \Delta_r G_{P_r}^\circ + \Delta_r V^\circ(P - P_r) \tag{1.71}$$

assuming that $\Delta_r V^\circ$ is a constant, which is usually quite acceptable for solid phases at crustal pressures. Therefore Equation (1.66) becomes, for changes in both T and P of solid phases,

$$\begin{aligned} \Delta_r G_{T,P}^\circ &= \Delta_r G_{T_r,P_r}^\circ - \Delta_r S_{T_r}^\circ(T - T_r) \\ &\quad + \Delta_r a\left[T - T_r - T\ \ln\left(\frac{T}{T_r}\right)\right] \\ &\quad + \Delta_r \frac{b}{2}\left(2TT_r - T^2 - T_r^2\right) \\ &\quad + \frac{\Delta_r c\,(T^2 + T_r^2 - 2TT_r)}{2TT_r^2} \\ &\quad + \Delta_r V^\circ(P - P_r) \end{aligned} \tag{1.72}$$

for reactions not involving solutes or gases, for which the constant $\Delta_r V°$ assumption is inappropriate.

Expressions have been proposed for the pressure dependence of $V°$ for solids, which complicates the integration of (1.70), but the constant volume assumption is quite common.

For gases, the variation of G with temperature is conveniently handled by the Maier-Kelley approach, but the variation with pressure is handled in a completely different way. The temperature and pressure dependence of aqueous solute properties will be discussed in terms of the HKF model.

The mixing process: Entropy (III). Equilibrium thermodynamics deals with homogeneous bodies of matter in equilibrium states. The mathematics of thermodynamics is the calculus, with its assumption of a continuum in the space occupied by thermodynamic variables, in which reversible processes are possible. This mathematical model of energy relationships has no way of providing for individual particles.

But we know beyond any doubt that the universe and everything it contains is made up of particles, which we call atoms and molecules. The universe is also not a continuum. Therefore, a model of energy relationships based on a mathematics of particles might be expected to yield deeper insights into the way nature works than one that is not. Such a model is statistical mechanics, which incorporates statistical thermodynamics. It leads to a parameter indistinguishable from entropy in any way, and therefore identified with entropy, but based on completely different reasoning. In this model, entropy is a parameter that is a measure of the probability of a given configuration or system structure, and processes are spontaneous if they lead to a more probable state of the system.

Entropy and probability. The relationship between entropy and probability can be found by analyzing a simple process for which both the entropy change and the probabilities are known. Such a process is the expansion of an ideal gas into a vacuum. Consider the expansion of N molecules of an ideal gas, initially at P_1 and V_1, into an evacuated chamber of volume V_2. The final pressure is P_2 and the final volume is $V_1 + V_2$. For this change, the entropy change is [from (1.63), and changing S to S/n],

$$\Delta S = nR\ln\left(\frac{V_1}{V_1+V_2}\right) \tag{1.73}$$

where n is the number of moles of gas. After expansion the probability of finding any particular molecule in the original volume is $V_1/(V_1 + V_2)$. The probability of finding all N molecules in the original volume V_1 at the same time without being constrained to be there is $[V_1/(V_1 + V_2)]^N$ (because there are N molecules and probabilities are multiplicative). Therefore, the probability of the initial state arising spontaneously after expansion is

$$p_{initial} = \left(\frac{V_1}{V_1+V_2}\right)^N$$

This is an extremely small probability. For example if $V_1/(V_1 + V_2)$ is 0.5 and $N = 10^{23}$ (i.e., $n \approx 1$), it is about $1/(2^{10^{23}})$.

After the expansion, the probability (p_{final}) of finding all N molecules in the final volume $V_1 + V_2$ must be 1.0. The ratio of these two probabilities is

$$\frac{p_{final}}{p_{initial}} = \left(\frac{V_1+V_2}{V_1}\right)^N \tag{1.74}$$

Comparison of (1.73) and (1.74) gives

$$\Delta S = nR\ln\left(\frac{p_{final}}{p_{initial}}\right)^{1/N}$$

or

$$\Delta S = \frac{nR}{N}\ln\left(\frac{p_{final}}{p_{initial}}\right)$$

The number of molecules divided by the number of moles (N/n) is Avogadro's number, N_a, so that the equation becomes

$$\Delta S = \frac{R}{N_a}\ln\left(\frac{p_{final}}{p_{initial}}\right) \tag{1.75}$$

Thus there is a direct relationship between entropy and probability in this simple case, and by analogy, generally. In the example mentioned above where $V_1/(V_1 + V_2) = 0.5$, (1.75) becomes, for one mole of gas,

$$\begin{aligned}\Delta S &= (R/10^{23})\ln(2^{10^{23}})\\ &= R\ln 2\\ &= 5.76\,\mathrm{J\,K^{-1}}\end{aligned}$$

(10^{23} is an abbreviation for Avogadro's number, 6.022136×10^{23}).

This general relationship between entropy and probability is more generally expressed as Boltzmann's famous equation

$$S = k\ln W \tag{1.76}$$

which is engraved on his tombstone in Vienna. Here k is R/N_a, and W is called variously the statistical probability or the statistical weight of a state whose entropy is S.

The Third Law

By now you are accustomed to being told that we cannot know the absolute values of thermodynamic parameters, only differences. But this applies only to the internal energy, U, and any parameters that contain U, such as H and G. Entropy is different in that we *can* get absolute values, by virtue of the Third Law of thermodynamics.

Third law entropies. The Third Law says:

> The entropy of all pure, crystalline, perfectly ordered substances is zero at absolute zero temperature, and the entropy of all other substances is positive.

Thus the entropy of all pure, crystalline minerals such as diamond, corundum, gibbsite, and so on are all zero at $T = 0$ K, but the entropy of, say, glass would not be zero, because its structure is amorphous and not crystalline. If we let T_1 be absolute zero in equation (1.59), the entropy of minerals at any temperature, say our standard temperature of 298.15 K, is then

$$S_{298.15} = \int_{T=0}^{T=298.15} \frac{C_p}{T} dT \qquad (1.77)$$

and all that is required to determine "absolute" values for the entropy of minerals is to measure their heat capacity at a series of temperatures between zero and 298.15 K and to evaluate the integral. This gives rise to another kind of calorimetry: *cryogenic*, or low-temperature calorimetry.

These formulas for the temperature dependence of the Gibbs energy, enthalpy, and entropy, are very well suited to computerized computation. You need only to have data for $\Delta_f G^\circ$, $\Delta_f H^\circ$, S°, and the parameters *a*, *b*, and *c*, for each substance of interest in a database. All of these are available from calorimetric studies. As for the effect of pressure, we have derived a general relationship [equation (1.69)], but have so far only considered solids explicitly.

Solutions and Activities

If the world was composed of pure substances, our theory of spontaneous processes would now be almost complete. However, there are in fact no pure natural substances; all are solutions to a greater or lesser extent, although some are sufficiently pure (e.g., most quartz crystals) that our theory as so far developed can apply to them.

Restating our general goal, we wanted to define a quantity (a thermodynamic potential) that tells us which way chemical reactions will proceed, and how that quantity varies with *T*, *P*, and concentration. We have defined such a quantity (*G*), and derived expressions for its variation with *T* and *P*. We must now deal with the effect of concentration on *G*.

The relationship between Gibbs energy and solute concentration is handled most conveniently and most generally by introducing the concept of *activity*. This is a dimensionless term used in place of a concentration or partial pressure of a particular component, and which allows calculation of the difference between the Gibbs energy of that component in solution and in some reference state. No simple definition such as this can suffice to make the activity concept clear. The rest of this whole section is an attempt to do that.

Ideal Solutions

Solutions are complicated systems. Much simplification is introduced by not describing the solutions themselves, but by how much they differ from some relatively simpler ideal case. There are two very useful idealized solution models, to which real solutions may be compared. Both are referred to as *ideal solutions*, so some care is required in using this term. We will save considerable space by not going into the historical usage of these two concepts of ideality, but define them in terms of our present understanding of component activity.

Henryan solutions. A Henryan solution is one that obeys Henry's Law, which means that activity of dissolved component *i* is directly proportional to its concentration. The coefficient of proportionality is the Henry's Law Constant, k_H. The concentration may be measured in various ways, notably mole fraction or molality. For example,

$$a_i = k_{H_i} m_i \qquad (1.78)$$

where m_i is the molality of *i*. In molecular terms, Henryan behavior for a solute means that there exist only solute-solvent forces, and of course solvent–solvent forces; there is no solute-solute interaction. This in turn means that the solute must be very dilute so that solute molecules are widely spaced. This leads to the concept of "infinite dilution", where pure Henryan behavior must be observed.

One of the most common applications follows from the original formulation of the law, and that is that the partial pressure (or fugacity, discussed later) of a gas phase component is directly proportional to its concentration in a coexisting liquid phase. In this case, $P_i = k_{H_i} m_i$, so the slope $(\partial P_i/\partial m_i = P_i/m_i)$ is constant.

Raoultian solutions. A Raoultian solution is one that obeys Raoult's Law, which in modern terms means that the activity of component *i* equals the mole fraction of *i*,

$$a_i = X_i \qquad (1.79)$$

It is in effect a special case of Henry's Law. In molecular terms, Raoultian behavior means that intermolecular forces are the same for all pairs of species in solution. In other words, for a binary solution A–B, the forces between A–A, B–B, and A–B, are all identical at all concentrations.

The Properties of Solutions

When we mix two substances together, the properties of each substance may or may not be affected. If we mix together black marbles and white marbles, the properties (density, heat capacity, etc.) of each marble remain exactly the same as they were before mixing, and most properties of the mixture are just the sums of the properties of the individual components of the mixture. If the black marbles have a total volume of V_b and the white marbles have a total volume V_w, then the volume of them mixed together is

$$V = V_b + V_w \qquad (1.80)$$

Using total volumes is usually inconvenient in chemical modeling. If the volume per mole of black marbles is V_b and the volume per mole of white marbles is V_w (note the change in notation from V to *V*), then the total volume is

$$V = n_b V_b + n_w V_w \qquad (1.81)$$

where n_b and n_w are the number of moles of black and white marbles in the mixture. Dividing by the total number of moles $n_b + n_w$ we get

$$V = X_b V_b + X_w V_w \tag{1.82}$$

where V is the *molar volume* of the mixture, and X is the *mole fraction.*

Ideal mixing. A pile of marbles is not a solution, but a mechanical mixture. Nevertheless, these simple relationships depend on the equality of forces between all particles, and are used to define the *Raoultian* ideal solution, i.e., a solution that obeys Raoult's Law. They can be generalized in the form

$$V_{ideal\ sol'n} = \sum_i X_i V_i^\circ \tag{1.83}$$

which is a generalization of (1.82), where V is the molar volume of an ideal solution, and V_i° is the molar volume of the pure component i.

The form of equation (1.83) applies also to any thermodynamic parameter which does not contain entropy in its definition. The main example is enthalpy, so that

$$H_{ideal\ sol'n} = \sum_i X_i H_i^\circ \tag{1.84}$$

The essential idea in these equations is that the properties of the pure components are not changed when they dissolve. In other words, the volume and enthalpy "of mixing" ($\Delta_m V$; $\Delta_m H$; i.e., the volume or enthalpy change during the mixing of components to form a solution) is zero. Thus, from (1.83),

$$\Delta_m V = V_{ideal\ sol'n} - \sum_i X_i V_i^\circ = 0 \tag{1.85}$$

and similarly for $\Delta_m H$.

However, entropy and other potential quantities that contain entropy (such as G) are specifically defined so as to change in spontaneous processes, and two or more substances dissolving into one another is a perfect example of a spontaneous process.

Consider two gases which are allowed to mix ideally at constant P and T. In the final mixture, the partial pressure of gas 1 is $P_1 = X_1 P$, and of gas 2 is $P_2 = X_2 P$, where X_1 and X_2 are the mole fractions. The ΔS of mixing is equal to the ΔS involved in expanding each gas from its initial pressure P to its partial pressure in the gas mixture. From equation (1.64), this process is for each gas

$$\Delta S_1 = R \ln(P/P_1)$$

and

$$\Delta S_2 = R \ln(P/P_2)$$

and the total change in entropy is

$$\begin{aligned} \Delta S &= X_1 R \ln(P/P_1) + X_2 R \ln(P/P_2) \\ &= X_1 R \ln(1/X_1) + X_2 R \ln(1/X_2) \\ &= -R(X_1 \ln X_1 + X_2 \ln X_2) \end{aligned} \tag{1.86}$$

or in general for any number of gases, for the mixing process,

$$\Delta_m S = -R \sum_i (X_i \ln X_i) \tag{1.87}$$

Because the X terms are fractional, $\Delta_m S$ is inherently positive. Equation (1.87), though derived here for gases, applies to any ideal (Raoultian) solution, solid, liquid, or gaseous.

It may not be clear to what difference the Δ in (1.87) refers. It is the difference in S between the i gases forming an ideal solution, and the same gases in their unmixed (pure) states, or

$$\Delta_m S = S_{ideal\ sol'n} - \sum_i X_i S_i^\circ \tag{1.88}$$

Thus we can also write

$$S_{ideal\ sol'n} = \sum_i X_i S_i^\circ - R \sum_i (X_i \ln X_i) \tag{1.89}$$

It is important to note the fundamental difference between the ideal mixing of volumes and other terms not containing entropy [equations (1.83), (1.84)], which are just linear combinations of the pure end-member terms, and the ideal entropy of mixing, equation (1.87), which is non-linear, and results in all mixtures having a higher entropy than points on the $\sum_i X_i S_i^\circ$ line or plane. It is this property that gives the entropy, Gibbs energy and other thermodynamic potentials (all of which contain an entropy term) their ability to predict energy differences, and hence reaction directions.

It follows from equations (1.54), (1.87), and the fact that $\Delta_m H = 0$, that the Gibbs free energy of (ideal) mixing is

$$\begin{aligned} \Delta_m G &= \Delta_m H - T \Delta_m S \\ &= RT \sum_i (X_i \ln X_i) \end{aligned} \tag{1.90}$$

and, as in (1.88),

$$\Delta_m G = G_{ideal\ sol'n} - \sum_i X_i G_i^\circ \tag{1.91}$$

so

$$G_{ideal\ sol'n} = \sum_i X_i G_i^\circ + RT \sum_i (X_i \ln X_i) \tag{1.92}$$

The $\sum_i X_i G_i^\circ$ term defines a straight line (or plane surface) between points representing end-member components, and the $\sum_i (X_i \ln X_i)$ term (which is inherently negative) describes how far *below* this line or plane is the surface representing the G of the (ideal) solution. For real solutions, somewhat more complex expressions containing correction factors derived in various ways must be used.

Partial Molar Properties

The molar volume of a substance that is dissolved in something else is not directly measurable, but it is possible to calculate it from measurements of the molar volume of the solution as a whole. The result is the *partial molar volume*, $\overline{V}$. This is the molar volume of each solute, which, when all are added together in linear fashion, gives the molar volume of the whole solution. Thus we can use equation (1.83), just changing V_i° to $\overline{V}$,

$$V = \sum_i X_i \overline{V}_i \qquad (1.93)$$

The formal definition of a partial molar property is

$$\overline{Z}_i = \left(\frac{\partial Z}{\partial n_i}\right)_{T,P,\hat{n}_i} \qquad (1.94)$$

where Z is the total or extensive form of any thermodynamic parameter, $\overline{Z}$ the partial molar form, n_i is the number of moles of component i, and $\hat{n}_i$ is the number of moles of all components other than i in the same solution. Note particularly that the partial derivative is taken of the total quantity Z, not the molar Z, and that the main constraints are T and P. However, the important thing to know about partial molar properties is not this differential equation, but that they are the properties per mole of substances at a particular concentration in a particular solution. You think about partial molar properties in exactly the same way that you think about molar properties. The only difference is that for a given substance, they are not fixed quantities at a given T and P, but vary with the concentration of the substance and the nature of the solution.

Gibbs Energies of Solutes

The partial molar Gibbs energy is particularly important, and gets its own symbol, μ , and its own name, the *chemical potential*. Thus

$$\mu_i \equiv \overline{G}_i = \left(\frac{\partial G}{\partial n_i}\right)_{T,P,\hat{n}_i} \qquad (1.95)$$

Many thermodynamic relationships remain the same in partial molar form. For example, equations (1.45) and (1.46) become, for solute i,

$$(\partial \mu_i/\partial T)_P = -\overline{S}_i \qquad (1.96)$$

and

$$(\partial \mu_i/\partial P)_T = \overline{V}_i \qquad (1.97)$$

The chemical potential is arguably the property of most interest for solution components, because it can be used to calculate equilibrium solution compositions, including saturation states for minerals and gases. This follows from our definition of G becoming minimized for a system at equilibrium at a given T and P. Once we know how μ_i changes with composition in existing phases or possible new phases, it is possible to calculate that configuration of phases and compositions that result in a minimum G for the system as a whole. It also follows from our definitions that at equilibrium, μ_i for each i must be the same in all phases; if it is greater in some parts of the system than in others, it should migrate down the potential gradient until it is everywhere equal. This then defines the minimum G for the system. So the question now is, how is μ related to concentrations, and how do we use it to predict equilibrium concentrations of solutes?

To get at the variation of μ with concentration, it would seem natural to find an expression for the derivative of μ with a concentration term, and then integrate. The derivative of μ_i with respect to the molality of i, m_i, is $(\partial\mu_i/\partial m_i)_{T,P,\hat{m}i}$, where, as before, $\hat{m}_i$ means the molality of all solution components *except i*.

At this point, some intuition tells us that it would be useful to expand this expression by introducing P_i, the vapor pressure of solute i. If i is a gas, this may be a measurable quantity; if i is a solid, it may not be, but the principles involved are unchanged. Thus

$$\left(\frac{\partial \mu_i}{\partial m_i}\right)_{\hat{m}_i} = \frac{\partial \mu_i}{\partial P_i}\frac{\partial P_i}{\partial m_i} \qquad (1.98)$$

where μ_i is the same in the solution and in the vapor phase, where it can be called G_i (the vapor being assumed an ideal gas), so that $(\partial\mu_i/\partial P_i) = (\partial G_i/\partial P_i) = V_i = RT/P_i$, and where $(\partial P_i/\partial m_i) = P_i/m_i$ is an expression of Henry's Law, as mentioned earlier. Combining all this we get

$$\left(\frac{\partial \mu_i}{\partial m_i}\right)_{\hat{m}_i} = \frac{RT}{m_i} \qquad (1.99)$$

for ideal (Henryan) solutions. Integrating this equation between two values of molality, m_i' and m_i'', we get

$$\mu_i'' - \mu_i' = RT \ln \frac{m_i''}{m_i'} \qquad (1.100)$$

showing the effect of changing solute concentration on the chemical potential, as we wanted. However, it is limited to ideal (Henryan) solutions. The relationship is generalized to any kind of solution by introducing a correction factor at each concentration. Thus

$$\mu_i'' - \mu_i' = RT \ln \frac{\gamma_H'' m_i''}{\gamma_H' m_i'} \qquad (1.101)$$

where γ_H is the Henryan activity coefficient.

Solute activity. Equation (1.101) can be generalized and so made more useful by choosing a single concentration m_i' for all solutes. In choosing this concentration, we should realize that (1) γ_H in the denominator will be different for all different solutes unless we choose some idealized state, and (2) it would be convenient to have the denominator ($\gamma'_H m'$) disappear, i.e., be unity. The only state that satisfies these conditions and is equal to 1 molal for all solutes is the ideal (Henryan) one molal solution, and this is universally used as the standard state for solutes. Introducing superscript ° for the standard state, and dropping the now unnecessary superscript ″, we get

$$\mu_i - \mu_i^\circ = RT \ln \frac{\gamma_{H_i} m_i}{\gamma_{H_i}^\circ m_i^\circ} \tag{1.102}$$

and because $\gamma_{Hi}^\circ = 1$ and $m_i^\circ = 1$, this is usually written

$$\mu_i - \mu_i^\circ = RT \ln(\gamma_{H_i} m_i) \tag{1.103}$$

The quantity $(\gamma_{Hi} m_i)/(\gamma_{Hi}^\circ m_i^\circ)$ is one definition of the *activity*, a_i, so

$$\mu_i - \mu_i^\circ = RT \ln a_i \tag{1.104}$$

The activity thus allows calculation of the difference between the μ_i in a solution and μ_i in the ideal one molal standard state at the same T and P as the solution. This sounds like a fairly esoteric thing to do, but because standard free energies of formation are determined for this ideal standard state (albeit at 25°C, 1 bar), it is immensely useful, as we will see. But first we note that the activity comes in two other useful forms.

Activities in solids, liquids, and gases. The activity as defined in (1.104) is so far only useful for aqueous solutes, for which molality is the common concentration term. An equivalent activity term for gases can be derived starting with the intensive form of equation (1.46),

$$(\partial G/\partial P)_T = V$$

Integrating from P_1 to P_2, we have

$$G_{P_2} - G_{P_1} = \int_{P_1}^{P_2} V\,dP \tag{1.105}$$

or, for an ideal gas in which $V = RT/P$,

$$\begin{aligned} G_{P_2} - G_{P_1} &= \int_{P_1}^{P_2} (RT/P)dP \\ &= RT \ln(P_2/P_1) \end{aligned} \tag{1.106}$$

If P_1 is 1 bar and this is designated a standard or reference state denoted by a superscript °, then P_2 becomes simply P, and

$$G - G^\circ = RT \ln(P/P^\circ) \tag{1.107}$$

$$= RT \ln P \text{ since } P^\circ = 1 \tag{1.108}$$

Thus for ideal gases $RT \ln P$ all by itself gives the value of $\int_{P=1}^{P} dG$, or in other words of $\int_{P=1}^{P} V\,dP$. Unfortunately, this doesn't work for real gases, although it's not a bad approximation at low pressures and high temperatures where real gases approach ideal behavior. However, the *form* of the relationship

$$\int_{P=1}^{P} V\,dP = \int_{P=1}^{P} dG = \int_{P=1}^{P} RT\,d\ln P$$

is sufficient to suggest that we could define a function such that the relationship *would* hold true for real gases. This function is the *fugacity*, *f*, where

$$V\,dP = dG = RT d\ln f \tag{1.109}$$

and

$$\int_{P_1}^{P_2} V\,dP = \int_{P_1}^{P_2} dG$$

$$G_{P_2} - G_{P_1} = RT \ln(f_{P_2}/f_{P_1}) \tag{1.110}$$

To complete the definition, we stipulate that f becomes equal to P at low pressures,

$$\lim_{P\to 0} (f/P) = 1 \tag{1.111}$$

and the ratio f/P is called the *fugacity coefficient*, γ_f, so

$$f_i = \gamma_{f_i} P_i \tag{1.112}$$

where P_i is the partial pressure of i.

Fugacity is thus a quantity that we use in place of pressure for gases when we want to calculate a free energy difference. You can generally think of it as a pressure or as a partial pressure, but remember that it is at the same time a thermodynamic model parameter. Thus it still has significance at values of say 10^{-60} bars, whereas a pressure of this value would have no physical significance.

Equation (1.110) has a meaning more general than just giving the difference in G on raising the pressure of a gas from P_1 to P_2. Changing the pressure from P_1 to P_2 is just one way of affecting the free energy of a component. Actually, the equation can be applied to *any* two states at the same T. If the first state is a reference state, denoted by superscript °, and the second state is unsuperscripted, we have

$$\mu_i - G_i^\circ = RT \ln(f_i/f_i^\circ) \tag{1.113}$$

$$= RT \ln(\gamma_{f_i} P_i)/(\gamma_{f_i}^\circ P_i^\circ) \tag{1.114}$$

where we change G_i to μ_i because of the generalization from one pure component to one component in any situation, including solutions. We have added the subscript i to emphasize that we are talking about a specific component, not some mixture of components.

Now we have another equation [(1.113) or (1.114)] relating a chemical potential difference to some measurable quantities, just as in (1.102), and (f_i/f_i°) or $(\gamma f_i P_i)/$

$(\gamma_{fi}^{\circ}P_i^{\circ})$ is obviously analogous to $(\gamma_{Hi}m_i)/(\gamma_{Hi}^{\circ}m_i^{\circ})$, so we define another activity as

$$a_i = f_i/f_i^{\circ} \tag{1.115}$$

We arrive again at equation (1.104), but this time with terms more useful for gases. Again, the denominator refers to our standard state, and in order for it to be unity, both γ_f and P in that state must simultaneously be unity. The only state for which this is true at all temperatures is an ideal gas at one bar, and so that is the definition of the standard state for gases, at least in databases. When this choice $f^{\circ} = 1$ bar) is made,

$$a_i = f_i \tag{1.116}$$

Thus if you know or can calculate γ_f, then knowing the partial pressure of any i allows calculation of the difference in chemical potential between i in whatever state it is in, and i acting as an ideal gas at one bar at the same T, by (1.114). However, we will note later that the standard state pressure is often chosen as the system pressure, i.e., the pressure of interest, rather than 1 bar. If this is the case, then f° is not 1 bar but must be calculated along with f itself.

Finally, for an ideal gas f_i/f_i° is of course equal to P_i/P_i°, which is easily shown to be equal to the mole fraction, X_i. So, for ideal gaseous solutions, and by extension, for any ideal (Raoultian) solution,

$$\mu_i - G_i^{\circ} = RT \ln X_i \tag{1.117}$$

For solutions covering a wide range of compositions, such as many solid and liquid solutions, this equation can be used by introducing another correction factor, the Raoultian activity coefficient, γ_R. Thus

$$\mu_i - G_i^{\circ} = RT \ln(\gamma_{R_i} X_i) \tag{1.118}$$

As before, we now define another activity term

$$a_i = \gamma_{R_i} X_i \tag{1.119}$$

which is useful for solutions covering a wide range of concentrations, and for which γ_R is known or can be estimated. In geochemistry, this tends to be for solid and gaseous solutions only, but it is widely used in metallurgy for liquids as well. The standard state, as before, is that state for which $a = 1$, in this case the pure liquid or solid ($X = 1$; $\gamma_R = 1$ in this state by definition).

Activities and chemical potentials are thus intimately related.The fact that absolute values of μ cannot be known, so that we must always use differences in μ, is a nuisance. The activity concept has evolved to reduce the nuisance to a minimum, but in doing so we have had to introduce several different standard states. Thermodynamic properties are determined and tabulated for these various standard states, and how they interact can be seen when we consider the equilibrium constant. Finally, note that fugacities have units of pressure (e.g., bars), but that activities and activity coefficients are always dimensionless.

Activity Coefficients

From the discussion of activities, it is clear that if we are interested in calculating chemical potential differences, we must first know or be able to calculate activity coefficients. Activity coefficients can of course be measured by various methods, but no amount of measurements will ever suffice to supply the coefficients needed in all applications of thermodynamics to complex natural systems. Obviously, a calculation method is required that has some theoretical support, and which reproduces the measured values. The development of these methods, for Raoultian, Henryan, and fugacity coefficients is an ongoing task. Because of our focus on hydrothermal solutions, we will concentrate on Henryan activity coefficients, with only a mention of Raoultian and fugacity coefficients.

Henryan coefficients: Debye-Hückel equations. Henryan activity coefficients can be calculated for relatively low concentrations by variations of the Debye-Hückel equation. These all make use of the ionic strength I, defined as

$$I = \tfrac{1}{2}\sum_i m_i z_i^2 \tag{1.120}$$

where m_i is the molality of ionic species i, and z_i is its charge. For very low concentrations,

$$\log \gamma_{H_i} = -Az_i^2\sqrt{I} \tag{1.121}$$

where A is a constant. This is called the Debye-Hückel Limiting Law, because it works in the limit of essentially zero concentration of m_i (<0.01 m for univalent ions). It gives the Henry's Law slope. At higher concentrations, up to about 0.1 m, the Debye-Hückel expression is

$$\log \gamma_{H_i} = \frac{-Az_i^2\sqrt{I}}{1 + B\mathring{a}_i\sqrt{I}} \tag{1.122}$$

where B is another constant, and $\mathring{a}_i$ is theoretically a distance between ions, or an ion-size parameter, but is in practice an adjustable parameter. Values of $\mathring{a}_i$ for various ions can be found in tables in books on physical chemistry.

At concentrations beyond about 0.1 m, a variety of methods have been used to calculate γ_H. Most of them add a term or terms to the Debye-Hückel expression. A common one is the Davies equation,

$$\log \gamma_{H_i} = \frac{-Az_i^2\sqrt{I}}{1+\sqrt{I}} + 0.3Az_i^2 I \tag{1.123}$$

Here the $B\mathring{a}$ term in the denominator has been changed to 1.0, partly because that is its approximate value and partly because it is theoretically undesirable to have a solute-specific term ($\mathring{a}_i$) in a general equation for γ_H. The 0.3 in the last term is sometimes replaced by 0.2.

Another approach is the "B-dot" equation of Helgeson (1969),

$$\log \gamma_{H_i} = \frac{-Az_i^2\sqrt{I}}{1 + B\mathring{a}_i\sqrt{I}} + \dot{B}I \tag{1.124}$$

$\dot{B}$ is an empirical parameter designed to reproduce the activity coefficients of NaCl solutions, and therefore (1.124) works reasonably well for Na^+ and Cl^- for concentrations to several molar. For other solutes it also works reasonably well in solutions in which the dominant ions are Na^+ and Cl^-.

Neutral species. As might be expected, measured activity coefficients for neutral (uncharged) aqueous species are generally fairly close to 1.0, although they are a function of solution concentration. However, only those neutral species that are directly measurable by chemical analysis [such as $SiO_2(aq)$, $H_2S(aq)$, $CO_2(aq)$] have had their activity coefficients measured. More difficult is the problem of the activity coefficients of uncharged metal complexes, present in low concentrations, and which may form only a small proportion of the metal in solution. These are usually assumed to have coefficients similar to the measured ones just referred to, without much justification.

Modelers should realize that activity coefficients are affected by all solution components, and that simple, all-inclusive equations such as those above cannot be expected to be very accurate. Moreover, the degree to which they are inaccurate in specific cases is usually not known. Undoubtedly, the situation is helped by the fact that in equilibrium calculations the errors in calculated activity coefficients of products and reactants cancel one another to some extent. Nevertheless, uncertainties in activity coefficients in geochemical models are always a major concern.

Other activity coefficients: Most other approaches to the calculation of activity coefficients for solution components, including solid and gaseous as well as liquid solutions, have used some form of a virial equation as a starting point. A virial equation is simply an equation for the ideal state (e.g., the ideal gas equation) followed by an ascending polynomial in one of the state variables. It seems to work well as a basis for activity coefficients because the form of the equation has a basis in statistical mechanics.

In the 1970s, Kenneth Pitzer and his associates developed a theoretical model for electrolyte solutions that combined the Debye-Hückel equation with additional terms in the form of a virial equation, which has proven to be extraordinarily successful at fitting the behavior of mixed-salt solutions to very high concentrations. This model has no provision for adjusting standard state parameters, or for considering individual reactions between species. It is also limited at the present time to relatively low temperatures and pressures.

In both solid and gaseous solutions, virial equation-based Raoultian coefficients have often been proposed. For example, the Margules equations, often used in binary and sometimes in ternary solid solutions and which have a virial equation basis, were proposed originally for gaseous solutions. However, there is no satisfactory general model for Raoultian coefficients in multicomponent solid solutions, and the tendency in modeling has been to treat these solutions as ideal. Fugacity coefficients are quite important in calculations of boiling, and have been approached from the virial equation as well as from numerous modifications of the van der Waals equation, the best known of these being the (modified) Redlich-Kwong equation.

We will not discuss these methods, except to say that satisfactory generalized equations for the calculation of activity coefficients in solid, liquid, and gaseous solutions under geological conditions will probably remain an important research goal for many years to come.

Equilibrium Constants

We are rarely interested in components by themselves, in solution or otherwise. We combine components into *chemical reactions* that we think are part of the natural processes we are investigating. These chemical reactions eventually reach a state of equilibrium, if left to themselves, and it is this state of equilibrium which can be treated by our thermodynamic methods. Our natural systems of course rarely reach equilibrium, but our model systems do. The comparison of the two is surprisingly informative.

To find out what we can say about this balanced equilibrium state when several solutes and other phases are involved, let's consider a general chemical reaction

$$a\,\mathrm{A} + b\,\mathrm{B} = c\,\mathrm{C} + d\,\mathrm{D} \tag{1.125}$$

where A, B, C, and D are chemical formulae, and *a, b, c, d* (called stoichiometric coefficients) are any numbers (usually small integers) that allow the reaction to be balanced in both composition and electrical charges, if any. When this reaction reaches equilibrium,

$$c\,\mu_\mathrm{C} + d\,\mu_\mathrm{D} = a\,\mu_\mathrm{A} + b\,\mu_\mathrm{B}$$

and

$$\begin{aligned}\Delta_r\mu &= c\,\mu_\mathrm{C} + d\,\mu_\mathrm{D} - a\,\mu_\mathrm{A} - b\,\mu_\mathrm{B}\\ &= 0\end{aligned} \tag{1.126}$$

By our definition of activity, equation (1.104),

$$\mu_\mathrm{A} = \mu_\mathrm{A}^\circ + RT\ln a_\mathrm{A}$$

$$\mu_\mathrm{B} = \mu_\mathrm{B}^\circ + RT\ln a_\mathrm{B}$$

$$\mu_\mathrm{C} = \mu_\mathrm{C}^\circ + RT\ln a_\mathrm{C}$$

$$\mu_\mathrm{D} = \mu_\mathrm{D}^\circ + RT\ln a_\mathrm{D}$$

Substituting these expressions into (1.126), we get

$$\begin{aligned}\Delta_r\mu &= c\mu_C + d\mu_D - a\mu_A - b\mu_B \\ &= c(\mu_C^\circ + RT\ln a_C) + d(\mu_D^\circ + RT\ln a_D) \\ &\quad - a(\mu_A^\circ + RT\ln a_A) - b(\mu_B^\circ + RT\ln a_B) \\ &= (c\mu_C^\circ + d\mu_D^\circ - a\mu_A^\circ - b\mu_B^\circ) \\ &\quad + RT\ln a_C^c + RT\ln a_D^d \\ &\quad - RT\ln a_A^a - RT\ln a_B^b \\ &= \Delta_r\mu^\circ + RT\ln\left(\frac{a_C^c a_D^d}{a_A^a\, a_B^b}\right)\end{aligned}$$

There may be any number of reactants and products, and so to be completely general we can write

$$\Delta_r\mu = \Delta_r\mu^\circ + RT\ln\prod_i a_i^{\nu_i} \qquad (1.127)$$

where i is an index that can refer to any product or reactant, v_i refers to the stoichiometric coefficients of the products and reactants, with v_i positive if i is a product, and negative if i is a reactant. $\prod_i$ (or Π_i) is a symbol meaning "product of all i terms," which means that all the $a_i^{v_i}$ terms are to be multiplied together (much as $\sum_i a_i$ would mean that all a_i terms were to be added together). So in our case, the v terms are c, d, $-a$, and $-b$, and

$$\begin{aligned}\prod_i a_i^{\nu_i} &= a_C^c\, a_D^d\, a_A^{-a}\, a_B^{-b} \\ &= \frac{a_C^c\, a_D^d}{a_A^a\, a_B^b}\end{aligned}$$

In the general case, $\Pi_i a_i^{v_i}$ is given the symbol Q, so (1.127) becomes

$$\Delta_r\mu = \Delta_r\mu^\circ + RT\ln Q \qquad (1.128)$$

No equation is more central to geochemical modeling, so the terms in this equation deserve some discussion. First, the term $\Delta_r\mu^\circ$ refers to the difference in free energies of products and reactants when each product and each reactant, whether solid, liquid, gas, or solute, is in its pure standard state. This means the pure phase for solids and liquids [e.g., most minerals, $H_2O(s)$, $H_2O(l)$, etc.], pure gases acting ideally at 1 bar [e.g., $O_2(g)$, $H_2O(g)$, etc.], and dissolved substances [solutes, e.g., NaCl(aq), Na^+, etc.] in ideal solution at a concentration of 1 molal. Although we do have at times fairly pure solid phases in our real systems (minerals such as quartz and calcite are often quite pure), we rarely have pure liquids or gases, and we never have ideal solutions as concentrated as 1 molal. Therefore, $\Delta_r\mu^\circ$ usually refers to quite a hypothetical situation. It is best not to try to picture what physical situation it might represent, but to think of it as just the difference in numbers that are obtained from tables.

$\Delta_r\mu$, on the other hand, is the difference in free energy of reactants and products as they actually occur in the system you are considering, which may or may not have reached equilibrium. The activities in the Q term (the concentrations, fugacities, mole fractions, etc. of the products and reactants, together with their activity coefficients) change during the reaction as it strives to reach equilibrium and at any particular moment result in a particular value of $\Delta_r\mu$. Thus $\Delta_r\mu^\circ$ is a number obtained from tables that is independent of what is happening in the real system you are considering, but $\Delta_r\mu$ and Q are linked together—whatever activities (think *concentrations*) are in Q will result in a certain value of $\Delta_r\mu$.

It is perhaps better to write equation (1.128) as

$$\Delta_r\mu - \Delta_r\mu^\circ = RT\ln Q \qquad (1.129)$$

which shows that whatever terms are in Q control how different the chemical potentials ($\Delta_r\mu$) are from their standard tabulated values ($\Delta_r\mu^\circ$). When all activities in Q are 1.0, then there is no difference, $\Delta_r\mu = \Delta_r\mu^\circ$.

We are especially interested in the value of Q when our systems reach equilibrium; that is, when the product and reactant activities have adjusted themselves spontaneously such that $\Delta_r\mu = 0$. In this state, the $\Pi_i a_i^{v_i}$ term is called K, instead of Q, and (1.129) becomes

$$\Delta_r\mu^\circ = -RT\ln K \qquad (1.130)$$

Standard states usually refer to pure substances (except for the aqueous standard states) in which $\mu = G$, so this equation is often written

$$\Delta_r G^\circ = -RT\ln K \qquad (1.131)$$

Note that the activity product ratio (K) on the right-hand side is independent of variations in the system composition. Its value is controlled completely by a difference in (tabulated) standard state free energies ($\Delta_r G^\circ$) and so is a function only of the temperature and pressure. It is a constant for a given system at a given temperature or temperature and pressure (depending on the particular standard states used) and is called the *equilibrium constant.* Its numerical value for a given reaction is not dependent on the system involved actually achieving equilibrium, or in fact even existing. Its value is fixed when the reacting substances and their standard states are chosen. The left-hand side refers to a difference in free energies of a number of different physical and ideal states, which do not represent any real system or reaction. The right-hand side, on the other hand, refers to a single reaction that has reached equilibrium, or more exactly, to the activity product ratio that would be observed if the system did reach equilibrium.

Dependence of K on Temperature and Pressure

Combining equations (1.131) and (1.54), we get

$$\ln K = \frac{-\Delta_r H^\circ}{RT} + \frac{\Delta_r S^\circ}{R} \qquad (1.132)$$

showing that if $\Delta_r H^\circ$ and $\Delta_r S^\circ$ are assumed to be independent of T, ln K will be a linear function of $1/T$. This is often a useful approximation over small temperature intervals. To find a more exact expression for the effect of T on ln K, we first differentiate (1.132), obtaining

$$\frac{\partial}{\partial T}(\ln K) = \frac{\Delta_r H^\circ}{RT^2} \tag{1.133}$$

To integrate this from T_r to T, we need to know $\Delta_r H^\circ$ as a function of T. Using the Maier-Kelley formulation (1.22), this results in

$$\begin{aligned}\ln K_T = \ln K_{T_r} &- \frac{\Delta_r H_r^\circ}{R}\left(\frac{1}{T} - \frac{1}{T_r}\right)\\ &+ \frac{\Delta_r a}{R}\left(\ln\frac{T}{T_r} + \frac{T_r}{T} - 1\right)\\ &+ \frac{\Delta_r b}{2R}\left(T + \frac{T_r^2}{T} - 2T_r\right)\\ &+ \frac{\Delta_r c}{R}\frac{(-T^2 - T_r^2 + 2TT_r)}{2T^2T_r^2}\end{aligned} \tag{1.134}$$

for reactions not involving solutes.

The effect of pressure on K depends on the standard states chosen, because these determine the nature of $\Delta_r G^\circ$. It is now standard practice in geochemistry to define standard states for solid, liquid, and solute components as existing at the T and P of the system of interest, rather than at some fixed pressure such as 1 bar, so that equations (1.103) and (1.118) can be used without modification at any T and P. The standard state for gases is commonly but not always fixed at 1 bar, as noted previously. In reactions consisting only of gaseous components, where standard states are fixed at 1 bar, the effect of pressure on $\Delta_r G^\circ$ and hence on log K is zero. In all other cases, the effect of P is calculated using equations (1.46) and (1.97). Note that although the activity of each reactant and product must have the same standard state temperature, they do not necessarily all have the same standard state pressure. So solutes could use equation (1.103), and gases could use equation (1.116) in the same equilibrium constant expression.

The fact that we define our standard states as being at any T and P does not mean that we need tables of data for every possible combination of T and P. Data are tabulated for 25°C, 1 bar, but values for any other T and P are readily calculated using the equations we have derived [e.g., (1.22), (1.64), (1.65)]. Such calculations are relatively simple, because no mixing (dissolution) is involved.

Equilibrium Constant Names

The equilibrium constant is a central concept in chemical thermodynamic thinking. There is a wide variety of chemical systems and hence a wide variety of equilibria, but there is only one equilibrium constant concept. However, it does get a variety of names, depending on the situation. For example we have solubility product constants, Henry's Law constants, stability constants, dissociation and ionization constants, and so on. Because the activity can take on a variety of forms and is often approximated by omitting activity coefficients (giving rise to distribution coefficients, partition coefficients), the equilibrium constant can look quite different in different situations. It is best to realize that there is not a variety of equilibrium constants, just a variety of names for it.

Open Systems

In multiphase closed systems, each phase within the overall closed system is an open system, or subsystem, which can change composition in response to changes in other state variables such as T and P. We need to consider these compositional changes.

Thermodynamic Potentials in Open Systems

The Fundamental Equations (1.29) and (1.44) enable us to consider energy changes in reversible and irreversible processes, but have no provision for energy changes due to changes in composition. Up to this point, we have used the term *component* a little loosely, referring generally to compositional terms. Actually, it has a very strict definition.

For a given system, one first determines the minimum number of chemical formulae required to define the composition of all parts of the system. I use the term *formulae* rather than *substances*, because the chemical formulae need not correspond to actual substances, but may, for example, contain negative amounts of some elements. The choice of components for any system is therefore quite wide, but the minimum *number* of formulae required will be fixed by the nature of the system. The individual formulae chosen are the *components* of the system. Don't forget, too, that although we are interested in some *real* system, we choose components for a *model* system; we are not required to include in the model all the substances that exist in our real system, only those we think are important.

Starting with (1.44)

$$d\mathrm{G} = -\mathrm{S}\,dT + \mathrm{V}\,dP$$

which shows the function $\mathrm{G} = \mathrm{G}(T, P)$ for a closed system having two constraints (T and P). What we need now is the function $\mathrm{G} = \mathrm{G}(T, P, n_1, n_2, \ldots, n_c)$, meaning G as a function of T, P, and the number of moles n_1, n_2, etc., of each of the c components which make up the system. This is the total differential

$$d\mathrm{G} = \left(\frac{\partial \mathrm{G}}{\partial T}\right)_{P,n} dT + \left(\frac{\partial \mathrm{G}}{\partial P}\right)_{T,n} dP + \sum_{i=1}^{c}\left(\frac{\partial \mathrm{G}}{\partial n_i}\right)_{T,P,\hat{n}_i} dn_i \tag{1.135}$$

where n means n_1, n_2, . . . ,n_c (all components), n_i is any individual component i, and $\hat{n}_i$ means all components except i. This equation refers to a system capable of changing composition (an open system), but we recall that each individual phase in any system is in fact an open system. There is therefore an equation (1.135) for every phase. Recalling the definition of the chemical potential, (1.95), this becomes

$$dG = -S\,dT + V\,dP + \sum_{i=1}^{c} \mu_i\,dn_i \qquad (1.136)$$

where dG refers to a single phase. There is also however a G for the system as a whole, which, as an extensive property, is the sum of the G terms of all the individual phases. It is possible to show from (1.136) that for G to be minimized ($dG = 0$) for the system as a whole, T, P, and all μ_i must be the same in every part of the system, i.e., in every phase. This means there must be no gradients in T, P, or composition, which accords with our intuitive understanding of equilibrium.

Components and species. Consider the two-component system N_2-H_2. Components N_2 and H_2 refer to the result you would get if you analyzed the system for total nitrogen and total hydrogen. The actual molecular form taken by each element in the system is irrelevant. However, N_2 and H_2 might also refer to the *species* in the system, i.e., diatomic nitrogen molecules and diatomic hydrogen molecules. In real systems, for example, species N_2 and H_2 combine to form ammonia,

$$N_2(g) + 3\,H_2(g) = 2\,NH_3(g) \qquad (1.137)$$

so that there are at least three major species. In many systems, there may be only a few components, but dozens or hundreds of species.

Equation (1.136) has been derived for systems of c components. For example, in the two component system N_2-H_2, $c = 2$, and the final term on the right side would be $\mu_{N_2}dn_{N_2} + \mu_{H_2}dn_{H_2}$. However, the equation can also be used with i representing some or all of the *species* in the system, rather than the components, as long as the species are related to one another in balanced chemical reactions, such that the number of independent compositional parameters remains equal to c. Thus the final term on the right side of (1.136) could also read $\mu_{N_2}dn_{N_2} + \mu_{H_2}dn_{H_2}$, where N_2 and H_2 are now species and not components. Although we now have three compositional terms, we also have an equation (1.137) relating them (assuming equilibrium), so there are still only two independent compositional terms.

Changing from components to species in this way provides for some flexibility that we shall take advantage of shortly. In a closed system, we cannot change the chemical potentials of components N_2 and H_2, and the last term in (1.136) is zero. However, the chemical potentials of the species in (1.137) *can* change in a closed system, if the reaction progresses to the left or the right from some metastable state toward the stable equilibrium state. The last term in (1.136) (which would look a bit different in having $\sum_{i=1}^{s}$, rather than $\sum_{i=1}^{c}$, that is, s species rather than c components) would not be zero, even in a closed system, if we were considering chemical reactions progressing toward equilibrium. Furthermore, in such cases this last term must always be negative, to be consistent with (1.43).

The phase rule. Some manipulation of (1.136) results in another Fundamental Equation, the celebrated Gibbs-Duhem relationship,

$$S\,dT - V\,dP + \sum_{i=1}^{c} n_i\,d\mu_i = 0 \qquad (1.138)$$

where the i are again the c independent components, and $X_i = n_i/(n_1 + n_2 + \cdots + n_c)$, the mole fraction of i. From (1.138), we can see the number of independent intensive variables in any homogeneous phase. There are c compositional (chemical potential) terms, and two other intensive variables T and P, giving a total of $c + 2$ intensive variables.

In a single homogeneous phase, these $c + 2$ variables are linked by one equation (1.138), so only $c + 2 - 1$ of them are independent. If there are p phases, there are still only $c + 2$ intensive variables, because they have the same value in every phase (at equilibrium), but now there is one equation (1.138) for each phase, and $c + 2 - p$ independent intensive variables. These independent intensive variables are called degrees of freedom, f, so

$$f = c - p + 2 \qquad (1.139)$$

which is the Phase Rule.

Constraints and degrees of freedom. If you trace the origin of the "2" in equation (1.139), you find it is introduced in the derivation of equation (1.28), when we decided to consider only one kind of work, and therefore only two ways to change the energy content of systems. If there are work terms other than $P\Delta V$ work, there is an extra degree of freedom for each, because each provides a new way of changing the energy of the system. These extra degrees of freedom are in fact our third or higher *constraints.* There is therefore some overlap between the concepts of constraints and of degrees of freedom.

Imposing a third constraint (imposing a voltage; changing the degree of order or of stress, recrystallizing to a different polymorphic form, etc.) on a closed system in a stable equilibrium state (one at equilibrium and having only two constraints, such as T and P) *always* requires doing work on the system, and releasing that constraint always allows the system to do work, whatever the nature of the constraint. Therefore each added constraint is a degree of freedom, as are the two initial constraints (U and V; T and P). Constraints are included among the degrees of freedom a system has—they are a subset of the degrees of freedom concept. However, they apply only to closed systems (eliminating all compositional variables), and are independent of the number of phases.

Constraints are ways of changing the energy of systems. Therefore the number of constraints equals the number of terms on the right side of Fundamental Equations such as (1.29), (1.34), (1.35), and (1.47), in most cases either two (stable) or three (metastable). Also, there is always a state variable associated with each constraint, in our cases U, V, and ξ, or T, P, and ξ.

The HKF Model for Aqueous Electrolytes

Overall Structure

Modeling of hydrothermal solutions would be difficult without some provision for determining the Gibbs energies of aqueous ions and electrolytes, and how these vary with T, P, and composition. The variation of the Gibbs free energy of individual ions with T, P, and composition (and switching to HKF notation, in which j is used for ions) can be represented by writing the total differential of the partial molar free energy of the jth ion, giving

$$d\overline{G}_j = -\overline{S}_j dT + \overline{V}_j dP + (\partial\mu_j/\partial m_j)_{T,P} dm_j \quad (1.140)$$

where j is an ion of molality m_j in an aqueous solution of any composition. Changes in $\overline{G}_j$ due to changes in T, P, or m_j, are found by integrating this equation,

$$\int_{T_r,P_r,m_r}^{T,P,m} d\overline{G}_j = -\int_{T_r}^{T} \overline{S}_{j,P_r,m_r} dT + \int_{P_r}^{P} \overline{V}_{j,T,m_r} dP + \int_{m_r}^{m} d\mu_{j,T,P} \quad (1.141)$$

The first two integrals on the right-hand side take place at concentration m_r. If we equate this with the standard state (ideal one molal solution), then $\overline{S}_j$ and $\overline{V}_j$ become $\overline{S}_j^\circ$ and $\overline{V}_j^\circ$ respectively. The third integral takes care of departures from standard state conditions (change of composition) at T and P. Integration of $\int_{T_r}^{T} \overline{S}_j^\circ\, dT$ requires knowledge of $\overline{C}_{pj}^\circ$, and integration of $\int_{m_r}^{m} d\mu_j$ $(= \mu_j - \mu_j^\circ = RT \ln a_j = RT \ln m_j\gamma_{Hj})$ requires knowledge of γ_{Hj}. Therefore, the information needed to know how the Gibbs energy of an ion j varies with T, P, and composition is how $\overline{C}_{pj}^\circ$ and $\overline{V}_j^\circ$ vary with T and P respectively, and how γ_{Hj} varies with composition.

Earlier we said that the temperature dependence of the heat capacity for pure substances (solids, liquids, and gases) was described by equation (1.19). This works well because the heat capacity for pure substances is a continuously increasing function of T. Dissolved substances, and particularly electrolytes (which dissociate into charged particles or ions in solution), have a more complex behavior for which the Maier-Kelley equation (1.19), or any other such polynomial, is entirely inadequate. Therefore we must devise another equation for the effect of T on C_p. We evidently also need an expression for the effect of T and P on the partial molar volumes of ions, i.e., an equation of state for ions. To complete the model, we also need an activity coefficient expression that gives γ_{Hj} as a function of composition at any T and P. The various modifications of the Debye-Hückel equation are usually considered adequate for this purpose. However, even without activity coefficients, we will be able to calculate standard state properties and hence equilibrium constants at T and P. This is the major contribution of the HKF model.

How to avoid reading the rest of this section. The rest of this section is a very brief description of the HKF model, proposed by Helgeson and Kirkham (1974a, b; 1976) and Helgeson et al. (1981), and revised by Tanger and Helgeson (1988). This section is somewhat like the old IBM computer manuals—you had to understand the subject completely before you could understand the manuals, which were supposed to explain it. The model is too complex to "explain" in the space available; nevertheless, it is now an essential tool, and it is possible to at least have some appreciation for what is going on when you press a few keys and obtain reasonably accurate data for your important reactions at high temperatures and pressures.

The main points are these:

1. Equation (1.141) shows that to calculate changes in the standard free energy of ion j with T and P, we need to know how $\overline{C}_{pj}^\circ$, and $\overline{V}_j^\circ$ vary with T and P respectively. The HKF model provides semi-empirical equations of state and tables of data that permit this.

2. These equations and data have been incorporated into the program SUPCRT92 (Johnson et al., 1992), together with the Haar et al. (1984) equation of state for water and Maier-Kelley coefficients for minerals and gases, which permits calculation of log K and other parameters for chemical reactions over a very wide range of T and P.

3. The HKF model also proposes a method for calculating activity coefficients (γ_{Hj}), but this has not been incorporated into SUPCRT92.

4. The Gibbs energy of formation ($\Delta_f\overline{G}^\circ$) of ions is a bit more complicated than that for compounds, because no properties of single ions can be measured, and so additional conventions must be introduced. However, the effects of these conventions all cancel out in balanced reactions, just as the elemental properties cancel out [see discussion of equation (1.12)].

Solvation: The Born Functions

We saw that the Gibbs energy that we use for compounds ($\Delta_f G^\circ$) is actually the difference between the Gibbs energy (G°) of the compound and the sum of the Gibbs energies of the constituent elements, each in its most stable state. The $\Delta_f G^\circ$ of an element in its most stable state, such as $\Delta_f G^\circ_{Na}$, is then the difference between the G° of the element and the G° of its constituent elements ($G^\circ_{Na} - G^\circ_{Na}$) or zero (it does not follow that the G of elements is zero). What then, for example, is the (partial molar) Gibbs energy of formation of the sodium ion in water, $\Delta_f\overline{G}^\circ_{Na^+}$? It will not be zero, because Na^+ is in a totally different energetic state than metallic Na. The difference consists mostly in what happens when Na is (conceptually) immersed in water and then given a positive charge.

It can be argued (Bockris and Reddy; 1970, v. 1, p. 56) that the Gibbs energy of ion-solvent interaction is equivalent to the work done in discharging an ion in a vacuum and charging the ion again in the solvent having a dielectric constant ϵ. Assuming the ion to be a simple sphere, Born (1920) showed that this quantity is

$$\Delta\overline{G}^{\circ}_{s,j} = \frac{N_a(Z_je)^2}{2r_j}\left(\frac{1}{\epsilon}-1\right) \qquad (1.142)$$

where $\Delta\overline{G}_{s,j}$ is the Gibbs energy of solvation (or hydration in the case of water) for ion j, N_a is Avogadro's number, e is the electronic charge, Z_j is the number of electronic charges (i.e., the valence of ion j), r_j is the ionic radius, and ϵ is the dielectric constant of the solvent (water).

This simple equation—based on coulombic forces only—when combined with other data, predicts enthalpies of hydration that have the same order of magnitude as experimental values. The fact that it succeeds as well as it does suggests that it contains a large part of the truth, and might serve as the basis of a more satisfactory model.

In the HKF model, a number of theoretical difficulties in equating the Born function with ion-solvent interaction are accommodated in two ways. First, the ionic radius is treated as an adjustable parameter called $r_{e,j}$, the *effective* ionic radius. It is derived from crystallographic ionic radii, with corrections modeled on data for aqueous NaCl to high T and P. Second, thermodynamic properties predicted by the Born function are compared to experimental data, and the differences are fitted to empirical functions. The contribution of the Born function in the HKF model is called the *solvation* contribution, and the empirical part is called the *non-solvation* contribution.

Single ion properties. The Born function for individual ions, and in fact any single ionic property, is not experimentally measurable. Thus we can measure properties for NaCl(*aq*), but not for Na^+ or Cl^-. Two conventions are required to get around this problem. The first convention is that the properties of electrolytes are taken to be the sum of the individual ionic species. Thus, for example, $\overline{V}^{\circ}_{NaCl(aq)} = \overline{V}^{\circ}_{Na^+} + \overline{V}^{\circ}_{Cl^-}$. The second convention is that an ionic property (e.g., $\overline{V}_j$; $\overline{G}_j$) is taken to be the *difference* between the property for ion j and the same property in the same solution for the hydrogen ion, H^+. What this amounts to in practice is that the properties of aqueous Cl^- are taken to be exactly those of HCl(*aq*), and similarly for other completely dissociated acids. This convention is often expressed by saying that we assume all properties of the hydrogen ion to be zero, which is not really necessary.

Having properties for Cl^-, it is then possible to obtain properties for Na^+ from those of NaCl(*aq*), and similarly for all other individual ions. The properties thus obtained are "conventional" properties, though this word is often omitted. The definitions of ionic Gibbs energies and enthalpies, being themselves differences, get a bit more complicated, but the principle is the same—having conventional properties for the chloride ion, we can derive conventional properties for all ions.

We now define a "conventional" Born parameter for ion j as

$$\begin{aligned}\omega_j &= \frac{N_a(Z_je)^2}{2r_{e,j}} - \left[\frac{N_a(Z_{H^+}e)^2}{2r_{e,H^+}}\right].\\ &= \frac{N_a(Z_je)^2}{2r_{e,j}} - 0.5387Z_j\end{aligned} \qquad (1.143)$$

where 0.5387 is the value of $N_a(Z_{H^+}e)^2/(2r_{e,H^+})$ (Helgeson and Kirkham, 1976). The Born function in the HKF model is therefore

$$\Delta\overline{G}^{\circ}_{s,j} = \omega_j\left(\frac{1}{\epsilon}-1\right) \qquad (1.144)$$

which is the difference in ion-solvent interaction between ion j and that of H^+.

Having defined the $\Delta\overline{G}^{\circ}_s$, for ion-solvent interaction, the $\Delta\overline{V}^{\circ}_s$, $\overline{C}^{\circ}_{ps}$ and other properties are derived by differentiation [equations (1.58), (1.96), (1.97)], giving rise to a number of Born functions that define the "solvation contribution" to each property calculated in the HKF model. In practice this means fitting data for the dielectric constant of water to an empirical equation in T and P, inserting this into (1.144), then differentiating. Because $r_{e,j}$ is also a function of T and P, the whole process is a rather large project in data processing.

The Non-Solvation Contribution

After defining the Born function as described above, comparison of experimental values of $\Delta\overline{V}^{\circ}$ and $\Delta\overline{C}^{\circ}_p$ with calculated values of $\Delta\overline{V}^{\circ}_s$ and $\Delta\overline{C}^{\circ}_{ps}$ showed that the discrepancies could be fitted with functions of the form

$$\Delta\overline{V}^{\circ}_n = a_1 + a_2f(P) + a_3f_1(T) + a_4f(P)f_1(T) \qquad (1.145)$$

and

$$\Delta\overline{C}^{\circ}_{pn} = c_1 + c_2f_2(T) \qquad (1.146)$$

where subscript n stands for non-solvation, and

$$f_1(T) = 1/(T-\Theta)$$

$$f_2(T) = 1/(T-\Theta)^2$$

$$f(P) = 1/(\Psi + P)$$

where Θ, a variable in the original model, is now fixed at 228 K. The Ψ parameter is also fixed at 2,600 bars.

Combining the solvation and non-solvation parts of the model gives

$$\overline{V}^{\circ}_{T,P} = \Delta\overline{V}^{\circ}_{n} + \Delta\overline{V}^{\circ}_{s}$$
$$= \underbrace{a_1 + \frac{a_2}{\Psi + P} + \frac{a_3}{T - \Theta} + \frac{a_4}{(\Psi + P)(T - \Theta)}}_{\textit{non-solvation part}}$$
$$\underbrace{-\,\omega Q + \left(\frac{1}{\epsilon} - 1\right)\left(\frac{\partial\omega}{\partial P}\right)_T}_{\textit{solvation part}} \qquad (1.147)$$

for the (conventional) standard partial molar volume of ion j or electrolyte k as a function of T and P, and

$$\overline{C}^{\circ}_{PT} = \Delta\overline{C}^{\circ}_{Pn} + \Delta\overline{C}^{\circ}_{Ps}$$
$$= \underbrace{c_1 + \frac{c_2}{(T - \Theta)^2}}_{\textit{non-solvation part}}$$
$$\underbrace{+\,\omega T X + 2TY\left(\frac{\partial\omega}{\partial T}\right)_P - T\left(\frac{1}{\epsilon} - 1\right)\left(\frac{\partial^2\omega}{\partial T^2}\right)_P}_{\textit{solvation part}} \qquad (1.148)$$

for the (conventional) standard partial molar heat capacity of ion j or electrolyte k as a function of T only, where Q, X and Y are Born functions, that is, temperature and pressure derivatives of the dielectric constant of pure water.

As mentioned above, having the standard state volume and heat capacity terms as a function of T and P permits calculation of the standard state Gibbs energy and hence the equilibrium constant over a range of T and P. The essential parameters required to use the HKF model to obtain the properties of an ion j or an electrolyte k are then the four volume fit coefficients $a_1 \ldots a_4$, the two heat capacity coefficients, c_1, c_2, the Born function for that property, and ω_j, another Born parameter which includes the effective ionic radius.

We omit presentation of the various complete HKF equations for the thermodynamic properties of ions and electrolytes, but those presented thus far will give you an appreciation of the complexities of the model, and the work involved in developing it.

Phase Separation

So far, the relevance of this chapter to ore formation modeling has been limited to the choice of material included and excluded. We now get a bit closer to the subject of real interest. With the concepts so far developed, we could in principle combine experimental data with our equations to calculate values of all our thermodynamic parameters for minerals, gases, and ions over a range of T and P. We could, therefore, calculate solubility products, and even solubilities of minerals and gases, if we knew the species involved and had data for them. But that is not enough.

The process of phase separation is important in studies of the phase relations in any system. In geological systems, phase separation from a fluid phase arises in the study of both silicate melts and aqueous solutions. The thermodynamic properties of silicate melts are less well understood than those of aqueous solutions, so that the application of thermodynamics to melt crystallization and exsolution of volatiles is less useful from the point of view of discussing principles, such as in this chapter. Therefore the discussion here will focus on hydrothermal solutions.

One of the more important events in the life of any hydrothermal solution is the splitting of the homogeneous or single-phase solution into two or more phases. This generally means generation of a gas phase or precipitation of minerals from a hydrothermal liquid, as a result of some changing conditions during the travels of the solution. We have laid the groundwork for the consideration of this process with the concept of the Gibbs energy, and the idea that μ_i will be the same in all phases and for all i at equilibrium. It follows that we can predict phase separation by comparing, at any T and P, the μ of the dissolved gas or mineral with the μ of the separated gas or mineral. For a homogeneous solution, μ of the dissolved gas or mineral will be less than μ of the separate (pure) gas or mineral at the same T and P, and the separate phase will either not exist, or will tend to dissolve if it does exist. But as conditions change, it may happen that the reverse becomes the case, and the gas or mineral will separate from the solution in order to keep the G of the system as a whole to a minimum.

Of course, because we cannot measure or calculate μ directly, what we actually do is compare activities or fugacities, which we *can* measure or calculate, and which are directly related to μ. Assuming that we are able to write a balanced reaction for the coexistence of a gas or mineral and its dissolved components, we can also calculate the equilibrium constant for that reaction, and knowing the activities or fugacities of the dissolved components and the pure separated phases, we can predict whether phase separation should take place or not.

Speciation Calculations

First, we must mention a procedure that is not exactly thermodynamic in nature, but which is essential to considerations of phase separation. This is the process of calculating, for any given bulk fluid composition at specified T and P, the activities (molalities and activity coefficients) of all the ionic and molecular dissolved species in the fluid. There are many more species than components in any solution. Even a two-component solution such as $NaCl$-H_2O will have many species such as Na^+, Cl^-, H^+, OH^-, $NaCl^\circ$, $NaOH^\circ$, and perhaps others not yet discovered, or perhaps neglected because of low concentration. In this simple two-component case, the speciation calculation consists of determining, at whatever the T and P of the solution, both the molality and activity coefficient of each of the six species mentioned. Since there are thus 12 unknown quantities, we must formulate 12 equations involving these unknowns, and be able to solve them. Six of these equations will be activity coefficient equations, and the other six will consist of equilibrium constant expressions and mass and charge balances.

There is no need to go into details here; suffice it to say that it is now a routine problem, and many programs are available for solving it for any number of components, often resulting in literally hundreds of species (see Chap. 2). A single note of caution is warranted. You can only solve for the species you know about, or perhaps that your database knows about, and that you have data for. It is quite possible to arrive at incorrect conclusions simply by not considering all the relevant species, or by having poor data for those that you do consider.

Precipitation

Our G minimization concept means that for any chemical reaction, if $\Delta_r\mu$ (*not* $\Delta_r\mu^\circ$) is negative, the reaction as written will proceed to the right; if $\Delta_r\mu$ is positive, the reaction as written will proceed to the left. In principle, we determine $\Delta_r\mu$ from equation (1.128), by using the activities of all products and reactants to determine the quantity Q. In practice, we proceed as follows. To determine whether a mineral is undersaturated or supersaturated in a solution, we write for that mineral

$$\text{solid mineral} = \text{dissolved mineral} \qquad (1.149)$$

If this reaction goes to the right, the solution is undersaturated. If it goes to the left, the solution is supersaturated. For example, equation (1.149) for calcium carbonate is

$$CaCO_3(s) = Ca^{2+} + CO_3^{2-} \qquad (1.150)$$

and the equilibrium constant is

$$\frac{a_{Ca^{2+}}a_{CO_3^{2-}}}{a_{CaCO_3(s)}} = K_{150} \qquad (1.151)$$

If we assume that $CaCO_3$ will precipitate as a pure mineral, either calcite or aragonite, then $a_{CaCO_3(s)} = 1$, and K becomes the *solubility product*, K_{sp}, the ion activity product *required for equilibrium* with the pure solid phase, which can be calculated from equation (1.131). It is of course different for calcite and aragonite. Note that K and K_{sp} are numerically identical for reaction (1.150); the only difference is how we use them.

Any particular solution being considered at a particular T and P, either the chemical analysis of a real solution or some hypothetical solution, will have particular values of $a_{Ca^{2+}}$ and $a_{CO_3^{2-}}$, which are determined by the speciation calculation. The product of these ion activities is the ion activity product *in the actual solution*, and is called IAP. We compare the values of IAP and K_{sp} for the reaction, usually with the quantity $\log(\mathrm{IAP}/K_{sp})$, called the *Saturation Index*, SI. If SI = 0 for a reaction, the solution being considered is theoretically saturated with the pure mineral phase for that reaction. If SI > 0, the pure mineral is supersaturated, and should precipitate, and if SI < 0 it is undersaturated, and should dissolve if present.

However, $CaCO_3$ may be part of a solid solution, say ankerite. In this case, the ratio IAP/K_{sp} gives $a_{CaCO_3(s)}$, the solid phase activity required for equilibrium with the ion activities in the solution. This activity is transformed into a mole fraction using equation (1.119), which requires that we have a solid solution model giving us values of the Raoultian activity coefficient in this case. Equation (1.150) is then rewritten for the other components of the solid solution, in this case substituting Fe and Mg for Ca, and the mole fractions of those components ($FeCO_3$ and $MgCO_3$) are calculated in a similar way. If the sum of the mole fractions $X_{CaCO_3} + X_{FeCO_3} + X_{MgCO_3} = 1$, the solution is saturated with the solid solution phase. If the sum >1, the solution is supersaturated, and if it is <1, it is undersaturated.

It does not matter whether or not Ca^{2+} and CO_3^{2-} are the dominant forms of calcium and carbonate in solution; in fact they may be very minor forms. In fact, virtually any species formed from the dissolved mineral can be used in (1.150). The important thing is to be able to solve for the activities of those species. Thus the dissolution of K-feldspar could be written

$$KAlSi_3O_8(s) = K^+ + AlO_2^- + 3\,SiO_2(aq) \qquad (1.152)$$

or as

$$KAlSi_3O_8(s) + 9\,H_2O(l) = KOH^\circ + H^+ + Al(OH)_4^- + 3\,H_4SiO_4(aq) \qquad (1.153)$$

or in several other ways. Each will give the same answer about the precipitation of K-feldspar, as long as the activities of all the various species can be correctly calculated.

Boiling

The term "boiling" is often used as a shorthand way of referring to the often complex process of the separation of a less dense phase from a more dense fluid phase. We will consider here only a gas phase separating from a hydrothermal solution. Whatever the process of fluid phase separation is called, it is generally more complex than mineral precipitation because the separation of the vapor phase involves vaporization of the solvent (water) itself, not just dissolved components. The enthalpy change is therefore a major factor, in contrast with the fairly minor enthalpy of crystallization associated with mineral precipitation. Crystallization of minerals from a melt is analogous in this respect, in the sense that part of the solvent itself is changing phase.

To understand the boiling calculation, consider first some pure water at depth in the crust. Pure water has a known vapor pressure which varies from 1 bar at 100°C to 221 bars at 374°C , the critical temperature. At a particular place in the crust, whether water will boil or not depends only on its T and P. If the confining pressure exceeds the vapor pressure at that temperature, no vapor phase will form. If the vapor pressure exceeds the confining pressure, a vapor phase will form, and the water will boil until it is gone or until the confining pressure increases or until T decreases. Each of these possibilities can be further explored in a geological context. For example, it is often assumed that conduction of heat to the water through the wall rocks is slow compared to the boiling process, so that the enthalpy of vaporization must come from the water itself, resulting in a cooling effect (*adiabatic boiling*). Alternatively, it could be assumed that the boiling process is very slow, and that the enthalpy of vaporization is supplied entirely from the wall rocks (*isothermal boiling*). Also, some assumption must be made about the volume available to the vapor phase. If it is a fixed volume, the vapor pressure will build up to the equilibrium value; if the vapor can escape, boiling will continue (*closed* vs. *open system* boiling).

Suppose now that the water is in contact with a limestone, and therefore contains some carbonate. Whatever the nature of the solution or other conditions, some dissolved gas (CO_2 and perhaps CO) will form because of reactions between the dissolved CO_3^{2-} and $H_2O(l)$, for example

$$CO_3^{2-} + 2H^+ = CO_2(aq) + H_2O(l) \qquad (1.154)$$

and a speciation calculation will give us $a_{CO_2(aq)}$. We can then consider the reaction between $CO_2(aq)$ and $CO_2(g)$, which is

$$CO_2(aq) = CO_2(g) \qquad (1.155)$$

to determine the fugacity of $CO_2(g)$ (the speciation program could of course do this for us). This f_{CO_2} can then be converted into a partial pressure [equation (1.112)], by calculating an appropriate fugacity coefficient. This is the partial pressure of CO_2 in a vapor phase in equilibrium with the liquid, *if there is a vapor phase.* Note that the fugacity, f_{CO_2}, being a thermodynamic model parameter, has meaning whether or not there is a vapor or gas phase, but the partial pressure is a physical quantity, defined as the mole fraction times the total pressure of the gas, which cannot exist unless there is a gas. We now have a pressure term for CO_2 gas, which we can add to the vapor pressure of water. Carrying out similar calculations for other gases, we arrive at a total pressure which we then compare with the confining pressure to see if a gas phase will form.

Actually, as noted by Reed (1982), the calculation is identical in form to the "solid mineral = dissolved mineral" problem, only changing the solid solution to a gaseous solution, and using fugacities instead of activities. The role of the aqueous solution is the same in both cases. In addition, there must be provision for the changing activity of the solvent, which will decrease as water evaporates, and this in turn has an effect on activity coefficients and the water vapor pressure. Also, in a multicomponent gas phase, the contribution of each gas to the enthalpy of vaporization must be separately calculated, and the effects of non-ideal mixing incorporated.

All these relationships are solved in an iterative manner simultaneously. This is easy to say, but it presents a number of numerical and conceptual problems that have been the focus of much research over the last 30 years.

Redox Reactions

A number of elements can occur with more than one electron configuration, and these differ widely in their chemical properties (e.g., sulfur as H_2S is poisonous; sulfur as SO_4^{2-} is harmless). Therefore it becomes important to have a parameter that characterizes the oxidation state of fluids, much as T characterizes the temperature, and pH characterizes the acidity (recall that $pH = -\log a_{H^+}$). At Earth surface conditions, the most widely used such parameter is the *oxidation potential, Eh*, probably because it can be directly measured with suitable electrodes. However, *Eh* is a function of *pH* for many important reactions, and it becomes more difficult to use at elevated temperatures, so geochemical modeling more often uses another parameter, *oxygen fugacity*, or f_{O_2}.

We introduced the fugacity concept in the usual way, by considering real gas pressures, and the correction factor (γ_f) required to change a partial pressure into a fugacity. It then becomes habitual to think of fugacity as a kind of partial pressure. However, the actual definition of fugacity has no such restrictions. Consider the following reaction:

$$H_2S(aq) + 2O_2(g) = SO_4^{2-} + 2H^+ \qquad (1.156)$$

for which the equilibrium constant is

$$\frac{a_{SO_4^{2-}} a_{H^+}^2}{a_{H_2S(aq)} f_{O_2}^2} = K_{156} \qquad (1.157)$$

where f_{O_2} has been substituted for a_{O_2} [equation (1.116)]. If you look up the values of $\Delta_f G^\circ$ for each of these four species and calculate K [equation (1.131)], you will find it is about 10^{126} at 25°C. If you now choose a pH of 7.0 ($a_{H^+} = 10^{-7}$) and rearrange equation (1.157), you find

$$f_{O_2} = 10^{-70} \left(\frac{a_{SO_4^{2-}}}{a_{H_2S(aq)}} \right)^{\frac{1}{2}} \qquad (1.158)$$

Thus f_{O_2} is a quantity that is proportional to the sulfate–sulfide ratio. If we choose conditions such that $a_{SO_4^{2-}} = a_{H_2S(aq)}$, we find $f_{O_2} = 10^{-70}$ bars. Considered as a partial pressure of oxygen, this doesn't make much sense, because it would correspond to something like one molecule of oxygen in the entire universe. So the fugacity of oxygen, while it does approximate a partial pressure under some conditions, is better thought of as simply a thermodynamic parameter that is a useful index of the oxidation state of aqueous solutions (or almost any other system) under all conditions. In the above case, if the sulfate–sulfide ratio is 100 (solution more oxidized), the f_{O_2} is 10^{-69}; if the sulfate–sulfide ratio is 0.01 (solution more reduced), the f_{O_2} is 10^{-71}. Of course the same relationships hold for any redox pair, such as Fe^{3+}/Fe^{2+}, CO_2/CH_4, U^{6+}/U^{4+}, and so on. Each ratio may be different, but each pair can appear in a balanced reaction involving $O_2(g)$, and if the solution is at equilibrium, each pair will result in the same f_{O_2}. Note that in this example, we were careful to use the labels (g) and (aq), because $O_2(aq)$ and $O_2(g)$ are thermodynamically and physically quite different things, and similarly for $H_2S(aq)$ and $H_2S(g)$.

So we see that although f_{O_2} is a useful indicator of redox conditions, it does become very small under reducing conditions. In these cases it is often more convenient to use hydrogen instead of oxygen as the indicator substance. The fugacities f_{O_2} and f_{H_2} are related in aqueous systems by the reaction

$$2\,H_2O(l) = O_2(g) + 2\,H_2(g) \tag{1.159}$$

for which the equilibrium constant is

$$K_{159} = \frac{f_{O_2} \cdot f_{H_2}^2}{a_{H_2O(l)}} \tag{1.160}$$

Therefore in hydrothermal systems, in which $a_{H_2O(l)} \approx 1$ [equation (1.119)], the oxygen and hydrogen fugacities are inversely related, so that as f_{O_2} becomes very small, f_{H_2} (or a_{H_2}) becomes large, and in many cases is actually a measurable quantity, i.e., a partial pressure (or a molality).

For example, at 300°C, $K_{159} = 10^{-35.61}$, and $K_{156} = 10^{47.75}$. If, as before, the pH is 7.0, and $a_{H_2S(aq)} = a_{SO_4^{2-}}$, f_{O_2} is $10^{-30.88}$ bars, an unmeasurably small quantity. However, by (1.160), f_{H_2} is $10^{-2.37}$ bars, which may be a measurable parameter. Thus in aqueous systems, both f_{O_2} and f_{H_2} can serve as redox indicators. Which is more convenient depends on whether the system is relatively oxidized or reduced.

Buffered Components

It sometimes happens that the number of phases is the same or greater than the number of components, resulting in the number of degrees of freedom being ≤ 2 [equation (1.139)]. This results in the system being "buffered", meaning it will resist change. For example, a rock consisting of hematite and magnetite has $p = 2$ and $c = 2$, so $f = 2$. This means that at a specified T and P (our two degrees of freedom), all properties of the rock are fixed and determinable (whether or not anyone has actually determined them is irrelevant here). For example, because hematite and magnetite are related by equation (1.49), for which the equilibrium constant is

$$\frac{a_{Fe_3O_4}^2 a_{O_2}^{\frac{1}{2}}}{a_{Fe_2O_3}^3} = K_{49} \tag{1.161}$$

and because both minerals are quite pure and have unit activity [equation (1.119)], then $a_{O_2} = K_{49}^2$, which is a constant. In other words, the oxygen activity [or fugacity, equation (1.116)] along with all other properties of the rock, has a fixed value at the specified T and P. This means that the oxidation state of the rock, and of any fluid in equilibrium with the rock, is fixed. There may of course be no oxygen molecules in the rock or the fluid, as discussed earlier, but changes in the fluid or in the rock tending to change its oxidation state (e.g., introduction of oxidizing agents) will not in fact change that state, but will only change the ratio of hematite to magnetite. Only when one of these phases disappears will the oxidation state of the system change.

It may happen that the rock contains pure hematite and magnetite, but it contains a lot of other minerals as well, and we are not sure how many components or degrees of freedom there are. No matter, the oxygen fugacity is still fixed by the presence of the two oxides, as long as they remain pure and at equilibrium with the rest of the system. In effect, they constitute a two-component system within the multicomponent rock, buffering f_{O_2} for the whole rock. This concept has been transferred to the laboratory, where mineral pairs are often used to control oxidation states in experiments.

In fact, in view of the emphasis given to oxygen fugacity buffering in experimental systems, it is worth emphasizing that buffering reactions can control all kinds of chemical species. For example, the activity of Fe is also buffered in hematite + magnetite. Similarly, the activity of SiO_2 will be buffered by the presence of quartz, or, at a different value, by the presence of (pure) albite and (pure) nepheline. A three component system with three phases is also buffered. For example, K-feldspar + muscovite + quartz will buffer not only a_{SiO_2}, but $a_{Al_2O_3}$, a_{KOH}, a_{K^+}/a_{H^+}, and other activities as well. In each case, it is possible to write a reaction in which all three minerals appear, plus the species being buffered. It is then buffered for the same reasons given for oxygen in the case of hematite + magnetite.

Naturally, we must always be cautious in applying these concepts to real systems. In this case, for example, the hematite grains in our rocks may be completely mantled by another phase, so that hematite and magnetite cannot reach equilibrium, and the rock is therefore not buffered. Our model systems are always at equilibrium, but our real systems may not be.

Process Modeling

Because thermodynamics deals primarily with equilibrium states, whereas natural systems seem to be in continual flux and rarely reach equilibrium, it is natural to wonder to what extent this subject can help in the study of natural processes. We have already seen that we can calculate some useful things such as solubilities, gas phase compositions, and even stable assemblages in metamorphic rocks (well, we have perhaps not seen all this, but we have seen all the tools needed to do all this). But these situations represent equilibrium states. What about the processes between these states? What can thermodynamics tell us about irreversible processes, beyond the fact that they can happen or cannot happen in certain circumstances?

Earlier we introduced the progress variable and the affinity. It is time to take a closer look at these concepts.

Affinity and the Progress Variable

We have developed two examples of Fundamental Equations [equations (1.29) and (1.44)]. These are equations that relate three state variables, but not just any three. Two of the state variables define the stable equilibrium state (S and V; T and P), and the third (U; G) becomes a thermodynamic potential (becomes minimized) under those chosen conditions. However, we also said that systems can be at equilibrium (not changing), though not at the minimum possible U or G values. These other equilibrium states are metastable, and they have a natural tendency to decrease their $U_{S,V}$ or $G_{T,P}$ contents, but they are constrained from doing so. Without this constraint, they would spontaneously slide down the $U_{S,V}$ or $G_{T,P}$ gradient to minimize these quantities.

We call the two state variables required to define the system the first two constraints, and the constraint resulting in the metastable state the third constraint. The third constraint may just be the fact that some reactants are separated from each other, or it may be that the system is somehow "frozen" in its higher energy state, such as diamond or sanidine at room temperature. It could also be an imposed voltage in an electrolytic cell, or some osmotic arrangement. Whatever the nature of the metastable state, or the third constraint, we can imagine that constraint being released in a stepwise manner. Each time the constraint is released, the system changes irreversibly towards stable equilibrium—a bit of diamond changes to graphite; imposed voltage is reduced; the Al and Si in sanidine become a bit more ordered. When the constraint is reapplied, the system stops changing in a new metastable state. This doesn't happen in real life of course—we are talking about model systems here.

The following discussion could take place in terms of U, S, and V, or of G, T, and P. We prefer the latter, so we start with our Fundamental Equation (1.44),

$$dG = -SdT + VdP$$

This describes the shape of the G–T–P surface for stable equilibrium of any system (Figure 2B); knowing S as a function of T and V as a function of P, we could integrate to find ΔG resulting from any change in T and P, as long as the beginning and final states are both stable equilibrium states. However, for a change from a metastable equilibrium state to a stable equilibrium state on release of a constraint, $dG_{T,P}$ is always negative, which we indicate by equation (1.43), or by

(1.162)

analogous to (1.33). As before [equation (1.34)], we can invent a variable to represent the third constraint that results in the negative quantity,

$$dG = \left(\frac{\partial G}{\partial T}\right)_{P,\xi} dT + \left(\frac{\partial G}{\partial P}\right)_{T,\xi} dP + \left(\frac{\partial G}{\partial \xi}\right)_{T,P} d\xi \qquad (1.163)$$

Comparing this with (1.47), we see that another definition of the affinity A is $(\partial G/\partial \xi)_{T,P}$, and (1.163) becomes

$$dG = -S\,dT + V\,dP - A\,d\xi \qquad (1.164)$$

as before. The fact that we define the affinity in different ways, i.e., as $-(\partial U/\partial \xi)_{S,V}$ or as $-(\partial G/\partial \xi)_{T,P}$, just means we refer to the same reaction taking place under different constraints.

If A is zero, equation (1.164) represents the shape of a stable equilibrium G–T–P surface. If A is nonzero, (1.164) represents the shape of a metastable equilibrium G–T–P surface (Figure 2B). For any increment $d\xi$ of a spontaneous change, we know that $A d\xi$ is always positive, so that

$$dG_{T,P} = -A\,d\xi \qquad (1.165)$$

is always negative (or zero, if A is zero), consistent with equation (1.43). We must now investigate the consequences of this.

In the cases of most interest to us ξ represents some small number of moles of reactants changed to products in a chemical reaction. Consider again the generalized chemical reaction in equation (1.125). Let's say that the reaction proceeds from left to right as written. During the reaction, A and B disappear and C and D appear, but the *proportions* of A/B/C/D that appear and disappear are fixed by the stoichiometric coefficients. If the reaction is

$$A + 2B \rightarrow 3C + 4D \qquad (1.166)$$

then for every mole of A that reacts (disappears), 2 moles of B must also disappear, while 3 moles of C and 4 moles of D must appear. This is simply a mass balance, independent of thermodynamics or kinetics, and can be expressed as

$$\frac{dn_A}{\nu_A} = \frac{dn_B}{\nu_B} = \frac{dn_C}{\nu_C} = \frac{dn_D}{\nu_D} = \frac{dn_i}{\nu_i} \qquad (1.167)$$

where the differentials dn_A, dn_B, and so on, refer to a change in the amount of A, B, and so on, of any convenient magnitude, not necessarily an infinitesimal change, and we use v_A, v_B . . . in place of a, b . . . . Whatever the amount of change in A or B, etc., we can consider these increments to be increments in our step variable, ξ, so

$$\frac{dn_A}{\nu_A} = \frac{dn_B}{\nu_B} = \frac{dn_C}{\nu_C} = \frac{dn_D}{\nu_D} = d\xi \qquad (1.168)$$

from which it appears that

$$\frac{dn_A}{d\xi} = \nu_A; \qquad \frac{dn_B}{d\xi} = \nu_B; \ldots \qquad \frac{dn_i}{d\xi} = \nu_i \qquad (1.169)$$

Equation (1.169) says that in reaction (1.166), $(dn_A/d\xi) = -1$, $(dn_B/d\xi) = -2$, $(dn_C/d\xi) = 3$, and $(dn_D/d\xi) = 4$, which simply means that for every mole of A that disappears,

2 moles of B also disappear, 3 moles of C appear, and so on.

As an example of this, consider again the anhydrite → gypsum reaction (1.10), in which, as written, $v_A = -1$, $v_B = -2$, $v_C = 1$, and $v_D = 0$. This is also illustrated as process $A \rightarrow A'$ in Figure 2B. From (1.169),

$$dn_{anhydrite} = -d\xi$$
$$dn_{water} = -2\,d\xi$$
$$dn_{gypsum} = d\xi$$

where $n_{anhydrite}$ is some number of moles of anhydrite, and similarly for water and gypsum. If n° is the number of moles of each to start with, then integrating these equations from n° to some new value of n gives

$$\int_{n^\circ}^{n} dn_{anhydrite} = -\int d\xi$$
$$n_{anhydrite} - n^\circ_{anhydrite} = -\Delta\xi$$

or

$$n_{anhydrite} = n^\circ_{anhydrite} - \Delta\xi$$

and similarly

$$n_{water} = n^\circ_{water} - 2\,\Delta\xi$$
$$n_{gypsum} = n^\circ_{gypsum} + \Delta\xi$$

which shows that whatever amounts of each mineral we have to start with, this amount is decreased by $\Delta\xi$ moles for anhydrite and increased by $\Delta\xi$ moles for gypsum, every time we allow the reaction to proceed by $\Delta\xi$. If we let $n^\circ_{gypsum} = 0$ and $n^\circ_{anhydrite} = 1$ (point A in Figure 2B), and we release the constraint preventing anhydrite from reacting with water in four steps of $\Delta\xi = 0.25$ moles, then after one step $n_{anhydrite} = 0.75$ moles, $n_{gypsum} = 0.25$ moles, and so on. In this case the reaction proceeds until either anhydrite or water is used up, but more commonly an equilibrium between reactants and products is reached. Note too, that $\Delta\xi$ and $d\xi$ will be negative if the reaction proceeds from right to left.

Considering a system at constant T and P, equation (1.136) shows that

$$dG_{T,P} = \sum_{i=1}^{s} \mu_i dn_i \tag{1.170}$$

where the i are not the c independent components, but the s species we are considering that form from those components. In our ammonia example [equation (1.137)], $s = 3$. Into this we substitute the relation $dn_i = v_i d\xi$ from (1.169), to get

$$dG_{T,P} = \sum_{i=1}^{s} (\nu_i \mu_i) d\xi \tag{1.171}$$

Comparing this to (1.165), we see that another definition of the affinity is

$$A = -\sum_i \nu_i \mu_i \tag{1.172}$$

Recalling that our v_i are positive for products and negative for reactants, the quantity $\sum_i v_i \mu_i$ is simply the difference in (partial) molar free energy between products and reactants. For (1.166) this is

$$\underbrace{(3\,\mu_C + 4\,\mu_D)}_{products} - \underbrace{(\mu_A + 2\,\mu_B)}_{reactants} \tag{1.173}$$

If this sum is zero, the reaction is at stable equilibrium, there is no third constraint, the affinity is zero, the third term on the right side of (1.164) disappears, and equation (1.44) applies to the (closed) system. If some constraint prevents reaction (1.166) from proceeding to equilibrium, then the sum in (1.173) is not zero, but may be positive or negative, depending on whether (1.166) wants to go to the left or right. If the sum $\sum_i v_i \mu_i$ is positive (A negative), the reaction wants to go to the left as written, $d\xi$ is negative, and $Ad\xi$ is positive. If the sum is negative (A positive), the reaction proceeds to the right, $d\xi$ is positive, and $Ad\xi$ is positive. So $Ad\xi$ is inherently positive, and $dG_{T,P}$ is inherently negative for a spontaneous reaction, consistent with (1.165).

Equation (1.172) shows that the affinity is a $\Delta\mu_{T,P}$ term, giving the "distance" in G between stable and metastable equilibrium surfaces, or states, and the amount of useful work that a chemical reaction can do as it reaches equilibrium. For reaction (1.10), it is in fact represented by the vector $A \rightarrow A'$ in Figure 2B.

Reaction Path Models

This discussion may seem rather removed from the practical problems of understanding how ore deposits form, but Helgeson (1968, 1979) showed how to use these concepts to follow complex irreversible processes including any number of individual chemical reactions, and since then these techniques have become a standard tool in geochemical modeling. The original example used by Helgeson was the dissolution of K-feldspar in water. In the terms we have used here, the (closed) system consisted of K-feldspar plus water at a specified T and P. The third constraint was the separation of these two phases. This constraint was released in small increments by adding small amounts ($d\xi$ in moles) of K-feldspar to the water, and performing a speciation calculation to determine the equilibrium activities of all species. Then IAP and K_{sp} were compared for all possible solid phases, and if precipitation or dissolution was observed, the composition of the solution was adjusted, and the next $d\xi$ of K-feldspar added. This was continued until overall system equilibrium was attained. A surprising number of precipitations, buffering reactions, and dissolutions occur during this "simple" process. This simulation of an irreversible process using nothing but equilibrium thermodynamic concepts may not reproduce what happens in real processes in all respects, but nevertheless it always provides useful insights.

Ammonia formation example. As an example of several things discussed to this point, we will consider the formation of ammonia from hydrogen and nitrogen [reaction (1.137)] patterned after a similar presentation in Denbigh (1981). Consider a system at T and one bar consisting of one mole of pure N_2 and three moles of pure H_2 kept separate from one another. This system has four constraints. In addition to T and P (the only constraints needed to define stable equilibrium), a third constraint is the separation of the gases, and the fourth is a constraint on the reaction to form NH_3. We release one constraint by allowing the gases to mix, resulting in a metastable gaseous solution of N_2 and H_2. Then we allow reaction (1.137) to take place in the forward direction in ten increments, from pure N_2 + 3 H_2 to two moles of pure NH_3. Thus $dn_{NH_3}/d\xi = 2$, and ξ increases from 0 to 1.0 during the reaction. After each increment of reaction, $n_{N_2} = (1 - \xi)$, $n_{H_2} = 3\,(1 - \xi)$, and $n_{NH_3} = 2\xi$, and the mole fractions are

$$\left.\begin{aligned} X_{N_2} &= \frac{1-\xi}{4-2\xi} \\ X_{H_2} &= \frac{3-3\xi}{4-2\xi} \\ X_{NH_3} &= \frac{2\xi}{4-2\xi} \end{aligned}\right\} \tag{1.174}$$

Equation (1.92) written in terms of total Gibbs energy is obtained by multiplying both sides of (1.92) by the denominator of the mole fraction term, $(4 - 2\xi)$, so

(1.175)

Substituting for n_i,

$$\begin{aligned} G &= (1-\xi)\mu^\circ_{N_2} + (3-3\xi)\mu^\circ_{H_2} + 2\xi\mu^\circ_{NH_3} \\ &\quad + RT[(1-\xi)\ln X_{N_2} + (3-3\xi)\ln X_{H_2} \\ &\quad + 2\xi \ln X_{NH_3}] \\ &= (\mu^\circ_{N_2} + 3\mu^\circ_{H_2}) + \xi(2\mu^\circ_{NH_3} - \mu^\circ_{N_2} - 3\mu^\circ_{H_2}) \\ &\quad + RT[(1-\xi)\ln X_{N_2} + (3-3\xi)\ln X_{H_2} \\ &\quad + 2\xi \ln X_{NH_3}] \end{aligned} \tag{1.176}$$

so

$$\begin{aligned} G - (\mu^\circ_{N_2} + 3\mu^\circ_{H_2}) &= \xi(\Delta_r\mu^\circ) + RT[(1-\xi)\ln X_{N_2} \\ &\quad + (3-3\xi)\ln X_{H_2} \\ &\quad + 2\xi \ln X_{NH_3}] \\ &= \xi(\Delta_r\mu^\circ) + \Delta_m G \end{aligned} \tag{1.177}$$

where G is the total Gibbs energy of the system containing $(4 - 2\xi)$ moles of nitrogen, hydrogen, and ammonia gases, $\Delta_r\mu^\circ$ is the standard Gibbs energy of reaction (1.137) at T from SUPCRT92, and ξ is the progress variable which can have any value between 0 and 1.0. Note that the $RT[\ldots]$ term is simply the total energy form of (1.90), and can be called $\Delta_m G$, the total Gibbs energy of mixing. Evidently we can plot values of $[G - (\mu^\circ_{N_2} + 3\mu^\circ_{H_2})]$ as a function of reaction progress at various Ts, and because the two μ° terms are constants, the curve will show the true shape of the Gibbs energy variation and the minimum at the equilibrium value of ξ. Recall that $\xi = 0$ means a solution of one mole N_2 and three moles H_2, and $\xi = 1$ means two moles of pure NH_3. Somewhere in between there is an equilibrium composition where reaction (1.137) is at equilibrium, and $\mu_{N_2} + 3\mu_{H_2} = 2\mu_{NH_3}$. Table 1 shows the values of the terms in equation (1.177) at 200°C , and they are plotted in Figure 3. The values of $\Delta_r\mu^\circ$ ($\equiv \Delta_r G^\circ$) are obtained from a least squares fit of data from SUPCRT92, which is $\Delta_r\mu^\circ = -97116.2 + 213.536\,T$(K).

Note how the mixing term alone gives a minimum at $\xi = 0.34$, but the curve is "tilted" to lower ξ values by the contribution of the $\Delta_r\mu^\circ$ term. Also note that there is a large energy drop at $\xi = 0$, before any ammonia has formed. This is due entirely to the mixing of N_2 and H_2 before the reaction starts. At $\xi = 1$, there is zero energy of mixing, and the system (pure NH_3) has a higher Gibbs energy than pure N_2 + 3 H_2.

Equation (1.177) can be differentiated with respect to ξ, and the resulting expression equated to zero to solve for the minimum value of ξ. You won't want to do this without a program that does symbolic algebra because the differentiated expression is quite lengthy, but the result at 200°C is $\xi = 0.252$.

Performing the same calculations at temperatures from 25 to 300°C reveals that the equilibrium ξ value for this reaction changes considerably with temperature, from almost pure product at 25°C to almost pure reactants at 300°C, as shown in Figure 4.

Ammonia speciation. The mixing curve in Figure 3 is useful to show that the G function actually does have a minimum, and how the progress variable can be used to

TABLE 1. Data from equation (1.177) for T = 200°C.

ξ	$\xi(\Delta_r\mu^\circ)$ J	$\Delta_m G^\circ$ J	$G - (\mu^\circ_{N_2} + 3\mu^\circ_{H_2})$ J
0.0	0	− 8,849	− 8,849
0.1	392	−11,047	−10,655
0.2	784	−12,020	−11,236
0.3	1,176	−12,427	−11,252
0.4	1,567	−12,389	−10,821
0.5	1,959	−11,937	− 9,977
0.6	2,351	−11,062	− 8,711
0.7	2,743	− 9,714	− 6,971
0.8	3,135	− 7,780	− 4,645
0.9	3,527	− 4,989	− 1,462
1.0	3,918	0	3,918

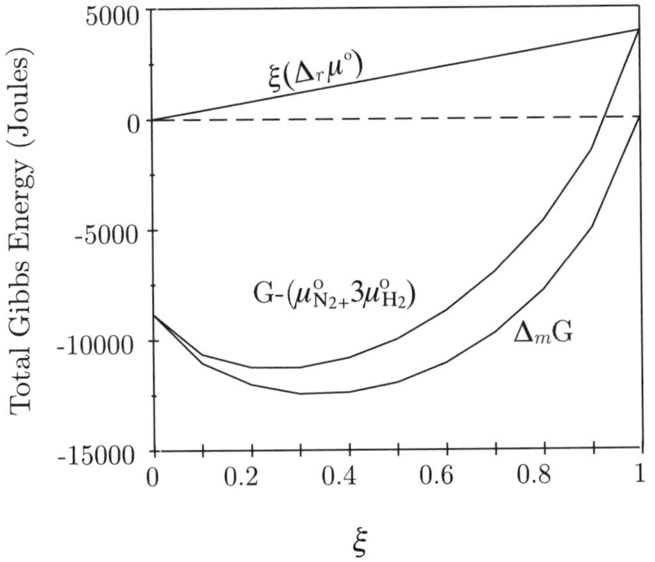

FIG. 3. The energy of mixing and the reaction energy combine to give a minimum in system G at $\xi = 0.252$ at 200°C.

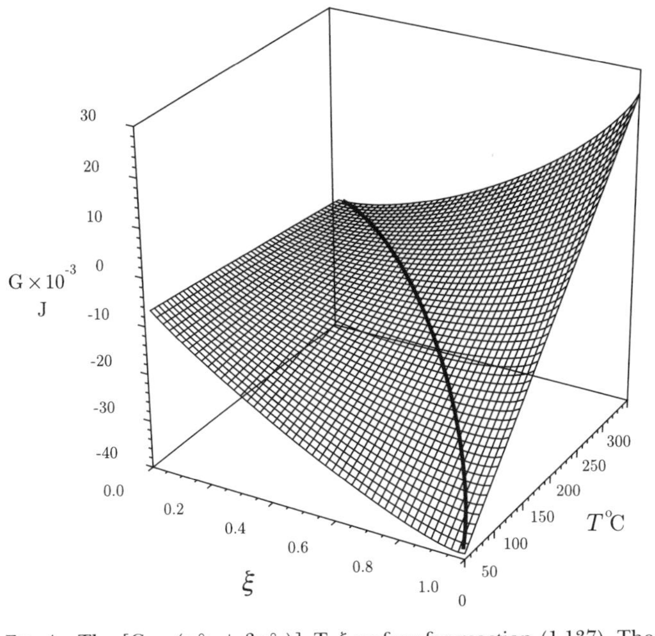

FIG. 4. The $[G - (\mu^\circ_{N_2} + 3\mu^\circ_{H_2})]$–T–$\xi$ surface for reaction (1.137). The approximate location of the equilibrium ξ (Table 2) is shown by the heavy line.

simulate stages in an irreversible reaction. In fact in progressing past the equilibrium composition, we actually drove the reaction "backwards" all the way to pure NH_3. But apart from reaction path models, we are usually interested in the stable equilibrium state of a system, rather than "artificially" constructed mixing curves like Figure 3.

A more usual thing to do with reactions like this would be to use the equilibrium constant,

$$\frac{a^2_{NH_3}}{a_{N_2}a^3_{H_2}} = K_{137} \tag{1.178}$$

values for which are also obtainable from SUPCRT92. It is of interest to note in passing that this program gives identical K values at all elevated pressures at a given T. This is because, as mentioned earlier, the standard state for gases used in the program is the ideal gas state at T and *one bar*. Because the reaction contains only gases, $\Delta_r G^\circ$ is therefore independent of pressure, as is log K. We will assume ideal gas conditions (where $f_i/f_i^\circ = X_i$), so the activity terms in (1.178) are the mole fractions in equations (1.174).

Because the mole fractions are all a function of a single variable ξ, equation (1.178) then contains a single unknown, and can be solved for ξ and hence the mole numbers and mole fractions of the three species that satisfy the equilibrium constant. Not surprisingly, these results agree with the G-minimization calculation (to within a few places in the third decimal), and are shown in Table 2 as a function of temperature.

Finally, we can have a look at the affinity values. The easiest way to calculate A is to first multiply equation (1.104) by v_i, then sum over all species, resulting in

$$\sum_{i=1}^{s} v_i\mu_i = \sum_{i=1}^{s} v_i\mu_i^\circ + \sum_{i=1}^{s} v_i RT \ln a_i \tag{1.179}$$

Combining this with (1.172) we get

$$-A = \Delta_r G^\circ + RT \ln Q \tag{1.180}$$

where $Q = \prod_i a_i^{v_i}$, and where the a_i are not necessarily the equilibrium values. Then substituting $-RT \ln K$ for $\Delta_r G^\circ$ [equation (1.131)], we get

$$A = RT \ln(K/Q) \tag{1.181}$$

Note the similarity of this expression to the Saturation Index, because for a simple solubility product expression, Q becomes the same as IAP.

Values of the mole fractions (activities) of each of the three species are calculated from the mole numbers in Table 2, and combined into values of Q at each ξ. The results are shown in Table 3 and Figure 5.

TABLE 2. Species mole numbers that satisfy K_{137} and equations (1.174).

T °C	log K_{137}	n_{N_2} mol	n_{H_2} mol	n_{NH_3} mol	ξ
25	5.764	0.03177	0.09530	1.9365	0.9682
50	4.508	0.06535	0.1961	1.8693	0.9347
100	2.467	0.2074	0.6223	1.5851	0.7895
150	0.8740	0.4684	1.4059	1.0627	0.5314
200	−0.4061	0.7425	2.2275	0.5150	0.2575
250	−1.4611	0.8975	2.6923	0.2051	0.1026
300	−2.3460	0.9591	2.8772	0.8190	0.04095

TABLE 3. Calculation of the affinity at T = 200°C from equation (1.181).

ξ	Q	K/Q	A J mol^{-1a}
0.05	0.006916	56.7648	15,889
0.10	0.03260	12.0408	9,789
0.20	0.1875	2.09387	2,907
0.2575	0.3925	1.000	0
0.30	0.6420	0.6116	− 1,935
0.40	1.8729	0.2096	− 6,147
0.50	5.3333	0.07361	−10,263
0.60	16.333	0.0240	−14,667
0.70	60.583	0.00648	−19,823
0.80	341.33	0.00115	−26,625
0.90	5,805	0.000068	−37,774

[a]Actually, Joules per 2 moles of NH_3

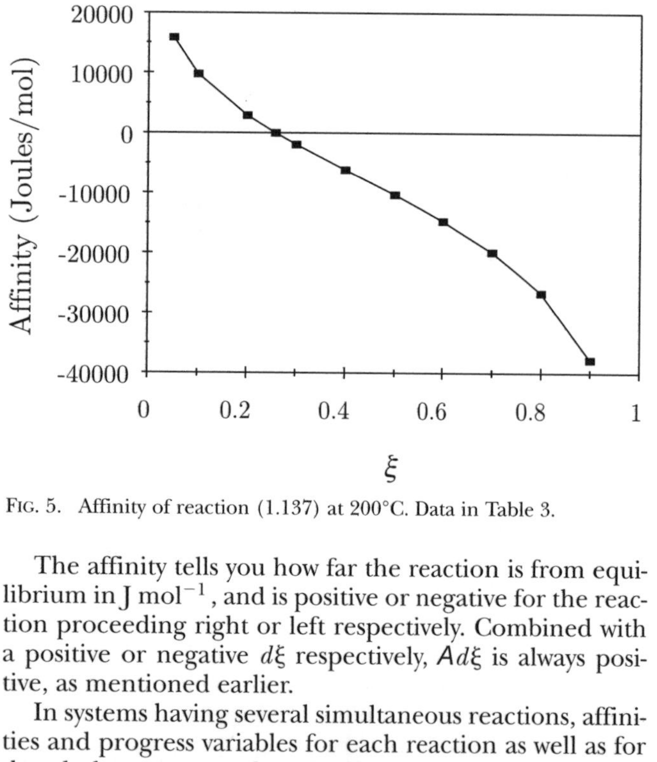

FIG. 5. Affinity of reaction (1.137) at 200°C. Data in Table 3.

The affinity tells you how far the reaction is from equilibrium in J mol^{-1}, and is positive or negative for the reaction proceeding right or left respectively. Combined with a positive or negative $d\xi$ respectively, $Ad\xi$ is always positive, as mentioned earlier.

In systems having several simultaneous reactions, affinities and progress variables for each reaction as well as for the whole system may be calculated. Unfortunately, affinities of individual reactions in such systems are not related in any simple way to the order in which those reactions will reach equilibrium, due to the effects of reaction coupling [Helgeson, (1979)]. Similarly, although the affinity is commonly used in theoretical expressions for reaction rate constants, it is never the only determining factor. Nevertheless, it is always a central concept in thinking about irreversible processes.

Concluding Remarks

There are many difficulties in constructing models of natural systems, but understanding thermodynamics should not be one of them. As shown in this chapter, the various equations are not mathematically difficult, and there is a fairly short chain of reasoning between useful equations and the first principles they are based on. However, generations of students can testify that it *is* somehow difficult:

> The first time I heard about Chemical Thermodynamics was when a second-year undergraduate brought me the news early in my freshman year. He told me a spine-chilling story of endless lectures with almost three hundred numbered equations, all of which, it appeared, had to be committed to memory and reproduced in exactly the same form in subsequent examinations. Not only did these equations contain all the normal algebraic symbols but in addition they were liberally sprinkled with stars, daggers, and circles so as to stretch even the most powerful of minds.
>
> *Smith (1977).*

At several points in this presentation I have tried to make the distinction between thermodynamics as a clean, simple model of energy relationships, and messy natural systems. Making this distinction is one of the secrets to understanding thermodynamics, because the hypothetical systems, impossible processes, and unknowable parameters are then seen to be parts of a mathematical framework, a model, related to real systems only by virtue of using measured parameters as variables. We make simple models of systems using thermodynamics (thermodynamic systems), and we compare them to much more complex natural systems. In the process, we use many of the same terms in both kinds of systems. As a result, some simple thermodynamic concepts get unnecessarily confused. Natural systems are mostly open, and never achieve thermodynamic equilibrium. They don't really have components or degrees of freedom, only thermodynamic systems do. Thermodynamic systems have only perfect equilibrium states, stable or metastable. They have no need of "local equilibrium," which is something natural systems must have if thermodynamics is to be applied to them. And so on.

The really difficult parts of thermodynamics have nothing to do with the simple mathematical framework which makes up most of this chapter. The hard parts are in the measurement of property data, the massaging of these into coherent databases, and the development of complex equations of state and of the correction factors required due to the fact that most of our simple equations refer to idealized systems. Readers may have noticed the very brief space given to these subjects here, and the distinctly more uncertain tone in discussing them. These subjects are vital to real applications of thermodynamics, and will be more fully treated in the chapters to follow. This chapter has focused on the easy part.

Acknowledgments

I thank Graham Layne, Dave Polya, and Jeremy Richards for comments which led to significant improvements in the manuscript.

REFERENCES

Bockris, J.O'M., and Reddy, A.K.N., 1970, Modern Electrochemistry, Volume 1: New York, Plenum, 622 p.

Born, M., 1920, Volumen und Hydrationswarme der Ionen: Zeitschrift für Physik., v. 1, p. 45–48.

Callen, H.B., 1960, Thermodynamics: New York, John Wiley, 376 p.

Denbigh, K., 1981, The Principles of Chemical Equilibrium, 4th edition, Cambridge, Cambridge University Press, 494 p.

Haar, L., Gallagher, J.S., and Kell, G.S., 1984, NBS/NRC steam tables: Thermodynamic and transport properties and computer programs for vapor and liquid states of water in SI units: Washington, Hemisphere Publishing Corporation, 320 p.

Helgeson, H.C., 1968, Evaluation of irreversible reactions in geochemical processes involving minerals and aqueous solutions: I. Thermodynamic relations: Geochimica et Cosmochimica Acta., v. 32, p. 853–877.

—— 1969, Thermodynamics of hydrothermal systems at elevated temperatures and pressures: American Journal of Science, v. 267, p. 729–804.

—— 1979, Mass transfer among minerals and hydrothermal solutions, in H.L. Barnes, ed., Geochemistry of hydrothermal ore deposits, 2nd ed.: New York, Wiley-Interscience, p. 568–610.

Helgeson, H.C., and Kirkham, D.H., 1974a, Theoretical prediction of the thermodynamic behavior of aqueous electrolytes at high temperatures and pressures: I. Summary of the thermodynamic/electrostatic properties of the solvent: American Journal of Science, v. 274, p. 1089–1198.

—— 1974b, Theoretical prediction of the thermodynamic behavior of aqueous electrolytes at high pressures and temperatures: II. Debye-Hückel parameters for activity: American Journal of Science, v. 274, p. 1199–1261.

—— 1976, Theoretical prediction of the thermodynamic properties of aqueous electrolytes at high pressures and temperatures: III. Equation of state for aqueous species at infinite dilution: American Journal of Science, v. 276, p. 97–240.

Helgeson, H.C., Kirkham, D.H., and Flowers, G.C., 1981, Theoretical prediction of the thermodynamic properties of aqueous electrolytes at high pressures and temperatures: IV. Calculation of activity coefficients, osmotic coefficients, and apparent molal and standard and relative partial molal properties to 600°C and 5 kbar: American Journal of Science, v. 281, p. 1249–1493.

Johnson, J.W., Oelkers, E.H., and Helgeson, H.C., 1992, SUPCRT92: A software package for calculating the standard molal thermodynamic properties of minerals, gases, aqueous species, and reactions as functions of temperature and pressure: Computers and Geosciences, v. 18, p. 899–947.

Knapp, R.A., 1989, Spatial and temporal scales of local equilibrium in dynamic fluid-rock systems. Geochimica et Cosmochimica Acta, v. 53, p. 1955–1964.

Maier, C.G., and Kelley, K.K., 1932, An equation for the representation of high temperature heat content data: Journal of the American Chemical Society, v. 54, p. 3243–3246.

Reed, M.H., 1982, Calculation of multicomponent chemical equilibria and reaction processes in systems involving minerals, gases and an aqueous phase: Geochimica et Cosmochimica Acta, v. 46, p. 513–528.

Smith, E. B., 1977, Basic chemical thermodynamics, 2nd edition: Oxford, Clarendon Press, 130 p.

Tanger, J.C. IV, and Helgeson, H.C., 1988, Calculation of the thermodynamics and transport properties of aqueous species at high pressures and temperatures: Revised equations of state for the standard partial molal properties of ions and electrolytes: American Journal of Science, v. 288, p. 19–98.

Chapter 2

Solubility of Ore Minerals and Complexation of Ore Metals in Hydrothermal Solutions

Scott A. Wood

Department of Geology and Geological Engineering, University of Idaho, Moscow, Idaho 83844-3022

and Iain M. Samson

Earth Sciences, University of Windsor, Windsor, Ontario, Canada N9B 3P4

Introduction

Knowledge of the solubility of ore minerals and the speciation of ore metals in hydrothermal solutions is required for a complete understanding of the genesis of hydrothermal ores. In this chapter, we explore the factors that control solubility and speciation, demonstrate how to carry out quantitative calculations, and review the current state of knowledge for a number of economically important metals. The term solubility refers to the sum of the concentrations of all dissolved forms of a given metal in a hydrothermal solution in equilibrium with a mineral (or minerals) containing that metal. We use the term speciation to denote the relative concentrations of the various forms of a metal in solution.

The solubility of a mineral provides an upper limit to the amount of dissolved metal that a hydrothermal fluid can transport, assuming thermodynamic equilibrium. Although a given solution may temporarily carry more metal than permitted by the equilibrium solubility of relevant minerals owing to sluggish reaction kinetics, the equilibrium solubility is nevertheless an important benchmark. Given enough time, equilibrium solubility cannot be exceeded, and systems will proceed in a direction toward the equilibrium state. Also, knowledge of equilibrium solubilities is required for modeling rate processes. Metal concentrations may be maintained below the equilibrium solubility either by sorption processes, which remove metals from solution before saturation is reached with respect to a given mineral, or if there is insufficient metal available in the system to saturate the solution. As pointed out in Chapter 1, the extent to which a solution is saturated with respect to a given mineral can be determined by comparing the actual ion activity product, or IAP, of the solution with the solubility product, or K_{SP}, of that mineral.

Speciation is important because, as will be demonstrated below, it controls the equilibrium solubility and depositional mechanisms for a particular mineral, and speciation also can have significant effects on sorption processes and reaction rates. We will therefore illustrate methods of determining which species are important and their relative concentrations in aqueous solutions.

In what follows we employ the following convention regarding notation for oxidation states of cations. When referring to the simple, hydrated metal ion we write M^{q+}, where q represents the ionic charge. However, when referring to the general oxidation state of a cation, or a cation's oxidation state in a complex with ligands other than water, we write M(Q), with Q being the oxidation state in upper case Roman numerals. Thus, the simple hydrated divalent zinc ion is written Zn^{2+}, but we would refer to zinc chloride complexes as Zn(II)-chloride complexes.

Complexation

It is generally accepted that when simple aqueous ions (e.g., Zn^{2+}, Pb^{2+}, Au^{+}, Bi^{3+}) predominate in a hydrothermal solution, ore mineral solubilities (especially sulfides) are too low for the transport of significant quantities of ore metals (Czamanske, 1959; Barnes, 1979). This fact is evident from Table 1, where it can be seen that the solubility of several important ore minerals as the simple aqueous ion is less than (usually much less than) 1 ppm under all conditions considered. To attain solubilities necessary for ore deposit formation, ore metal ions must form complexes. A complex is simply a combination of one or more metal ions (including protons, i.e., H^{+}) with one or more anionic or neutral species. The anions and/or neutral species participating in the complex are referred to as ligands. Complexes may be divided into two general classes: coordination complexes and ion pairs. Coordination complexes are formed by metals and ligands capable of bonding with a high degree of covalency. Thus, their bonds are highly directional in character (because they depend on the overlap of atomic orbitals) and they have a definite structure that can be identified by spectroscopic methods (cf. Crerar et al., 1985, and references therein). Coordination complexes tend to be formed by the transition metal ions (all three rows) and As, Sb, Bi, Sn, Pb, Tl, Se, Ga, and Al. Ion pairs comprise a single cation and a single anion, held together solely by electrostatic attraction, i.e., ionic bonding. As a result, the bonds are non-directional and the geometry of these types of complexes is not well-defined. The ligands can be in direct contact with the metal ion, in which case they form contact or inner-sphere ion pairs, or they may be separated by water molecules, in which case they form solvent-separated or outer-sphere ion pairs (Stumm and Morgan, 1981; Crerar et al., 1985). It is possible also to form triple, quadruple, or higher-order ion combinations (Oelkers and Helgeson, 1990, 1993). The alkalis, alkaline earths, rare earth elements, Sc, Y, and actinides

TABLE 1. Solubilities (in ppm) of selected ore minerals as the simple, hydrated ion at saturated water vapor pressure (SWVP) and Σsulfide = 0.001 molal, as a function of pH and temperature. Calculated using data from SUPCRT92 (Johnson et al., 1992).

Mineral	pH	Temp (°C)			
		25	100	200	300
galena	3	2.8×10^{-6}	4.6×10^{-4}	4.7×10^{-2}	9.1×10^{-1}
	5	2.8×10^{-10}	4.6×10^{-8}	4.7×10^{-6}	9.1×10^{-5}
sphalerite	3	2.3×10^{-3}	8.5×10^{-3}	3.8×10^{-2}	9.9×10^{-2}
	5	2.3×10^{-7}	8.5×10^{-7}	3.8×10^{-6}	9.9×10^{-6}
cinnabar	3	2.1×10^{-30}	9.5×10^{-24}	6.7×10^{-18}	4.9×10^{-14}
	5	2.1×10^{-34}	9.5×10^{-28}	6.7×10^{-22}	4.9×10^{-18}
acanthite	3	2.0×10^{-11}	5.0×10^{-7}	9.6×10^{-5}	1.5×10^{-2}
	5	2.0×10^{-15}	5.0×10^{-11}	9.6×10^{-9}	1.5×10^{-6}

(U, Th) tend to form ion pairs rather than coordination complexes, owing to a relatively large difference in electronegativity between cation and anion, leading towards ionic bonding. However, it is important to realize that there is actually a continuum between the extremes of purely ionic and purely covalent bonding.

Stability Constants

The degree to which a metal and a ligand tend to form a complex is measured by the equilibrium constant for a reaction such as:

$$M^{+q} + nL^{-p} = ML_n^{q-np} \qquad (2.1a)$$

Such an equilibrium constant is generally referred to as a stability or complexation constant. A larger value of the stability constant implies a stronger or more stable complex. There are a number of different terms used to describe stability constants. For example, stability constants for a complexation reaction such as reaction (2.1a) are referred to as cumulative or overall stability constants, and are assigned the symbol β_n. Stability constants for a stepwise complexation reaction such as:

$$ML_{n-1}^{q-(n-1)p} + L^{-p} = ML_n^{q-np} \qquad (2.1b)$$

are referred to as stepwise stability constants and given the symbol K_n. We will follow these conventions in this chapter. However, the terminology and symbols are not universal, which can lead to confusion. Thus, care is required in extracting stability constants from the literature and in reporting or tabulating stability constants. Cumulative and stepwise stability constants are related to one another as follows:

$$\beta_n = \prod_{i=1}^{n} K_i = K_1K_2K_3...K_n \qquad (2.2)$$

In order to calculate the solubility of a mineral in a given solution, the following thermodynamic data are required: the solubility product for the mineral of interest (see Chapter 1), the stability constants for all complexes likely to be important, equilibrium constants for reactions among various forms of the ligand (e.g., HSO_4^- and SO_4^{2-}), and activity coefficients (see Chapter 1) for all relevant aqueous species at the temperature(s) and pressure(s) of interest. If the solid of interest is a solid solution or non-stoichiometric phase, then activity coefficients of solid components are also required (see Wood and Fraser, 1978, Anderson and Crerar, 1993, or Nordstrom and Munoz, 1994, for details on solid solution modeling).

Cation Hydrolysis

The term cation hydrolysis refers to the following type of complex-forming reaction:

$$M^{+q} + nH_2O(l) = M(OH)_n^{q-n} + nH^+ \qquad (2.3a)$$

where a metal ion-hydroxide complex is formed as a result of the breaking (lysis) of water (hydro). The equilibrium constant for a reaction like (2.3a) is called the hydrolysis constant and is denoted by the symbol $K_{h,n}$. The hydrolysis constant is related to the cumulative stability constant for a hydroxide complex by the expression:

$$K_{h,n} = \beta_n \bullet K_w^n \qquad (2.3b)$$

where K_w is the equilibrium constant for the water dissociation reaction (reaction 2.31 below). Thus, cation hydrolysis and hydroxide complex formation are synonymous. Factors that control the degree to which a given cation is hydrolyzed, i.e., the magnitude of $K_{h,n}$, have been thoroughly discussed by Baes and Mesmer (1976) and Stumm and Morgan (1981). In general, the smaller and/or the more highly charged the cation, the greater the degree of hydrolysis. Notable exceptions are Au^+, Hg^{2+}, and Pd^{2+}, which have large ionic radii, and are among the most strongly hydrolyzed cations known (see below).

Effect of Complexation on Solubility

We now demonstrate how complexation can increase solubility using galena (PbS) as an example. In what follows, square brackets [] denote concentrations and curly brackets {} denote activities (see Chapter 1 for the definition of activity). First, consider the solubility of galena in water at sufficiently low pH that Pb^{2+} and H_2S^0 are the only important dissolved lead and sulfide species, respectively. We will initially ignore the contribution of Pb bisulfide and hydroxide complexes, which will be small at the low pH and H_2S concentrations used here (Tugarinov et al., 1975; Giordano and Barnes, 1979). In this case:

$$\text{solubility of galena} = \Sigma Pb = [Pb^{2+}] \qquad (2.4)$$

Note that solubility is always defined in terms of concentration, not activity. The concentration of Pb^{2+}, i.e., $[Pb^{2+}]$, can be calculated from the equilibrium constant for the reaction:

$$PbS(s) + 2H^+ = Pb^{2+} + H_2S^0 \qquad (2.5a)$$

which is

$$K_{s2} = \frac{\{H_2S^0\}\{Pb^{2+}\}}{\{H^+\}^2} \quad (2.5b)$$

Rearranging (2.5b) and substituting $\{Pb^{2+}\} = \gamma_{Pb^{2+}}[Pb^{2+}]$ (see Chapter 1) yields:

$$[Pb^{2+}] = \{Pb^{2+}\}/\gamma_{Pb^{2+}} = K_{s2}\{H^+\}^2/(\{H_2S^0\}\gamma_{Pb^{2+}}) \quad (2.5c)$$

Here we follow the notation of Stumm and Morgan (1981) for the equilibrium constant of reaction (2.5a), where the subscript "s2" denotes a "solubility constant" in which S^{2-} is written in the doubly protonated form, H_2S^0. We use reaction (2.5a) and K_{s2} here instead of the solubility product because K_{SP} refers to the reaction: $PbS(s) = Pb^{2+} + S^{2-}$, and thermodynamic data for the species S^{2-} are poorly known. If pH, the activity of H_2S^0, and the activity coefficient of Pb^{2+} remain constant, then the concentration of Pb^{2+} is fixed at a constant value (at constant P and T).

When chloride ion is added to the solution, lead chloride complexes may form according to:

$$Pb^{2+} + Cl^- = PbCl^+ \quad (2.6)$$

$$Pb^{2+} + 2Cl^- = PbCl_2^0 \quad (2.7)$$

$$Pb^{2+} + 3Cl^- = PbCl_3^- \quad (2.8)$$

$$Pb^{2+} + 4Cl^- = PbCl_4^{2-} \quad (2.9)$$

In this case the solubility becomes:

$$\text{solubility of galena} = \Sigma Pb = [Pb^{2+}] + [PbCl^+] + [PbCl_2^0] + [PbCl_3^-] + [PbCl_4^{2-}] \quad (2.10)$$

If pH and H_2S^0 activity are the same as in the previous example, then $\{Pb^{2+}\}$ is still fixed by reaction (2.5a), i.e., it has the same value as in the absence of chloride. Furthermore, if $\gamma_{Pb^{2+}}$ remains constant, then $[Pb^{2+}]$ is also "fixed". Although Pb^{2+} is consumed in complexation reactions (2.6–2.9), reaction (2.5) shifts to the right to replace the Pb^{2+} lost to complexation. Thus, the total concentration of Pb in solution must increase if any significant complexation takes place, and consequently the solubility of galena increases.

Let us now calculate the solubility of galena at 200°C, saturated water vapor pressure (SWVP), $[H_2S^0] = 10^{-3}$ molal, and pH = 3.0, both in the presence and absence of 1.0 molal Cl^-. At first we will assume all activity coefficients to be unity, i.e., activity may be replaced by concentration; the effect of this assumption will be investigated later in this chapter. The value of $[Pb^{2+}]$ may be calculated from equation (2.5b) as follows:

$$[Pb^{2+}] = K_{s2}[H^+]^2[H_2S^0]^{-1} \quad (2.11)$$

and equation (2.10) can be rewritten:

$$\Sigma Pb = [Pb^{2+}] + \beta_1[Pb^{2+}][Cl^-] + \beta_2[Pb^{2+}][Cl^-]^2 + \beta_3[Pb^{2+}][Cl^-]^3 + \beta_4[Pb^{2+}][Cl^-]^4 \quad (2.12)$$

Eliminating $[Pb^{2+}]$ by substituting equation (2.11) into equation (2.12) we obtain:

$$\Sigma Pb = K_{s2}[H^+]^2[H_2S^0]^{-1}(1 + \beta_1[Cl^-] + \beta_2[Cl^-]^2 + \beta_3[Cl^-]^3 + \beta_4[Cl^-]^4) \quad (2.13)$$

The following values of the required equilibrium constants have been calculated using SUPCRT92 (Johnson et al., 1992; see below for a description of SUPCRT92 and a review of Pb(II)-complexes) for 200°C and SWVP: $K_{s2} = 10^{-3.64}$; $\beta_1 = 10^{2.64}$; $\beta_2 = 10^{3.97}$; $\beta_3 = 10^{3.94}$; $\beta_4 = 10^{3.52}$.

For the solubility of galena in the absence of chloride complexation (i.e., reaction 2.5a) we obtain:

$$\Sigma Pb = [Pb^{2+}] = K_{s2}[H^+]^2[H_2S^0]^{-1} = 10^{-3.64}(10^{-3})^2(10^{-3})^{-1} = 10^{-6.64} \text{ molal (moles/kg } H_2O) \quad (2.14)$$

This corresponds to a solubility of 2.29×10^{-7} molal or 47.4 μg/L (ppb) Pb. The solubility in a solution containing one molal free chloride (by free we mean that portion of total chloride not already bound in a complex or ion pair) is calculated according to:

$$\Sigma Pb = 10^{-6.64}(1 + 10^{2.64}(1) + 10^{3.97}(1)^2 + 10^{3.94}(1)^3 + 10^{3.52}(1)^4) = 10^{-6.64}(10^{4.34}) = 10^{-2.30} = 5.01 \times 10^{-3} \text{ molal} = 1038 \text{ mg/L (ppm)} \quad (2.15)$$

Thus, chloride complexation at $[Cl^-] = 1.0$ (~ 5.5 wt % NaCl, if Na-Cl ion pairs are neglected) has increased the solubility of galena by nearly four and a half orders of magnitude. It should be noted that, in this simple case, the solubility increase owing to complexation is proportional to the term:

$$(1 + \beta_1[Cl^-] + \beta_2[Cl^-]^2 + \beta_3[Cl^-]^3 + \beta_4[Cl^-]^4)$$

which further emphasizes that the degree to which complexation affects mineral solubility depends on the strength of the complexes (i.e., the magnitude of the β's) and the concentration or activity of the free ligand(s). As we will show below, galena solubility calculations in any real-world situation will be more complicated because what we usually know is total, not free, chloride concentration. To calculate the latter we have to take into account the formation of complexes between chloride and Pb^{2+} (a relatively small correction in this case), as well H^+, Na^+, K^+, Fe^{2+}, etc. (potentially much more important corrections). Nevertheless, the above calculations illustrate the effect that complexation can have on mineral solubilities and why speciation is so important in solubility calculations.

From the discussion so far, it should be evident that, to obtain high ore mineral solubilities, either large solubility constants (K_{SP} or K_{s2}) or large stability constants for the predominant complexes, or both, are required. In the case of gold, the equilibrium constant for the dissolution reaction: $Au(s) + \frac{1}{4}O_2(g) + H^+ = Au^+ + \frac{1}{2}H_2O(l)$ is extremely low, but this is balanced by the fact that Au complexes tend to have very high stability constants, resulting in sufficient solubility of gold to form ore deposits under at least some conditions. On the other hand, stability constants for common complexes of metals such as Zn, Fe, and Mn are somewhat lower, but the K_{s2} (K_{SP}) values for many minerals containing these metals are higher, resulting in comparatively high solubilities. However, even in the latter case, complexation is usually required to attain solubilities that would permit the formation of economic deposits.

Effect of Complexation on Depositional Mechanisms

An important aspect of developing a genetic or exploration model for a particular type of hydrothermal ore deposit is gaining an understanding of the reasons for ore metal deposition. This, after all, ultimately controls the location and, to some extent, the grade and tonnage of the ore deposit. Knowledge of the speciation of a metal in solution is critical if one is to understand why a particular ore mineral is deposited where it is. It is therefore important to be able to relate physico-chemical changes in the mineralizing solution to the solubility and speciation of the metal or metals of interest. A given metal can be deposited for a variety of reasons and different metals in the same solution can be deposited by different mechanisms. These relationships are examined in detail in Chapter 5, but some fundamental points are worth mentioning here.

For illustrative purposes, we will consider a somewhat simplistic model reaction for galena deposition (cf. the multi-component equilibria considered later in this chapter):

$$PbCl_4^{2-} + H_2S^0 = PbS(s) + 2H^+ + 4Cl^- \qquad (2.16)$$

A shift in the equilibrium of such a reaction to the right will obviously result in the precipitation of galena. Such a shift may be brought about by a decrease in temperature (if the mineral has prograde solubility), an increase in the activity of H_2S^0, or a decrease in the activity of H^+ (increase in pH) or Cl^-. Note that, when attempting to draw qualitative conclusions from simple reactions as we have done here, it is important to write the reaction in terms of the predominant aqueous species and the solid phases stable over the range of conditions considered, otherwise, erroneous inferences will be made.

It should be obvious that the changes in fluid chemistry necessary to cause deposition in the above example apply to the precipitation of sulfides from chloride complexes and that the potential reasons for the precipitation of ore minerals other than sulfides or from complexes other than chlorides may be very different. For example, suppose the predominant lead species was the bisulfide complex $Pb(HS)_3^-$. We would then write:

$$Pb(HS)_3^- + H^+ = PbS(s) + 2H_2S^0 \qquad (2.17)$$

In this case, precipitation of galena would result from a decrease in pH or an increase in the activity of H_2S^0, precisely the opposite of the effect if lead is transported as a chloride complex.

Even species of the same general type but different stoichiometries can result in subtle but important differences in the mechanism required to deposit an ore mineral. For example, if the predominant Pb species were $PbCl^+$ instead of $PbCl_4^{2-}$, the reaction governing deposition is:

$$PbCl^+ + H_2S^0 = PbS(s) + 2H^+ + Cl^- \qquad (2.18)$$

In this case, the dependence of galena solubility on pH and H_2S^0 activity are identical to that of reaction (2.16), but the dependences on Cl^- activity and (most likely) temperature are different.

Mineral deposition can occur as a result of a number of processes including water-rock interaction, boiling, dilution, fluid mixing, conductive cooling, etc. Quantification of the various effects can only be achieved if thermodynamic data are available for the appropriate precipitation reaction and any related equilibria. In reality, the effect of such processes on all the relevant equilibria in a system should be considered simultaneously, a task which can be achieved practically with software packages such as CHILLER (Reed, 1982) or EQ3/6 (Wolery, 1979; 1983; see also Chapter 5). The main point we wish to emphasize here is that, if one hopes to realistically model and understand the reasons for the deposition of metals in hydrothermal ore deposits, knowledge of the ways in which metals are complexed is essential. Quantification of the depositional process requires thermodynamic data on appropriate aqueous equilibria (including complexation reactions) and solubility products for the minerals of interest. A given metal may form a variety of complexes depending on the temperature and pressure of transport, as well as on fluid chemistry. This requires a knowledge of the speciation of the metal under varying conditions of P, T, and fluid chemistry as well as a knowledge of the values these parameters had in the deposit of interest. The latter are gleaned from mineralogical, fluid inclusion, and isotopic studies, topics which are covered in Chapters 6, 7, 8, and 9.

Which Complexes to Include in Solubility Calculations

In an ideal world, reliable, experimentally-measured stability constants would be available for all complexes of possible importance for a given metal, and given the power of modern computers, it would be a relatively simple task to include all of these complexes in solubility and speciation calculations. However, thermodynamic data are lacking for a large number of important complexes, especially at elevated temperatures and pressures, and in some cases the stoichiometry and even the existence of certain complexes are in question. As we shall see, it is possible to estimate stability constants for many complexes, but in order to limit the number of estimates required, it is desirable to have a means of deciding which ligands are most likely to complex a given metal in any given instance. It would also be useful to be able to assess whether any important complexes might be missing from a solubility model, because we can only estimate thermodynamic data for complexes that we expect to be present.

A given complex will be an important contributor to the solubility of an ore mineral when: (1) the total, stoichiometric concentration of the constituent ligand is relatively high and (2) the particular complex has a relatively large stability constant. In the absence of stability constant data, the relative stabilities of competing complexes are difficult to determine. However, it is possible to make a qualitative assessment of the relative stabilities of complexes using a tool called the HSAB (Hard-Soft Acid-Base) principle, first described by Pearson (1963). In the next two sections we briefly discuss the relative abundances of ligands in hydrothermal fluids and describe the HSAB principle in detail.

Relative natural abundances of ligands. Inorganic ligands of potential importance in natural hydrothermal fluids include fluoride (F^-), chloride (Cl^-), bromide (Br^-), iodide (I^-), bisulfide (HS^-), polysulfide (S_nS^{2-}), thiosulfate ($S_2O_3^{2-}$), sulfite (SO_3^{2-}), bisulfate (HSO_4^-), sulfate (SO_4^{2-}), bicarbonate (HCO_3^-), carbonate (CO_3^{2-}), ammonia (NH_3), hydroxide (OH^-), dihydrogen phosphate ($H_2PO_4^-$), hydrogen phosphate (HPO_4^{2-}), phosphate (PO_4^{3-}), thioarsenites (e.g., $As_3S_6^{3-}$), thioantimonites (e.g., $Sb_3S_6^{3-}$), telluride (HTe^-, Te^{2-}, Te_2^{2-}), and cyanide (CN^-). Organic ligands that exist in some hydrothermal fluids include carboxylic acid anions such as acetate (CH_3COO^-), propionate ($CH_3CH_2COO^-$), oxalate ($C_2O_4^{2-}$), and malonate ($^-OOCCH_2COO^-$), thiols (organic compounds containing an -SH group), amino acids, and porphyrins. Table 2 gives representative ranges of total stoichiometric concentrations of selected ligands in natural hydrothermal fluids for which these data are relatively well constrained. The ranges listed in Table 2 represent the most probable concentrations, but specific environments may exist in which the concentration of a given ligand exceeds the maximum indicated.

Chloride is the most abundant ligand in the majority of hydrothermal fluids. Because many metals form reasonably strong complexes with this ligand, chloride complexation is often the dominant form of ore metal transport in mineralizing fluids. Bromide and iodide are generally several orders of magnitude less concentrated than chloride in hydrothermal fluids, and so with rare exception, complexes with these ligands are far less important than with chloride (Gammons and Yu, 1997). The concentration of fluoride is often restricted to relatively low values by the solubilities of fluorite and topaz, but for certain "hard" metal ions such as Be^{2+}, fluoride complexes may be important (cf. Wood, 1992b).

TABLE 2. Representative ranges of ligand concentrations in natural hydrothermal fluids

Ligand	Concentration range (moles/kg H_2O)	Source
ΣCl^-	<0.03 to >7	Barnes (1979)
ΣSO_4^{2-}	10^{-10} to 0.3	Barnes (1979)
ΣS^{2-}	10^{-4} to 0.1	Barnes (1979)
ΣNH_3^{2-}	$10^{-3.9}$ to $10^{-1.5}$	Barnes (1979)
ΣCO_3	$10^{-3.4}$ to 1	Barnes (1979)
Σacetate	0 to 0.17	Kharaka et al. (1998)
Σpropionate	0 to 0.059	Kharaka et al. (1998)
Σoxalate	0 to 0.005	Kharaka et al. (1998)
Σmalonate	0 to 0.025	Kharaka et al. (1998)

Whether or not sulfide or sulfate predominates in a hydrothermal system is mainly a function of the oxygen fugacity, with sulfate and sulfide predominating under oxidizing and reducing conditions, respectively (see Chapter 3). Sulfate forms relatively weak complexes with most ore metals and hence rarely competes favorably with chloride. On the other hand, bisulfide can form very strong complexes with "soft" metal ions such as Au^+ and Ag^+. Thus, bisulfide is probably the next most important ligand after chloride in most hydrothermal solutions. The concentrations of total carbonate and total ammonia can be relatively high (Table 2) and these ligands can be important complexers of ore metals in certain limited environments. Because hydroxide is always present in aqueous solutions as a result of the self-dissociation of water (reaction 2.31), it may be an important form of transport for some metals at higher pH.

So far, carboxylic acid anions have only been reported from relatively low temperature (<200°C) hydrothermal environments such as sedimentary basinal brines (Kharaka et al., 1998), which are considered to be analogues of Mississippi Valley-type ore-forming fluids, and in the pore waters of hydrothermally altered sediments in the Guayamas Basin (Martens, 1990). As is evident from Table 2, concentrations of acetate and malonate in particular can be quite high in some of these environments. The concentrations of amino acids, porphyrins, and thiols in natural hydrothermal fluids are not well constrained.

Pearson's HSAB principle. All metal ions may be considered to be Lewis acids, because they accept electrons, and all ligands may be considered to be Lewis bases, because they donate electrons. Therefore, all metal-ligand complexes are Lewis acid-base adducts. Hard acids are small, highly charged metal ions, generally with d^0 electron configurations. As a result, the electron clouds of these metals are not easily deformed, and they tend to prefer ionic or electrostatic bonding. Soft acids are large metal ions of low charge, typically with d^{10} electron configurations, and consequently have easily deformed electron clouds. Soft acids therefore prefer to bond covalently. Hard and soft bases can be similarly defined, and metal ions or ligands with intermediate properties (e.g., partially filled d-orbitals) are called borderline. Table 3 presents a useful classification of metals and ligands with respect to their hard-soft character.

TABLE 3. Classification of metals and ligands in terms of Pearson's (1963) HSAB principle

Hard	Borderline	Soft
Acids		
H^+	Fe^{2+}, Mn^{2+}, Co^{2+}, Ni^{2+},	$Au^+ > Ag^+ > Cu^+$
$Li^+ > Na^+ > K^+ > Rb^+ > Cs^+$	Cu^{2+}, Zn^{2+}, Pb^{2+}, Sn^{2+},	$Hg^{2+} > Cd^{2+}$
$Be^{2+} > Mg^{2+} > Ca^{2+} > Sr^{2+} > Ba^{2+}$	As^{3+}, Sb^{3+}, Bi^{3+}	$Pt^{2+} > Pd^{2+}$ other PGE^{2+} *$Tl^{3+} > Tl^+$
$Al^{3+} > Ga^{3+}$		
$Sc^{3+} > Y^{3+}$; REE^{3+} ($Lu^{3+} > La^{3+}$);		
Ce^{4+}; Sn^{4+}		
$Ti^{4+} > Ti^{3+}$, $Zr^{4+} \approx Hf^{4+}$		
$Cr^{6+} > Cr^{3+}$; $Mo^{6+} > Mo^{5+} > Mo^{4+}$;		
$W^{6+} > W^{4+}$; Nb^{5+}, $Ta^{5+}Re^{7+} >$;		
$Re^{6+} > Re^{4+}$; $V^{6+} > V^{5+} > V^{4+}$;		
Mn^{4+}; Fe^{3+}; Co^{3+}; $As^{5+}Sb^{5+}$;		
Th^{4+}; $U^{6+} > U^{4+}$		
$PGE^{6+} > PGE^{4+}$, etc. (Ru, Ir, Os)		
Bases		
F^-; H_2O, OH^-, O^{2-}; NH_3;NO_3^-;	Cl^-	$I^- > Br^-$; CN^-; CO;
$CO_3^{2-} > HCO_3^-$; $SO_4^{2-} > HSO_4^-$;		$S^{2-} > HS^- > H_2S$;
$PO_4^{3-} > HPO_4^{2-} > H^2PO_4^-$;		organic phosphines
carboxylates (i.e., acetate, oxalate, etc.);		(R_3P); organic thiols (RP);
MoO_4^{2-}; WO_4^{2-}		polysulfide (S_nS^{2-}),
		thiosulfate ($S_2O_3^{2-}$),
		sulfite (SO_3^{2-});
		HSe^-, Se^{2-}, HTe^-, Te^{2-};
		AsS_2^-; SbS_2^-

Note: In the case of hard species, the > symbol denotes "harder than," and in the case of soft species, it denotes "softer than." The symbol "R" denotes an organic carbon chain.
*According to Pearson (1968), Tl^{3+} is softer than Tl^+ in spite of being more highly charged.

Pearson's HSAB principle states that, in a competitive situation, hard acids tend to complex with hard bases, and soft acids tend to complex with soft bases (Pearson, 1963). In other words, given the choice, metal ions will complex with those ligands that tend to bond in the same way. Metals that tend to bond covalently will generally preferentially form complexes with ligands that bond covalently, and similarly for ionic bonding. Returning to our distinction between coordination complexes and ion pairs, it should be evident that ion pairs are formed in interactions between hard metal ions and hard ligands, whereas coordination complexes are more likely to be formed in soft-soft interactions.

The words "competitive situation" are important to Pearson's principle, because given no choice, a soft metal ion may be forced to form a complex with a hard or borderline ligand. For example, the soft Au^+ ion would prefer to complex with the soft HS^- ion, rather than the harder Cl^-, but in a situation where the HS^- concentration is very low and the Cl^- is very high, Au^+ is forced to form a complex with Cl^- (which is preferable to forming a complex with the even harder ligand, H_2O).

The HSAB principle is most useful in determining the direction of a ligand exchange reaction, such as:

$$HgF^+ + CaBr^+ = HgBr^+ + CaF^+ \tag{2.19}$$

In this case, the HSAB principle predicts that the reaction will go from left to right, so that the harder Ca^{2+} is complexed with the harder F^-, and the softer Hg^{2+} with the softer Br^-. The reason the HSAB principle works so well in predicting which ligands are preferred by a metal ion in an aqueous medium is that in such a medium a competitive situation always exists. For example, the complexation reaction:

$$Zn^{2+} + 4Cl^- = ZnCl_4^{2-} \tag{2.20}$$

is more correctly written as

$$Zn(H_2O)_6^{2+} + 4Cl^- = ZnCl_4^{2-} + 6H_2O(l) \tag{2.21}$$

because metal ions do not exist as "bare" ions but are always hydrated to some extent (note that, although not shown in equation (2.21) for simplicity, the ligand is also generally hydrated, but to a lesser extent). Thus, Pearson's principle works well in predicting complexation tendencies of metal ions in aqueous solution because competition between water and a second ligand always occurs.

The behavior of hydroxide is another example of the importance of keeping in mind that complexation reactions actually involve competition between H_2O and another ligand. The hydroxide ion (OH^-) commonly appears to violate Pearson's principle by forming extremely strong complexes with soft metal ions such as Pd^{2+}. In fact, the stability constants for Pd-hydroxide complexes are among the strongest known for any metal (Baes and Mesmer, 1976). This apparent violation of Pearson's principle occurs because formation of a hydroxide complex is actually the exchange of the hard H_2O ligand for the hard OH^-, i.e.,

$$Pd(H_2O)_4^{2+} + nOH^- = Pd(H_2O)_{4-n}(OH)_n^{2-n} + nH_2O \quad (2.22)$$

Although both H_2O and OH^- are hard, OH^- may be slightly softer (Pearson, 1968), because the electrons on oxygen in H_2O are more tightly constrained (and less available for covalent bonding) owing to the presence of two H^+ ions as opposed to one H^+ in OH^-. This slight difference in hardness, combined with a negative charge on OH^-, making it more attractive to the positively charged Pd^{2+}, may tip the balance in favor of OH^-.

One problem with the use of Pearson's principle is that predictions for interactions among borderline metal ions and ligands are usually not definitive. Nevertheless, the HSAB principle remains a useful geochemical tool for many situations (see the reviews of individual metals below).

The HSAB principle also can be useful in helping to identify erroneous experimental data, and in guiding extrapolations of experimental data to higher temperatures. The thermodynamics of hard-hard interactions are different from those of soft-soft interactions. The standard state Gibbs free energy of complexation may be written in terms of the enthalpy and entropy of complexation according to the previous chapter:

$$\Delta_r G^o = \Delta_r H^o - T\Delta_r S^o \quad (2.23)$$

As shown by equation (1.43), complexation is favored if $\Delta_r G^o < 0$. For electrostatic, hard-hard interactions, complexation is endothermic ($\Delta_r H^o > 0$), so the reaction must be driven forward by the increase in entropy that occurs when waters of hydration of the metal and ligand ions are released upon complexation (Ahrland, 1968, 1973; Seward, 1981). As a result, the stability constants of complexes between hard metal ions and ligands increase monotonically with temperature (cf. eq. 1.132), and simple electrostatic theories will be very successful in guiding extrapolations of these constants to higher temperatures. On the other hand, soft-soft complexation reactions tend to be exothermic ($\Delta_r H^o < 0$) owing to the strong covalent bonds formed (Ahrland, 1968, 1973; Seward, 1981). The $\Delta_r S^o$ of reaction is generally much smaller, because soft metal ions and ligands are much less strongly hydrated than their hard counterparts. Soft-soft complexation reactions are thus driven by an exothermic enthalpy change and their stability constants show a tendency to decrease with increasing temperature, at least over the range 0° to 100°C. Simple electrostatic models will be less successful in guiding extrapolations of stability constants to higher temperature for such reactions. However, as Seward (1981) points out, all complexation reactions tend to increase in hardness, i.e., become more electrostatic, as temperature increases. Therefore, stability constants for soft-soft complexation reactions eventually pass through a minimum, and subsequently increase with increasing temperature (see below for an example).

The Pearson HSAB principle is a useful tool for determining the relative stabilities of metal-ion complexes. However, to understand fully the chemical controls on the thermodynamics of metal-ion complex formation, it is necessary to consider a variety of additional factors, such as the dielectric constant of water, ion hydration, ligand-field stabilization, and relativistic electron orbital effects. For a detailed explanation of these and other factors, see Barnes (1979), Seward (1981), Crerar et al. (1985), Eugster (1986), Brimhall and Crerar (1987), and Seward and Barnes (1997).

Ab initio calculations. A relatively recent development in aqueous geochemistry has been the use of ab initio calculation methods to determine stoichiometries, geometries and relative stabilities of aqueous complexes. Although a full exposition of ab initio methods is beyond the scope of this paper (cf. Tossell and Vaughan, 1992), we would like to point out that such methods hold considerable promise as an aid to choosing which complexes to include in geochemical models of ore-forming processes. Such calculations are based on the principles of quantum mechanics and statistical mechanics and require powerful computers. Only in the last decade or so has the field developed to the point where heavy metal complexes of relevance to economic geology can be investigated. In the future it may be possible to quantitatively calculate stability constants using ab initio methods, but this day may be some way off. However, ab initio methods already have been used in the study of species of relevance to ore deposits, such As(III)-sulfide and -hydroxide (Helz et al., 1995; Tossell, 1997), Sb(III)-sulfide (Tossell, 1994), Zn- and Cd-bisulfide (Kothekar et al., 1978; Tossell and Vaughan, 1993), Zn-chloride (Tossell, 1991), and Au-chloride and -bisulfide (Tossell, 1996) complexes, primarily to make conclusions regarding preferred stoichiometries and geometries to facilitate the interpretation of experimental solubility and spectroscopic measurements.

More Complicated Solubility Calculations

Effect of Activity Coefficients on Solubility

We will next illustrate the effect of activity coefficients on solubility by returning to the simple galena solubility calculation carried out above for the conditions: 200°C, saturated water vapor pressure, $[H_2S^0] = 10^{-3}$ molal, pH = 3.0, and 1.0 molal Cl^-. For this calculation we will ignore any reduction in the concentration of free chloride by complexation or ion pair formation and assume the true ionic strength to be 1.0 molal. We will use the Davies equation (Stumm and Morgan, 1981) to calculate the activity coefficients of all charged aqueous species and we will make the widely used assumption (Helgeson, 1969) that the activity coefficients of neutral species remain equal to unity. The Davies equation may be expressed as:

$$\log\gamma_i = \frac{-Z_i^2 A\sqrt{I}}{1+\sqrt{I}} + 0.2AZ_i^2 I \quad (2.24)$$

where I is the true ionic strength calculated according to the equation:

$$I = \frac{1}{2}\sum_{i=1}^{N} m_i Z_i^2 \quad (2.25)$$

In the above equations, γ_i is the activity coefficient, Z_i is the charge, and m_i is the molal concentration of the ith species. The Debye-Hückel parameter, A, at 200°C and SWVP, is taken from Helgeson and Kirkham (1974b) and is equal to 0.8099.

If we include activity coefficients, equation (2.13) above becomes:

$$\Sigma Pb = (K_{s2}\{H^+\}^2\{H_2S^0\}^{-1})(1/\gamma_{Pb^{2+}} + \beta_1[Cl^-]\gamma_{Cl^-}/\gamma_{PbCl^+} + \beta_2[Cl^-]^2\,\gamma_{Cl^-}{}^2/\gamma_{PbCl^o_2} + \beta_3[Cl^-]^3\,\gamma_{Cl^-}{}^3/\gamma_{PbCl_3^-} + \beta_4[Cl^-]^4\gamma_{Cl^-}{}^4/\gamma_{PbCl_4{}^{2-}}) \quad (2.26)$$

Before proceeding, we should emphasize that one of the greatest sources of uncertainty in geochemical solubility and speciation calculations is the activity coefficient, especially for minor species such as the lead chloride complexes considered here. For the purpose of illustrating the effect of including activity coefficients in solubility calculations, we use equation (2.24) in conjunction with equation (2.26). The values calculated from equation (2.24) should be treated as approximations but should be of the right order of magnitude. The activity coefficients calculated in this manner are: $\gamma_{Pb^{2+}} = \gamma_{PbCl_4{}^{2-}} = 0.107$; $\gamma_{Cl^-} = \gamma_{PbCl^+} = \gamma_{PbCl_3^-} = 0.572$. Substituting these and all other required data into equation (2.26) yields:

$$\Sigma Pb = (10^{-6.64})(1/0.107 + 10^{2.64}(1)(0.572)/(0.572) + 10^{3.97}(1)^2(0.572)^2/(1) + 10^{3.94}(1)^3(0.572)^3/(0.572) + 10^{3.52}(1)^4(0.572)^4/(0.107)) = (10^{-6.64})(10^{3.99}) = 10^{-2.65} = 2.23\times10^{-3}\text{ molal} = 462\text{ mg/kg (ppm)} \quad (2.27)$$

Thus, inclusion of activity coefficient effects has resulted in a decrease in the solubility of galena by a factor of approximately two. Note that, at the temperature and ionic strength of these calculations, the activity coefficients of all charged species are less than 1.0. A decrease in the activity coefficients of the individual lead species alone would tend to increase galena solubility. This is because, in effect, reactions (2.5–2.9) fix the activity of each of the lead species in solution, assuming temperature, pH, and the activities of chloride and hydrogen sulfide are all held constant. If the activity of a species is constant, and the activity coefficient decreases, then the concentration of the species must increase, according to the following equation:

$$\{PbCl_n{}^{2-n}\} = \gamma_{PbCl_n{}^{2-n}} \bullet [PbCl_n{}^{2-n}] \quad (2.28)$$

However, the effect of activity coefficients described above is more than compensated for by the decrease in the activity of Cl^-, which has the effect of decreasing the solubility of galena by decreasing the degree of complexation of Pb^{2+}. Thus, in cases where the solubility of a mineral is controlled by the formation of complexes with relatively high ligand numbers, the inclusion of activity coefficient effects usually leads to a decrease in solubility. On the other hand, if the mineral solubility is controlled by the free ion or complexes of relatively low ligand number, then inclusion of activity coefficient effects will usually result in increased solubility (this is the case with anhydrite, for example). The effects of activity coefficients become increasingly important as the charge on the species increases, owing to the Z_i^2 term in equation (2.24). These calculations, although relatively simplistic, illustrate the importance of the activity coefficient correction, and also the need for reducing the uncertainty in activity coefficient computation.

As mentioned above, uncertainties in the activity coefficients of aqueous species represent a major source of uncertainty in solubility and speciation calculations. For simplicity, we have chosen the Davies equation, which is a relatively convenient equation to use but is probably not very accurate at high ionic strengths. Other activity coefficient models, appropriate for high ionic strengths, include the B-dot method (Helgeson, 1969; Helgeson et al., 1981), the Pitzer equations (Pitzer, 1979, and references therein), and specific interaction theory or SIT (Grenthe and Wanner, 1989; Giridhar and Langmuir, 1991). Space does not permit a full exposition of these models here (see Langmuir, 1997, for a good summary), but we would like to make a few comments to guide the reader in the selection of the appropriate model to use. At ionic strengths less than 0.1 molal, the Davies equation should yield adequate accuracy, and it has the advantage of simplicity. The Pitzer equations are applicable up to quite high ionic strengths (up to at least 6 molal, and perhaps as high as 20 molal) and have been shown to work well at elevated temperatures and pressures. Use of the Pitzer equations requires that the Pitzer parameters be available for the species in question, and these are currently unavailable for nearly all metal complexes (and probably will remain so in the foreseeable future). However, Pitzer parameters are available for many major electrolytes such as NaCl, KCl, etc., even at elevated temperatures (see for example Holmes and Mesmer, 1983). SIT theory is valid for use up to ionic strengths intermediate between those of the Davies and Pitzer equations, but currently suffers from even poorer availability of equation parameters. Helgeson's B-dot equation was devised especially to estimate the activity coefficients of trace components in a solution dominated by one electrolyte (usually NaCl in most geochemical applications) and it remains the best means of estimating activity coefficients of minor species (i.e., most metal complexes). However, improved methods are desperately required. For the time being, the best course of action is to use the Pitzer approach to calculate activity coefficients for the major ions in solution, e.g., Cl^-, but to use another method (e.g., Helgeson's B-dot) for trace ions.

Simultaneous Equilibrium Calculations

As already indicated above, a complete solubility calculation in any given system will be more complicated than the simple examples demonstrated so far, owing to the interdependence of a large number of related equilibria. We now reconsider the problem of the calculation of the solubility of galena at 200°C, pH = 3, $[\Sigma S] = 10^{-3}$ molal, and $[\Sigma Cl] = 1.0$ molal (with chloride "added" as HCl and NaCl). To carry out this calculation in the most rigorous manner, we must consider all relevant species that might turn out to be significant. In the case under consideration, these species include: Pb^{2+}, $PbCl^+$, $PbCl_2^0$, $PbCl_3^-$, $PbCl_4^{2-}$, H^+, Cl^-, Na^+, HCl^0, $NaCl^0$, OH^-, $NaOH^0$, H_2S^0, HS^-, S^{2-}, $NaHS^0$, $PbOH^+$, $Pb(OH)_2^0$, $Pb(OH)_3^-$, $Pb(HS)_3^-$, $Pb(HS)_2^0$, and $PbS(H_2S)_2^0$. One can quibble about this list of species, and in fact, some of these species can be shown to be insignificant with relatively little effort. However, we will include all the species in the above list for illustrative purposes. In the problem as we have set it up, there are 22 unknowns (the concentration of each of the species). To solve this problem we need to find 22 independent constraints or equations relating the unknowns, and solve this system of equations using numerical methods. Some of the constraints come in the form of equilibrium constant expressions for relevant reactions among the species. These constraints are often referred to as mass action constraints. We already have identified five mass action constraints: they are the equilibrium constant expressions for reactions (2.5–2.9). In addition we have 13 more mass action constraints corresponding to the following equilibria:

$$H^+ + Cl^- = HCl^0 \quad (2.29)$$

$$Na^+ + Cl^- = NaCl^0 \quad (2.30)$$

$$H_2O(l) = H^+ + OH^- \quad (2.31)$$

$$Na^+ + OH^- = NaOH^0 \quad (2.32)$$

$$H_2S^0 = H^+ + HS^- \quad (2.33)$$

$$HS^- = H^+ + S^{2-} \quad (2.34)$$

$$Na^+ + HS^- = NaHS^0 \quad (2.35)$$

$$Pb^{2+} + H_2O = PbOH^+ + H^+ \quad (2.36)$$

$$Pb^{2+} + 2H_2O = Pb(OH)_2^0 + 2H^+ \quad (2.37)$$

$$Pb^{2+} + 3H_2O = Pb(OH)_3^- + 3H^+ \quad (2.38)$$

$$PbS + H_2S^0 = Pb(HS)_2^0 \quad (2.39)$$

$$PbS + H_2S^0 + HS^- = Pb(HS)_3^- \quad (2.40)$$

$$PbS + 2H_2S^0 = PbS(H_2S)_2^0 \quad (2.41)$$

We now have 18 mass action constraints. Note that in providing mass action constraints, none of the reactions can be linear combinations of any other two or more reactions. For example, the reaction:

$$H_2S^0 = 2H^+ + S^{2-}$$

is a linear combination of reactions (2.33) and (2.34) and does not represent an independent constraint on the species concentrations.

An additional constraint that must normally be satisfied when dealing with species concentrations in aqueous solutions is that of charge balance or electroneutrality; the sum of the concentrations of positively charged species must equal the sum of the concentrations of the negatively charged species. Thus,

$$2[Pb^{2+}] + [PbCl^+] + [H^+] + [Na^+] + [PbOH^+] = [Cl^-] + [OH^-] + [HS^-] + 2[S^{2-}] + [PbCl_3^-] + 2[PbCl_4^{2-}] + [Pb(OH)_3^-] + [Pb(HS)_3^-] \quad (2.42)$$

The three remaining constraints come from mass balance expressions. The following mass balances are appropriate to our example:

$$[\Sigma S] = 10^{-3} \text{ molal} = [H_2S^0] + [HS^-] + [S^{2-}] + [NaHS^0] + 3[Pb(HS)_3^-] + 2[Pb(HS)_2^0] + 3[PbS(H_2S)_2^0] \quad (2.43)$$

$$[H^+] = 10^{-pH}/\gamma_{H^+} \quad (2.44)$$

$$[\Sigma Cl] = m_{NaCl} = 1.0 \text{ molal} = [Cl^-] + [HCl^0] + [NaCl^0] + [PbCl^+] + 2[PbCl_2^0] + 3[PbCl_3^-] + 4[PbCl_4^{2-}] \quad (2.45)$$

Note that we could also have chosen to include a mass balance on total Na, but this would have given us too many constraints on the system, i.e., the system would be overdetermined, and no solution can be found that satisfies all 23 constraints. In the model we have defined, we are fixing pH, total sulfide and total chloride, and the total sodium concentration is permitted to "float" so that the charge balance is satisfied. Another possible way of setting up the calculation would be to constrain total sulfide, chloride, and sodium, and let pH "float" to satisfy charge balance. However, we cannot specify saturation with respect to galena, and fix pH, total sulfide, total chloride, and total sodium all at the same time. The choice of which constraints to employ should be dictated by the nature of the natural process one is trying to model.

Having 22 equations in 22 unknowns, one may now solve for the concentrations of all species, provided the equilibrium constants for all mass action expressions are available at the pressures and temperatures of interest (see Table 4). Such a problem can be solved using an equilibrium-solver algorithm such as EQBRM, originally developed by Crerar (1975). Anderson and Crerar (1993) provide a source listing for a FORTRAN version of this algorithm that includes provision for activity coefficient corrections using the Davies equation. In Appendix 1, we illustrate the use of this code in solving the above system of equations. As shown in the Appendix, the calculated solubility of galena under the conditions of interest is equal to 1.02×10^{-3} molal or 211 mg/kg. Thus, in this particular example, competition for Cl^-, primarily by Na^+ to form $NaCl^0$, reduces the solubility by a factor of approximately two

TABLE 4. Equilibrium constants employed for the EQBRM calculation of galena solubility at 200°C and SWVP

Reaction	Log K	Reaction	Log K
(2.5a) $PbS(s) + 2H^+ = Pb^{2+} + H_2S^0$	-3.64[1]	(2.33) $H_2S^0 = H^+ + HS^-$	-7.12[6]
(2.6) $Pb^{2+} + Cl^- = PbCl^+$	2.64[1]	(2.34) $HS^- = H^+ + S^{2-}$	-10.75[6]
(2.7) $Pb^{2+} + 2Cl^- = PbCl_2^0$	3.97[1]	(2.35) $Na^+ + HS^- = NaHS^0$	0.09[4]
(2.8) $Pb^{2+} + 3Cl^- = PbCl_3^-$	3.94[1]	(2.36) $Pb^{2+} + H_2O = PbOH^+ + H^+$	-3.78[3]
(2.9) $Pb^{2+} + 4Cl^- = PbCl_4^{2-}$	3.52[1]	(2.37) $Pb^{2+} + 2H_2O = Pb(OH)_2^0 + 2H^+$	-11.37[3]
(2.29) $H^+ + Cl^- = HCl^0$	-0.09[5]	(2.38) $Pb^{2+} + 3H_2O = Pb(OH)_3^- + 3H^+$	-20.76[3]
(2.30) $Na^+ + Cl^- = NaCl^0$	0.09[1]	(2.39) $PbS + H_2S^0 = Pb(HS)_2^0$	-4.78[2]
(2.31) $H_2O(l) = H^+ + OH^-$	-11.28[1]	(2.40) $PbS + H_2S^0 + HS^- = Pb(HS)_3^-$	–[7]
(2.32) $Na^+ + OH^- = NaOH^0$	0.09[4]	(2.41) $PbS + 2H_2S^0 = PbS(H_2S)_2^0$	-4.88[2]

[1]SUPCRT92 (Johnson et al., 1992); [2]Barnes (1979); [3]Tugarinov et al. (1975); [4]approximated by the log K of $NaCl^0$; [5]Ruaya and Seward (1987); [6]Crerar and Barnes (1976); [7]Barnes (1979) gives values for this constant, but not at 200°C.

from that calculated above in equation (2.27). The magnitude of the effect of including all relevant equilibria in solubility calculations of course depends on the particular set of pH, m_{NaCl}, T, and P conditions selected.

Multi-component equilibria calculations of the type described above are greatly facilitated through the use of a number of currently available software packages for hydrothermal conditions, such as SOLMINEQ.88 (Kharaka et al., 1988), EQ3 (Wolery, 1979, 1983), and SOLVEQ (Reed, 1982). A detailed description of the use of SOLVEQ is given in Chapter 5.

Uncertainties in Speciation and Solubility Calculations

When computing speciation and solubility, it is important to keep in mind the possible sources of error. A major source of potential error is the combined uncertainties in all the thermodynamic data employed, whether measured experimentally, or estimated theoretically, and including the computation of activity coefficients. In general, the degree of uncertainty will increase with increasing temperature, pressure, and ionic strength of the problem at hand. A detailed discussion of the propagation of errors in thermodynamic calculations is given by Anderson (1977) and Taylor (1997). Here we simply point out that it is rare that the total uncertainty in speciation and solubility calculations involving hydrothermal solutions is less than 0.5 to 1.0 log units. However, even calculations with greater uncertainties often can provide useful constraints on the behavior of natural systems or indicate directions for fruitful experimental measurements, as long as the limitations of the data are kept in mind.

Methods of Extrapolation of Equilibrium Constants

Ideally, all the equilibrium constants required for a solubility or speciation calculation at elevated pressures and temperatures would be available from well designed, executed, and interpreted experiments. However, this is rarely the case, nor is it likely to be the case for many years to come. Therefore it is desirable to have some means of extrapolating thermodynamic data from 25 °C and 1 bar to elevated temperatures and pressures. Here we briefly describe and illustrate the use of several techniques for the extrapolation of stability constants.

In order to extrapolate an equilibrium constant rigorously from a reference temperature to another temperature, it is necessary to know the heat capacity change for the reaction ($\Delta_r C_p^o$) as a function of temperature for use in equations (1.21) and (1.133). For reactions involving only minerals and gases, $\Delta_r C_p^o$ can usually be expressed in terms of the Maier-Kelley equation (eq. 1.20), and then equation (1.133) can be integrated to yield equation (1.134). Thus, in order to accomplish the extrapolation, it is necessary to know the Maier-Kelley coefficients (or coefficients for a similar heat capacity equation) for each reactant and product in the reaction of interest. However, there are two problems with this procedure. The first is that the Maier-Kelley equation does not have the correct form to express heat capacities of reactions involving aqueous solutes, the values of which asymptotically approach negative infinity at the critical point of water, i.e., 374°C (Helgeson et al., 1981). The second problem is that heat capacity data are generally unavailable for the vast majority of aqueous complexes of interest to economic geologists. A number of methods that have been developed to circumvent these problems will be reviewed below. We will extrapolate the stability constant for a lead chloride complexation reaction from 25° to 300°C using each of the methods discussed. The results will be compiled and compared with actual experimental data. However, we caution that no definitive conclusions regarding the general validity of the individual methods of extrapolation should be drawn from the single example chosen here.

Isocoulombic Methods

Two-term isocoulombic extrapolation. If it can be assumed that $\Delta_r C_p^o \approx 0$, then equation (1.134) can be simplified to the van't Hoff equation:

$$\log K_T - \log K_{T_r} = \frac{-\Delta_r H^0}{2.30259R}\left(\frac{1}{T} - \frac{1}{T_r}\right) \quad (2.46)$$

Where T is the temperature of interest, and T_r is a reference temperature. This equation indicates that a plot of log K versus 1/T should be linear, if the above assumption holds, and a set of log K values at lower temperatures can be extrapolated to higher temperatures using such a linear plot. However, for the general chemical reaction involving aqueous ions, it is unlikely that $\Delta_r C_p^o \approx 0$ For example, consider the ionization reaction:

$$HF^0 = H^+ + F^- \quad (2.47)$$

On one side of this equation, we have a neutral molecule, and on the other side we have two univalent ions. When ions are placed in water, their resultant hydration has a very large effect on the heat capacity and other thermodynamic properties of the solution, whereas the hydration of a neutral molecule has considerably less effect. Thus, we cannot expect that the heat capacities of the products will exactly balance the heat capacity of the reactant in reaction (2.47) such that $\Delta_r C_p^o \approx 0$, and therefore, we cannot use the van't Hoff equation (2.46) as a basis for the extrapolation of equilibrium constants. In other words, for the general reaction involving aqueous ions, we should expect significant curvature in a plot of log K versus 1/T.

However, if a reaction is written such that it has the same number and type of charges on both sides of the reaction, e.g.,

$$HF^0 + OH^- = F^- + H_2O(l) \quad (2.48)$$

then the heat capacity effects of the ions will cancel to a large extent, and $\Delta_r C_p^o$ will be relatively small, if not zero. Reactions such as (2.48) above were termed isocoulombic by Lindsay (1980), and the fact that $\Delta_r C_p^o$ should be near zero for such reactions has been referred to as the "Principle of Balance of Identical Like Charges" by Cobble et al. (1982). Because $\Delta_r C_p^o$ is close to zero for isocoulombic reactions, the van't Hoff equation has a greater probability of guiding accurate extrapolation of lower temperature equilibrium constants than is the case with non-isocoulombic reactions. Use of the van't Hoff equation to extrapolate equilibrium constants of isocoulombic reactions to higher temperatures has been referred to by Gu et al. (1994) as the two-term isocoulombic method, because two terms, log K_{T_r} and $\Delta_r H_p^o$, are required to accomplish the extrapolation. Lindsay (1980) showed that the isocoulombic approach works well for a number of truly isocoulombic reactions up to approximately 300°C, and also that it works reasonably well for quasi-isocoulombic reactions such as:

$$HSO_4^- + OH^- = SO_4^{2-} + H_2O(l) \quad (2.49)$$

This reaction is not truly isocoulombic because it has an anion with a –2 charge on one side and two anions with a –1 charge on the other.

Most ionic reactions can be made isocoulombic if combined with a suitable model reaction. For example, reaction (2.47) above can be transformed into the isocoulombic form (2.48) by adding the following reaction:

$$OH^- + H^+ = H_2O(l) \quad (2.50)$$

Reaction (2.50) is an ideal model reaction because its thermodynamic parameters are relatively well-known over a wide temperature and pressure range. The equilibrium constant for reaction (2.48) may then be expressed as $K_{2.48} = K_{2.47}K_{2.50}$, or $\log K_{2.48} = \log K_{2.47} + \log K_{2.50}$.

We will now illustrate the use of the two-term isocoulombic method for the extrapolation of the equilibrium constant for the reaction:

$$Pb^{2+} + Cl^- = PbCl^+ \quad (2.51)$$

for which $\log K_{2.51,25°C} = 1.41$ (Seward, 1984). Obviously, the above equation is not isocoulombic. The reaction can be made quasi-isocoulombic by subtracting reaction (2.50) from it to obtain:

$$Pb^{2+} + Cl^- + H_2O(l) = PbCl^+ + OH^- + H^+ \quad (2.52)$$

To apply the two-term isocoulombic method, we must calculate the equilibrium constant and the enthalpy of reaction for reaction (2.52) at the reference temperature, here chosen to be 25°C, as follows:

$$\log K_{2.52,\,25°C} = \log K_{2.51,\,25°C} - \log K_{2.50,\,25°C} \quad (2.53)$$

$$\log K_{2.52,\,25°C} = 1.41 - 13.995 = -12.585 \quad (2.54)$$

and

$$\Delta_r H^o_{2.52} = \Delta_r H^o_{2.51} - \Delta_r H^o_{2.50} \quad (2.55)$$

where each $\Delta_r H^o$ refers to the reference temperature (we have dropped the temperature subscripts on the $\Delta_r H^o$ symbols for simplicity). Now, substituting the actual values into equation (2.55), we obtain

$$\Delta_r H^o_{2.52} = 2{,}460\ J/mole - (-55{,}815\ J/mole) = 58{,}275\ J/mole \quad (2.56)$$

where $\Delta_r H^o_{2.51}$ = 2,460 J/mole is taken from Seward (1984), and $\Delta_r H^o_{2.50}$ = 55,815 J/mole is calculated using SUPCRT92 (Johnson et al., 1992). The values of $\log K_{2.52,\,25°C}$ and $\Delta_r H^o_{2.52}$ so obtained are then substituted into the van't Hoff equation (eq. 2.46) to obtain $\log K_{2.52}$ at any desired temperature. The values for $\log K_{2.51,T}$ at any elevated temperature (T) are obtained by adding $\log K_{2.50,T}$ (compiled in Table 5) to $\log K_{2.52,T}$. For example, at 300°C, we have:

$$\log K_{2.51,300°C} = \log K_{2.52,\,300°C} + \log K_{2.50,300°C} = -7.69 + 11.3 = 3.61 \quad (2.57)$$

TABLE 5. Equilibrium constants employed in the text calculated using SUPCRT92 (Johnson et al., 1992)

T(°C)	log $K_{2.50}$	log $K_{2.59}$
25	13.995	0.20
50	13.27	0.83
100	12.26	2.00
150	11.63	3.09
200	11.28	4.14
250	11.17	5.21
300	11.30	6.40

The resultant values of log $K_{2.51,T}$ are tabulated from 50° to 300°C in Table 6 (column 5).

Obviously, the value of log $K_{2.51,T}$ calculated depends on the value of $\Delta_r H^o{}_{2.51}$. For comparison, the value of $\Delta_r H^o{}_{2.51}$ = 4,531 J/mole obtained from SUPCRT92 is considerably different from the corresponding value given by Seward (1984), and it is of interest to compare estimates of log $K_{2.51,T}$ determined using this value. In this case we calculate:

$$\Delta_r H^o{}_{2.52} = 4{,}531 \text{ J/mole} - (-55{,}815 \text{ J/mole}) = 60{,}346 \text{ J/mole} \quad (2.58)$$

Once again, we substitute this value and log $K_{2.52,\ 25°C}$ = −12.585 into equation (2.46) and calculate values of log $K_{2.52,T}$ at other temperatures, and recover log $K_{2.51,T}$ as in equation (2.57). The resultant values of log $K_{2.51,T}$ are given in Table 6 (column 6). As can be seen from Table 6, the values of log $K_{2.51,T}$ calculated using the two-term isocoulombic method and either of the two $\Delta_r H^o{}_{2.52}$ values are in relatively good agreement (maximum deviation ±0.3 log unit at 300°C) with the original measurements of Seward (1984). However, slightly better agreement is obtained using $\Delta_r H^o{}_{2.52}$ = 4,531 J/mole calculated from SUPCRT92.

The better the match between the model reaction and the reaction of interest, the greater the probability that the isocoulombic method will yield reliable results. Thus, it is somewhat surprising that the quasi-isocoulombic equation (2.52) yields as good an approximation as it does. Very frequently, excellent estimates can be obtained with quasi-isocoulombic equations. However, in general, it is better to use a complexation reaction involving a metal ion and ligand with properties similar to the metal ion and ligand in the reaction of interest. This approach was taken previously by Ruaya (1988) and Wood et al. (1992), among others. For example, we could use the following reaction as the model reaction for equation (2.51):

$$Zn^{2+} + Cl^- = ZnCl^+ \quad (2.59)$$

to form the strictly isocoulombic reaction

$$Pb^{2+} + ZnCl^+ = PbCl^+ + Zn^{2+} \quad (2.60)$$

For this reaction, the assumption that $\Delta_r C^o_p \approx 0$ is likely to be a better approximation than for reaction (2.52), because the types and magnitudes of the charges are perfectly balanced, and the structures of the ions in solution are more similar. We calculate the equilibrium constant and the enthalpy of reaction for reaction (2.60) at the reference temperature according to:

$$\log K_{2.60,\ 25°C} = \log K_{2.51,\ 25°C} - \log K_{2.59,\ 25°C} \quad (2.61)$$

$$\log K_{2.60,\ 25°C} = 1.41 - 0.2 = 1.21 \quad (2.62)$$

where log $K_{2.59,\ 25°C}$ = 0.2 comes from SUPCRT92, and

$$\Delta_r H^o{}_{2.60} = \Delta_r H^o{}_{2.51} - \Delta_r H^o{}_{2.59} \quad (2.63)$$

$$\Delta_r H^o{}_{2.60} = 2{,}460 \text{ J/mole} - 43{,}317 \text{ J/mole} = -40{,}857 \text{ J/mole} \quad (2.64)$$

where $\Delta_r H^o{}_{2.51}$ = 2,460 J/mole comes from Seward (1984) and $\Delta_r H^o{}_{2.59}$ = 43,317 J/mole comes from SUPCRT92. The values log $K_{2.60,\ 25°C}$ = 1.21 and $\Delta_r H^o{}_{2.60}$ = −40,857 J/mole are then substituted into equation (2.46) and values of log $K_{2.60,T}$ are computed at the desired temperature. Then, values of log $K_{2.51,T}$ are computed from the equation:

$$\log K_{2.51,T} = \log K_{2.60,T} + \log K_{2.59,T} \quad (2.65)$$

which at 300°C becomes

$$\log K_{2.51,T} = -2.22 + 6.40 = 4.18 \quad (2.66)$$

The values of log $K_{2.51,T}$ from 50° to 300°C resulting from application of these equations are presented in Table 6 (column 7). Once again, values of log $K_{2.51,T}$ can also be calculated with $\Delta_r H^o{}_{2.51}$ = 4,531 J/mole from SUPCRT92, and these are given in Table 6, column 8. From Table 6, it is evident that, for this particular reaction (2.51), the estimates using equation (2.59) as a model reaction are actually worse than those using equation (2.50) as a model reaction, in spite of the fact that the former should be more suitable in terms of cancellation of heat capacities. This situation probably is a result of uncertainties in the thermodynamic data for equation (2.59), whereas the thermodynamic data for reaction (2.50) are much better defined.

In summary, it can be concluded that the two-term isocoulombic method can yield reasonable estimates of stability constants at elevated temperatures provided that (1) the reaction can be made isocoulombic or quasi-isocoulombic by addition or subtraction of an appropriate model reaction, (2) reliable values of log K and $\Delta_r H^o$ are available for both the reaction of interest and the model reaction at some reference temperature (usually, but not necessarily always, 25°C), and (3) reliable log K values are available for the model reaction at each elevated temperature of interest. The choice of which model reaction to use is a trade-off between finding a reaction that provides as close a match as possible to the structure and charges of ions on both sides of the isocoulombic reaction and a reaction for which the thermodynamic data are reasonably well known.

Before leaving this subject, several other points should be made. First, estimates of high temperature stability constants using the two-term isocoulombic method (or any method) of extrapolation will be more accurate the shorter the extrapolation from the reference conditions. Thus, if permitted by the availability and quality of experimental thermodynamic data, use of a reference temperature higher than 25°C is often desirable if a long extrapolation would otherwise be made. Second, if values for the enthalpy of reaction are not available, or are of questionable quality, a two-term isocoulombic extrapolation can still be made by plotting two or more experimentally determined log Ks determined at different temperatures on a plot of log K versus 1/T, fitting a straight line to these data, and graphically determining

TABLE 6. The first stability constant for $PbCl^+$ estimated using various methods described in the text

T(°C)	1 Expt.	2 SUPCRT	3 Dens. A	4 Dens. B	5 2-term A	6 2-term B	7 2-term C	8 2-term D	9 1-term A	10 1-term B
25	1.41	1.44 (0.03)	1.41 (0.00)	1.41 (0.00)	1.41 (0.00)	1.41 (0.00)	1.41 (0.00)	1.41 (0.00)	1.41 (0.00)	1.41 (0.00)
50	1.47	1.53 (0.06)	1.46 (-0.01)	1.50 (0.03)	1.47 (0.00)	1.50 (0.03)	1.49 (0.02)	1.51 (0.04)	1.66 (0.19)	1.95 (0.48)
100	1.67	1.81 (0.14)	1.63 (-0.04)	1.76 (0.09)	1.73 (0.06)	1.80 (0.13)	1.77 (0.10)	1.84 (0.17)	2.20 (0.53)	2.97 (1.30)
150	2.09	2.19 (0.10)	1.85 (-0.24)	2.08 (-0.01)	2.06 (-0.03)	2.17 (0.08)	2.19 (0.10)	2.29 (0.20)	2.76 (0.67)	3.94 (1.85)
200	2.55	2.64 (0.09)	2.09 (-0.46)	2.44 (-0.11)	2.47 (-0.08)	2.60 (0.05)	2.70 (0.15)	2.84 (0.29)	3.35 (0.80)	4.90 (2.35)
250	3.18	3.20 (0.02)	2.39 (-0.79)	2.87 (-0.31)	2.98 (-0.20)	3.13 (-0.05)	3.34 (0.16)	3.50 (0.32)	4.00 (0.82)	5.90 (2.72)
300	3.89	3.94 (0.05)	2.80 (-1.09)	3.45 (-0.44)	3.61 (-0.28)	3.79 (-0.10)	4.18 (0.29)	4.35 (0.46)	4.75 (0.86)	7.03 (3.14)

Figures in parentheses represent the difference between estimated value and experimental value.
1) Experimentally determined by Seward (1984).
2) Calculated using SUPCRT92.
3) Calculated using the density model with $\Delta_r H^\circ (PbCl^+) = 2460$ J/mole and $\Delta_r C_p^\circ (PbCl^+) = 140$ J/K-mole from Seward (1984).
4) Calculated using the density model with $\Delta_r H^\circ (PbCl^+) = 4531$ J/mole and $\Delta_r C_p^\circ (PbCl^+) = 196$ J/K-mole from SUPCRT92.
5) Calculated using the two-term isocoulombic method with $H_2O = H^+ + OH^-$ as the model reaction, $\Delta_r H^\circ (PbCl^+) = 2460$ J/mole from Seward (1984) and $\Delta_r H^\circ (H_2O) = 55{,}815$ J/mole from SUPCRT92 .
6) Calculated using the two-term isocoulombic method with $H_2O = H^+ + OH^-$ as the model reaction and $\Delta_r H^\circ (PbCl^+) = 4531$ J/mole and $\Delta_r H^\circ (H_2O) = 55{,}815$ J/mole from SUPCRT92.
7) Calculated using the two-term isocoulombic method with $Zn^{2+} + Cl^- = ZnCl^+$ as the model reaction, $\Delta_r H^\circ (PbCl^+) = 2460$ J/mole from Seward (1984), and $\Delta_r H^\circ (ZnCl^+) = 43{,}317$ J/mole from SUPCRT92.
8) Calculated using the two-term isocoulombic method with $Zn^{2+} + Cl^- = ZnCl^+$ as the model reaction and $\Delta_r H^\circ (PbCl^+) = 4531$ J/mole and $\Delta_r H^\circ (ZnCl^+) = 43{,}317$ J/mole from SUPCRT92.
9) One-term isocoulombic model with $H_2O = H^+ + OH^-$ as the model reaction.
10) One-term isocoulombic model with $Zn^{2+} + Cl^- = ZnCl^+$ as the model reaction.

log K of the isocoulombic reaction. Third, although we do not demonstrate this use here, the isocoulombic method can be used to guide extrapolations of equilibrium constants from one pressure to another, or from one ionic strength to another. Finally, it should be realized that use of any isocoulombic method may be risky at temperatures near or beyond the critical temperature of water (374°C), because the partial molar heat capacities of ions approach negative infinity at this point (Helgeson et al., 1981), and the heat capacities of the products and reactants of even well-balanced isocoulombic reactions may not cancel sufficiently well to make $\Delta_r C_p^o = 0$ a good approximation.

One-term isocoulombic extrapolation. Unfortunately, for many reactions of interest in economic geology, the only thermodynamic datum available is a single stability constant at a single temperature. In this case, it is impossible to use the two-term isocoulombic extrapolation method, or any of the other extrapolation methods described below, without estimating $\Delta_r H^o$ in some manner. Although such methods of estimation exist, considerable error may be introduced. However, Gu et al. (1994), have suggested that, if for an isocoulombic reaction the assumption that $\Delta_r C_p^o \approx 0$ is valid, then it should also be true that $\Delta_r S^o \approx 0$. If this is the case, then the equation

$$\Delta_r G^o = \Delta_r H^o - T\Delta_r S^o \qquad (2.67)$$

becomes

$$\Delta_r G^o = \Delta_r H^o \qquad (2.68)$$

If $\Delta_r C_p \approx 0$, then $\Delta_r H^o$ is a constant, because by definition

$$\Delta_r C_p^o = \left(\frac{\partial \Delta_r H^0}{\partial T}\right)_p .$$

Then, according to equation (2.68), $\Delta_r G^o$ is a constant. This is very useful because $\Delta_r G^o(T)$ is directly related to log K_T via the equation:

$$\log K_T = -\frac{\Delta_r G^o(T)}{2.303RT} \qquad (2.69)$$

Thus, if $\Delta_r G^o(T)$ is constant, then

$$\log K_{T_r} = -\frac{\Delta_r G^o(T_r)}{2.303RT_r} \qquad (2.70)$$

Taking the ratio of equations (2.69) and (2.70) and rearranging we obtain

$$\log K_T = \left(\frac{T_r}{T}\right) \log K_{T_r} \qquad (2.71)$$

So with the one-term isocoulombic method, the only datum required to calculate log K_T is log K_{T_r}. We again return to the extrapolation of the stability constant for reaction (2.51) to illustrate the use of this method. Once again, we take T_r to be 298.15K, so log $K_{2.51,\ 25°C} = 1.41$ (Seward, 1984). First we use equation (2.50) as the model reaction so that log $K_{2.52,\ 25°C} = -12.585$. At 300°C then, we calculate log K_T according to

$$\log K_{2.52,300°C} = \left(\frac{298.15}{573.15}\right) \cdot (-12.585) = -6.55 \qquad (2.72)$$

and

$$\log K_{2.51,\ 300°C} = \log K_{2.52,\ 300°C} + \log K_{2.50,\ 300°C} = -6.55 + 11.3 = 4.75 \qquad (2.73)$$

In this particular case, the predictions obtained with the one-term isocoulombic method using equation (2.50) as the model reaction (Table 6, column 9) diverge from the experimental values until at 300°C the prediction is nearly one order of magnitude higher than the experimental value. Using reaction (2.59) as the model reaction and applying equation (2.71) and an equation of the form of (2.73) we obtain log $K_{2.51,\ 300°C} = 7.03$. For this example, the one-term isocoulombic method, using reaction (2.59) as the model reaction, gives a much poorer approximation of log $K_{46,573.15}$ than the two-term method, or any of the other methods attempted here (cf. Table 6, column 10). However, Gu et al. (1994) provide numerous examples where the one-term method gives a comparable or better approximation than the two-term method. These authors attribute the success of the one-term method vis-à-vis the two-term method to the cancellation of errors in the $\Delta_r C_p^o$ and $\Delta_r S^o$ terms. Again, the very poor estimate of log $K_{2.51,\ 300°C}$ obtained from the one-term method here using reaction (2.59) as the model reaction is probably attributable to errors in the thermodynamic data for reaction (2.59), which is supported by the better results obtained using reaction (2.50) as the model reaction. Alternatively, the assumption that $\Delta_r S^o = 0$ for an isocoulombic reaction may simply not be valid for some reactions. As Gu et al., (1994) point out, it is often very difficult to determine a priori whether the one-term or the two-term method will yield more accurate results. The one-term isocoulombic method does appear to yield comparatively poor results for chloride complexation reactions (C.H. Gammons, pers. commun., 1996); it yields much better results when applied to acid dissociation, ligand exchange or hydroxide complexation reactions. We would recommend the use of the two-term method in those cases where reliable $\Delta_r H^o$ values are known for both the reaction of interest and the model reaction, or for any chloride complexation reaction. However, the one-term equation may be useful for other types of reactions, especially when neither $\Delta_r H^o$ nor $\Delta_r C_p^o$ are available or they are of questionable quality.

The Density Model

A complete presentation of the density model has been given by Anderson et al. (1991). This method of extrapolation of equilibrium constants is based on the empirical observation that equilibrium constants for the ionization of many solutes at elevated temperatures and pressures display nearly linear relationships with respect to the density of water (see references in Anderson et al., 1991).

Anderson et al. (1991) show that this empirical observation leads to an equation expressing the equilibrium constant as a function of temperature, pressure, and volumetric properties of water (density, coefficient of isothermal expansion, etc.). Anderson et al.'s (1991) equation for reactions involving only dissolved species is as follows:

$$\ln K_T = \ln K_{T_r} - \frac{\Delta_r H^o}{R}\left(\frac{1}{T}-\frac{1}{T_r}\right) + \frac{\Delta_r C_{Pr}}{RT_r(\partial\alpha/\partial T)_{P_r}} \left(\frac{1}{T}\ln\frac{\rho_r}{\rho} - \frac{\alpha_r}{T}(T-T_r)\right) \quad (2.74)$$

where $\Delta_r C^o_p$ is the change in heat capacity of the reaction at the reference temperature, T_r, α_r is the coefficient of thermal expansion of water at the reference temperature and pressure, ρ_r is the density of water at the reference temperature and pressure, ρ is the density of water at the pressure and temperature of interest, $(\partial\alpha/\partial T)_{P_r}$ is the change in the coefficient of thermal expansion with respect to temperature at constant pressure for water at the reference temperature and pressure, and all other symbols are as defined previously. Note that ln K = 2.30259 log K. The parameters, ρ_r, ρ, and $(\partial\alpha/\partial T)_{P_r}$ are properties of water alone and can be found in tables 2, 3, and 5, respectively, in Anderson et al. (1991), as well as in Helgeson and Kirkham (1974a). Thus, three reaction-specific parameters need be known to use this method: ln K_{T_r}, $\Delta_r H^o$, and $\Delta_r C^o_p$ Anderson et al. (1991) give additional equations for extrapolation of equilibrium constants for reactions involving minerals as well as aqueous species, and Anderson (1995) provides some further guidance regarding their use.

As an illustration of the use of the density model for extrapolating stability constants, we once again extrapolate the stability constant for equation (2.51) to 300°C. From Seward (1984) we obtain the following values: log $K_{2.51,\,25°C}$=1.41; $\Delta_r H^o$ = 2,460 J/mole; $\Delta_r C^o_p$ = 140 J/mole-K. The values for the water properties required are (Anderson et al., 1991): $\alpha_{25°C} = 2.593 \times 10^{-4}\ K^{-1}$; $(\partial\alpha/\partial T)_{P_{25°C}} = 9.5714 \times 10^{-6}\ K^{-2}$; $\rho_{25°C}$ = 0.997 g/cm^3; and $\rho_{300°C}$ = 0.7124 g/cm^3. Substituting these values into equation (2.74), we obtain log $K_{2.51,\,300°C}$ = 2.80. Values of log $K_{2.51,\,300°C}$ between 25° and 300°C are given in Table 6, column 3. To test the sensitivity of the density model to the thermodynamic parameters for equation (2.51), we repeat the calculation above using the following data from SUPCRT92: $\Delta_r H^o$ = 4,531 J/mole; $\Delta_r C^o_p$ = 196 J/mole–K. The values of ln $K_{2.51,\,25°C}$, $\alpha_{25°C}$, $(\partial\alpha/\partial T)_{P_{25°C}}$, $\rho_{25°C}$, and $\rho_{300°C}$ are the same as before. We then obtain log $K_{2.51,\,300°C}$ = 3.45; values at other temperatures are given in Table 6, column 4.

For this particular example, the estimates of the stability constant provided by the density model are less accurate than those of the two-term isocoulombic method, but are significantly better than the one-term isocoulombic method. It is also evident that the density model predictions are quite sensitive to the input thermodynamic data (Table 6) for the reaction of interest. The density model is likely to yield the best estimates when relatively well-constrained $\Delta_r H^o$ and $\Delta_r C^o_p$ values are available. Two other advantages of the density model are (1) extrapolations to higher pressures are relatively straightforward (it is only necessary to input ρ at the temperature and pressure of interest), and (2) modifications to equation (2.74) permit the incorporation of mineral and gas phases in the reaction(s) to be evaluated.

The Modified HKF Equation

One of the most sophisticated methods for extrapolation of stability constants to elevated temperatures and pressures is the modified Helgeson-Kirkham-Flowers (HKF) equation for aqueous species which has been developed by Helgeson and coworkers in a series of publications (Helgeson and Kirkham, 1974a, b, 1976; Helgeson, 1981; Helgeson et al., 1981; Shock and Helgeson, 1988; Tanger and Helgeson, 1988; Shock et al., 1992). The HKF equation describes the thermodynamic properties of aqueous species in terms of a modification of the Born (1920) equation. The theory behind the HKF equation has been well-covered in the above references (see also Chap. 1), and will not be repeated here. Our main purpose is to provide the reader with a basic appreciation of the intricacies involved in the use of this equation.

The HKF equation does not yield equilibrium constants directly, but is used to calculate the so-called apparent partial molal Gibbs free energy, which may be defined by:

$$\Delta_f\bar{G}^o(P,T) \equiv \Delta_f\bar{G}^o(P_r,T_r) + (\bar{G}^o_{P,T} - \bar{G}^o_{P_r,T_r}) \quad (2.75)$$

where

$$\Delta_f\bar{G}^o(P_r,T_r)$$

is the partial molal Gibbs free energy of formation of the aqueous species from the elements at the reference temperature and pressure, and

$$\bar{G}^o_{P,T} \text{ and } \bar{G}^o_{P_r,T_r}$$

are the partial molal Gibbs free energy of the aqueous species at the pressure and temperature of interest, and the reference pressure and temperature, respectively. The term in parentheses in equation (2.75) represents a correction of the partial molal Gibbs free energy of the aqueous species for deviations from the reference temperature and pressure. Note that in this convention, the Gibbs free energy of the elements are not corrected to the temperature and pressure of interest. In other words, the reference state in this convention is the elements in their most stable form at the reference pressure and temperature. An alternative reference state (used by Cobble et al., 1982, for example) is the elements in their most stable form at the temperature and pressure of interest, in which case the partial molal Gibbs free energies of the elements are also corrected to the temperature and pressure of interest. For more details on reference state conventions for the Gibbs free energy of formation, see Chapter 1, and Anderson and Crerar (1993). Once $\Delta_r\bar{G}^o(P,T)$ for the reaction of interest has been computed, log K can then be calculated using equation (2.69).

Calculation of

$$\Delta_f\overline{G}^o(P,T)$$

for an aqueous species using the HKF equation requires knowledge of

$$\Delta_f\overline{G}^o(P_r,T_r) \text{ and } S^0{}_{Pr,Tr,}$$

and $S^0{}_{P_r,\,T_r}$, the standard partial molal Gibbs free energy of formation, and the partial molal entropy for the aqueous species at the reference temperature and pressure (usually 25°C and 1 bar). Also required are the parameters c_1, c_2, a_1, a_2, a_3, a_4, and $r_{e,j}$, which represent properties of the aqueous species under consideration and are referred to as the HKF equation parameters. In addition, we require values of ε (the dielectric constant) and g, which are properties of the solvent, water, and depend on both temperature and pressure.

Thus, in order to use the HKF equation to calculate

$$\Delta_f\overline{G}^o(P,T)$$

for an aqueous species you need to know nine species-dependent parameters

$$\Delta_f\overline{G}^o(P_r,T_r),$$

$S^0{}_{P_r,\,T_r}$, c_1, c_2, a_1, a_2, a_3, a_4, and $r_{e,j}$). These parameters are available for a large number of species in Shock and Helgeson (1988, 1990), Shock et al. (1989), Sassani and Shock (1992), Haas et al. (1995), Pokrovskii and Helgeson (1995), Shock (1995), Shock et al. (1997), and Sverjensky et al. (1997). In some cases, the parameters have been extracted from experimental data and in other cases they have been estimated using correlation algorithms (cf. Shock and Helgeson, 1988).

The computer code SUPCRT92 (Johnson et al., 1992), which permits computation of thermodynamic data including equilibrium constants for reactions involving minerals, aqueous species, and gases, facilitates calculations involving the HKF equation. Performing these calculations by hand, or even within a computer spreadsheet, can be tedious and prone to errors. However, the original version of SUPCRT92 does not contain all of the HKF parameters currently available, and unfortunately, HKF parameters are not yet available for a variety of species relevant to mineralizing hydrothermal systems. Thus, for a particular problem it may be necessary to modify the SUPCRT92 database to include (1) additional published HKF parameters, (2) HKF parameters extracted from published experimental data by the user, or (3) HKF parameters estimated by the user employing some of the correlation algorithms developed by Shock and Helgeson (1988), Shock et al. (1989), and Sassani and Shock (1992). Approach (1) is relatively straightforward, but (2) and (3) require an in-depth understanding of the theory behind the HKF model and of the determination and evaluation of thermodynamic data. An updated version of SUPCRT92 containing HKF equation parameters for all the species considered by Sverjensky et al. (1997) can be obtained from the Laboratory of Theoretical Geochemistry at the University of California, Berkeley. Database updates are also available via the World Wide Web (http://zonvark.wustl.edu/geopig/).

When all the HKF equation parameters for the species of interest have been derived directly from reliable experimental data, the modified HKF equation does a remarkably good job of interpolating and extrapolating equilibrium constants over a wide range of temperatures and pressures. Even when some of the parameters have to be estimated from correlation algorithms, quite accurate predictions can be obtained. However, when most or all of the parameters have been estimated, the HKF equation can yield variable results. The HKF approach is particularly useful when extrapolating beyond the critical point, where the isocoulombic approaches may not be reliable. On the other hand, under subcritical conditions, especially when experimentally-derived HKF parameters are missing for a large number of species, it is often more convenient, and probably more accurate, to use one of the simpler methods of extrapolation described above.

Estimating Standard State Equilibrium Constants

In many cases, even stability constants under standard state conditions (e.g., 25° and 1 bar) are unavailable for species of potential interest. It is thus desirable to have a relatively reliable means of estimating these constants. We present here one of the simplest of such methods. It has been demonstrated that, if two sets of related equilibrium constants are plotted versus one another in logarithmic form, then very often such a plot is highly linear (Hancock et al., 1977; Langmuir, 1979; Nordstrom and Munoz, 1994). Such a linear relationship is referred to as a Linear Free Energy Relationship (LFER). For example, if we plot the log of the stability constants for a variety of complexes of the type $PtX_4{}^{2-4q}$ versus those for complexes of the type $PdX_4{}^{2-4q}$, where X^{-q} is a ligand of charge of $-q$, then a linear relation results (Fig. 1a). A similar plot involving Cd^{2+} and Zn^{2+} is shown in Figure 1b. The poorer correlation in Figure 1b compared to Figure 1a is a result of the fact that the complexes in Figure 1b are generally much weaker than those in Figure 1a. Nevertheless, it is apparent that stability constants can be estimated from Figure 1b with an uncertainty of approximately ±1 log unit. An LFER also can be constructed relating the stability constants of complexes involving two different ligands and a variety of metal ions, as in Figure 2. Finally, a linear relationship often exists among the cumulative (and also stepwise) stability constants of two different metal-ligand pairs (Fig. 3).

We illustrate the use of LFERs to estimate stability constants via two examples. In the first example, we estimate log β_4 for the $Pt(CN)_4{}^{2-}$ complex using the LFER shown in Figure 1a. From Hancock and Evers (1976), we obtain a value of log β_4 for $Pd(CN)_4{}^{2-}$ of 63. Substituting this value into the equation of the line shown in Figure 1a (i.e.,

$\log \beta_4(Pt^{2+}) = 1.2627 \log \beta_4(Pd^{2+}) - 1.5523$), we calculate $\log \beta_4$ ($Pt(CN)_4^{2-}$) = 78. In the second example, we wish to obtain a value for $\log \beta_6$ ($TlCl_6^{3-}$) given a value of $\log \beta_6$ ($BiCl_6^{3-}$) = 7.3 (Högfeldt, 1982) and the LFER equation from Figure 3, $\log \beta_n$ ($TlCl_n^{3-n}$) = 2.393 $\log \beta_n$ ($BiCl_n^{3-n}$) – 0.241. The resulting value of $\log \beta_6$ ($TlCl_6^{3-}$) is 17.2.

Thus, it can be seen that LFERs are a useful tool for estimating unknown stability constants. However, the accuracy of the LFER approach depends highly on the quality of the data from which the LFER is constructed. In order to maximize the probability that an LFER will yield an acceptable result, certain factors should be taken into consideration. First, and perhaps most obvious, is the fact that all the data used in constructing an LFER should refer to the same temperature, pressure, and ionic strength. Second, the greater the range of values of stability constants employed in the LFER, the better constrained the regression equation will be. Finally, the more similar the metal-ions or the ligands being compared with respect to their Pearson hard-soft properties, the better the observed correlation is likely to be. For example, in Figure 1a, we have chosen to compare the stability constants of the soft metal ions Pt^{2+} and Pd^{2+}, and have obtained a very good correlation. We would expect a significantly poorer correlation in comparing Pd^{2+} with Be^{2+}, for instance. Examples of the use of LFERs in estimating geochemically relevant stability constants can be found in Mountain and Wood (1988), and Lee and Byrne (1992).

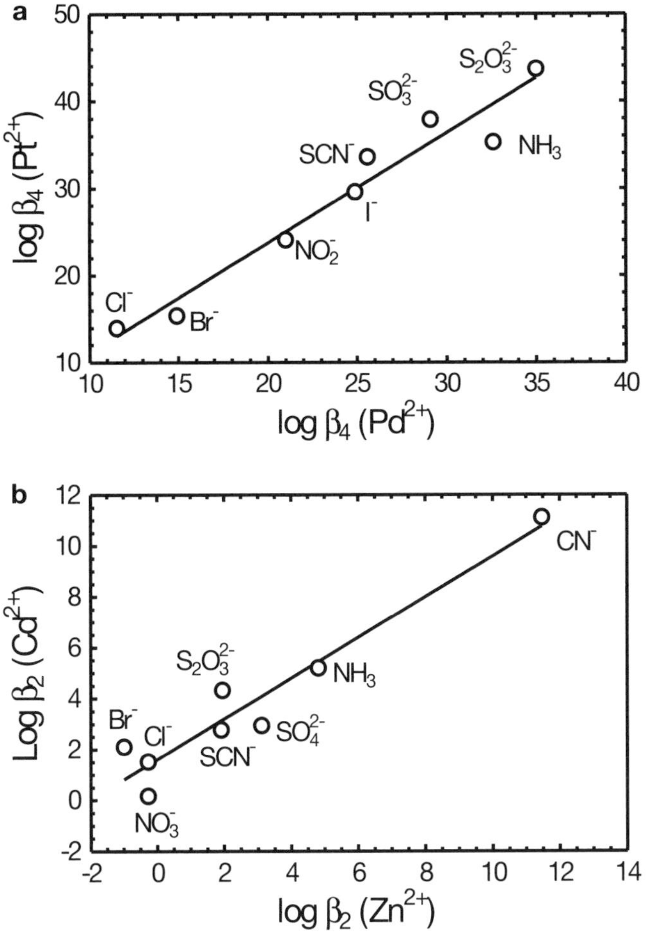

FIG. 1. Linear free energy relationships for: (a) $\log \beta_4$ for Pt^{2+} complexes versus $\log \beta_4$ for Pd^{2+} complexes with a variety of ligands. See Mountain and Wood (1988) for sources of data. The equation of the straight line is: $\log \beta_4(Pt^{2+}) = 1.2627 \log \beta_4(Pd^{2+}) - 1.5523$; (b) $\log \beta_2$ for Cd^{2+} complexes versus $\log \beta_2$ for Zn^{2+} complexes with a variety of ligands. The data are from Högfeldt (1982); the equation of the straight line is: $\log \beta_2(Cd^{2+}) = 0.7986 \log \beta_2(Zn^{2+}) + 1.6054$.

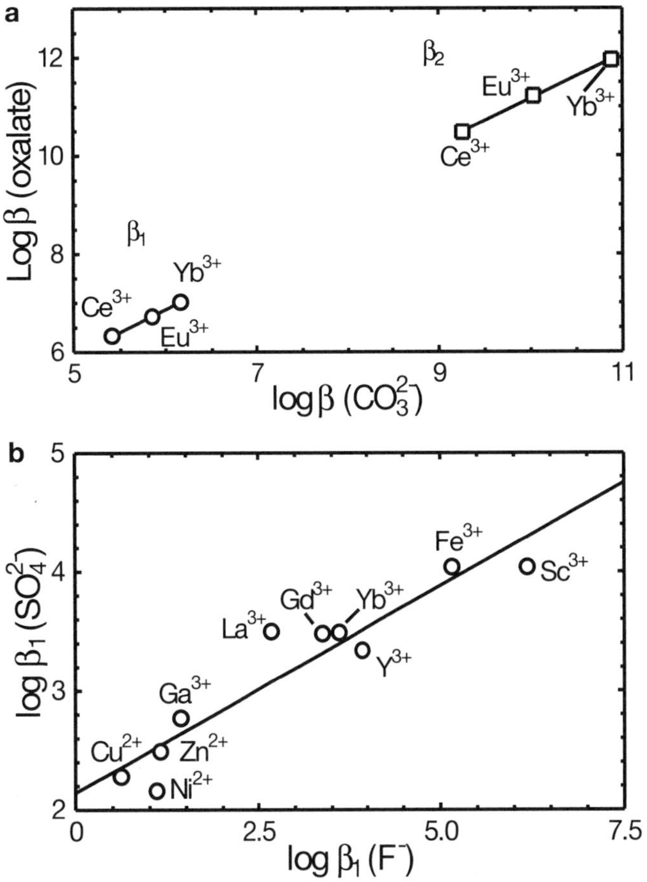

FIG. 2. Linear free energy relationships for: (a) $\log \beta_1$ for oxalate ($C_2O_4^{2-}$) complexes versus $\log \beta_1$ for carbonate (CO_3^{2-}) complexes with the rare earth elements. Also shown is the analogous LFER for $\log \beta_2$. The data come from Cantrell and Byrne (1987). The equations of the lines are: $\log \beta_1$ ($C_2O_4^{2-}$) = 0.918 $\log \beta_1$ (CO_3^{2-}) + 1.361, and $\log \beta_2$ ($C_2O_4^{2-}$) = 0.907 $\log \beta_2$ (CO_3^{2-}) + 2.100; (b) $\log \beta_1$ for sulfate (SO_4^{2-}) complexes versus $\log \beta_1$ for fluoride (F^-) complexes with a variety of metals. The data are from Högfeldt (1982). The equation of the line is: $\log \beta_1$ (SO_4^{2-}) = 0.348 $\log \beta_1$ + 2.142.

Review of Thermodynamic Data for Selected Metals

In the following sections, we critically review current knowledge of stability constants of inorganic complexes for a variety of metals (As, Sb, Cu, Au, Ag, Fe, Pb, Mn, Hg, Mo, W, Sn, and Zn). The discussion of individual metals is organized in terms of the Pearson hard-soft classification, starting with the hardest metal ions and progressing to the softest. Because a metal ion's hard-soft character is partially dictated by its oxidation state, a given metal's position in the review is determined by its most important

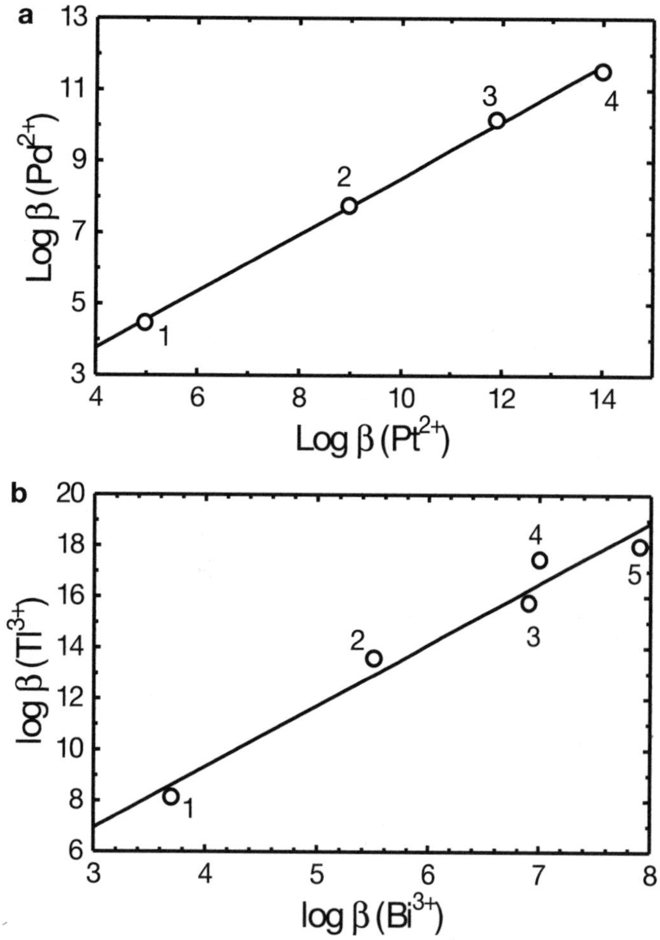

FIG. 3. Linear free energy relationships for: (a) the cumulative stability constants of Pd^{2+}-chloride complexes versus the cumulative stability constants of Pt^{2+}-chloride complexes. The data are from sources listed in Mountain and Wood (1988). The equation of the line is: log β_n ($PdCl_n^{2-n}$) = 0.7921 log β_n ($PtCl_n^{2-n}$) + 0.5993; (b) the cumulative stability constants of Tl^{3+}-chloride complexes versus the cumulative stability constants of Bi^{3+}-chloride complexes. The data come from Sillén and Martell (1964) and Högfeldt (1982), respectively. The equation of the line is: log β_n ($TlCl_n^{3-n}$) = 2.393 log β_n ($BiCl_n^{3-n}$) – 0.241.

oxidation state in hydrothermal solutions. Where possible, we direct the reader to recommended thermodynamic data for important complexes for each metal. In some selected cases we also comment on mineral solubility products or other thermodynamic data for minerals containing these metals. In general, thermodynamic data calculated using SUPCRT92 (Johnson et al., 1992) and various updates (Shock et al., 1997; Sverjensky et al., 1997) are in reasonable to excellent agreement with the most reliable experimental data, and in such cases we encourage readers to employ this code in their calculations. However, in a few cases, which we point out below, SUPCRT92 or the recent updates provide estimates of thermodynamic properties that are inconsistent with what we consider to be the most reliable experimental data.

Hard Metals

Tungsten. The predominant oxidation state of tungsten in most hydrothermal solutions is W(VI), but under very reducing conditions, W(V) may become important (Wood and Vlassopoulos, 1989). The W^{6+} and W^{5+} ions are hard acids and so can be predicted to form strong complexes with hard bases such as O^{2-}, F^-, OH^-, CO_3^{2-}, and PO_4^{3-}, and should be less likely to complex, in a competitive situation, with Cl^-. Indeed, most of the above anions have been proposed as important ligands for W(VI) (there are no data for W(V)). However, there is now considerable evidence that WO_4^{2-} and its protonated equivalents, HWO_4^- and $H_2WO_4^0$, are important species, and probably the predominant ones, in the transport of tungsten under hydrothermal conditions (Wesolowski et al., 1984; Wood and Vlassopoulos, 1989; Gibert et al., 1992; Wood, 1992a; and references therein). These species are related through the following dissociation reactions:

$$HWO_4^- = WO_4^{2-} + H^+ \quad (2.76)$$

$$H_2WO_4^0 = HWO_4^- + H^+ \quad (2.77)$$

so that $H_2WO_4^0$ will be more important in more acidic fluids, and WO_4^{2-} in more alkaline fluids (Fig. 4). The only experimentally-derived thermodynamic data available for these species and reactions under hydrothermal conditions are the log K values of Wesolowski et al. (1984) for reaction (2.76) up to 300°C and the free energy data of Wood (1992a) for $H_2WO_4^0$ from 300° to 600°C at 1 kbar. Thus, modeling of wolframite and scheelite solubility under geologically reasonable conditions requires considerable extrapolation using the methods outlined above (cf. Heinrich, 1990; Polya, 1990; Samson and Wood, 1997; and Wood and Samson, in prep.), in addition to thermodynamic data on ferberite, huebnerite, and scheelite, and relevant Fe^{2+}, Mn^{2+}, and Ca^{2+} species. Unfortunately, there are few experimentally-derived thermodynamic data on the solubility of these W minerals (see Wood and Samson, in prep.). However, the thermodynamic data for reaction (2.76) given by Wesolowski et al. (1984) provide a solid basis for extrapolations to higher temperatures and pressures, and Wood and Samson (in prep.) show that their estimates (based on the density model) for the equilibrium constants for reaction (2.76) are in good agreement with those calculated using HKF equation parameters from Shock et al. (1997) up to 500°C.

Chloride complexes, including species such as $H(WO_3)_2Cl^0$, WCl_6^0, HWO_3Cl^0, WO_3Cl^-, $Na_3WO_4Cl^0$, and $CaWO_4 \cdot \times CaCl_2$, have been attributed an important role in hydrothermal transport of W by a number of authors (Manning, 1984; Haselton and d'Angelo, 1986; Shironosova et al., 1988; Khodorevskaya, 1989; Malinin and Kurovskaya, 1993). However, both theoretical calculations (Ivanova, 1966; Schröcke et al., 1984) and experimental studies (Wesolowski et al., 1984; Wood and Vlassopoulos, 1989; Wood, 1990, 1992a; Keppler and Wyllie, 1992) have shown that such complexes are unimportant under geologically reasonable conditions. In the experiments of Wood and Vlassopoulos (1989), W solubility increased with NaCl, NaOH, and KCl concentration, but was independent of HCl. These results were interpreted to indicate the

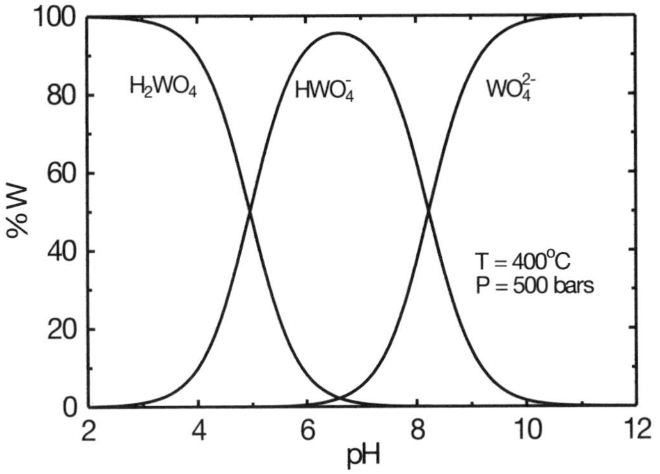

FIG. 4. Diagram showing fields of predominance of tungstate species at 400°C and 500 bars. Data from Wood and Samson (in prep.).

presence of Na-tungstate and K-tungstate ion pairs (e.g., $NaHWO_4^0$, $NaWO_4^-$), complexes that had previously been proposed by Eugster (1985), Shironosova et al. (1988), and Galkin et al. (1989), and that in concentrated brines these may be the dominant species. Indeed, the observation in many studies that W-mineral solubilities increase with LiCl, NaCl, or KCl concentration, which usually has been interpreted in terms of W-chloride complexes, may be a result of alkali ion-tungstate ion pairing. On the other hand, theoretical modeling of W transport by Gibert et al. (1992) has shed doubt on the importance of alkali ion-tungstate ion pairs.

Wesolowski et al. (1984) present definitive potentiometric evidence for the existence of polytungstate species (e.g., $H_7(WO_4)_6^{5-}$ and $H_{10}(WO_4)_6^{2-}$) at temperatures up to 290°C in relatively W-rich (0.01 molal), acidic solutions. Such species become less important with increasing temperature (at least up to 250°C), increasing ionic strength and decreasing W concentration, and are therefore thought unlikely to contribute to W mass transfer in ore-forming systems. However, the data of Wesolowski et al. (1984) show an increase in the formation constants of some of these species with increased temperature above 250°C and an investigation of polynuclear species at even higher temperatures could prove interesting.

In melt-vapor partitioning experiments (Manning, 1984; Keppler and Wyllie, 1992), W partitions preferentially into the melt phase in fluorine-bearing systems, indicating that W-fluoride complexes are unlikely to increase significantly the solubility of tungsten minerals in ore-forming solutions, a conclusion previously reached by Ivanova (1966) on the basis of theoretical thermodynamic calculations. Finally, Higgins (1980) suggested that carbonate complexes might be important in the transport of tungsten in hydrothermal solutions. However, Raman spectroscopic studies by Wood (1990) showed that such complexes were not present up to 280°C and total carbonate concentrations of 1 molal, a finding which is consistent with the results of Manning (1984).

In summary, evidence for the existence of significant concentrations of dissolved tungsten species other than WO_4^{2-}, HWO_4^-, and $H_2WO_4^0$ in ore-forming hydrothermal solutions is questionable, and thermodynamic data for these putative species are scarce. Furthermore, calculations carried out by a number of authors (Wesolowski, 1984; Polya, 1989, 1990; Gibert et al., 1992; Wood, 1992a; Wood and Samson, in prep.) suggest that ore-forming quantities of tungsten can be transported in hydrothermal solutions by WO_4^{2-}, HWO_4^-, and $H_2WO_4^0$ alone; no other species are required to explain the formation of wolframite and scheelite deposits. However, reliable, experimentally derived thermodynamic data are still lacking, particularly for the solubility products of important W minerals. Until more experimental data are available, an internally consistent data set that may be employed in the calculation of scheelite and ferberite solubilities is provided by Wood and Samson (in prep.).

Molybdenum. Molybdenum is more readily reduced than tungsten in hydrothermal solutions, and species containing Mo(VI), Mo(V), Mo(IV), or Mo(III) have been proposed (Cao, 1989; Gu, 1993). All of these oxidation states result in relatively hard ion behavior, and complexes with hard ligands such as O^{2-} and OH^- should be preferred especially for the higher oxidation states.

Several lines of evidence suggest that chloride complexing is not important in Mo transport under geologically reasonable conditions. Smith et al. (1980) carried out thermodynamic extrapolations from low-temperature data and concluded that chloride and sulfide complexes were unimportant. Kudrin (1985) showed that chloride complexing occurs only at m_{HCl} values above 0.1, i.e., under very acidic conditions. Wood et al. (1987) found little correlation between Mo and NaCl concentrations in their experiments at mildly acidic to neutral pH, suggesting that chloride complexes of Mo(VI) were unimportant under these conditions. This conclusion is supported by melt-vapor partitioning experiments (Tingle and Fenn, 1982; Candela and Holland, 1984; Keppler and Wyllie, 1992) in which neither Cl nor F influenced the partition coefficients of Mo. Furthermore, Raman spectroscopic measurements by Kiddie and Wood (1989) showed that Mo(VI)-chloride complexes only become important at HCl concentrations that are geologically unrealistic. Although, Gu (1993) suggested that Mo(IV)- and/or Mo(III)-chloride complexes could possibly be important under reducing conditions, using both theoretical and experimental techniques, he showed that complexation of Mo(VI) and Mo(V) by chloride only occurs at very acidic, high-salinity conditions that are geologically unrealistic. On the other hand, Cao (1989) concluded that Mo(V)-oxychloride complexes, such as $MoO(OH)_2Cl^0$, and Na-molybdate ion pairs, such as $NaHMoO_4^0$ or $Na_2MoO_4^0$, are important in the hydrothermal transport of Mo, based on measurements of the solubilities of MoO_2 and MoS_2. However, the proposed species are not well constrained by Cao's (1989) data. First, it is extremely difficult to separate the effects of

Cl-complexation from Na-ion pairing when using only NaCl as the source of these components. Second, the pH at the temperature of the experiments was not measured or calculated.

The theoretical calculations of Smith et al. (1980) suggest that bimolybdate is the dominant species under slightly acidic conditions at 250° to 350°C. A number of solubility experiments using molybdenite (Wood et al., 1987; Cao, 1989) and tugarinovite (MoO_2); (Kudrin, 1985) indicate that both molybdic acid ($H_2MoO_4^0$) and bimolybdate ($HMoO_4^-$) are important complexes between 250° and 450°C over a wide range of oxygen fugacities. Kudrin (1985) and Gu (1993) provide the only experimentally-derived thermodynamic data for any molybdate species under hydrothermal conditions. In spite of the above evidence for Mo(VI) species, Gu (1993) suggests that oxy-hydroxide complexes of Mo(V), Mo(IV), and Mo(III) (e.g., MoO_2^+, $Mo(OH)_3^+$) may be more important under geologically reasonable conditions.

Macdonald and Spooner (1982) have suggested that molybdenum may form carbonate complexes. This is based on the fact that molybdenite deposition coincides with CO_2 effervescence in the Boss Mountain deposit in British Columbia. However, such evidence is circumstantial and there are no experimental or theoretical studies with which such a model can be tested. Based on comparison with tungsten, it seems unlikely that carbonate or bicarbonate would be capable of displacing O^{2-} and OH^- from Mo, at least in the higher oxidation states.

The studies quoted above are also contradictory with respect to the magnitude and temperature dependence of molybdenite solubility. In the multicomponent solubility experiments of Wood et al. (1987), molybdenite solubility was low (<1 ppm) and showed little variation with temperature. Calculations of molybdenite solubility by Smith et al. (1980) and Kudrin (1985; based on his tugarinovite experimental data), indicate a significant positive temperature dependence, with, in the case of Smith et al. (1980), predicted concentrations of several thousand ppm at 350°C. Cao (1989) found a difference of several orders of magnitude between solubilities in S-rich and S-poor systems between 300° and 450°C. In S-poor systems, solubilities exceeded 3,000 ppm in some experiments and were relatively independent of temperature. Measured solubilities were two to three orders of magnitude lower in S-rich systems and decreased with temperature (i.e., were retrograde).

From the above discussion it is clear that additional, well-constrained experiments on molybdenite solubility and Mo speciation in hydrothermal solutions are required before accurate modeling of the mass transfer of this element will be possible. However, based on available data, it seems unlikely that carbonate, bicarbonate, fluoride, or bisulfide play significant roles, and chloride complexation will be significant only in very acidic, saline, and reducing fluids. The possibility that multiple oxidation states of Mo may exist under geologically relevant conditions must be entertained, and oxy-hydroxy species are probably most important.

Borderline Metals

Arsenic. There is general agreement that the most important form of arsenic in most hydrothermal solutions is the As(III) species $H_3AsO_3^0$ (Ballantyne and Moore, 1988; Webster, 1990; Akinfiyev et al., 1992; Pokrovski et al., 1996; and references therein). This species will predominate under moderately oxidizing to moderately reducing, low-sulfide conditions over a range of temperatures, becoming increasingly predominant at temperatures above 200°C, and a range of pH from <2 to approximately 8 to 9. At the same redox conditions and sulfide concentrations, the species $H_2AsO_3^-$, $HAsO_3^{2-}$, and AsO_3^{2-} become successively predominant with increased pH above 8 (Baes and Mesmer, 1976; Ivakin et al., 1976). In low-temperature, sulfide-rich solutions, thioarsenite complexes predominate (see below), and in near-surface, oxidizing waters the As(V) species $H_3AsO_4^0$ or one of its dissociation products may be predominant (Criaud and Fouillac, 1986; Ballantyne and Moore, 1988). Under extremely reducing conditions dissolved arsine gas, AsH_3^0, becomes increasingly stable (Heinrich and Eadington, 1986), but such conditions are unlikely to be attained in ore-forming environments. The only arsenic species currently in the SUPCRT92 database are the As(III) species, $H_2AsO_3^-$, and the As(V) species, $H_2AsO_4^-$ and $HAsO_4^{2-}$. However, Shock et al. (1997) have recently published modified HKF equation parameters for the As(V) species, AsO_4^{3-}, $HAsO_4^{2-}$, $H_2AsO_4^-$, and $H_3AsO_4^0$, and the As(III) species AsO_2^- (i.e., $H_2AsO_3^-$) and $HAsO_2$ (i.e., H_3AsO_3), based on correlation algorithms.

Values of the equilibrium constant for the reaction:

$$\tfrac{1}{2}\,As_2S_3(\text{orpiment}) + 3H_2O(l) = H_3AsO_3^0 + \tfrac{3}{2}H_2S^0 \qquad (2.78)$$

have been determined experimentally by Mironova et al. (1984), Webster (1990), and Pokrovski et al. (1996). Pokrovski et al. (1996) derived HKF equation parameters for $H_3AsO_3^0$ and thermodynamic data for orpiment based on their experimental data. Equilibrium constants for reaction (2.78) calculated using these data are in good agreement with the independently measured values of Webster (1990), and are in fair agreement with those of Mironova et al. (1984; see fig. 9 in Pokrovski et al., 1996). On the other hand, Sergeyeva and Khodakovskiy (1969) and Akinfiyev et al. (1992) provide thermodynamic data yielding equilibrium constants for reaction (2.78) which are in agreement with each other, but differ by up to two log units from those of Pokrovski et al. (1996). The estimated HKF equation parameters of Shock et al. (1997) for $H_3AsO_3^0$ also yield equilibrium constants for reaction (2.78) that are not consistent with those of Pokrovski et al. (1996). We believe that the thermodynamic data given by Pokrovski et al. (1996) are the most reliable and therefore recommend their use to calculate equilibrium constants for reaction (2.78) over a wide range of pressure and temperature. Thermodynamic data for the species $H_2AsO_3^-$, $HAsO_3^{2-}$, and AsO_3^{2-}, which are internally consistent with the database of Pokrovski et al. (1996), are not available. However, because these species are not predominant at pH values less than 8 at any temperature, they can be neglected in calculations of orpiment solubility for most hydrothermal environments.

Nakagawa (1971) has shown that chloride does not affect the solubility of orpiment and therefore chloride complexing does not appear to play a role in hydrothermal As(III) transport. On the other hand, As(III)-sulfide (thioarsenic) species may be important at low temperatures in sulfide-rich solutions (Spycher and Reed, 1989; Mironova et al., 1990; Webster, 1990; Eary, 1992; Helz et al., 1995; and references therein). However, there has been much debate as to the stoichiometry of the predominant As(III) species. Spycher and Reed (1989, 1990a,b) reviewed the literature on As(III)-sulfide complexes up until that time and, based on an analysis of what they considered to be the more reliable studies, proposed that the most important As(III)-sulfide species are the trimers $H_3As_3S_6^0$, $H_2As_3S_6^-$, and $HAs_3S_6^{2-}$. Krupp (1990a,b) has pointed out some of the pitfalls of such an approach and suggests that, by analogy with Sb, some form of the dimer ($H_2As_2S_4^0$, $HAs_2S_4^-$, or $As_2S_4^{2-}$) is more probable. Meanwhile, Webster (1990) and Eary (1992) measured the solubilities of crystalline and amorphous As_2S_3, respectively, and both were able to explain their results in terms of the trimer $H_2As_3S_6^-$, whereas Mironova et al. (1990) interpret their own solubility studies in terms of dimeric species. Helz et al. (1995) have brought EXAFS, Raman spectroscopy, and ab initio molecular orbital calculations to bear on the problem. Their spectroscopic results pertain to solutions undersaturated with respect to either orpiment or amorphous As_2S_3, and suggest that, under these conditions, monomeric species ($H_2AsS_3^-$ and $HAsS_3^{2-}$, actually formulated by Helz et al. as $AsS(SH)_2^-$ and $AsS_2(SH)^{2-}$) are predominant. However, they show, via a reinterpretation of previous solubility experiments (Mironova et al., 1990; Webster, 1990; Eary, 1992), that at saturation the predominant species are the trimer $As_3S_4(SH)_2^-$ and the monomer $AsS(OH)(SH)^-$. The ab initio calculations of Helz et al. (1995) indicate that dimeric As(III)-sulfide species should be highly unstable relative to monomers and trimers.

Thus, the picture that emerges from the work of Helz et al. (1995) is that, near saturation with respect to orpiment or amorphous As_2S_3 and over the pH range 1 to 9, $As_3S_4(SH)_2^-$ and $AsS(OH)(SH)^-$ are the predominant As species, with the latter more important at higher pH. However, at lower As concentrations (i.e., in solutions undersaturated with respect to As sulfides), the monomer species $AsS(SH)_2^-$ and $AsS_2(SH)^{2-}$ are predominant. For the most part, we agree with this interpretation. However, the assignment of the stoichiometries of the species in undersaturated solutions by Helz et al. (1995) may not be entirely correct. In their Raman spectra they observed a band with peaks at 325 and 412 cm^{-1} for one species and a band with a peak at 382 cm^{-1} for the other species. They observed a change in the relative intensities of these peaks with changing pH, and therefore concluded that the two species were related by a simple protonation reaction, i.e.,

$$AsS(SH)_2^- = AsS_2(SH)^{2-} + H^+ \tag{2.79}$$

However, Raman data of Wood et al. (1995) show that a change in S/As ratio of the solution at constant pH can also generate the same relative shift in intensities, suggesting that the relationship among the two species may be more complicated than proposed by Helz et al. (1995).

To summarize As speciation, the neutral species $H_3AsO_3^0$ is predominant in solutions with low total sulfide concentrations under moderately reducing to moderately oxidizing conditions over a range of temperatures, pressures, and pH. Chloride complexes do not appear to play a role in hydrothermal As transport. Finally, at low temperatures and high sulfide concentrations, As-sulfide species may become important. The latter species may be polynuclear, with the number of As atoms increasing with total dissolved As concentration. The exact stoichiometries of the As-sulfide species remain uncertain. It is extremely difficult to differentiate among polynuclear species based on solubility studies alone, so that spectroscopic techniques may be required to resolve thioarsenite speciation.

Antimony. There are a number of similarities between the aqueous geochemistry of As and Sb, but there are also some differences. For example, both Sb(III) and Sb(V) oxidation states are known, but the field of predominance of Sb(III) relative to Sb(V) species is much greater than is the case for As(III) species. As with As(III), Sb(III)-chloride complexes would appear to play no role in hydrothermal Sb transport (Ovchinnikov et al., 1982; Wood et al., 1987), and the neutral $Sb(OH)_3^0$ species is predominant in low-sulfide solutions over a wide range (<0–10) of pH (Popova et al., 1975; Wood et al., 1987; Shikina et al., 1988; and references therein). Kolpakova (1982) and Wood et al. (1987) both provide equilibrium constants for the reaction:

$$Sb_2S_3(\text{stibnite}) + 6H_2O(l) = 2Sb(OH)_3^0 + 3H_2S^0 \tag{2.80}$$

but over different temperature ranges (25°–90°C and 200°–350°C, respectively). As shown in figure 9 in Wood et al. (1987), the data fit a straight line on a log K versus 1/T plot, as would be expected given that reaction (2.80) is isocoulombic.

As is the case with As(III), Sb(III) forms sulfide complexes (thioantimonites) when sulfide concentrations are relatively high. The stoichiometry of these complexes and/or the solubility of Sb phases (mainly stibnite) have been studied by many authors (Krupp, 1988a; Spycher and Reed, 1989; Wood, 1989; Tossell, 1994; and references therein). Many stoichiometries for Sb(III)-sulfide complexes have been proposed (see table 2 in Spycher and Reed, 1989, for a summary of studies published prior to 1988). Spycher and Reed (1989), derived stoichiometries and thermodynamic data for such complexes based on what they considered to be the most reliable experimental studies published at the time. They proposed the species $H_2Sb_2S_4^0$, $HSb_2S_4^-$, and $Sb_2S_4^{2-}$ to be the most important complexes. Based on new stibnite solubility measurements, Krupp (1988a) proposed that, in addition to the three species suggested by Spycher and Reed (1989), the species $Sb_2S_2(OH)_2$ may also be important, particularly as temperature increases. From Raman spectroscopic data, Wood (1989) deduced that the most likely stoichiometry for the Sb(III)-sulfide complex in alkaline solutions in equilibrium with amorphous $Sb_2S_3(s)$ is $Sb_2S_4^{2-}$, in agreement with Krupp (1988a) and Spycher and Reed (1989). On dilution this species may give way to the monomeric SbS_2^- or SbS_3^{3-} species. Tossell (1994) used ab initio molecular orbital calculations to show that the species observed by Wood (1989) may in fact be $H_2Sb_2S_4^0$ in the concentrated solutions, and $HSbS_3^{2-}$ and $H_2SbS_3^-$ in more dilute solutions. However, predominance of the neutral $H_2Sb_2S_4^0$ complex (as opposed to $HSb_2S_4^-$ or $Sb_2S_4^{2-}$) at the pH of the studies of Wood (1989), i.e., approximately 13, is in contradiction to the dissociation constants of either Krupp (1988a) or Spycher and Reed (1989), which predict that $H_2Sb_2S_4^0$ should predominate only at pH values less than 4.9 or 3.0, respectively, at 25°C. In any event, there is agreement that some form of the dimer ($H_2Sb_2S_4^0$, $HSb_2S_4^-$, or $Sb_2S_4^{2-}$) is the predominant species in sulfide solutions saturated with respect to stibnite or amorphous antimony sulfide at low temperatures. The existence of the $Sb_2S_2(OH)_2$ species as postulated by Krupp (1988a) also is supported by the ab initio calculations of Tossell (1994).

Spycher and Reed (1989) give equilibrium constants for the reactions:

$$Sb_2S_3(\text{stibnite}) + HS^- = HSb_2S_4^- \quad (2.81)$$

and

$$Sb_2S_3(\text{stibnite}) + HS^- = Sb_2S_4^{2-} + H^+ \quad (2.82)$$

whereas Krupp (1988a) gives log K values for the analogous reactions written in terms of H_2S^0. Thus, in order to compare the two sets of constants, we have converted reactions (2.81) and (2.82) to the form employed by Krupp (1988a) using the H_2S^0 dissociation reaction (2.33) and its corresponding equilibrium constant calculated from SUPCRT92. The comparison is made in Figure 5, from which it is evident that the agreement among the two studies is poor for log K for the reaction:

$$Sb_2S_3(\text{stibnite}) + H_2S^0 = HSb_2S_4^- + H^+ \quad (2.83)$$

and only fair for the reaction:

$$Sb_2S_3(\text{stibnite}) + H_2S^0 = Sb_2S_4^{2-} + 2H^+ \quad (2.84)$$

There is also a significant discrepancy among the two studies with respect to the equilibrium constants derived for the reaction:

$$HSb_2S_4^- = Sb_2S_4^{2-} + H^+ \quad (2.85)$$

which is to be expected given the discrepancies noted among the two studies for reactions (2.83) and (2.84). Because the study of Krupp (1988a) covers a relatively

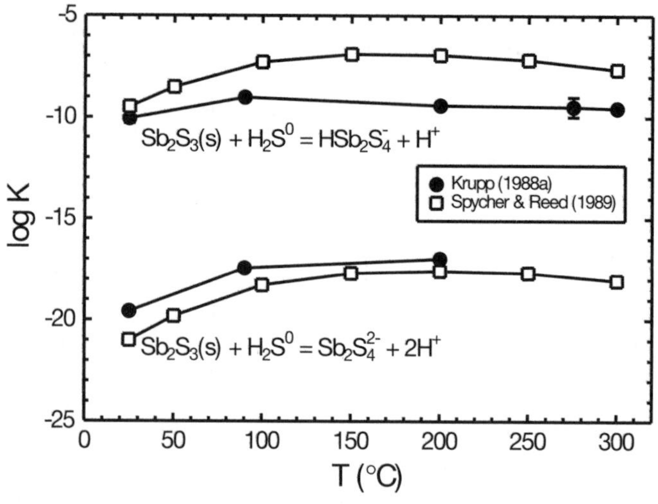

FIG. 5. Plot of log K values from literature for dissolution of stibnite as dimeric thioantimonite species at SWVP as a function of temperature

wide range of pH, ΣS, and temperature using the same methodology, whereas the study of Spycher and Reed (1989) relies on several different studies each covering a narrower range of the above variables, the former is likely to be the most internally consistent. Also, Krupp (1988a) was well aware of the many experimental difficulties that may have plagued some of the earlier experiments on which Spycher and Reed (1989) based their analysis. Thus, at this time we recommend the use of Krupp's (1988a) equilibrium constants for Sb(III)-sulfide and -hydroxysulfide species. However, the magnitude of the discrepancies exhibited between the two data sets are of concern, and there is justification for further experimental work on these species.

In summary, the generally most important species for Sb transport in hydrothermal solutions is the hydroxide complex, $Sb(OH)_3^0$. However, at low temperatures and high ΣS under reducing conditions, thioantimonite species are probably important, but the stoichiometries and thermodynamics of these species are somewhat uncertain. For a recent review of the hydrothermal geochemistry of Sb, including the calculation of the solubility of stibnite and other antimony minerals, see Williams-Jones and Normand (1997).

Iron. It is generally accepted that the most important oxidation state of iron in hydrothermal solutions is Fe(II), because the solubility of iron-bearing minerals is very low under log f_{O_2}-pH conditions where dissolved Fe(III) species predominate. Being a borderline ion in the Pearson sense, the Fe^{2+} ion does not exhibit a strong preference for either soft or hard ligands. As such, chloride, hydroxide, or bicarbonate complexes may be important in the hydrothermal mass transfer of iron, depending upon the particular physicochemical conditions and geological environment. Although Fe(II)-bisulfide complexes may be important as intermediates in the precipitation of iron sulfide minerals from hydrothermal solutions and during diagenesis (Luther, 1991; Luther et al., 1996), it is believed that they are not significant agents of hydrothermal transport of iron (Crerar and Barnes, 1976).

Studies of the solubility of iron minerals in hydrothermal chloride solutions (Chou and Eugster, 1977; Crerar et al., 1978; Boctor et al., 1980; Heinrich and Seward, 1990; Ding and Seyfried, 1992; Fein et al., 1992; Palmer and Hyde, 1993; and references therein) show that the predominant species are Fe^{2+}, $FeCl^+$, and $FeCl_2^0$, and that complexes with higher chloride ligand number become increasingly important with increasing temperature, increasing chloride concentration, and decreasing pressure. However, Koplitz et al. (1987), Wood et al. (1987), and McPhail (1991) have presented spectroscopic and solubility evidence for the possible importance of higher ligand number species such as $FeCl_3^-$ and $FeCl_4^{2-}$, respectively, at high chloride concentrations.

Stability constants for the species $FeCl^+$ measured by various authors are compared in Figure 6a, along with the values calculated using SUPCRT92. Although Figure 6a exhibits considerable scatter, there is some agreement among the various studies. The HKF equation parameters for $FeCl^+$ in SUPCRT92 are based on the stability constants measured by Heinrich and Seward (1990) at SWVP, so it is not surprising that SUPCRT92 yields stability constants identical to the latter. However, it is also evident that the data of Crerar et al. (1978) at 300°C, Palmer and Hyde (1993) at or below 250°C, and Ohmoto et al. (1994) at 300° and 350°C are in good agreement with the stability constants calculated using SUPCRT92. On the other hand, the stability constants of Crerar et al. (1978) at 200° and 250°C, that of Palmer and Hyde (1993) at 300°C, and that of Ohmoto et al. (1994) at 250°C deviate significantly from the values calculated by SUPCRT92. At 500 bars, the stability constants measured by Ding and Seyfried (1992) at 200° and 400°C appear to be too large, but their constant at 350°C agrees fairly well with the value calculated using SUPCRT92. Thus, the stability constants for $FeCl^+$ at SWVP calculated using SUPCRT92 seem to be reasonably well constrained by experimental data, in contrast to those at higher pressures. However, we recommend the use of SUPCRT92 to calculate stability constants of $FeCl^+$ at elevated temperatures and pressures until more experimental data at pressures greater than SWVP become available. The estimated stability constants given by Sverjensky et al. (1997) are essentially identical to those calculated using SUPCRT92.

As can be seen from Figure 6b, the stability constants ($\log \beta_2$) of $FeCl_2^0$ calculated using SUPCRT92 are in excellent agreement with the data of Crerar et al. (1978) and Heinrich and Seward (1990) from which the HKF equation parameters for $FeCl_2^0$ in SUPCRT92 are probably derived. The value of Ohmoto et al. (1994) at 250°C and SWVP is also relatively close to the curve representing the values calculated using SUPCRT92, but their stability constants at higher temperatures are more than an order of magnitude higher. The Ding and Seyfried (1992) measurements at 500 bars are also greater than expected based on the SWVP values calculated using SUPCRT92 (stability constants should decrease with increasing pressure, Crerar et al., 1985). Finally, the stability constants measured by Fein et al. (1992) at all pressures are higher than the corresponding values calculated from SUPCRT92. Fein et al. (1992) have computed stability constants for $FeCl_2^0$ from the solubility data of Chou and Eugster (1977), Boctor et al. (1980), and Korzhinskiy (1987). Their calculations (see fig. 2, Fein et al., 1992) show that the $\log \beta_2$ values computed from the data of Boctor et al. (1980), and Korzhinskiy (1987) at 1 kbar are in reasonably good agreement with $\log \beta_2$ values derived experimentally by Fein et al. (1992). On the other hand, the $\log \beta_2$ values calculated by Fein et al. (1992) from the data of Chou and Eugster (1977) and Korzhinskiy (1987) at 2 kbars are lower and have a lesser temperature dependence than the values measured at 2 kbars by Fein et al. (1992; see their fig. 2). Clearly more experimental data are required to resolve the discrepancies among reported values of $\log \beta_2$. Meanwhile, the measured values of Fein et al. (1992) would appear to be the most reliable at supercritical conditions. Sverjensky et al. (1997) have recently published

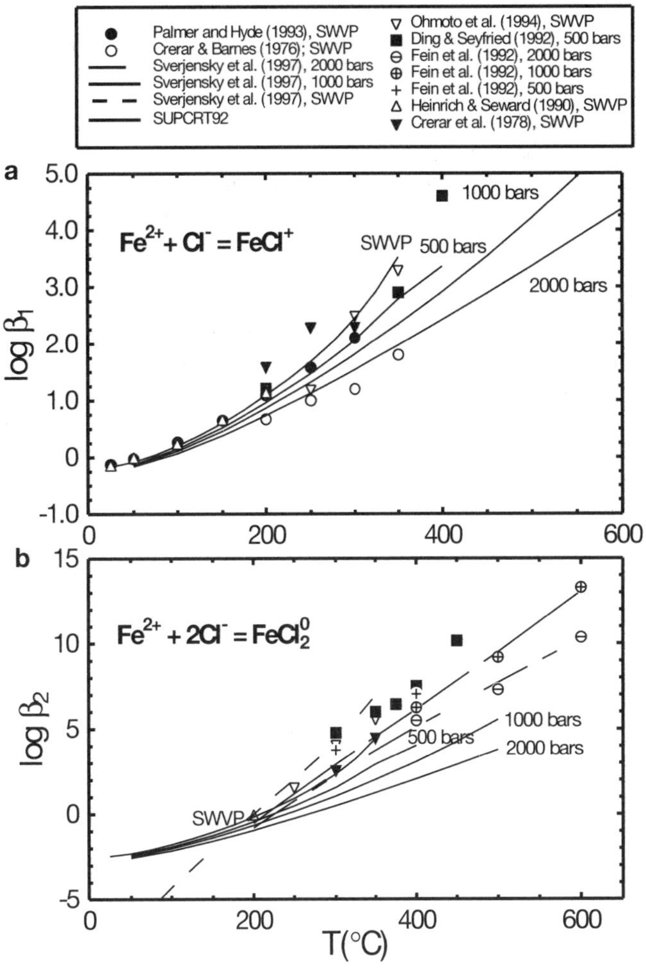

FIG. 6. (a) Plot of $\log \beta_1(FeCl^+)$ values from the literature versus temperature at various pressures. Note that the values measured by Palmer and Hyde (1993) fall practically on top of those reported by Heinrich and Seward (1990); (b) Plot of $\log \beta_2(FeCl_2^0)$ values from the literature versus temperature at various pressures.

revised HKF equation parameters for $FeCl_2^0$, which result in log β_2 values in good agreement with those of Fein et al. (1992). The data of Ding and Seyfried (1992) above 350°C, and of Ohmoto et al. (1994), are also in better agreement with the estimates of Sverjensky et al. (1997) than those of SUPCRT92. We therefore recommend use of the estimates of Sverjensky et al. (1997).

Hydrolysis of Fe^{2+} in hydrothermal solutions has been studied at temperatures up to 300°C by Sweeton and Baes (1970) and Tremaine and LeBlanc (1980), both of whom derived hydrolysis constants from measurements of the solubility of magnetite using a flow-through hydrothermal apparatus. The equilibrium constants measured in the two studies for the dissolution of magnetite as the simple hydrated Fe^{2+} ion are in reasonable agreement with each other, as well as with the values calculated by SUPCRT92 (Fig. 7). However, the hydrolysis constants determined by Sweeton and Baes (1970) are 1 to 4 log units higher than those reported by Tremaine and LeBlanc (1980). The original database of SUPCRT92 does not contain any Fe^{2+} hydroxide complexes. Shock et al. (1997) provide HKF parameters for these species based on the data of Sweeton and Baes (1970), but they point out that neither the Sweeton and Baes nor the Tremaine and LeBlanc data sets are completely consistent with the correlations they developed for hydroxide complexes. Tremaine and LeBlanc (1980) and Palmer and Hyde (1993) suggest reasons for the observed discrepancies among the studies of Sweeton and Baes (1970) and Tremaine and LeBlanc (1980). However, in the absence of any concrete evidence as to a serious deficiency in either study, these discrepancies remain unresolved. This situation should not seriously affect solubility calculations in mildly to strongly acidic NaCl solutions owing to the predominance of chloride complexes under such conditions. However, at high temperature, low chloride concentrations, and relatively high pH, hydroxide complexes may predominate, and under these conditions, solubility calculations for iron-bearing minerals are relatively uncertain.

It is possible that iron-bicarbonate complexes may play a role in Fe mass transfer in some hydrothermal solutions (cf. Wood et al., 1987). No experimental data are available for these species, but estimated stability constants for the $FeHCO_3^+$ complex are given by Cobble et al. (1982) up to 300°C.

It was shown above and in Figure 7 that the equilibrium constant for the dissolution of magnetite as the free ferrous ion, i.e., for the reaction:

$$\tfrac{1}{3}Fe_3O_4(s) + 2H^+ + \tfrac{1}{3}H_2(g) = Fe^{2+} + \tfrac{4}{3}H_2O(l) \quad (2.86)$$

is fairly well known, which indicates that the thermodynamic data in SUPCRT92 should result in reasonably accurate calculated solubilities of magnetite in hydrothermal solutions. Thermodynamic data for the reaction:

$$FeS_2(s) + 2H^+ + H_2O(l) = Fe^{2+} + 2H_2S^0 + \tfrac{1}{2}O_2(g) \quad (2.87)$$

derived from various studies are compared to each other and to values calculated from SUPCRT92 in Figure 8. It can be seen that data from various sources differ from one another by approximately one-half to two orders of magnitude, depending on temperature. These discrepancies need to be resolved, but until then, use of SUPCRT92 to calculate the equilibrium constant for reaction (2.87) is recommended.

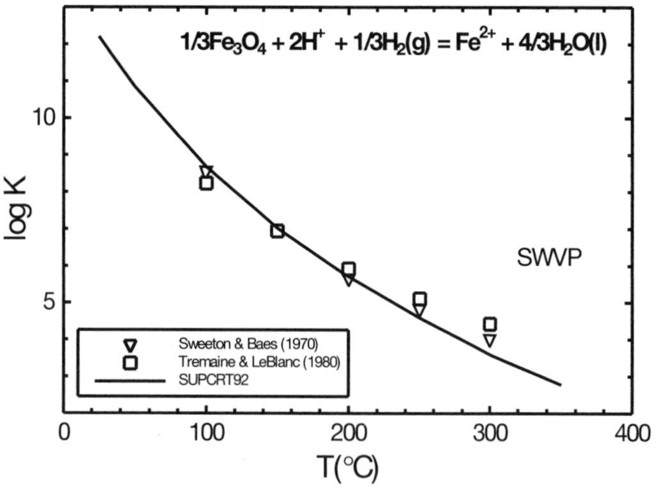

FIG. 7. Plot of log K versus temperature for the reaction: $\tfrac{1}{3}Fe_3O_4(s) + 2H^+ + \tfrac{1}{3}H_2(g) = Fe^{2+} + \tfrac{4}{3}H_2O(l)$ from various sources.

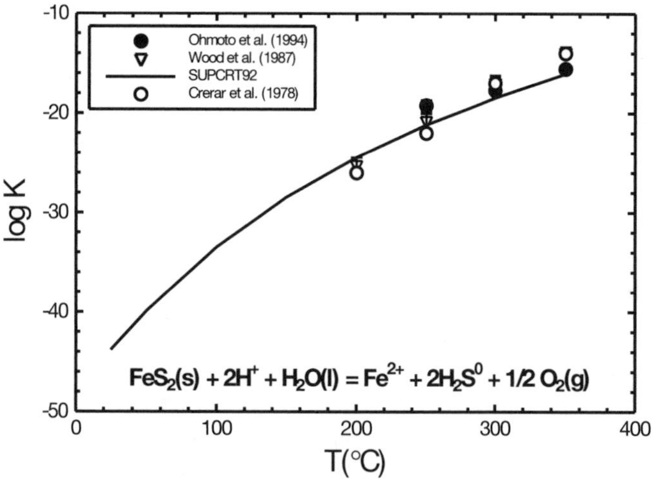

FIG. 8. Plot of log K versus temperature for the reaction: $FeS_2(s) + 2H^+ + H_2O(l) = Fe^{2+} + 2H_2S^0 + \tfrac{1}{2}O_2(g)$ from various sources. Crerar et al. (1978) tabulated values of log K for the above reaction. Wood et al. (1987) provide log K values for the reaction: $\tfrac{1}{4}Fe_3O_4(s) + \tfrac{1}{2}FeS(s) + 2H^+ = Fe^{2+} + \tfrac{1}{4}FeS_2(s) + H_2O(l)$, which were converted to the form required using equations (ii) and (iv) of table 2 in Crerar et al. (1978). Ohmoto et al. (1994) give log K values for the reaction: $FeS_2(s) + 2H^+ + H_2(g) = Fe^{2+} + 2H_2S$, which were converted to the required form using equations 11 and 12 in table 4 of Ohmoto et al. (1994).

Manganese. As a borderline cation, Mn^{2+} should exhibit similar preferences with respect to ligands as the Fe^{2+} ion. As such, chloride, hydroxide, and bicarbonate complexes would be expected to be the most important species in hydrothermal ore-forming solutions. The thermodynamic database for aqueous Mn(II) complexes at elevated temperatures and pressures is surprisingly poor, although the situation recently improved with the publication of studies by Gammons and Seward (1996), and Wolfram and Krupp (1996).

Gammons and Seward (1996) measured the stability constants of Mn-chloride complexes to 300°C using the indirect AgCl(s) solubility technique. They have obtained cumulative stability constants for the complexes $MnCl^+$ and $MnCl_2^0$. Their results are compared with stability constants for the same complexes from other data sources in Figures 9a and 9b. Figure 9a shows that there is considerable disagreement among measured values of log β_1. As shown by Gammons and Seward (1996), there is a very wide range of measured stability constants (over three orders of magnitude) even at 25°C, and their value determined at that temperature is at the low end of the range. The only other experimental data for temperatures above 50°C are those of Wheat and Carpenter (1988) from 50° to 170°C, and these are as much as an order of magnitude greater than those of Gammons and Seward (1996). The values of log β_1 calculated by SUPCRT92 and those estimated by Böttcher and Usdowski (1990) are evidently based on the measured values of Wheat and Carpenter (1988) because these are in relatively good agreement at low temperatures. However, the estimates of Böttcher and Usdowski (1990) and SUPCRT92 diverge strongly at temperatures above 120°C. The estimates obtained using HKF parameters given by Sverjensky et al. (1997) are very similar to those obtained using SUPCRT92.

Figure 9b shows that the agreement among the only two studies providing values of log β_2 at elevated temperature, i.e., the experimental measurements of Gammons and Seward (1996) and the estimates of Böttcher and Usdowski (1990), is also poor. Gammons and Seward (1996) demonstrated that, although some data manipulation is necessary to permit a comparison, their results are consistent with the results of Boctor and Frantz (1980) and Boctor (1985) at 350° to 500°C (see fig. 12 in Gammons and Seward, 1996).

The reason for the observed discrepancies is not entirely clear. The log β_1 values of Wheat and Carpenter (1988), on which the estimates of SUPCRT92 and Böttcher and Usdowski (1990) are based, may be overestimated because they apparently did not account for the possible formation of the $MnCl_2^0$ complex, which would be most likely to be important at the higher temperatures. Given that Gammons and Seward (1996) derived stability constants for both $MnCl^+$ and $MnCl_2^0$ over the widest range of temperature of any study, their data show consistent trends, and their measurements appear to have been carefully done, we recommend use of their data for Mn-chloride complexes.

Experimental measurements of the stability constant of the Mn(II)-bicarbonate complex $MnHCO_3^+$ have been made only at temperatures up to and including 55°C

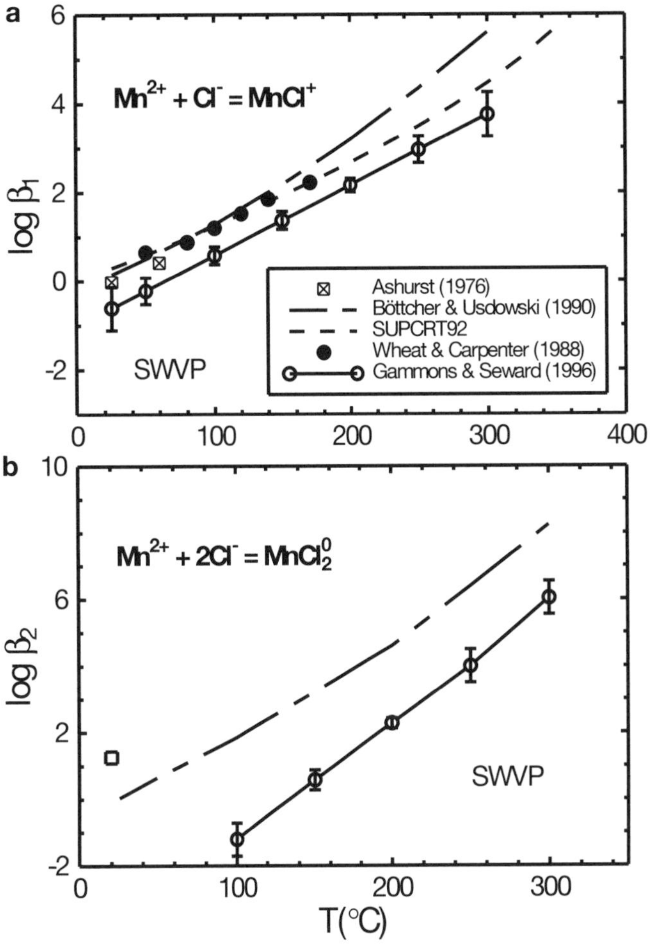

FIG. 9. (a) Plot of log $\beta_1(MnCl^+)$ values from the literature versus temperature; (b) plot of log $\beta_2(MnCl_2^0)$ values from the literature versus temperature.

(Lesht and Baumann, 1978; Wolfram and Krupp, 1996). However, a number of authors have attempted to make estimates of these stability constants up to as high as 300°C (Cobble et al., 1982; Phillips and Silvester, 1983; Böttcher and Usdowski, 1990). All three estimates are in relatively good agreement with one another, although the Böttcher and Usdowski (1990) estimates diverge to become higher than those of Cobble et al. (1982) by approximately 0.6 log units at 300°C. None of these studies is really independent of any of the others, inasmuch as all use the data of Lesht and Baumann (1978) as a base, and then apply some type of isocoulombic extrapolation. Wolfram and Krupp (1996) obtained a stability constant at 25°C that is almost an order of magnitude greater than that of Lesht and Baumann (1978), and furthermore, they did not detect the Mn(II)-bicarbonate complex in their rhodochrosite solubility studies at higher temperatures. These findings cast doubt on the validity of the extrapolated stability constants for $MnHCO_3^+$. In addition, Wolfram and Krupp (1996) provide evidence of, and thermodynamic data for, the carbonate complex $MnCO_3^0$ and the hydroxycarbonate complex $Mn(OH)CO_3^-$ up to

275°C and 200°C, respectively. Thus, there is still considerable uncertainty concerning the nature and thermodynamics of Mn-carbonate/bicarbonate complexes. It is important to resolve these discrepancies because Mn(II)-carbonate/bicarbonate could contribute significantly to Mn(II) mass transfer in low-chloride, low-temperature, high-CO_2 systems (e.g., some epithermal/geothermal fluids). At 150°C the stability constants for various Mn(II)-complexes are: log β_1 ($MnHCO_3^+$) = 2.20 (Cobble et al., 1982); log β_1 ($MnCO_3^0$) = 5.3 (Wolfram and Krupp, 1996); and log β_1 ($MnCl^+$) = 1.4. These data suggest that the carbonate/bicarbonate complexes are more stable than the chloride complex, and at sufficiently high carbonate:chloride activity ratios, the carbonate/bicarbonate complexes could predominate. However, the temperature dependencies of the constants are such that the chloride complexes become stronger relative to the carbonate/bicarbonate complexes with increasing temperature.

Three independent estimates (Cobble et al., 1982; Böttcher and Usdowski, 1990; Shock et al., 1997) of the first three hydrolysis constants for Mn^{2+} are in relatively good agreement with one another and fair agreement with the only experimentally determined hydrolysis constant at elevated temperature, that of Wolfram and Krupp (1996) for $Mn(OH)_2^0$ (Fig. 10). The Shock et al. (1997) estimates are available in the form of estimated HKF equation parameters for the relevant species, which can be readily incorporated into SUPCRT92. We recommend use of the HKF parameters reported by Shock et al. (1997) together with SUPCRT92 to provide estimates of hydrolysis constants of Mn^{2+} over a wide range of temperature and pressure, until additional experimental data become available.

As is the case with Fe(II), Mn(II)-bisulfide complexes are not expected to play a significant role in hydrothermal Mn(II) mass transfer. However, such species may be important in bisulfide-rich, low-temperature environments, and Luther et al. (1996) have measured the stability constants for the species $MnSH^+$, $Mn_2(SH)^{3+}$, and $Mn_3(SH)^{5+}$ at 25°C.

The study of Wolfram and Krupp (1996) may indicate an important problem with respect to the solubility product of the mineral rhodochrosite. Values of K_{SP} for the reaction:

$$MnCO_3(\text{rhodochrosite}) = Mn^{2+} + CO_3^{2-} \tag{2.88}$$

determined by direct experimental measurements of rhodochrosite solubility at temperatures to 275°C are in gross disagreement with the theoretical estimates provided by SUPCRT92 and by Egorov and Titova (1962), which are in turn in disagreement with one another (cf. fig. 6a of Wolfram and Krupp, 1996). Not only are the data discrepant, but the three sets show entirely different temperature dependences. The experiments of Wolfram and Krupp (1996) appear to have been very carefully done. However, they report a K_{SP} for rhodochrosite at 25°C that is substantially lower than any other reported in the literature. Therefore, additional experiments would be desirable to confirm their results.

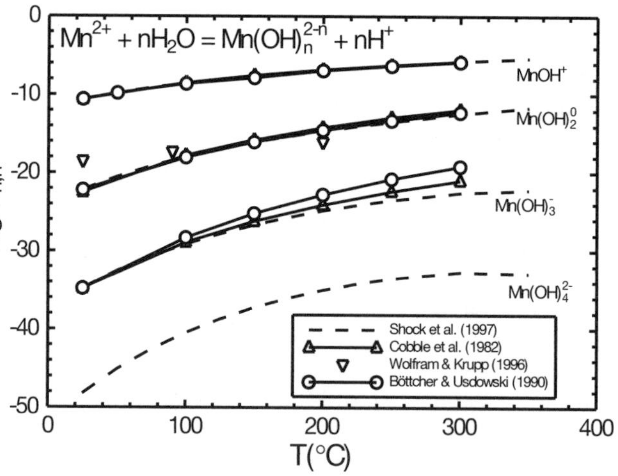

FIG. 10. Hydrolysis constants from the literature for Mn(II) as a function of temperature.

In summary, chloride, hydroxide, and bicarbonate/carbonate complexes of Mn(II) are likely to be the important agents of mass transfer of Mn(II) in hydrothermal environments, with chloride generally being the most important. The simple hydrated ion may also contribute to Mn transport. However, thermodynamic data for all but the hydroxide complexes are poorly constrained.

Tin. Tin can be present in two oxidation states in hydrothermal solutions: the Sn^{2+} ion is borderline and the Sn^{4+} ion is moderately hard. Pabalan (1986) measured the solubility of cassiterite in 0.1 to 5 m NaCl solutions between 200° and 350°C under vapor-saturated conditions. Under very oxidizing conditions (f_{O_2} > hematite-magnetite (HM) buffer), he found that Sn(IV) hydroxychloride complexes were the dominant form of Sn in solution. Cassiterite solubilities were low (<1 ppm) and defined by reactions such as:

$$\underset{\text{(cassiterite)}}{SnO_2} + 2Cl^- + 2H^+ = Sn(OH)_2Cl_2^0 \tag{2.89}$$

Under more reducing conditions, simple chloride complexes are dominant (Pabalan, 1986), and cassiterite solubility is significantly higher (>1000 ppm Sn in some experiments) and can be described by reactions of the form (Wilson and Eugster, 1990):

$$SnO_2 + XH^+ + nCl^- = SnCl_n^{X-n} + \frac{X}{2} H_2O + \frac{4-X}{4} O_2 \tag{2.90}$$

where X = oxidation state of Sn (2 or 4) and n = the ligation number for the chloride complex. Pabalan's reduced experiments were buffered by the Fe-magnetite system, where Sn^{2+} dominates over Sn^{4+}. Pabalan (1986) calculated cassiterite solubility for natural systems with pH constrained by the stability of muscovite (i.e., somewhat acidic), f_{O_2} by a CO_2/CH_4 ratio of 1, and m_{NaCl} = 1. Under such conditions, Sn concentrations were highest above ~260°C (up to 25 ppm) where Sn(II) complexes dominate ($SnCl_2{}^0$ at 350°C). At lower temperatures, cassiterite solubilities were significantly lower and $Sn(OH)_2Cl_2{}^0$ was the predominant species. In contrast, Kovalenko et al. (1986) concluded from experimental work that both chloride ($SnCl_2{}^0$) and hydroxychloride ($SnOHCl^0$) complexes were important at high temperatures (500°C, ~1kb) under acidic to neutral, reducing (nickel-nickel oxide, i.e., NNO) conditions in H_2O-HCl-NaCl solutions. Kovalenko et al. (1992) studied cassiterite solubility in more alkaline solutions (NaCl + NaOH, 500°C and NNO) and concluded that $Sn(OH)_2Cl^-$ was the dominant species.

Wilson and Eugster (1990) examined the solubility of cassiterite in HCl solutions at higher temperatures and pressures (400° to 700°C and 1.5 kb) at the NNO and HM buffers. They concluded that Sn(IV) species would only be important at relatively high f_{O_2} values and that in natural systems Sn(II) chloride complexes would dominate. Their experiments indicated that, for the NNO buffer, $SnCl^+$ and $SnCl_2{}^0$ were the important species between 400° and 600°C and that $SnCl_2{}^0$ dominated at 700°C. The complex $SnCl_3{}^+$ was the most abundant species at higher oxygen fugacities (HM buffer). Their calculated solubilities for natural systems were lower than those of Pabalan (1986): 7 ppm Sn at 600°C, NNO, 2m Cl^-, and pH constrained by K-feldspar-muscovite-quartz equilibria.

Various workers have calculated speciation and cassiterite solubility under a variety of conditions up to 350° to 400°C using thermodynamic data (Eadington and Giblin, 1979; Patterson et al., 1981; Eadington and Kinealy, 1983; Jackson and Helgeson, 1985a, b; Heinrich and Eadington, 1986; Heinrich, 1990). These mostly indicate that chloride complexes of Sn^{2+} dominate over hydroxy or fluoride complexes in moderately acidic, reducing solutions. The calculations of Jackson and Helgeson (1985a) indicate that at higher pH values (>3.5–5, depending on T), even in fluids with high m_{NaCl}, OH^- complexes such as $Sn(OH)_2{}^0$ and $Sn(OH)_4{}^0$ are more important than chloride complexes, as is the case for low-chloride fluids. However, cassiterite solubilities are significantly higher (up to several hundred ppm) at low pH and high temperature, where chloride complexes dominate. All indications are that fluoride complexes are unimportant given the low F-concentrations (buffered by fluorite or topaz precipitation) of natural fluids.

Equilibrium constants for the formation of simple Sn(II)-chloride complexes (reaction 2.90) are depicted in Figure 11. The theoretical estimates of Jackson and Helgeson (1985a) are in remarkably good agreement with the measured values of Pabalan (1986) over the temperature range 200° to 350°C at SWVP, and the experimental values of Wilson and Eugster (1990) at 400° to 700°C at 1.5 kbar conform to the trend established by the lower pressure and temperature data. No HKF parameters are available for Sn(II)-chloride complexes, but the data shown in Figure 11 cover a relatively wide temperature range, and are recommended for use in cassiterite solubility calculations.

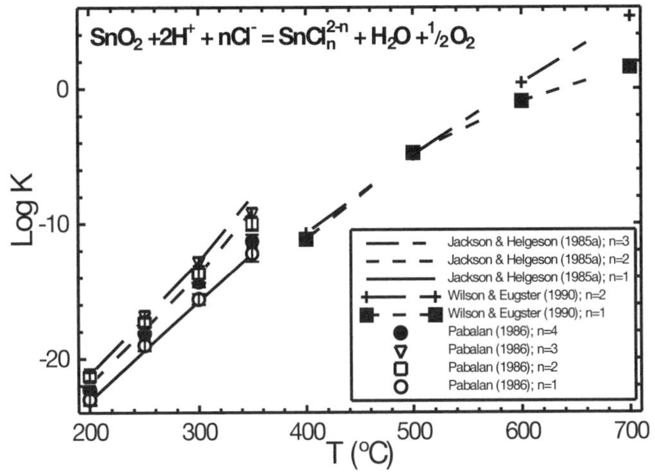

FIG. 11. Plot of log K versus temperature for the reaction: $SnO_2(s) + 2H^+ + nCl^- = SnCl_n^{2-n} + H_2O(l) + {}^1/_2O_2(g)$ from various sources.

More recently, Taylor and Wall (1993) measured the solubility of tin in chloride solutions at high temperatures and pressures (700°–800°C and 2 kb) using a variety of silicate buffer assemblages and relatively reducing conditions (QFM and QFM + 1.5; QFM = quartz-fayalite-magnetite). In these experiments they were able to achieve very high solubilities of up to tens of thousands of ppm Sn. Differences in solubility between different silicate assemblages for the same m_{HCl} led them to conclude that simple chloride complexes such as $SnCl_2{}^0$ could not alone explain their results and that a variety of hydroxychloride (e.g., $SnOHCl^0$) and mixed Na- and K-bearing chloride and hydroxychloride complexes (e.g., $NaSnOHCl_2{}^0$, $NaSnCl_3{}^0$, $KSnCl_3{}^0$, $K_2SnCl_4{}^0$) must exist. Taylor and Wall (1993) also conducted experiments in fluoride-bearing solutions and concluded that Sn-fluoride complexes are unimportant.

In summary, Sn(II) species are likely to be more important than Sn(IV) species in hydrothermal systems. Under the conditions typical of most Sn-depositing hydrothermal systems (i.e., >300°C, reducing and acidic), simple Sn(II)-chloride complexes are likely to be important and thermodynamic data for these species are relatively well constrained. Hydroxide, mixed hydroxychloride and alkali metal-bearing complexes of Sn(II) may be important, but the stability constants of these complexes are poorly known.

Zinc. The Zn^{2+} ion is another Pearson borderline acid that therefore forms complexes with a wide variety of ligands. Chloride, bisulfide, hydroxide, carbonate, and bicarbonate complexes all may play roles in hydrothermal Zn transport in certain environments, and experimental data have been obtained for each of these types of complexes over at least portions of the pressure-temperature range relevant to hydrothermal Zn transport.

Although there have been a number of studies of the solubility of Zn minerals (mostly sphalerite) in hydrothermal chloride solutions (cf. Barrett and Anderson, 1982; Ruaya and Seward, 1986; Bourcier and Barnes, 1987;

Wood et al., 1987; Barrett and Anderson, 1988; Cygan et al., 1994; and references therein), only a handful of these studies have resulted in stability constants for Zn chloride complexes at temperatures above 100°C. Ruaya and Seward (1986) determined stability constants up to 350°C at SWVP. Bourcier and Barnes (1987) derived Zn-chloride complex stability constants to 350°C and SWVP from zincite (ZnO) and smithsonite ($ZnCO_3$) solubilities, and Cygan et al. (1994) obtained stability constants from 300° to 600°C and 0.5 to 2.0 kbar from sphalerite solubility experiments. There is general agreement that Zn^{2+} forms a series of chloride complexes: $ZnCl^+$, $ZnCl_2^0$, $ZnCl_3^-$, and $ZnCl_4^{2-}$. However, the agreement among the stability constants from the various studies is only fair. Measurements of log β_1 for $ZnCl^+$ are summarized in Figure 12a, together with the values calculated from SUPCRT92. The SUPCRT92 database for Zn chloride complexes is based on the data of Ruaya and Seward (1986). Values of log β_1 obtained by Bourcier and Barnes (1987) are approximately an order of magnitude less than those of Ruaya and Seward (1986). The data of Cygan et al. (1994) at 0.5 kbars appear to be too high with respect to either of the other two sets of experimental data. On the other hand, the Cygan et al. (1994) data at 1.0 and 2.0 kbars are in reasonable agreement with the estimates provided by SUPCRT92, although the temperature dependences are not quite the same. The agreement among the three studies for log β_2 ($ZnCl_2^0$) is much better (Fig. 12b), being largely within the combined experimental uncertainties. Cygan et al. (1994) do not report stabilities for the higher complexes, and Figure 12c and d shows that there are significant discrepancies once again between Ruaya and Seward (1986) and Bourcier and Barnes (1987) for log β_3 ($ZnCl_3^-$) and log β_4 ($ZnCl_4^{2-}$), the disagreement being much worse for the former species than the latter. In a very recent study, Wesolowski et al. (1998) derive a value of log β_1 in good agreement with both Bourcier and Barnes (1987) and Ruaya and Seward (1986), and a value of log β_2 in better agreement with that of Bourcier and Barnes (1987) than with that of Ruaya and Seward (1986) at 200°C. Sverjensky et al. (1997) provide HKF parameters with which to calculate the stability constants of $ZnCl^+$,

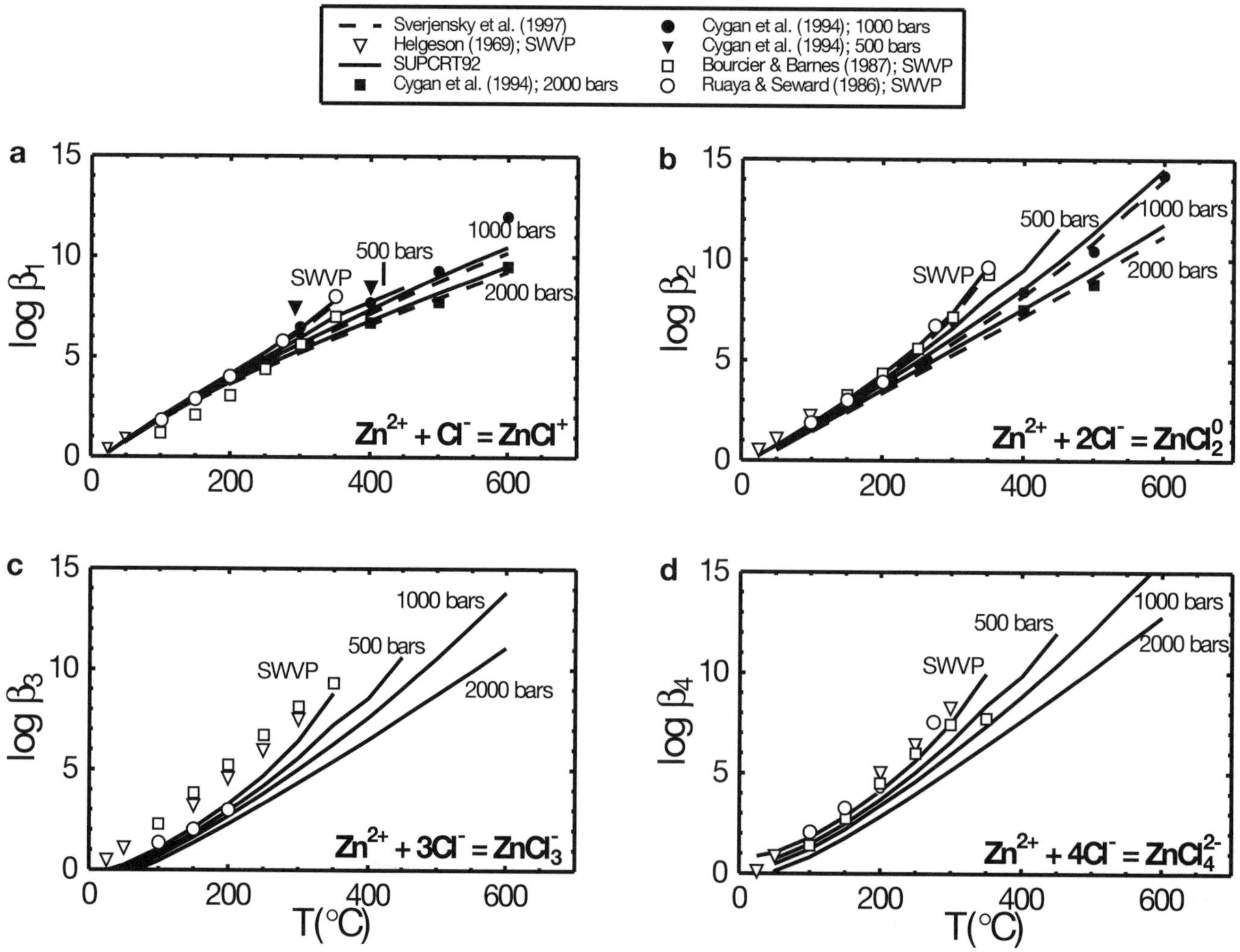

FIG. 12. Plot of literature values of (a) log β_1 ($ZnCl^+$); (b) log β_2 ($ZnCl_2^0$); (c) log β_3 ($PbCl_3^-$); and (d) log β_4 ($PbCl_4^{2-}$) versus temperature at various pressures.

$ZnCl_2^0$, and $ZnCl_3^-$, derived from Ruaya & Seward's (1986) data. The stability constants thus calculated are slightly lower than those calculated from SUPCRT92, and are in good agreement with the 2000 bar data of Cygan et al. (1994). Sverjensky et al. (1997) do not provide HKF parameters for $ZnCl_4^{2-}$ because of the uncertainties in the experimental data for this species. We recommend use of the parameters of Sverjensky et al. (1997) until experimental resolution of the discrepancies outlined above is obtained.

Barrett and Anderson (1988) calculated the solubility of sphalerite in hydrothermal chloride solutions using stability constants for the Zn(II)-chloride complexes from Ruaya and Seward (1986) and equilibrium constants for the reaction:

$$ZnS + 2H^+ = Zn^{2+} + H_2S^0 \quad (2.91)$$

calculated from data in Bowers et al. (1984), and compared the results to their experimental measurements from 25° to 95°C. The equilibrium constants for reaction (2.91) calculated from data in Bowers et al. (1984) are essentially identical to those calculated by SUPCRT92. Barrett and Anderson (1988) found excellent agreement among calculated and measured solubilities at 60° to 95°C, but at 25°C the calculated solubilities are too low by nearly an order of magnitude. Barrett and Anderson (1988) state that calculations using the Zn(II)-chloride stability constants of Bourcier and Barnes (1987) result in sphalerite solubilities differing by less than 0.5 log units from those using the data of Ruaya and Seward (1986). Evidently, in spite of important differences in detail between the data of Ruaya and Seward (1986) and Bourcier and Barnes (1987), these data sets yield similar calculated ZnS(s) solubilities. Thus, the calculations of Barrett and Anderson (1988) suggest that such solubility calculations are on a relatively good footing.

Bourcier and Barnes (1987) and Hayashi et al. (1990) both provide equilibrium constants, derived from sphalerite solubility measurements, for the following Zn-bisulfide complexation reactions at elevated temperatures:

$$ZnS(s) + H_2S^0 = Zn(HS)_2^0 \quad (2.92)$$

$$ZnS(s) + H_2S^0 + HS^- = Zn(HS)_3^- \quad (2.93)$$

$$ZnS(s) + H_2S^0 + 2HS^- = Zn(HS)_4^{2-} \quad (2.94)$$

There is reasonable agreement between the two studies on the equilibrium constants estimated for reactions (2.92) and (2.93), and these equilibrium constants exhibit a very weak temperature dependence between 25° and 350°C. However, the agreement is somewhat poorer for reaction (2.94), with the discrepancy among the two data sets increasing with decreasing temperature. It should also be noted that, in addition to the species $Zn(HS)_2^0$, $Zn(HS)_3^-$, and $Zn(HS)_4^{2-}$, Bourcier and Barnes (1987) employed the species $Zn(OH)(HS)^0$ in the model describing their solubility results, whereas Hayashi et al. (1990) employed the species $Zn(OH)(HS)_2^-$ and $Zn(OH)(HS)_3^{2-}$. Gübeli and Ste.-Marie (1967a) identified the species $Zn(OH)(HS)^0$ from their solubility experiments at room temperature. Bourcier and Barnes (1987) point out that the species $Zn(OH)(HS)^0$ will only be important in solutions with relatively low sulfide concentrations and high pH, and did not represent a significant proportion of total Zn in their experiments (they in fact derived equilibrium constants for the formation of this species from the solubility measurements of Hinners, 1963). They also concluded that this species would never be important in nature in equilibrium with sphalerite. From the results of Hayashi et al. (1990), it is evident that the species $Zn(OH)(HS)_2^-$ and $Zn(OH)(HS)_3^{2-}$, if they exist at all, are only important at pH values above approximately 8 (their fig. 3). Dyrssen (1991) notes that solubility experiments cannot distinguish among species such as $Zn(OH)(HS)_2^-$ and $Zn(OH)(HS)_3^{2-}$ and their stoichiometric equivalents ZnS_2H^- and $ZnS_3H_2^{2-}$, which differ in their empirical formulae only by the presence of a water molecule. However, the ab initio calculations of Tossell and Vaughan (1993) suggest that $Zn(OH)(HS)_3^{2-}$ should be more stable than $ZnS_3H_2^{2-}$, and is therefore the preferred stoichiometry.

Daskalakis and Helz (1993) studied the solubility of sphalerite in sulfidic solutions and proposed that the following species were essential to explain their solubility data: $Zn(HS)_4^{2-}$, $ZnS(HS)^-$, and $ZnS(HS)_2^{2-}$. The latter two species can be written in their hydrated forms as: $Zn(OH)(HS)_2^-$ and $Zn(OH)(HS)_3^{2-}$, respectively. The addition of the species $Zn(HS)_2^0$ improved slightly the fit of their model to their solubility data, but no polysulfide species were required. Thus, with the exception of the species $Zn(HS)_3^-$ proposed by Hayashi et al. (1990), the speciation schemes of Hayashi et al. (1990) and Daskalakis and Helz (1993) are identical. Daskalakis and Helz (1993) suggest that the $ZnS(HS)_2^{2-}$ species may actually be a tetranuclear species with the formula: $Zn_4(HS)_6(OH)_4^{2-}$ (see fig. 2 in Daskalakis and Helz, 1993, for the structure of this species) based on analogy with known Zn(II)-thiolate species such as $Zn_4(RS)_{10}^{2-}$ (where R is an organic group) and the EXAFS evidence of Helz et al. (1993). However, they admit that the question of the exact formulation of the $ZnS(HS)_2^{2-}$ species remains unresolved. The solubilities measured by Daskalakis and Helz (1993) are considerably lower than those measured by Gübeli and Ste.-Marie (1967a), probably due to the presence of ZnS colloids in the experimental solutions of the latter. The equilibrium constant for the formation of $Zn(HS)_2^0$ measured by Daskalakis and Helz (1993) is in reasonable agreement with those determined by Bourcier and Barnes (1987) and Hayashi et al. (1990). For reaction (2.94), the equilibrium constant determined by Daskalakis and Helz (1993) is in much better agreement with the values measured by Hayashi et al. (1990) than those measured by Bourcier and Barnes (1987). Furthermore, for the reaction:

$$ZnS(sphalerite) + 2HS^- = ZnS(HS)_2^{2-} \quad (2.95)$$

Hayashi et al. (1990) obtained log K = –4.9 compared to log K = –5.33 (Daskalakis and Helz, 1993) and for the reaction:

$$ZnS(sphalerite) + 2HS^- = ZnS(HS)^- \quad (2.96)$$

the respective equilibrium constants are log K = –4.64 (Daskalakis and Helz, 1993), and log K = –4.4 (Hayashi et al., 1990). The agreement between the two studies is therefore very good.

Luther et al. (1996), using voltammetry, determined that the species ZnS^0 and $Zn_2S_3^{2-}$ exist in sulfide-bearing solutions at 25°C, and measured their stability constants. These authors apparently did not find evidence for species bearing bisulfide (HS^-), although they did find such evidence for Fe(II), Mn(II), Co(II), and Ni(II). However, the species ZnS^0 can be formulated as the hydrated $Zn(OH)(HS)^0$, which was proposed by Gübeli and Ste.-Marie (1967a) and Bourcier and Barnes (1987). In fact, Luther et al. (1996) show that, if the solubility data of Gübeli and Ste.-Marie (1967a) are interpreted in terms of the species $Zn_2S_3^{2-}$, then a stability constant for the latter is obtained which is in relatively good agreement with that measured by Luther et al. (1996) using voltammetry. Luther et al., (1996) suggest that the species $Zn_2S_3^{2-}$ actually has a tetranuclear structure (Zn_4S_6), similar to a species proposed by Daskalakis and Helz (1993). However, Daskalakis and Helz (1993) found no evidence for the species ZnS^0. They exerted great efforts to avoid sampling colloidal ZnS (they used well-crystalline ZnS(s) preleached with EDTA solution to dissolve fine-grained solid and high-energy surfaces, they approached equilibrium only from undersaturation, and they employed a 0.2 μm filter), and as a result determined a solubility considerably lower than that measured by Gübeli and Ste.-Marie (1967a). These findings suggest that the Luther et al. (1996) ZnS^0 species may be a polynuclear species of sufficient size to be considered colloidal. Yet, Luther et al. (1996) present spectroscopic and electrochemical evidence that the species they identify as ZnS^0 is a complex in true solution. Additional work may be required to resolve this issue.

As is evident from the above discussion, the Zn-sulfide system is rather complicated. However, the agreement observed among the studies of Hayashi et al. (1990) and Daskalakis and Helz (1993), and some of the results of Bourcier and Barnes (1987), for Zn(II)-bisulfide complexes is encouraging, although further refinements would be desirable. We therefore recommend that the data set of Hayashi et al. (1990), which covers a wide range of temperature and is in excellent agreement with the data of Daskalakis and Helz (1993), be employed in solubility calculations for the time being. Zn(II)-bisulfide complexes will be important in relatively low temperature solutions with high bisulfide concentrations, low chloride concentrations, and relatively high pH.

There is generally poor agreement among the relatively large number of studies providing thermodynamic data for Zn(II)-hydroxide complexes. Figure 13a indicates that there is good agreement between the experimental measurements of the first stepwise hydrolysis constant for Zn(II) of Khodakovskiy and Yelkin (1975), Reichle et al. (1975), and Plyasunov et al. (1988) and the estimates derived from HKF parameters given by Shock et al. (1997) for $Zn(OH)^+$. The data of Perrin (1962) are lower than the rest by about one log unit. However, the agreement among various studies for $Zn(OH)_2^0$, $Zn(OH)_3^-$, and $Zn(OH)_4^{2-}$ is much less satisfactory (Figs. 13b, c, d), with discrepancies of up to two log units among the values obtained. In the absence of a definitive reason for choosing one data set over another, we recommend the use of the estimates of Shock et al. (1997), which in most cases fall within the scatter of the various experimental data. In most of the experimental studies, the primary thermodynamic data obtained are equilibrium constants for the dissolution of ZnO(s) as hydroxide complexes. When the various studies are compared in this form, as done in figure 29 of Shock et al. (1997), agreement is seen to be much better for the higher hydroxide complexes. Thus, some of the disagreement exhibited in Figure 13 may be a result of inconsistencies in the thermodynamic data for ZnO(s) employed in the various studies to derive hydrolysis constants. Recently, however, Wesolowski et al. (1998) reported an equilibrium constant for the reaction:

$$ZnO(s) + 2H^+ = Zn^{2+} + H_2O(l) \quad (2.97)$$

at 200°C that is in good agreement with values determined for this temperature by Khodakovskiy and Yelkin (1975) and Ziemniak (1992), and that calculated by SUPCRT92. The correspondence among these values indicates additional problems with the data for Zn-hydroxide complexes.

The only stability constants available for the $ZnHCO_3^+$ complex at elevated temperatures are those estimated by Murray and Cobble (1980), Cobble et al. (1982), and Phillips and Silvester (1983), and those reported by Ryan and Baumann (1978) and Baumann (1981). The stability constants from these studies agree reasonably well where they overlap. However, the estimated values of Murray and Cobble (1980) and Cobble et al. (1982) diverge at temperatures above 250°C. We assume that the values of Cobble et al. (1982) represent their final best estimates and recommend these values until experimental data become available at elevated temperatures.

Lead. The Pb^{2+} ion is one of the softest of the borderline cations and therefore should form stronger complexes with chloride and bisulfide, and weaker complexes with hydroxide, and bicarbonate (carbonate), than do other borderline cations. Some thermodynamic data are available for all these complexes at elevated temperatures.

Stability constants for Pb(II)-chloride complexes have been derived from the solubility measurements of Nriagu and Anderson (1971) and Rafal'skiy and Masalovich (1982), and from the spectroscopic studies of Yurchenko et al. (1976) and Seward (1984); they have also been estimated at elevated temperature via extrapolation of room temperature data (Helgeson, 1969). The available stability constants for Pb(II)-chloride complexes at elevated

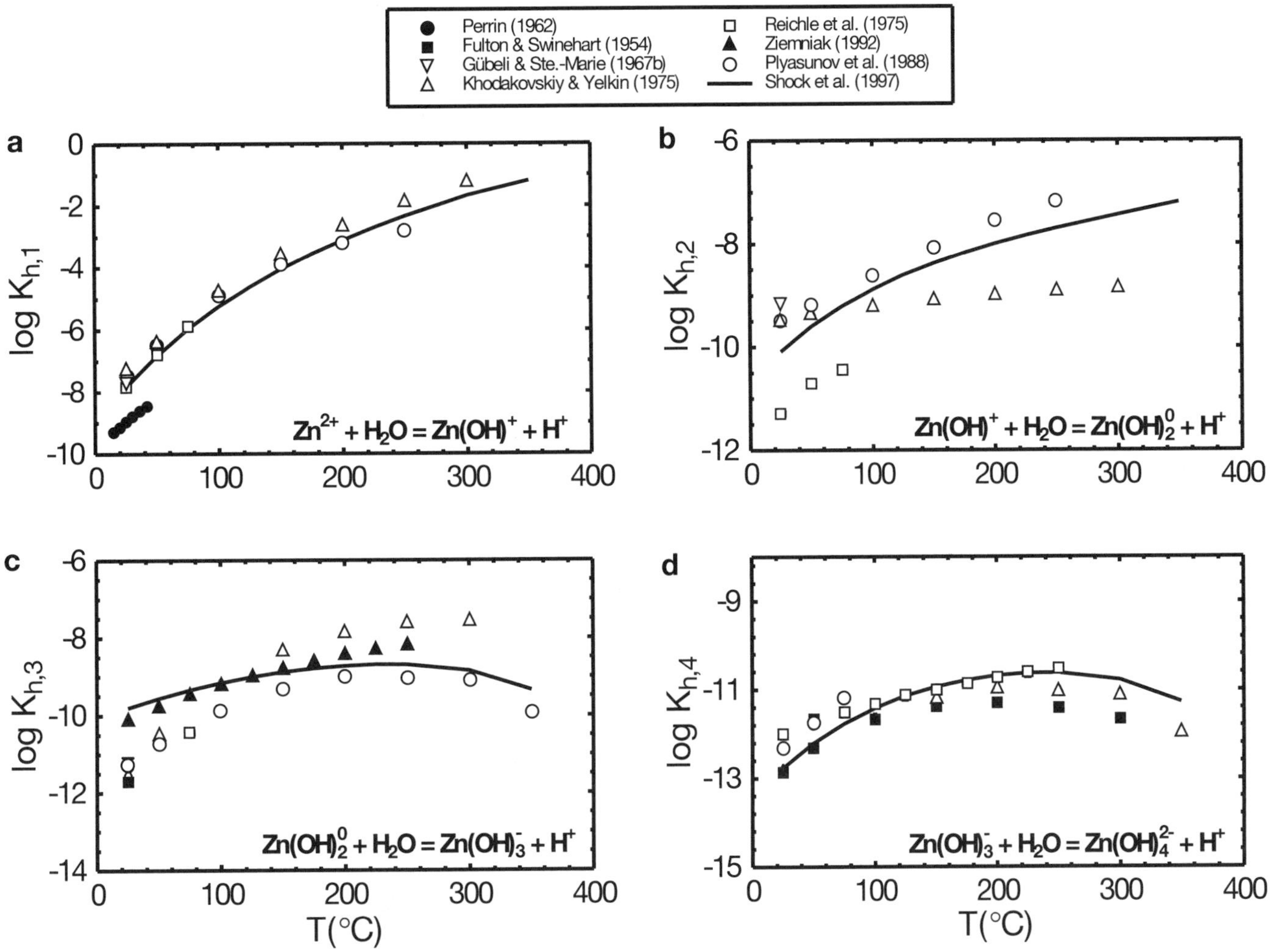

FIG. 13. Plot of stepwise hydrolysis constants from the literature versus temperature at SWVP for: (a) $Zn(OH)^+$; (b) $Zn(OH)_2^0$; (c) $Zn(OH)_3^-$; and (d) $Zn(OH)_4^{2-}$.

temperatures are compared in Figure 14a-d, together with those calculated using SUPCRT92 and HKF parameters from Sverjensky et al. (1997). The agreement among values of log β_1 for $PbCl^+$ is excellent, within 0.5 log units, except for the values of Rafal'skiy and Masalovich (1982) and the estimates of Helgeson (1969), both of which appear to be too low at elevated temperature by as much as a log unit. In the case of β_2 for $PbCl_2^0$, the agreement is good to fair among all the studies, except for the estimates of Helgeson (1969), which are too low by several orders of magnitude at 300°C. The amount of data is less and the agreement is poorer for β_3 and β_4, and the data of Seward (1984) are probably the best available. The HKF parameters for the Pb(II)-chloride complexes employed by SUPCRT92 were apparently derived from the data of Seward (1984), and so we recommend use of the stability constants for these complexes calculated using SUPCRT92. These HKF parameters yield practically the same estimates as those of Sverjensky et al. (1997).

Barrett and Anderson (1988) calculated the solubility of galena in hydrothermal chloride solutions using stability constants for the Pb(II)-chloride complexes from Seward (1984) and equilibrium constants for the reaction:

$$PbS + 2H^+ = Pb^{2+} + H_2S^0 \qquad (2.98)$$

calculated from data in Bowers et al. (1984) and compared the results to their experimental measurements from 25° to 95°C. The equilibrium constants for reaction (2.98) calculated from data in Bowers et al. (1984) are essentially identical to those calculated by SUPCRT92, and Seward's (1984) stability constants also are identical to those calculated by SUPCRT92 (see above paragraph). Barrett and Anderson (1988) found excellent agreement among calculated and measured solubilities at 60° to 95°C, although at 25°C the calculated solubilities are too low by nearly an order of magnitude. Barrett and Anderson (1988) point out that the value of the equilibrium constant for reaction (2.98) determined by Uhler and Helz (1984) is almost two orders of magnitude greater than the value employed in their calculations, and they therefore suggest that there is still some uncertainty connected with galena solubility calculations. However, the relatively good agreement Barrett and Anderson (1988) obtained between calculated and measured galena

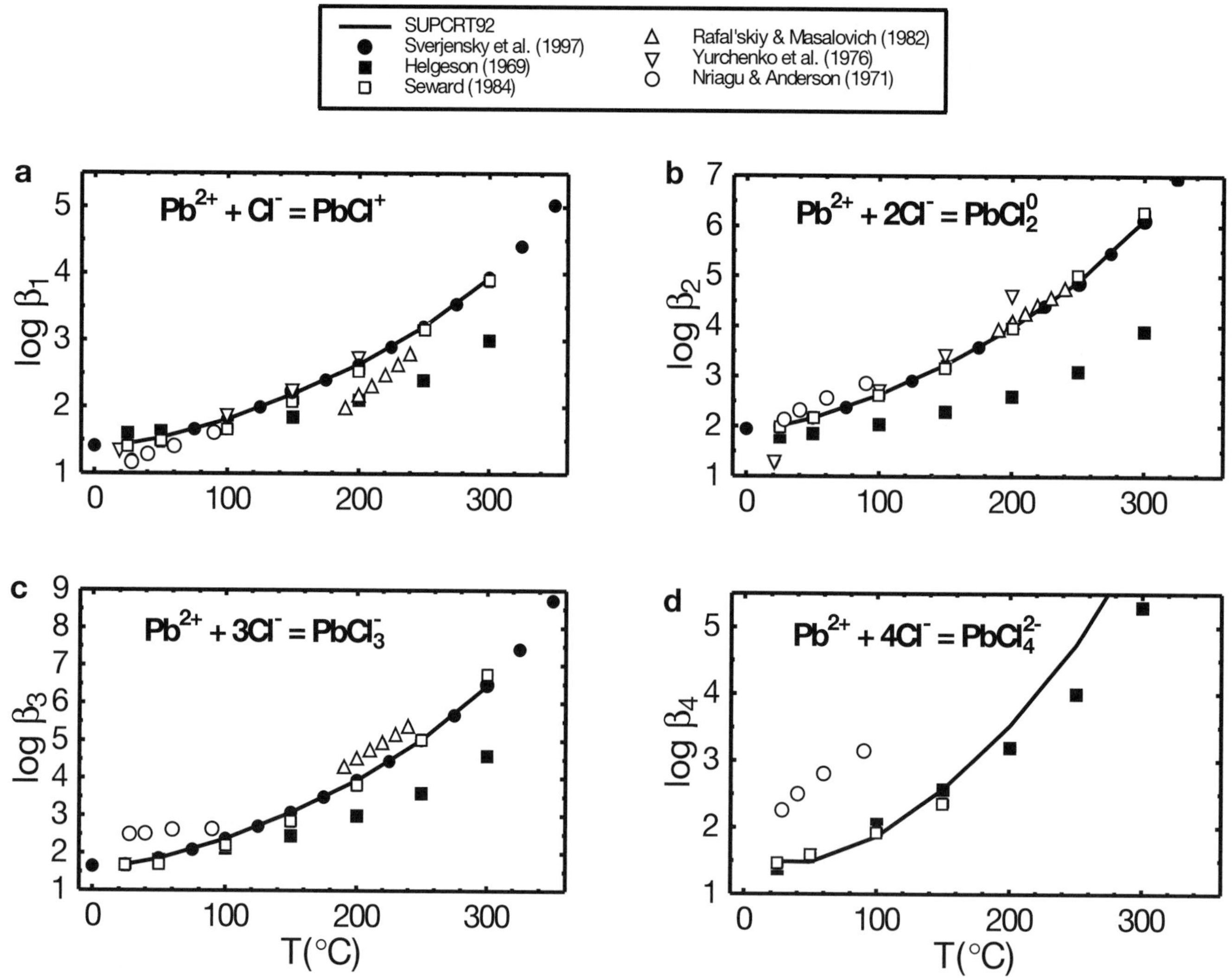

FIG. 14. Plot of literature values of (a) log β_1 ($PbCl^+$); (b) log β_2 ($PbCl_2^0$); (c) log β_3 ($PbCl_3^-$); and (d) log β_4 ($PbCl_4^{2-}$) versus temperature at various pressures.

solubilities, and the relatively good agreement among various measurements of Pb(II)-chloride solubility experiments is encouraging and suggests that galena solubility calculations using data from SUPCRT92 yield results of at least the right order of magnitude.

Hemley (1953) measured PbS solubility in H_2S-saturated solutions over the pH range 1 to 8 and determined the stoichiometries of the predominant complexes to be $Pb(HS)_2^0$ at low pH, and $Pb(HS)_3^-$ at high pH. Anderson (1962) measured PbS solubilities at 30°C and concluded that $Pb(HS)_3^-$ and $Pb(HS)_2(H_2S)^0$ were the predominant species at pH > 6 and pH < 6, respectively. However, neither Hemley (1953) nor Anderson (1962) varied H_2S in their experiments, which precludes definitive conclusions as to stoichiometry. Nriagu (1971) conducted solubility experiments at 90°C. He reported that $Pb(HS)_2(H_2S)^0$ is the predominant species at pH = 3.5 to 6.2, and $Pb(HS)_3^-$ at pH > 6.2. Hamann and Anderson (1978) made solubility measurements in an attempt to resolve the discrepancies in the reported Pb(II)-bisulfide complex stoichiometries. They did not succeed in obtaining stoichiometries in their experiments, but they obtained PbS solubilities in good agreement with those of Hemley (1953) and Anderson (1962), but lower than those of Nriagu (1971). Giordano and Barnes (1979) suggest that Nriagu's (1971) solubilities are too high owing to ineffective filtering of his samples. The most complete of these studies is that of Giordano and Barnes (1979) who provide equilibrium constants for the following reactions from 30° to 300°C:

$$PbS(s) + H_2S(g) + HS^- = Pb(HS)_3^- \qquad (2.99)$$

$$PbS(s) + H_2S(g) = Pb(HS)_2^0 \qquad (2.100)$$

$$PbS(s) + 2H_2S(g) = Pb(HS)_2(H_2S)^0 \qquad (2.101)$$

Their data suggest that $Pb(HS)_3^-$ is predominant at pH > 6 over a wide range of ΣS, $Pb(HS)_2^0$ is predominant at pH < 6 and ΣS less than approximately 1.0 molal, and that $Pb(HS)_2(H_2S)^0$ is predominant at pH < 6 and ΣS >

1.0 molal. Bisulfide complexes of Pb(II) will predominate over chloride complexes under low-temperature, near-neutral to alkaline, chloride-poor, and bisulfide-rich conditions. However, Giordano and Barnes (1979) carried out calculations that show that solubilities of galena as Pb(II)-bisulfide complexes greater than 1 ppm are attainable only in unusually sulfide-rich and/or alkaline solutions, and so it is unlikely that hydrothermal transport of Pb(II) as bisulfide complexes will lead to ore formation.

We are aware of only one study of Pb(II) hydrolysis at elevated temperatures, that of Tugarinov et al. (1975). Their data indicate that, in the absence of other ligands, Pb(II) hydrolysis will commence at pH = 3.8 at 200°C. Thus, Pb(II) hydrolysis will need to be taken into account in dilute hydrothermal solutions, although additional experimental measurements would be desirable in order to verify the experiments of Tugarinov et al. (1975). Hydrolysis constants derived from HKF parameters for Pb(II)-hydroxide complexes given by Shock et al. (1997) are in good agreement with those given by Tugarinov et al. (1975) for $Pb(OH)_3^-$, but hydrolysis constants from these two studies differ substantially for $Pb(OH)^+$ and $Pb(OH)_2^0$. However, as with Zn, when compared in terms of equilibrium constants for the dissolution of PbO(s) as hydroxide complexes, the agreement between Tugarinov et al. (1975) and Shock et al. (1997) is much better (cf. fig. 30 of Shock et al., 1997).

Faucherre and Bonnaire (1959) and Baranova (1968) determined stability constants for $Pb(CO_3)_2^{2-}$ at 25°C that are within about one log unit of each other, but the Baranova (1968) data refer to 1 molal ionic strength. Baranova and Barsukov (1965) determined stability constants at 20°C for $Pb(HCO_3)_2^0$ and $Pb(HCO_3)_3^-$, but their measurements were made in chloride solutions and the possible formation of Pb-chloride complexes was not taken into account. Baranova (1968) obtained stability constants for the complex $PbCO_3^0$ at 250° and 300°C. Finally, Leleu (1978) measured stability constants of the complexes $PbHCO_3^+$ and $Pb(CO_3)_2^{2-}$ at 120° to 180°C. The stability constants of Leleu (1978) for the $Pb(CO_3)_2^{2-}$ complex at 120° to 180°C form a reasonable trend with the value measured by Foucherre and Bonnaire (1959), although the 120°C value of Leleu (1978) may be too high. Wood (1987) showed that, based on the data of Baranova (1968), lead speciation in low-chloride, CO_2-rich fluids could be dominated by Pb-carbonate or Pb-bicarbonate complexes, but additional experimental data are required to fully evaluate the roles of these species. However, it seems unlikely that such complexes can be responsible for galena solubilities sufficiently high to form an ore deposit. In the experiments of Wood (1987), the solubility of galena under conditions where carbonate complexes predominated was less than 0.4 ppm, whereas in chloride-bearing solutions where Pb-chloride complexes predominated, solubilities of up to 89 ppm were attained.

Soft Metals

Copper. Although Cu may occur in aqueous solutions in both the Cu(I) and Cu(II) oxidation states, it is generally accepted that Cu(I) is predominant in most hydrothermal solutions (Helgeson, 1969; Crerar and Barnes, 1976). The Cu^+ ion is a moderately soft cation, softer than most of the transition metals, such as Fe^{2+}, Mn^{2+}, Zn^{2+}, etc., but harder than Ag^+ and Au^+. Thus, Cu^+ forms comparatively stable chloride and bisulfide complexes, and in basic solutions poor in other ligands, hydroxide complexes may need to be taken into account.

Crerar and Barnes (1976) were among the first to measure experimentally the stability of Cu(I)-chloride complexes at hydrothermal conditions. These authors concluded that the predominant Cu(I)-complex was $CuCl^0$ for which they derived stability constants. However, they employed a graphite-CO_2 f_{O_2} buffer which probably did not equilibrate sufficiently rapidly at the temperatures covered (cf. Ziegenbein and Johannes, 1980). Furthermore, the constants they derived appear to be much lower than expected, when compared to equivalent complexes of other soft metals, such as $AgCl^0$, and stability constants for $CuCl^0$ at room temperature reported in the literature. Var'yash and Rekharski (1982) and Var'yash (1992) conducted solubility experiments on Cu_2O(s) and Cu, in chloride solutions, and interpreted their results in terms of the species $CuClOH^-$ and $CuCl_2^-$, respectively. Var'yash (1992) produced a regression equation (based on his results, a re-interpretation of the data of Var'yash and Rekharski (1982), and a variety of data from the literature) that yields log β_2 for $CuCl_2^-$ from 15° to 300°C (Fig. 15). Var'yash's (1992) log β_2 values are remarkably close to the values estimated by Ruaya (1988) using an isocoulombic approach, differing by less than 0.5 log units over the entire temperature range. The older estimates of Helgeson (1969) for log β_2 are similar to those of Ruaya (1988) and Var'yash (1992) at low temperatures but increasingly diverge with increasing temperature (Fig. 15). Most recently, Xiao et al. (in press) have determined the equilibrium constants using solubility methods for the reactions:

$$Cu + \tfrac{1}{4}O_2(g) + H^+ + Cl^- = CuCl^0 + \tfrac{1}{2}H_2O(l) \tag{2.102}$$

$$Cu + \tfrac{1}{4}O_2(g) + H^+ + 2Cl^- = CuCl_2^- + \tfrac{1}{2}H_2O(l) \tag{2.103}$$

$$Cu + \tfrac{1}{4}O_2(g) + H^+ + 3Cl^- = CuCl_3^{2-} + \tfrac{1}{2}H_2O(l) \tag{2.104}$$

In order to derive stability constants for Cu(I)-chloride complexes from these data, it is necessary to calculate the equilibrium constant for the reaction:

$$Cu + \tfrac{1}{4}O_2(g) + H^+ = Cu^+ + \tfrac{1}{2}H_2O(l) \tag{2.105}$$

from SUPCRT92, and then subtract reaction (2.105) from reaction (2.102). The values of log β_1 and log β_2 thus obtained are also plotted in Figure 15. The values of log β_2 derived from Xiao et al. (in press) agree comparatively well with the estimates of Ruaya (1988) and measurements of Var'yash (1992). The results of all three studies are in near-perfect agreement at 25°C and 300°C, and deviate a maximum of 1 log unit from one another at intermediate temperatures. The values of log β_1 derived from the measurements of Xiao et al. (in press) deviate by more than an order of magnitude from the previous measurements of Crerar and Barnes (1976), except at higher temperatures where the two data sets appear to converge. There are no previous experimental measurements of log β_3 with which to compare the values of Xiao et al. (in press). Figure 15 illustrates that the estimates of log β_1 and log β_2 produced using the HKF parameters of Sverjensky et al. (1997) are in poor agreement with the experimental data of Xiao et al. (in press). We believe that the experimental results of Xiao et al. (in press) are the best available for Cu(I)-chloride complexes. Therefore, new HKF parameters that take this most recent experimental evidence into account should be derived.

Examination of Figure 15 shows that log β_2 for $CuCl_2^-$ is a U-shaped function of temperature, with a minimum at about 150° to 200°C. This is consistent with the "soft" character of Cu^+ and the "borderline" character of Cl^-. As discussed above, at low temperature, the soft-soft interaction between Cu^+ and Cl^- is driven by an exothermic enthalpy of complexation, resulting in decreasing log β_2 with increasing temperature. However, as temperature is increased further, the interaction switches to hard-hard, which is driven by a positive entropy of complexation, but has an endothermic enthalpy of complexation, resulting in increased log β_2 with increasing temperature.

Romberger and Barnes (1970) measured the solubility of covellite (CuS) in NaHS-H_2S solutions at 25° and 250°C and from these measurements derived stoichiometries for the Cu-bisulfide species present in their solutions, but they did not determine the oxidation state of Cu in the complexes. They assumed that Cu(II) was present,

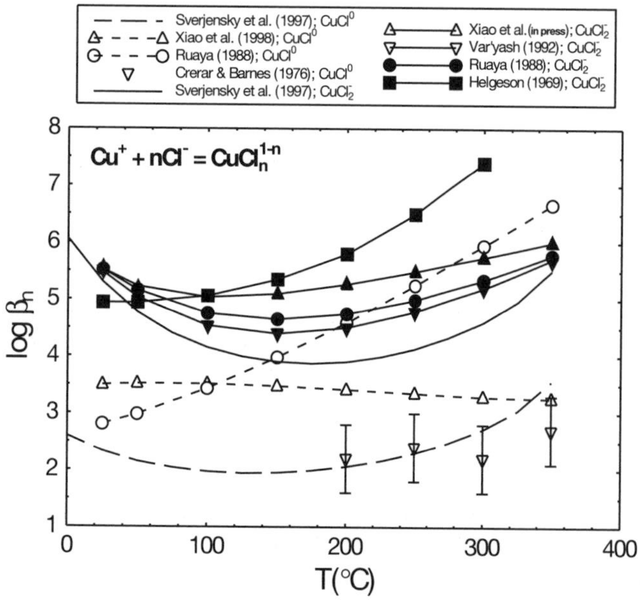

FIG. 15. Plot of log β_n ($CuCl_n^{1-n}$) values from the literature versus temperature at SWVP.

which subsequent spectroscopic and other data indicate is almost certainly an incorrect assumption (Snellgrove and Barnes, 1974; Crerar and Barnes, 1976; Shea and Helz, 1988). Crerar and Barnes (1976) measured the solubility of the assemblage chalcopyrite + pyrite + bornite in NaHS + H_2S solutions from 200° to 350°C, and determined that the important Cu(I)-bisulfide species in their solutions were $Cu(HS)_2^-$ and $Cu(HS)_2(H_2S)^-$. Unlike their solubility experiments in chloride complexation, there is little evidence to suggest that the bisulfide experiments did not reach equilibrium. Crerar and Barnes (1976) determined equilibrium constants for the following reactions:

$$\tfrac{1}{4}Cu_5FeS_4 + HS^- + \tfrac{3}{2}H_2S^0 = \tfrac{1}{4}CuFeS_2 + Cu(HS)_2(H_2S)^- \quad (2.106)$$

$$\tfrac{1}{4}Cu_5FeS_4 + HS^- + \tfrac{1}{2}H_2S^0 = \tfrac{1}{4}CuFeS_2 + Cu(HS)_2^- \quad (2.107)$$

Snellgrove and Barnes (1974) determined that the species $Cu(HS)_3^{2-}$ explained their measurements of the solubilities of CuS and Cu_2S at room temperature, but did not report a stability constant for this complex. Shea and Helz (1988) studied the solubility of covellite in bisulfide/polysulfide solutions at room temperature. They identified the complexes $CuS(HS)_2^{2-}$, $CuS(HS)_3^{3-}$, $Cu(S_5)_2^{3-}$, $Cu(S_4)(S_5)^{3-}$, and $CuS(S_5)^{2-}$ and report stability constants for each of these species. Note that, although the formulation of the species $CuS(HS)_2^{2-}$, $CuS(HS)_3^{3-}$, and $CuS(S_5)^{2-}$ suggests that the formal oxidation state of copper is Cu(II), Shea and Helz (1988) used optical spectroscopy to show that Cu is actually present as Cu(I). They suggest that there is an internal transfer of an electron from S to Cu in these complexes which produces the Cu(I) oxidation state. Helz et al. (1993) presented room-temperature EXAFS evidence that suggests the existence of polynuclear Cu(I)-bisulfide clusters such as $Cu_4(HS)_6^{2-}$.

Thompson and Helz (1994) measured the solubilities of two copper mineral assemblages, chalcocite + djurleite and anilite + covellite at room temperature in bisulfide/polysulfide solutions. They concluded that the species that best represent their solubility results and are consistent with the EXAFS evidence of Helz et al. (1993) for Cu-Cu bonds, are $Cu_3S_4H_3^{2-}$ and $Cu_4S_4H_2^{2-}$. They also reinterpret the measurements of covellite solubility made by Shea and Helz (1988) in terms of the species $Cu_2S_2(HS)_3^{3-}$, $Cu_2(S_3)(S_4)^{2-}$, and $Cu(S_9)(S_{10})^{3-}$ (the latter could also be $Cu_3(S_7)_3^{3-}$). Luther et al. (1996) have used voltammetry to study Cu-sulfide complexation and proposed the existence of species with the stoichiometries CuS^0 and $Cu_2S_3^{2-}$. Finally, very recently, Mountain and Seward (1997) have measured the solubility of Cu_2S(s) in bisulfide solutions at 22°C using a continuous flow apparatus. They have interpreted their data in terms of the following complexation reactions and stability constants:

$$Cu^+ + HS^- = Cu(HS)^0 \qquad \log\beta \approx 12.9 \qquad (2.108)$$

$$Cu^+ + 2HS^- = Cu(HS)_2^- \qquad \log\beta = 16.91 \pm 0.02 \qquad (2.109)$$

$$2Cu^+ + 3HS^- = Cu_2S(HS)_2^{2-} + H^+ \quad \log \beta = 29.83 \pm 0.04 \qquad (2.110)$$

It is evident that the geochemistry of Cu(I) in bisulfide solutions is complex, and there is relatively little agreement among the various studies. For example, the only bisulfide complex proposed in more than one study is $Cu(HS)_2^-$ (Crerar and Barnes, 1976; Mountain and Seward, 1997). Further investigations are required to establish definitively the stoichiometry and thermodynamics of Cu(I) complexes in bisulfide solutions over a wide range of temperature and pressure. A better understanding of these species is warranted because they, together with polysulfide complexes, may be important means of Cu transport under low-temperature, chloride-poor, and sulfide-rich conditions. Furthermore, Cu(I)-bisulfide/polysulfide complexes may represent important reaction intermediates during the precipitation of copper sulfide minerals from hydrothermal solutions.

Var'yash and Rekharskiy (1981) have determined equilibrium constants for the formation of $Cu(OH)^0$ and $Cu(OH)_2^-$ from Cu_2O(s) at 300°C. Their data (see their figure 1) suggest that significant hydrolysis of Cu(I) does not occur until pH > 5 in chloride-free solutions, and hydrolysis will be delayed to higher pH in the presence of chloride or at lower temperatures. Var'yash and Rekharskiy (1982) interpreted solubility measurements of Cu_2O(s) in chloride solutions from 25° to 250°C and pH = 5.5 to 10.5 in terms of a mixed hydroxychloride complex, $CuClOH^-$, but as mentioned above, Var'yash (1992) reinterpreted these data in terms of $CuCl_2^-$, so there is little experimental basis for the existence of mixed hydroxy chloride complexes at elevated temperatures.

Thus, it can be concluded that mass transfer of Cu(I) in most hydrothermal solutions will be accomplished via chloride complexation, and the most important chloride complex is likely to be $CuCl_2^-$ (according to Xiao et al., in press). Bisulfide or polysulfide complexes may play a role in certain limited environments, but there is still considerable uncertainty in both the stoichiometries and thermodynamics of these complexes. Finally, complexes with hard ligands such as carbonate, bicarbonate, hydroxide, fluoride, and sulfate can usually be neglected in most solubility calculations.

Silver. The Ag^+ ion is a soft ion, although not as soft as Au^+. Consequently, we would expect complexes of Ag^+ with chloride to be more important, and those with bisulfide to be less important, than the corresponding Au(I) complexes. There have been several studies of the stability of Ag(I)-chloride complexes ($AgCl^0$, $AgCl_2^-$, $AgCl_3^{2-}$) under hydrothermal conditions (e.g., Seward, 1976; Zotov et al., 1987; Levin, 1991; Gammons and Williams-Jones, 1995) and thermodynamic data have been measured up to 350°C at SWVP. These studies are in comparatively good agreement (see discussion by Gammons and Seward, 1996), and indicate that Ag chloride complexes are responsible for silver transport in a wide variety of hydrothermal environments. The HKF parameters for Ag-chloride complexes employed by SUPCRT92 and tabulated by Sverjensky et al. (1997), are based on the experimental data of Seward (1976) and are recommended for use in calculations involving these complexes.

The thermodynamics of Ag(I)-bisulfide complexes have been determined at 20°C and 1 bar by Schwarzenbach et al. (1958) and Schwarzenbach and Widmer (1966), at 25° to 250°C and SWVP by Sugaki et al. (1987), at 200° to 350°C and SWVP by Wood et al. (1987), and at 25° to 300°C and SWVP by Gammons and Barnes (1989). The most comprehensive study is that by Gammons and Barnes (1989), who suggest that $AgHS^0$ and $Ag(HS)_2^-$ are the predominant Ag-bisulfide complexes in acidic and near-neutral to slightly basic solutions, respectively. Gammons and Barnes (1989) provide equilibrium constants (their table 4) for the following reaction from 25° to 350°C:

$$\tfrac{1}{2}Ag_2S + \tfrac{1}{2}H_2S(aq) + HS^- = Ag(HS)_2^- \qquad (2.111)$$

These data are in good agreement with those derived by Schwarzenbach and Widmer (1966) at 25°C and those calculated by Gammons and Barnes (1989) from the solubility data of Melent'yev et al. (1969). Sverjensky et al. (1997) provide parameters for the HKF equation for $Ag(HS)_2^-$ based on correlation algorithms. However, values of log K for reaction (2.111) calculated using these parameters and thermodynamic data from SUPCRT92 deviate increasingly with rising temperature from those measured by Gammons and Barnes (1989), such that, at 300°C, the former is nearly 0.5 log units higher than the latter. Based on solubility data from Sugaki et al. (1987), Wood et al. (1987), and Melent'yev et al. (1969), Gammons and Barnes (1989) suggest that $AgHS^0$ is the predominant silver species in acidic sulfide solutions. However, they could not rule out the possibility that colloidal Ag_2S might have been sampled in the acid pH range in the above experiments. Sugaki et al. (1987) have proposed that polynuclear species (i.e., $Ag_2S(H_2S)^0$, $Ag_2S(H_2S)(HS)^-$, $Ag_2S(H_2S)(HS)_2^{2-}$, and $Ag_2S(HS)_2^{2-}$), are the predominant Ag-bisulfide complexes. Although this possibility cannot be excluded, evidence for these species is weak.

In addition to the species mentioned above, experiments have been conducted concerning the existence, and in some cases the stability, of the following aqueous silver species in hydrothermal solution: Ag^0 (Kozlov and Khodakovskiy, 1984; Zotov et al., 1986); $AgCl_2OH^{2-}$ and $AgClOH^-$ (Zotov et al., 1982); $AgOH^0$ and $Ag(OH)_2^-$ (Kozlov et al., 1983); and $AgCO_3^-$, $Ag(CO_3)_2^{3-}$, $Ag(OH)CO_3^{2-}$, and $Ag(OH)_2(CO_3)_2^{3-}$ (Kozlov, 1985). However, either the existence of these species remains controversial, (e.g., Ag^0; (Kozlov and Khodakovskiy, 1984; Zotov et al., 1986), or calculations show that these species cannot compete with chloride or bisulfide complexes in most hydrothermal solutions. Thiosulfate ($S_2O_3^{2-}$) or sulfite (SO_3^{2-}) may complex Ag in low-temperature oxidizing environments (Webster, 1986), but are not likely to be important at elevated temperatures owing to the metastability of these ligands. Telluride (Te^{2-}), thioarsenic, and thioantimony complexes with Ag(I) remain untested. Ammonia complexes are known to be relatively strong at room temperature (Maeda et al., 1979, 1983), and some limited thermodynamic data exist for these species at elevated temperatures (Kozlowska-Kolodziej and Bartecki, 1973). Gammons and Yu (1997) measured stability constants of Ag(I)-bromide and iodide complexes at 150° to 300°C, and compiled and critically evaluated all available data to provide a complete set of data for the chloride, bromide, and iodide complexes. They concluded that Ag(I)-iodide complexes may be important in iodide-rich sedimentary basin brines, and that in some cases, AgI(s) and AgBr(s) may limit Ag(I) concentrations.

Mercury. The hydrothermal geochemistry of mercury has been reviewed by a number of authors (Varekamp and Buseck, 1984; Krupp, 1988b; Wells and Ghiorso, 1988; Barnes and Seward, 1997; Fein and Williams-Jones, 1997; and references therein). Mercury, as Hg(II) in aqueous solutions, is extremely soft and is expected to bond preferentially with bisulfide and heavy halide (bromide, iodide) ligands. As a result, a large number of studies have focused on understanding the solubility of mercury minerals in bisulfide solutions and/or the stoichiometry and thermodynamics of Hg(II)-bisulfide complexes (Schwarzenbach and Widmer, 1963; Cooney and Hall, 1966; Barnes et al., 1967; Khodakovskiy et al., 1975; Shikina et al., 1982; Yefremova et al., 1982). Barnes et al. (1967) proposed the existence of the complexes $HgS{\cdot}2H_2S$, $Hg(HS)_3^-$, $HgS(HS)_2^{2-}$, and HgS_2^{2-} based on solubility studies at very high sulfide concentrations ($\Sigma S = 0.38$–3.7 molal). On the other hand, starting with Schwarzenbach and Widmer (1963), most authors have recognized only the species $Hg(HS)_2^0$, $HgS(HS)^-$, and HgS_2^{2-}. It is evident that Barnes et al. (1967) observed the species $HgS{\cdot}2H_2S$, $Hg(HS)_3^-$, and $HgS(HS)_2^{2-}$ as a result of their use of higher ΣS values than most other workers. Krupp (1988b) has pointed out that $HgS{\cdot}2H_2S$, $Hg(HS)_3^-$, and $HgS(HS)_2^{2-}$ are only stable under geologically unreasonable conditions, and are therefore not likely to be important in geological environments. Khodakovskiy et al. (1975), Shikina et al. (1982), and Yefremova et al. (1982) have determined equilibrium constants for one or more of the following reactions:

$$HgS(cinnabar) + OH^- + HS^- = HgS_2^{2-} + H_2O(l) \qquad (2.112)$$

$$HgS(cinnabar) + HS^- = HgS(HS)^- \qquad (2.113)$$

$$HgS(cinnabar) + H_2S^0 = Hg(HS)_2^0 \qquad (2.114)$$

Schwarzenbach and Widmer (1963) reported equilibrium constants for 25°C for analogs of each of the above reactions involving metacinnabar. Krupp (1988b) recalculated the data of Schwarzenbach and Widmer (1963) in terms of cinnabar. He then fitted a function of the form, $pK = -\log K = A/T(K) + B$, to all the available data for each of the above three reactions. The values calculated from these equations are shown in figure 1 of Krupp (1988b) along with the experimental values of log K on which these equations are based. However, there must be a typographical error in Krupp's (1988b) equation for reaction (2.113), because this equation does not reproduce the corresponding line shown in his figure 1. There is comparatively good agreement among the various studies and in addition, Krupp's equations (except for reaction 2.113) fit the data well. Furthermore, the existence of the species HgS_2^{2-} has been firmly established by Raman spectroscopy (Cooney and Hall, 1966).

The stability of carbonate, bicarbonate, and hydroxycarbonate complexes of Hg(II) have been studied at room temperature by Hietanen and Högfeldt (1976) and Khodakovskiy and Shikina (1981). The latter authors have shown that such complexes are probably not important in the hydrothermal mass transfer of Hg. It is also generally accepted that chloride and simple hydroxide complexes of Hg(II) are not significant in the relatively dilute fluids often characteristic of epithermal Hg deposits (Barnes, 1979; Varekamp and Buseck, 1984; Krupp, 1988b). Based on experimental studies, Kuznetsov et al. (1973) propose that mercury may be transported in sulfide-poor, chloride-rich fluids as chloride complexes, but their experiments are qualitative and do not unambiguously demonstrate the presence of significant chloride complexation. To our knowledge, there are no experimentally-determined stability constants available for Hg(II)-chloride complexes at elevated temperatures, but theoretical estimates of these are available in Helgeson (1969) and Sverjensky et al. (1997). These complexes could play a role in Hg mass transfer in very chloride-rich brines.

The solubility of Hg vapor in hydrothermal solutions has been studied by Glew and Hames (1971, 1972), Sorokin (1973), and Clever et al. (1985). The relatively high solubilities measured have led to the suggestion that mercury can be transported in hydrothermal solutions as hydrated elemental mercury, i.e., Hg^0 (Varekamp and Buseck, 1984; Shikina et al., 1986; Krupp, 1988b). Clever et al. (1985) summarize solubility data for Hg^0 in water up to 500°C. The data of Glew and Hames (1971, 1972) show that dissolved salts decrease Hg^0 solubility in solutions at temperatures below 50°C, but its solubility is increased by dissolved salts at higher temperatures. Krupp (1988b) further argues that mercury could be transported as Hg^0 in a liquid hydrocarbon phase under some ore-forming conditions, based on experimental data of Okouchi and Sasaki (1981). Fein and Williams-Jones (1997) quantitatively tested the latter hypothesis by extrapolating experimental data for the solubility of Hg in hydrocarbons (Clever and Iwamoto, 1987) from 63° to 150°C, and concluded that Hg transport in a liquid hydrocarbon phase is a very effective means of Hg transport in hydrothermal environments. Subsequently, Williams-Jones and Fein (pers. commun., 1998) have confirmed the results of their extrapolations with a series of measurements of the solubility of Hg in dodecane at temperatures up to 200°C.

We summarize the possibilities for Hg transport in hydrothermal solutions as follows (see also Krupp, 1988b; Fein and Williams-Jones, 1997): (1) carbonate, bicarbonate, hydroxide, and chloride complexes probably do not play important roles in most hydrothermal ore-forming environments, (2) significant quantities of Hg may be transported as sulfide complexes in neutral to alkaline, sulfide-rich ($\geq 10^{-2}$ m), moderately reducing, and moderately hot (>200°C) fluids, (3) aqueous elemental mercury Hg^0 may be important in sulfide-poor fluids, (4) transport as the vapor phase Hg(g) may occur under reducing, low-pressure conditions, (5) transport as elemental mercury Hg^0 in a liquid hydrocarbon phase may occur under sulfide-poor, organic-rich, reducing conditions, and (6) ammonia, thiosulfate, and polysulfide ligands may have limited roles in Hg transport, but no data are available by which to assess this.

Gold. The Au^+ ion is the prime example of a soft metal ion, and should strongly prefer soft ligands, such as bisulfide. This is borne out by considerable experimental evidence that gold is transported predominantly as bisulfide complexes in mildly oxidizing to reducing hydrothermal solutions over a wide range of pH and temperature (Seward, 1973, 1983; Renders and Seward, 1989; Shenberger and Barnes, 1989; Gibert et al., 1993; Pan and Wood, 1994; Benning and Seward, 1996; and references therein). It is now very well established that the predominant Au(I)-bisulfide complexes are $AuHS^0$ at acidic pH, $Au(HS)_2^-$ at weakly acidic to weakly basic pH and (Seward, 1973; Shenberger and Barnes, 1989; Benning and Seward, 1996). The experimental equilibrium constants of Benning and Seward (1996) for the following two reactions:

$$Au(s) + H_2S^0 = AuHS^0 + \tfrac{1}{2} H_2(g) \qquad (2.115)$$

$$Au(s) + H_2S^0 + HS^- = Au(HS)_2^- + \tfrac{1}{2} H_2(g) \qquad (2.116)$$

cover a wide range of temperature (150°–500°C) and pressure (500–1500 bars); they also extrapolated their data to SWVP (see their tables 2 and 3). Benning and Seward (1996) carefully demonstrated the attainment of equilibrium and avoided depending on the equilibration of solid redox buffers by using $H_2(g)$ to control f_{O_2}. Their data agree well with those of Seward (1973). The equilibrium constants of Shenberger and Barnes (1989) for reaction (2.116) at SWVP from 150° to 350°C differ from those of Benning and Seward's (1996) extrapolated values by approximately ±1 log unit, which the latter attribute to incomplete attainment of redox equilibrium in the study of Shenberger and Barnes (1989). Equilibrium constants for reaction (2.116) obtained by Gibert et al. (1993) differ by up to 2 log units from those of Benning and Seward (1996). Possible reasons for these discrepancies include uncertainties in the thermodynamic database for the mineral assemblage employed by Gibert et al. (1993), and/or different values of the H_2S^0 dissociation constant employed in the various studies (Benning and Seward, 1996). The values of the dissociation constant of H_2S employed by Benning and Seward (1996) are inconsistent with those employed by SUPCRT92 or Sverjensky et al. (1997), and, consequently, log K values for reaction (2.116) calculated from equation parameters given by Sverjensky et al. (1997) are inconsistent with the experimental values obtained by Benning and Seward (1996). Also, the log K value calculated by Sverjensky et al. (1997; see their fig. 28) for reaction (2.116) at 25°C and 1 bar is approximately one log unit higher than the only experimentally-derived value, that of Renders and Seward (1989). We believe that the Renders and Seward (1989) and Benning and Seward (1996) experiments are probably the most reliable for the reasons outlined above. Therefore the inconsistency between their data and the database of Sverjensky et al. (1997) should be resolved, which ostensibly requires agreement on a single set of values for the first dissociation constant of H_2S. New measurements of this quantity have been reported recently by Suleimenov and Seward (1997). Meanwhile, we recommend the use of the thermodynamic data from Renders and Seward (1989) and Benning and Seward (1996) for reactions (2.115) and (2.116) above, over the entire pressure and temperature range studied by these authors.

There has been considerable debate about the relative importance of Au chloride complexes in the hydrothermal transport of gold (Henley, 1973; Rytuba and Dickson, 1974; Wood et al., 1987; Zotov and Baranova, 1989; Zotov et al., 1990, 1991; Hayashi and Ohmoto, 1991; Gammons and Williams-Jones, 1995; Gammons et al., 1997). Substantial uncertainty in the thermodynamics of Au(I) chloride complexes, owing to the difficulty of making the measurements, has contributed to this debate. A reliable, complete, experimentally-based set of data for Au(I) chloride complexes, covering a wide range of pressure and temperature, is lacking. Most studies have focused on the equilibrium constant for the reaction:

$$Au(s) + 2Cl^- + H^+ = AuCl_2^- + \tfrac{1}{2} H_2(g) \qquad (2.117)$$

The most reliable values of equilibrium constants for this reaction have been measured by Nikolaeva et al. (1972) at 25° to 100°C and SWVP, Gammons and Williams-Jones (1995) at 300°C and SWVP, and by Zotov et al. (1991) at 400° to 500°C and 0.5, 1.0, and 1.5 kbars. Together these studies cover a wide range of pressure and temperature, although with considerable gaps in coverage. More importantly, the equilibrium constants for reaction (2.117) measured in all three of these studies all appear to be reasonably consistent with one another, and are in remarkably good agreement with the theoretical estimates of Helgeson (1969) (cf. fig. 10 in Gammons and Williams-Jones, 1995) and of Sverjensky et al. (1997; their fig. 28). Rytuba and Dickson (1974) and Hayashi and Ohmoto (1991) did not derive equilibrium constants from their solubility data, but their results are qualitatively consistent with the stability constants measured in the three studies mentioned above. Also, experimental study of the disproportionation reaction

$$3AuCl_2^- = 2Au(s) + AuCl_4^- + 2Cl^- \qquad (2.118)$$

by Gammons et al. (1997) at 100° to 200°C yields equilibrium constants in excellent agreement with those determined by Nikolaeva et al. (1972) from 25° to 80°C, which further supports the validity of the abovementioned thermodynamic data for the $AuCl_2^-$ complex. Much higher solubilities of gold as the $AuCl_2^-$ complex than those indicated by the above studies are implied by the work of Henley (1973) and Wood et al. (1987), but it now seems clear that these studies suffered from a number of problems that render the measured solubilities questionable. Owing to the lack of a complete, experimentally-derived data set for $AuCl_2^-$, and because they agree with the most reliable experimentally derived data available, we recommend use of the estimates of Sverjensky et al. (1997). Note that almost no reliable thermodynamic data are available for the Au(I) chloride complex, $AuCl^0$, nor for possible mixed Au(I)-hydroxychloride complexes (also little solid evidence has been obtained for their very existence). However, Sverjensky et al. (1997) provide estimates of the equilibrium constant for the reaction:

$$Au(s) + Cl^- + H^+ + \tfrac{1}{4}\,O_2 = AuCl^0 + \tfrac{1}{2}\,H_2O(l) \tag{2.119}$$

The Au(I) chloride complexes are considered to be more important than Au(III) chloride complexes for Au transport in most hydrothermal solutions (Seward, 1983). It has been well established that Au(III) chloride complexes such as $AuCl_4^-$ predominate at lower temperatures, and the Au(I) chloride complexes predominate at higher temperatures (Pan and Wood, 1991; Gammons and Williams-Jones, 1995; Gammons et al., 1997). Thus, there is a possibility of Au transport as $AuCl_4^-$ in low-temperature, highly oxidized and acidic fluids (e.g., Jaireth, 1992), but under less oxidizing conditions, especially at higher temperatures, Au(I) chloride complexes should predominate over Au(III) chloride complexes. Thus, the picture of gold speciation which emerges is the following: Au(III) chloride complexes will predominate under conditions of high chloride activity, low temperature, low pH, and high oxygen fugacity (i.e, near-surface conditions); Au(I) chloride complexes will be important at high chloride activity, high temperature, low pH, and moderately high oxygen fugacity; and Au(I)-bisulfide complexes will predominate over a wide temperature and pH range under mildly oxidizing to reducing conditions (i.e., most hydrothermal Au-transporting environments). Under comparatively oxidizing, near-neutral to basic conditions, and in the absence of bisulfide or chloride, Au(I)-hydroxide (Zotov et al., 1985; Vlassopoulos and Wood, 1990) or mixed Au(III)-hydroxychloride (Peck et al., 1991; Farges et al., 1993; Sharps et al., 1993) complexes may dominate Au speciation.

Other ligands that may have limited roles in gold transport include (1) thiosulfate and sulfite (Webster, 1986), which are probably limited to low-temperature, near-surface environments, (2) polysulfide (Berndt et al., 1994), (3) telluride, thioarsenic, and thioantimony species such as AsS_2^- or SbS_2^- (Nekrasov and Konyushok, 1982; Nekrasov et al., 1982; Seward, 1983), and (4) ammonia (Skibsted and Bjerrum, 1974; Wood et al., 1992). The possibilities under (3) have not been adequately tested, nor are thermodynamic data available for such species. Berndt et al. (1994) provide preliminary experimental thermodynamic data for Au-polysulfide complexes at 100° to 150°C and 100 bars. Their data suggest that these complexes may play a role in solutions saturated with respect to native sulfur at relatively low temperatures. Wood et al. (1992) provide theoretical estimates of the stability constants for the $Au(NH_3)_2^+$ complexes at elevated temperatures, but these may be subject to large errors. The cyanide complex, $Au(CN)_2^-$, has a very high stability constant (Seward, 1983), hence the use of cyanide in heap leaching operations to recover gold. However, cyanide is a metastable species even at room temperature and it is expected that it will rapidly break down at elevated temperatures, and is thus not likely to be important in hydrothermal gold mass transfer.

Concluding Remarks

In this chapter we have illustrated how to (1) carry out solubility and speciation calculations, (2) make a rational choice of which species to include in a given model, and (3) estimate data not available in the literature. We have also provided a detailed review of the data that are available, and shown the reader, by example, how to critically evaluate experimental data. Armed with these tools, readers should be capable of carrying out their own calculations with a reasonable degree of confidence. We have purposely avoided including a large number of solubility and speciation diagrams that readers could try to adapt to their own needs. The practice of "borrowing" such diagrams or other generalizations regarding ore transport and solubility is dangerous and one we hope this chapter (together with Chapters 1, 3, 4 and 5) will help eradicate. If we have done our job properly, we should see an increased number of articles on ore deposit genesis that include "home-made" solubility and speciation calculations. Our chapter also illustrates that, in spite of significant progress in understanding ore transport and solubility, much remains to be done. We hope that this will stimulate geochemists to continue and expand such studies. We also hope that this chapter will provide economic geologists with a deeper appreciation of the role experimental studies and thermodynamic modeling play in the development of genetic models for ore deposits.

Acknowledgments

We gratefully acknowledge financial support from a NATO Collaborative Research Grant. Insightful reviews of an earlier version of the manuscript were provided by Bill Bourcier, Chris Gammons, and Anthony (Willy) Williams-Jones. The manuscript also benefited from comments by Greg Anderson and Jeremy Richards.

REFERENCES

Ahrland, S., 1968, Thermodynamics of complex formation between hard and soft acceptors and donors: Structural Bonding, v. 5, p. 118–149.

—— 1973, Thermodynamics of stepwise formation of metal-ion complexes in aqueous solution: Structural Bonding, v. 15, p. 167–188.

Akinfiyev, N.N., Zotov, A.V., and Nikonorov, A.P., 1992, Thermodynamic analysis of equilibria in the system As(III)-S(II)-O-H: Geochemistry International, v. 29, p. 109–121.

Anderson, G.M., 1962, The solubility of PbS in H_2S-water solutions: Economic Geology, v. 70, p. 809–828.

—— 1977, Uncertainties in calculations involving thermodynamic data, *in* Greenwood, H.J., ed., Application of thermodynamics to petrology and ore deposits: Mineralogical Association of Canada Short Course, v. 2, p. 199–215.

—— 1995, Is there alkali-aluminum complexing at high temperatures and pressures: Geochimica et Cosmochimica Acta, v. 59, p. 2155–2161.

Anderson, G.M., and Cermignani, C., 1991, Mineralogical and thermodynamic constraints on the metasomatic origin of the York River gneisses, Bancroft, Ontario: The Canadian Mineralogist, v. 29, p. 965–980.

Anderson, G.M., and Crerar, D.A., 1993, Thermodynamics in geochemistry: The equilibrium model: Oxford, Oxford University Press, 588 p.

Anderson, G.M., Castet, S., Schott, J., and Mesmer, R.E., 1991, The density model for estimation of thermodynamic parameters of reactions at high temperatures and pressures: Geochimica et Cosmochimica Acta, v. 55, p. 1769–1779.

Ashurst, K.G., 1976, The thermodynamics of the formation of chlorocomplexes of iron(III), cobalt(II), iron(II), manganese(II), and copper(II) in perchlorate medium: National Institute of Metallurgy of South Africa Report No. 1820, 44 pp.

Baes, C.F., Jr., and Mesmer, R.E., 1976, The hydrolysis of cations: New York, Wiley-Interscience. 489 p.

Ballantyne, J.M., and Moore, J.N., 1988, Arsenic geochemistry in geothermal systems: Geochimica et Cosmochimica Acta, v. 52, p. 475–483.

Baranova, N.N., 1968, Composition of lead carbonate complexes and their dissociation constants at 25°, 250° and 300°C: Geochemistry International, v. 5, p. 13–20.

Baranova, N.N., and Barsukov, V.L., 1965, Transport of lead by hydrothermal solutions in the form of carbonate complexes: Geochemistry International, v. 2, p. 802–809.

Barnes, H.L., 1979, Solubilities of ore minerals, *in* Barnes, H.L., ed., Geochemistry of hydrothermal ore deposits, 2nd. ed.: New York, Wiley-Interscience, p. 404–460.

Barnes, H.L., and Seward, T.M., 1997, Geothermal systems and mercury deposits, *in* Barnes, H.L., ed., Geochemistry of hydrothermal ore deposits, 3rd. ed.: New York, Wiley, p. 699–736.

Barnes, H.L., Romberger, S.B., and Stemprok, M., 1967, Ore solution chemistry. II: Solubility of HgS in sulfide solutions: Economic Geology, v. 62, p. 957–982.

Barrett, T.J., and Anderson, G.M., 1982, The solubility of sphalerite and galena in NaCl brines: Economic Geology, v. 77, p. 1923–1933.

—— 1988, The solubility of sphalerite and galena in 1–5 m NaCl solutions to 300°C: Geochimica et Cosmochimica Acta, v. 52, p. 813–820.

Baumann, J.E., 1981, Information circular: U.S. Bureau of Mines, n. 8853, p. 268.

Benning, L.G., and Seward, T.M., 1996, Hydrosulphide complexing of Au(I) in hydrothermal solutions from 150°–400°C and 500°–1500 bar: Geochimica et Cosmochimica Acta, v. 60, p. 1849–1871.

Berndt, M.E., Buttram, T., Early, D., III, and Seyfried, W.E., Jr., 1994, The stability of gold polysulfide complexes in aqueous sulfide solutions: 100° to 150°C and 100 bars: Geochimica et Cosmochimica Acta, v. 58, p. 587–594.

Bethke, C.M., 1992, The question of uniqueness in geochemical modeling: Geochimica et Cosmochimica Acta, v. 56, p. 4315–4320.

Boctor, N.Z., 1985, Rhodonite solubility and thermodynamic properties of aqueous $MnCl_2$ in the system MnO-SiO_2-HCl-H_2O: Geochimica et Cosmochimica Acta, v. 49, p. 565–575.

Boctor, N.Z., and Frantz, J.D., 1980, Mineral-solution equilibria in the system Mn_3O_4-H_2O-HCl: Carnegie Institute of Washington Yearbook, v. 79, p. 345–347.

Boctor, N.Z., Popp, R.K., and Frantz, J.D., 1980, Mineral-solution equilibria, IV: Solubilities and the thermodynamic properties of $FeCl_2^0$ in the system Fe_2O_3-H_2-H_2O-HCl: Geochimica et Cosmochimica Acta, v. 44, p. 1509–1518.

Born, von M., 1920, Volumen und hydratationswärme der ionen: Zeitschrift für Physik, v. 1, p. 45–48.

Böttcher, M.E., and Usdowski, E., 1990, An estimation of dissociation constants for Mn(II) complexes in aqueous solutions to 300°C: Zeitschrift für Physik und Chemie, Neue Folge, v. 167, p. 81–86.

Bourcier, W.L., and Barnes, H.L., 1987, Ore solution chemistry—VII. Stabilities of chloride and bisulfide complexes of zinc to 350°C: Economic Geology, v. 82, p. 1839–1863.

Bowers, T., Jackson, K., and Helgeson, H.C., 1984, Equilibrium Activity diagrams: New York, Elsevier Press, 397 p.

Brimhall, G.H., and Crerar, D.A., 1987, Ore fluids: magmatic to supergene, *in* Carmichael, I.S.E., and Eugtser, H.P., eds., Thermodynamic modeling of geological materials: Minerals, fluids, and melts: Reviews in Mineralogy, v. 17, p. 235–322.

Candela, P.A., and Holland, H.D., 1984, The partitioning of copper and molybdenum between silicate melts and aqueous fluids: Geochimica et Cosmochimca Acta, v. 48, p. 373–380.

Cantrell, K.J., and Byrne, R.H., 1987, Rare earth element complexation by carbonate and oxalate ions: Geochimica et Cosmochimica Acta, v. 51, p. 597–605.

Cao, X., 1989, Solubility of molybdenite and the speciation of molybdenum in hydrothermal solutions: Unpublished Ph.D. thesis, Ames, Iowa, Iowa State University, 102 p.

Chou, I-M, and Eugster, H.P., 1977, Solubility of magnetite in supercritical chloride solutions: American Journal of Science, v. 277, p. 1296–1314.

Clever, H.L., and Iwamoto, M., 1987, Solubility of mercury in normal alkanes: Industrial Engineering Chemistry Research, v. 26, p. 336–337.

Clever, H.L., Johnson, S.A., and Derrick, M.E., 1985, The solubility of mercury and some sparingly soluble mercury salts in water and aqueous electrolyte solutions: Journal of Physical Chemical Reference Data, v. 14, p. 631–680.

Cobble, J.W., Murray, R.C., Jr, Turner, P.J., and Chen, K., 1982, High-temperature data for species in aqueous solution: Electric Power Research Institute Report No. NP-2400, 200 p.

Cooney, R.P.J., and Hall, J.R., 1966, Raman spectrum of thiomercurate(II) ion: Australian Journal of Chemistry, v. 19, p. 2179–2180.

Crerar, D.A., 1975, A method for computing multicomponent equilibria based on equilibrium constants: Geochimica et Cosmochimica Acta, v. 39, p. 1375–1384.

Crerar, D.A., and Barnes, H.L., 1976, Ore solution chemistry V: Solubilities of chalcopyrite and chalcocite assemblages in hydrothermal solution at 200° to 350°C: Economic Geology, v. 71, p. 772–794.

Crerar, D.A., Susak, N.J., Borcsik, M., and Schwartz, S., 1978, Solubility of the buffer assemblage pyrite + pyrrhotite + magnetite in NaCl solutions from 200° to 350°C: Geochimica et Cosmochimica Acta, v. 42, p. 1427–1437.

Crerar, D.A., Wood, S.A., Brantley, S., and Bocarsly, A., 1985, Chemical controls on the solubility of ore-forming minerals in hydrothermal solutions: Canadian Mineralogist, v. 23, p. 333–352.

Criaud, A., and Fouillac, C., 1986, Étude des eaux thermominérales carbogazeuses du Massif Central Français. II: Comportement de quelques métaux en trace, de l'arsenic, de l'antimoine et du germanium: Geochimica et Cosmochimica Acta, v. 50, p. 1573–1582.

Cygan, G.L., Hemley, J.J., and D'Angelo, W.M., 1994, An experimental study of zinc chloride speciation from 300° to 600°C and 0.5 to 2.0 kbar in buffered hydrothermal solutions: Geochimica et Cosmochimica Acta, v. 58, p. 4841–4855.

Czamanske, G.K., 1959, Sulfide solubility in aqueous solutions: Economic Geology, v. 54, p. 57–63.

Daskalakis, K.D., and Helz, G.R., 1993, The solubility of sphalerite (ZnS) in sulfidic solutions at 25°C and 1 atm. pressure: Geochimica et Cosmochimica Acta, v. 57, p. 4923–4931.

Ding, K., and Seyfried, W.E., Jr., 1992, Determination of Fe-Cl complexing in the low pressure supercritical region (NaCl fluid): Iron solubility constraints on pH of seafloor hydrothermal fluids: Geochimica et Cosmochimica Acta, v. 56, p. 3681–3692.

Dyrssen, D.W., 1991, Comment on "Solubility of sphalerite in aqueous sulfide solutions at temperatures between 25° and 240°C" by K. Hayashi, A. Sugaki, and A. Kitakaze: Geochimica et Cosmochimica Acta, v. 55, p. 2683–2684.

Eadington, P.J., and Giblin, A., 1979, Alteration minerals and the precipitation of tin in granitic rocks: CSIRO, Division Mineralogy, Technical Communications, 37 p.

Eadington, P.J., and Kinealy, K., 1983, Some aspects of the hydrothermal reactions of tin during skarn formation: Journal of the Geological Society of Australia, v. 30, p. 461–471.

Eary, L.E., 1992, The solubility of amorphous As_2S_3 from 25° to 90°: Geochimica et Cosmochimica Acta, v. 56, p. 2267–2280.

Egorov, A.M., and Titova, Z.P., 1962, Temperature dependence of solubility products of salts with polyatomic ions: Russian Journal of Inorganic Chemistry, v. 7, p. 141–142.

Eugster, H.P., 1985, Granites and hydrothermal ore deposits: A geochemical framework: Mineralogical Magazine, v. 49, p. 7–23.

—— 1986, Minerals in hot water: American Mineralogist, v. 71, p. 655–673.

Farges, F., Sharps, J.A., and Brown, G.E., Jr., 1993, Local environment around gold(III) in aqueous chloride solutions: An EXAFS spectroscopy study: Geochimica et Cosmochimica Acta, v. 57, p. 1243–1252.

Faucherre, M.J., and Bonnaire, J., 1959, Sur la constitution des carbonates complexes de cuivre et de plomb: Académie des Science [Paris] Comptes Rendus, v. 248, p. 26.

Fein, J.B., and Williams-Jones, A.E., 1997, The role of mercury-organic interactions in the hydrothermal transport of mercury: Economic Geology, v. 92, p. 20–28.

Fein, J.B., Hemley, J.J., D'Angelo, W.M., Komninou, A. and Sverjensky, D.A., 1992, Experimental study of iron-chloride complexing in hydrothermal fluids: Geochimica et Cosmochimica Acta, v. 56, p. 3179–3190.

Fulton, J.W., and Swinehart, D.F., 1954, The equilibria of crystalline zinc hydroxide in dilute hydrochloric acid and sodium hydroxide at 25: The first and second acidic dissociation constants of zinc hydroxide: Journal of the American Chemical Society, v. 76, p. 864–867.

Galkin, A.V., Shironosova, G.P., and Kolonin, G.R., 1989, Hydrothermal γ-tracer technique and study of tungsten minerals solubility [abs.]: Third International Symposium on Hydrothermal Reactions, September 12–15, 1989, Frunze, Kirghizia, Program and Abstracts, p. 31.

Gammons, C.H., and Barnes, H.L., 1989, The solubility of Ag_2S in near neutral aqueous sulfide solutions at 25° to 300°C: Geochimica et Cosmochimica Acta, v. 53, p. 279–290.

Gammons, C.H., and Seward, T.M., 1996, Stability of manganese(II) chloride complexes from 25° to 300°C: Geochimica et Cosmochimica Acta, v. 60, p. 4295–4311.

Gammons, C.H., and Williams-Jones, A.E., 1995, The solubility of Au–Ag alloy + AgCl in HCl/NaCl solutions at 300°C: New data on the stability of Au(I) chloride complexes in hydrothermal solutions: Geochimica et Cosmochimica Acta, v. 59, p. 3453–3468.

Gammons, C.H., and Yu, Y., 1997, The stability of aqueous silver bromide and iodide complexes at 25°-300°C: Experiments, theory and geologic applications: Chemical Geology, v. 137, p. 155–173.

Gammons, C.H., Yu, Y., and Williams-Jones, A.E., 1997, The disproportionation of gold(I) chloride complexes at 25° to 200°C: Geochimica et Cosmochimica Acta, v. 61, p. 1971–1984.

Gibert, F., Moine, B., Schott, J., and Dandurand, J.-L., 1992, Modeling of the transport and deposition of tungsten in the scheelite-bearing calc-silicate gneisses of the Montagne Noire, France: Contributions to Mineralogy and Petrology, v. 112, p. 371–384.

Gibert, F., Pascal, M.-L., and Pichavant, M., 1993, Solubility of gold in KCl (0.5 m) solutions under hydrothermal conditions (350°–450°C, 500 bars), *in* Cuney, M., and Cathelineau, M., eds., Proceedings of the 4th International Symposium on Hydrothermal Reactions: Institut Lorrain des Geosciences, Nancy, France, p. 65–68.

Giordano, T.H., and Barnes, H.L., 1979, Ore solution chemistry, VI: PbS solubility in bisulfide solutions to 300°C: Economic Geology, v. 74, p. 1637–1646.

Giridhar, J., and Langmuir, D., 1991, Determination of E^0 for the UO_2^{2+}/U^{4+} couple from measurement of the equilibrium: UO_2^{2+} + Cu(s) + $4H^+$ = U^{4+} + Cu^{2+} + $2H_2O$ at 25°C: Radiochimica Acta, v. 54, p. 133–138.

Glew, D.N., and Hames, D.A., 1971, Aqueous nonelectrolyte solutions: Part X. Mercury solubility in water: Canadian Journal of Chemistry, v. 49, p. 3114–3118.

—— 1972, Aqueous nonelectrolyte solutions: Part XI. Mercury solubility in 6.10 molal sodium chloride: Canadian Journal of Chemistry, v. 50, p. 3124–3128.

Grenthe, I., and Wanner, H., 1989, Guidelines for the extrapolation to zero ionic strength: Giv-sur Yvette, France, Report NEA-TDB-2.1, F-91191. OECD, Nuclear Energy Agency Data Bank.

Gu, Y., 1993, Theoretical and experimental studies of the hydrothermal geochemistry of molybdenum: Unpublished Ph.D. thesis, Clayton, Victoria, Australia, Monash University, 170 p.

Gu, Y., Gammons, C.H., and Bloom, M.S., 1994, A one-term extrapolation method for estimating equilibrium constants of aqueous reactions at elevated temperatures: Geochimica et Cosmochimica Acta, v. 58, p. 3545–3560.

Gübeli, A.O., and Ste.-Marie, J., 1967a, Constantes de stabilité de thiocomplexes et produits de solubilité de sulfures de mètaux II. Sulfure de zinc: Canadian Journal of Chemistry, v. 45, p. 2101–2108.

—— 1967b, Stabilité des complexes hydroxo et produits de solubilité des hydroxides de métaux. I. Argent et zinc: Canadian Journal of Chemistry, v. 45, p. 827–832.

Haas, J.R., Shock, E.L., and Sassani, D.C., 1995, Rare earth elements in hydrothermal systems: Estimates of standard partial molal thermodynamic properties of aqueous complexes of the rare earth elements at high temperatures and pressures: Geochimica et Cosmochimica Acta, v. 59, p. 4329–4350.

Hamann, R.J., and Anderson, G.M., 1978, Solubility of galena in sulfur-rich NaCl solutions: Economic Geology, v. 73, p. 96–100.

Hancock, R.D., and Evers, A., 1976, Formation constants of $Pd(CN)_4^{2-}$: Inorganic Chemistry, v. 15, p. 995–996.

Hancock, R.D., Finkelstein, N.P., and Evers, A., 1977, A linear free-energy relation involving the formation constants of palladium(II) and platinum(II): Journal of Inorganic Nuclear Chemistry, v. 39, p. 1031–1034.

Haselton, H.T., Jr. , and D'Angelo, W.M., 1986, Tin and tungsten solubilities (500°-700°C, 1 kbar) in the presence of a synthetic quartz monzonite [abs.]: EOS—Transactions of the American Geophysical Union, v. 67, p. 388.

Hayashi, K.-I., and Ohmoto, H., 1991, Solubility of gold in NaCl- and H_2S-bearing aqueous solutions at 250°–350°C: Geochimica et Cosmochimica Acta, v. 55, p. 2111–2126.

Hayashi, K., Sugaki, A., and Kitakaze, A., 1990, Solubility of sphalerite in aqueous sulfide solutions at temperatures between 25° and 240°C: Geochimica et Cosmochimica Acta, v. 54, p. 715–725.

Heinrich, C.A., 1990, The chemistry of hydrothermal tin (-tungsten) ore deposition: Economic Geology, v. 85, p. 457–482.

Heinrich, C.A., and Eadington, P.J., 1986, Thermodynamic prediction of the hydrothermal chemistry of arsenic, and their significance for the paragenetic sequence of some cassiterite-arsenopyrite-base metal sulfide deposits: Economic Geology, v. 81, p. 511–529.

Heinrich, C.A., and Seward, T.M., 1990, A spectrophotometric study of aqueous iron(II) chloride complexing from 25° to 200°C: Geochimica et Cosmochimica Acta, v. 54, p. 2207–2221.

Helgeson, H.C., 1969, Thermodynamics of hydrothermal systems at elevated temperatures and pressures: American Journal of Science, v. 63, p. 622–635.

—— 1981, Prediction of the thermodynamic properties of electrolytes at high pressures and temperatures, *in* Rickard, D.T, and Wickman, F.E., eds., Chemistry and geochemistry of solutions at high temperatures and pressures: Proceedings of a Nobel symposium organized by the Royal Swedish Academy of Sciences: Physics and Chemistry of the Earth, New York, Pergamon, v. 13-14, p. 133–177.

Helgeson, H.C., and Kirkham, D.H., 1974a, Theoretical prediction of the thermodynamic properties of aqueous electrolytes at high pressures and temperatures: I. Summary of the thermodynamic/electrostatic properties of the solvent: American Journal of Science, v. 274, p. 1089–1198.

—— 1974b, Theoretical prediction of the thermodynamic properties of aqueous electrolytes at high pressures and temperatures: II. Debye-Hückel parameters for activity: American Journal of Science, v. 274, p. 1199–1261.

—— 1976, Theoretical prediction of the thermodynamic properties of aqueous electrolytes at high pressures and temperatures: III. Equation of state for aqueous species at infinite dilution: American Journal of Science, v. 276, p. 97–240.

Helgeson, H.C., Kirkham, D.H., and Flowers, G.C., 1981, Theoretical prediction of the thermodynamic properties of aqueous electrolytes at high pressures and temperatures: Iv.c. Calculation of activity coefficients, osmotic coefficients, and apparent molal and standard and relative partial molal properties to 600°C and 5 kb: American Journal of Science, v. 281, p. 1249–1493.

Helz, G.R., Charnock, J.M., Vaughan, D.J., and Garner, C.D., 1993, Multinuclearity of aqueous copper and zinc bisulfide complexes: An EXAFS investigation: Geochimica et Cosmochimica Acta, v. 57, p. 15–25.

Helz, G.R., Tossell, J.A., Charnock, J.M., Pattrick, R.A.D., Vaughan, D.J., and Garner, C.D., 1995, Oligomerization in As(III) sulfide solutions: Theoretical constraints and spectroscopic evidence: Geochimica et Cosmochimica Acta, v. 59, p. 4591–4604.

Hemley, J.J., 1953, A study of lead sulfide solubility and its relation to ore deposition: Economic Geology, v. 48, p. 113–138.

Henley, R.W., 1973, Solubility of gold in hydrothermal chloride solutions: Chemical Geology, v. 11, p. 73–87.

Hietanen, S., and Högfeldt, E., 1976, On the complex formation between Hg(II) and CO_3^{2-}: Chemica Scripta, v. 10, p. 37–38.

Higgins, N.C., 1980, Fluid inclusion evidence for the transport of tungsten by carbonate complexes in hydrothermal solutions: Canadian Journal of Earth Science, v. 17, p. 823–830.

Hinners, N.W., 1963, The solubility of sphalerite in aqueous solutions at 80°C: Unpublished Ph.D. dissertation, Princeton, New Jersey, Princeton University, 180 p.

Högfeldt, E., 1982, Stability constants of metal-ion complexes: Part A: Inorganic ligands: IUPAC Chemical Data Series No. 21, New York, Pergamon, 310 p.

Holmes, H.F., and Mesmer, R.E., 1983, Thermodynamic properties of aqueous solutions of the alkali metal chlorides to 250°C: Journal of Physical Chemistry, v. 87, p. 1242–1255.

Ivakin, A.A., Vorob'eva, S.V., Gertman, E.M., and Voronova, E.M., 1976, Acid-base equilibria and self-association in arsenious acid solutions: Russian Journal of Inorganic Chemistry, v. 21, p. 237–240.

Ivanova, G.F., 1966, Thermodynamic evaluation of the possibility of tungsten transport as halogen compounds: Geochemistry International, v. 2, p. 964–973.

Jackson, K.J., and Helgeson, H.C., 1985a, Chemical and thermodynamic constraints on the hydrothermal transport and deposition of tin; I, Calculation of the solubility of cassiterite at high pressures and temperatures: Geochimica et Cosmochimica Acta, v. 49, p. 1–22.

—— 1985b, Chemical and thermodynamic constraints on the hydrothermal transport and deposition of tin; I. Interpretation of phase relations in the Southeast Asian tin belt: Economic Geology, v. 80, p. 1365–1378.

Jaireth, S., 1992, The calculated solubility of platinum and gold in oxygen-saturated fluids and the genesis of platinum-palladium and gold mineralization in the unconformity-related uranium deposits: Mineralium Deposita, v. 27, p. 42–54.

Johnson, J.W., Oelkers, E.H., and Helgeson, H.C., 1992, SUPCRT92: a software package for calculating the standard molal thermodynamic properties of minerals, gases, aqueous species, and reactions from 1–5000 bars and 0°–1000°C: Computers and Geosciences, v. 18, p. 899–947.

Keppler, H., and Wyllie, P.J., 1992, Partitioning of Cu, Sn, Mo, W, U, and Th between melt and aqueous fluid in the systems haplogranite-H_2O-HCl and haplogranite-H_2O-HF: Contributions to Mineralogy and Petrology, v. 109, p. 139–150.

Kharaka, Y.K., Gunter, W.D., Aggarwall, P.K., Perkins, E.H., and DeBraal, J.D., 1988, Solmineq.88: A computer program code for geochemical modeling of water-rock interactions: U. S. Geological Survey Water Investigations Report, 88–4227.

Kharaka, Y.K., Lundegard, P.D., and Giordano, T.H., 1998, Distribution and origin of organic ligands in subsurface waters from sedimentary basins: Reviews in Economic Geology, v. 9, in press.

Khodakovskiy, I.L., and Shikina, N.D., 1981, The role of carbonate complexes in mercury transport in hydrothermal solutions (experimental studies and thermodynamic analysis): Geochemistry International, v. 18, p. 32–43.

Khodakovskiy, I.L., and Yelkin, A.Ye., 1975, Measurement of the solubility of zincite in aqueous NaOH at 100°, 150°, and 200°C: Geochemistry International, v. 12, p. 127–133.

Khodakovskiy, I.L., Popova, M.Ya., and Ozerova, N.A., 1975, On the role of sulfide complexes in the transport of mercury by hydrothermal solutions: Geochemistry International, v. 12, p. 37–47.

Khodorevskaya, L.I., 1989, Study of influence of HCl concentration and density of hydrothermal fluid on WO_3 solubility [abs.]: Third International Symposium on Hydrothermal Reactions, September 12–15, 1989, Frunze, Kirghizia, Program and Abstracts, p. 36.

Kiddie, A.M., and Wood, S.A., 1989, Raman spectral studies on systematics of molybdate speciation at high temperatures and pressures [abs.]: Third International Symposium on Hydrothermal Reactions, September 12–15, 1989, Frunze, Kirghizia, Program and Abstracts, p. 37.

Kolpakova, N.N., 1982, Laboratory and field studies of ionic equilibria in the Sb_2S_3–H_2O–H_2S system: Geochemistry International, v. 19, p. 46–64.

Koplitz, L.V., McClure, D.S., and Crerar, D.A., 1987, Spectroscopic study of chloroiron(II) complexes in LiCl-DCl-D_2O solutions: Inorganic Chemistry, v. 26, p. 308–313.

Korzhinskiy, M.A., 1987, The calcium-iron ratio in a supercritical chloride fluid in equilibrium with skarn mineral assemblages: Geokhimiya, v. 2, p. 203–220.

Kothekar, V., Pullman, A., and Demoulin, D., 1978, Ab initio molecular-orbital study of the binding of Zn^{II} with SH_2 and SH^-: International Journal of Quantum Chemistry, v. 14, p. 779–791.

Kovalenko, N.I., Ryzhenko, B.N., Barsukov, V.L., Klintsova, A.P., Velyukhanova, T.K., Volynets, M.P., and Kitayeva, L.P., 1986, The solubility of cassiterite in HCl and HCl + NaCl (KCl) solutions at 500°C and 1000 atm under fixed redox conditions: Geochemistry International, v. 23, n. 7, p.1–16.

Kovalenko, N.I., Ryzhenko, B.N., Dorofeyeva, V.A., and Bannykh, L.N., 1992, The stability of $Sn(OH)_4^{2-}$, $Sn(OH)_2F^-$, and $Sn(OH)_2Cl^-$ at 500°C and 1 kbar: Geochemistry International, v. 29, n. 8, p. 84–94.

Kozlov, Vl.K., 1985, Laboratory data on the role of carbonate complexes in hydrothermal silver transport: Geochemistry International, v. 22, p. 85–95.

Kozlov, Vl.K., and Khodakovskiy, I.L., 1984, The thermodynamic parameters of atomic silver in aqueous solution at 25°–280°C: Geochemistry International, v. 21, p. 118–131.

Kozlov, Vl.K., Kuznetsov, V.N., and Khodakovskiy, I.L., 1983, The thermodynamic parameters of Ag_2O_c and silver(I) hydroxy complexes in aqueous solution at elevated temperatures: Geochemistry International, v. 20, p. 137–149.

Kozlowska-Kolodziej, B., and Bartecki, A., 1973, Solubility of silver oxide in aqueous ammonia solutions at elevated temperatures: Rocznijki Chemii, Annals of the Polish Chemical Society, v. 47, p. 1841–1848.

Krupp, R.E., 1988a, Solubility of stibnite in hydrogen sulfide solutions, speciation and equilibrium constants, from 25° to 350°C: Geochimica et Cosmochimica Acta, v. 52, p. 3005–3015.

—— 1988b, Physicochemical aspects of mercury metallogenesis: Chemical Geology, v. 69, p. 345–356.

—— 1990a, Comment on "As(III) and Sb(III) sulfide complexes: An evaluation of stoichiometry and stability from existing experimental data" by N.F. Spycher and M.H. Reed: Geochimica et Cosmochimica Acta, v. 54, p. 3239–3240.

—— 1990b, Response to the Reply by N.F. Spycher and M.H. Reed: Geochimica et Cosmochimica Acta, v. 54, p. 3245.

Kudrin, A.V., 1985, The solubility of tugarinovite MoO_2 in aqueous solutions at elevated temperatures: Geochemistry International, v. 22, p. 126–138.

Kuznetsov, V.A., Efremova, E.P., and Kolonin, G.R., 1973, On the stability of cinnabar in high temperature solutions: Geochemistry International, v. 10, p. 498–507.

Langmuir, D., 1979, Techniques of estimating thermodynamic properties for some aqueous complexes of geochemical interest, *in* Jeanne, E.A., ed., Chemical modeling in aqueous systems: American Chemical Society, Symposium Series 93, p. 353–387.

—— 1997, Aqueous environmental geochemistry: New Jersey, Prentice Hall, 600 p.

Lee, J.H., and Byrne, R.H., 1992, Examination of comparative rare earth element complexation behaviour using linear free-energy relationships: Geochimica et Cosmochimica Acta, v. 56, p. 1127–1137.

Leleu, M.G., 1978, L'association sulfures-carbonates: Application au cas de la galène en milieu hydrothermal: Chemical Geology, v. 22, p. 43–70.

Lesht, D., and Baumann, J.E., 1978, Thermodynamics of the manganese(II) bicarbonate system: Inorganic Geochemistry, v. 17, p. 3332–3334.

Levin, K.A., 1991, An experimental and thermodynamic study of the stabilities of silver chloride complexes in KCl and NaCl solutions up to 7 m at 300°C: Geokhimiya, v. 10, p. 1463–1468.

Lindsay, W.T., Jr., 1980, Estimation of concentration quotients for ionic equilibria in high temperature water: The model substance approach: Proceedings of the 41st International Water Conference, Pittsburg, Pennsylvania, October 20, 1980, p. 284–294.

Luther, G.W., III, 1991, Pyrite synthesis via polysulfide compounds: Geochimica et Cosmochimica Acta, v. 55, p. 2839–2850.

Luther, G.W., III, Rickard, D.T., Theberge, S., and Olroyd, A., 1996, Determination of metal (bi)sulfide stability constants of Mn^{2+}, Fe^{2+}, Co^{2+}, Ni^{2+}, Cu^{2+} and Zn^{2+} by voltammetric methods: Environmental Science and Technology, v. 30, p. 671–679.

Macdonald, J.A., and Spooner, E.T.C., 1982, Carbonate complexing of molybdenum in hydrothermal solutions: Evidence from Boss Mountain, British Columbia [abs.]: Geological Society of America Abstracts with Programs, v. 14, p. 552.

Maeda, M., Arnek, R., and Biedermann, G., 1979, A potentiometric and calorimetric study of the system Ag^+–NH_3 in 3 M $NaClO_4$, 3 M $LiClO_4$, and 3 M $NaNO_3$ media: Journal of Inorganic and Nuclear Chemistry, v. 41, p. 343–346.

Maeda, M., Nakagawa, G., and Biedermann, G., 1983, Estimation of medium effect on dissociation constant of ammonium ion and formation constants of silver(I)-ammine complexes in aqueous solution: Journal of Physical Chemistry, v. 87, p. 121–125.

Malinin, S.D., and Kurovskaya, N.A., 1993, The solubility of scheelite in aqueous NaCl, $CaCl_2$, and KCl solutions at 600°–800°C and 2 kbar: Geochemistry International, v. 30, p. 76–88.

Manning, D.A.C., 1984, Volatile control of tungsten partitioning in granitic melt-vapour systems: Institute of Mining and Metallurgy Transactions, sec. B, v. 93, p. B185–B190.

Martens, C.S., 1990, Generation of short chain organic acid anions in hydrothermally altered sediments of the Guayamas Basin, Gulf of California: Applied Geochemistry, v. 5, p. 71–76.

McPhail, D.C., 1991, Experimental determination of the solubility of magnetite-K-feldspar-biotite-quartz in hydrothermal chloride brines: Unpublished Ph.D. thesis, Princeton, New Jersey, Princeton University.

Melent'yev, B.N., Ivanenko, V.V., and Pamfilova, L.A., 1969, Solubility of some ore-forming sulfides under hydrothermal conditions: Geochemistry International, v. 6, p. 416–460.

Mironova, G.D., Zotov, A.V., and Gul'ko, N.I., 1984, Determination of the solubility of orpiment in acid solutions at 25°-150°C: Geochemistry International, v. 21, p. 53–59.

—— 1990, The solubility of orpiment in sulfide solutions at 25°-150°C and the stability of arsenic sulfide complexes: Geochemistry International, v. 27, p. 61–73.

Mountain, B.W., and Seward, T.M., 1997, Hydrosulphide complexes of copper at 22°C: A novel approach to the measurement of stability constants by the solubility method [abs.]: Seventh Annual V.M. Goldschmidt Conference, Tucson, Arizona, June 2–6, 1997, p. 145–146.

Mountain, B.W., and Wood, S.A.,1988, Chemical controls on the solubility, transport, and deposition of platinum and palladium in hydrothermal solutions: A thermodynamic approach: Economic Geology, v. 83, p. 492–510.

Murray, R.C., and Cobble, J.W., 1980, Chemical equilibria in aqueous systems at high temperatures: 41st International Water Conference Proceedings, Pittsburgh, Pennsylvania, October 20–22, 1980, p. 295–310.

Nagakawa, R., 1971, Solubility of orpiment (As_2S_3) in Tamagawa Hot Springs, Akita Prefecture: Nippon Kagaku Zaishi, v. 92, p. 154–159 (in Japanese).

Nekrasov, I.Ya., and Konyushok, A.A., 1982, Heteropolynucleate gold complexes in antimony-bearing sulfide solutions: Doklady Akademia Nauk SSSR, v. 267, p. 185–188.

Nekrasov, I.Ya., Konyushok, A.A., and Sorokin, V.I., 1982, Form of gold(I) in antimony-bearing sulfide solutions: Doklady Akademia Nauk SSSR, v. 264, p. 207–210.

Nikolaeva, N.M., Yerenburg, A.M., and Antipina, V.A., 1972, Temperature dependence of the standard potential of halide complexes of gold: Izvestiya Sibirskogo Otdeleniya Akademii Nauk SSSR, Seria Khimicheskikh, v. 4, p. 126–129 (in Russian).

Nordstrom, D.K., and Munoz, J.L., 1994, Geochemical Thermodynamics, 2nd. ed.: Cambridge, Massachusetts, Blackwell Scientific Publications, 493 pp.

Nriagu, J.O., 1971, Studies in the system PbS-NaCl-H_2S-H_2O: Stability of lead(II) thiocomplexes at 90°C: Chemical Geology, v. 8, p. 299–310.

Nriagu, J.O., and Anderson, G.M., 1971, Stability of the lead(II) chloride complexes at elevated temperatures: Chemical Geology, v. 7, p. 171–183.

Oelkers, E.H., and Helgeson, H.C., 1990, Triple ion anions and polynuclear complexing in supercritical electrolyte solutions: Geochimica et Cosmochimica Acta, v. 54, p. 727–738.

—— 1993, Calculation of dissociation constants and the relative stabilities of polynuclear clusters of 1:1 electrolytes in hydrothermal solutions at supercritical pressures and temperatures: Geochimica et Cosmochimica Acta, v. 57, p. 2673–2697.

Ohmoto, H., Hayashi, K.-I., and Kajisa, Y., 1994, Experimental study of the solubilities of pyrite in NaCl-bearing aqueous solutions at 250°–350°C: Geochimica et Cosmochimica Acta, v. 58, p. 2169–2185.

Okouchi, S., and Sasaki, S., 1981, The measurement of the solubility of metallic mercury in hydrocarbons by means of the cold-vapor atomic absorption method: Bulletin of the Chemical Society of Japan, v. 54, p. 2513–2514.

Ovchinnikov, L.N., Kozlov, Ye.D., and Rafal'skiy, R.P., 1982, The solubility of stibnite in chloride solutions at elevated temperatures: Geochemistry International, v. 19, p. 56–63.

Pabalan, R.T., 1986, Solubility of cassiterite (SnO_2) in NaCl solutions from 200°C–350°C, with geologic applications: Unpublished Ph.D. thesis, University Park, Pennsylvania State University, 140 p.

Palmer, D.A., and Hyde, K.E., 1993, An experimental determination of ferrous chloride and acetate complexation in aqueous solutions to 300°C: Geochimica et Cosmochimica Acta, v. 57, p. 1393–1408.

Pan, P., and Wood, S.A., 1991, Gold chloride complexes in very acidic aqueous solutions and at temperatures 25°–300°C: A laser Raman spectroscopic study: Geochimica et Cosmochimica Acta, v. 55, p. 2365–2371.

—— 1994, The solubility of Pt and Pd sulfides and Au metal in bisulfide solutions. II: Results at 200°–350°C and at saturated vapor pressure: Mineralium Deposita, v. 29, p. 373–390.

Patterson, D.J., Ohmoto, H., and Solomon, M., 1981, Geologic setting and genesis of cassiterite-sulfide mineralization at Renison Bell, Western Tasmania: Economic Geology, v. 76, p. 393–438.

Pearson, R.G., 1963, Hard and soft acids and bases: Journal of the American Chemical Society, v. 85, p. 3533–3539.

—— 1968, Hard and soft acids and bases, HSAB. Part I: Fundamental principles: Journal of Chemical Education, v. 45, p. 581–587.

Peck, J.A., Tait, C.D., Swanson, B.I., and Brown, G.E., Jr., 1991, Speciation of aqueous gold(III) chlorides from ultraviolet/visible absorption and Raman/resonance Raman spectroscopies: Geochimica et Cosmochimica Acta, v. 55, p. 671–676.

Perrin, D.D., 1962, The hydrolysis of metal ions. Part III. Zinc: Journal of the Chemical Society, p. 4500–4502.

Phillips, S.L., and Silvester, L.F., 1983, Use of balanced-like-charges approach to metal-bicarbonate reactions: Inorganic Chemistry, v. 22, p. 3848–3851.

Pitzer, K.S., 1979, Theory: Ion interaction approach, *in* Pytkowicz, R.M., ed., Activity coefficients in electrolyte solutions, v. 1: Boca Raton, CRC Press, p. 157–208.

Plyasunov, A.V., Belonozhko, A.B., Ivanov, I.P., and Khodakovskiy, I.L., 1988, Solubility of zinc oxide in alkaline solutions at 200°–350°C under saturated steam pressure: Geochemistry International, v. 25, p. 77–85.

Pokrovski, G., Gout, R., Schott, J., Zotov, A., and Harrichoury, J.-C., 1996, Thermodynamic properties and stoichiometry of As(III) hydroxide complexes at hydrothermal conditions: Geochimica et Cosmochimica Acta, v. 60, p.737–749.

Pokrovskii, V.A., and Helgeson, H.C., 1995, Thermodynamic properties of aqueous species and the solubilities of minerals at high pressures and temperatures; the system Al_2O_3-H_2O-NaCl: American Journal of Science, v. 295, p. 1255–1342.

Polya, D.A., 1989, Chemistry of the main-stage ore-forming fluids of the Panasqeira W-Cu(Ag)-Sn deposit, Portugal: Implications for models of ore genesis: Economic Geology, v. 84, p. 1134–1152.

—— 1990, Pressure-dependence of wolframite solubility for hydrothermal vein formation: Institute of Mining and Metallurgy, sec. B Transactions, v. 99, p. B120–B124.
Popova, M.Ya., Khodakovskiy, I.L., and Ozerova, N.A., 1975, Experimental determination of the thermodynamic properties of hydroxo and hydroxofluoride complexes of antimony at temperatures up to 200°C: Geokhimiyia, n. 6, p. 835–843 (in Russian).
Rafal'skiy, R.P., and Masalovich, A.P., 1982, Determination of the instability constants of lead chloride complexes at elevated temperatures: Geochemistry International, v. 19, p. 158–174.
Reed, M.H., 1982, Calculation of multicomponent chemical equilibria and reaction processes in systems involving minerals, gases, and an aqueous phase: Geochimica et Cosmochimica Acta, v. 46, p. 513–528.
Reichle, R.K., McCurdy, L.G., and Hepler, L.G., 1975, Zinc hydroxide: Solubility product and hydroxy-complex stability constants from 12.5° to 75°C: Canadian Journal of Chemistry, v. 53, p. 384–391.
Renders, P.J., and Seward, T.M., 1989, The stability of hydrosulphido- and sulphido complexes of Au(I) and Ag(I) at 25°C: Geochimica et Cosmochimica Acta, v. 53, p. 244–253.
Romberger, S.B., and Barnes, H.L., 1970, Ore solution chemistry, III. Solubility of CuS in sulfide solutions: Economic Geology, v. 65, p. 901–919.
Ruaya, J.R., 1988, Estimation of instability constants of metal chloride complexes in hydrothermal solutions up to 300°C: Geochimica et Cosmochimica Acta, v. 52, p. 1983–1996.
Ruaya, J.R., and Seward, T.M., 1986, The stability of chlorozinc(II) complexes in hydrothermal solutions up to 350°C: Geochimica et Cosmochimica Acta, v. 50, p. 651–662.
—— 1987, The ion-pair constant and other thermodynamic properties of HCl up to 350°C: Geochimica et Cosmochimica Acta, v. 51, p. 121–130.
Ryan, M.P., and Bauman, J.E., Jr., 1978, Thermodynamics of the zinc bicarbonate ion pair: Inorganic Chemistry, v. 17, p. 3329–3331.
Rytuba, J.J., and Dickson, F.W., 1974, Reactions of pyrite + pyrrhotite + gold with NaCl-H_2O solutions, 300°–500°C, 500–1500 bars, and genetic implications, *in* Bogdanov, B. ed., Problems of ore deposition. 4th IAGOD Symposium: Bulgarian Academy of Science, Varna, 1974, v. 2, p. 320–326.
Samson, I.M., and Wood, S.A., 1997, The relative solubilities of ferberite and scheelite as a function of temperature, pressure, pH and salinity: Applications to granitoid-related tungsten deposits, *in* Papunen, H., ed., Mineral Deposits: Research and Exploration—Where Do They Meet?: Proceedings 4th Biennial Meeting of the Societé Geologique Appliquée: Turku, Finland, August 11–13, 1997, p. 967–970.
Sassani, D.C., and Shock, E.L., 1992, Estimation of standard partial molal entropies of aqueous ions at 25°C and 1 bar: Geochimica et Cosmochimica Acta, v. 56, p. 3895–3908.
Schröcke, H., Trumm, A., and Hochleitner, R., 1984, Über den Transport von Wolfram und den Absatz von Wolfram-Doppel-Oxiden in fluiden wässrigren Lösungen: Geochimica et Cosmochimica Acta, v. 48, p. 1791–1805.
Schwarzenbach, G., and Widmer, M., 1963, Die Löslichkeit von Metallsulfiden. I. Schwarzes Quecksilbersulfid: Helvetica Chimica Acta, v. 46, p. 2613–2628.
—— 1966, Die Löslichkeit von Metalsulfiden. II: Silbersulfid: Helvetica Chemica Acta, v. 49, p. 111–123.
Schwarzenbach, G., Gübeli, O., and Zust, H., 1958, Thiocomplexe des Silbers und die Löslichkeit von Silbersulfid: Chimia, v. 12, p. 84–86.
Sergeyeva, E.I., and Khodakovskiy, I.L., 1969, Physicochemical conditions of formation of native arsenic in hydrothermal deposits: Geochemistry International, v. 6, p. 681–694.
Seward, T.M., 1973, Thio complexes of gold in hydrothermal ore solutions: Geochimica et Cosmochimica Acta, v. 37, p. 379–399.
—— 1976, The stability of chloride complexes of silver in hydrothermal solutions up to 350°C: Geochimica et Cosmochimica Acta, v. 40, p. 1329–1341.
—— 1981, Metal complex formation in aqueous solutions at elevated temperatures and pressures, *in* Rickard, D.T., and Wickman, F.E., eds., Chemistry and geochemistry of solutions at high temperatures and pressures: New York, Pergamon, p. 113–129.
—— 1983, The transport and deposition of gold in hydrothermal systems, *in* Foster, R.P., ed., The geology, geochemistry and genesis of gold deposits: Geological Society of Zimbabwe Special Publication No. 1, p. 165–181.
—— 1984, The formation of lead(II) chloride complexes to 300°C: A spectrophotometric study: Geochimica et Cosmochimica Acta, v. 46, p. 121–134.
Seward, T.M., and Barnes, H.L., 1997, Metal transport by hydrothermal ore fluids, *in* Barnes, H.L., ed., Geochemistry of hydrothermal ore deposits, 3rd. ed.: New York, Wiley, p. 435–486.
Sharps, J.A., Brown, G.E., Jr., and Stebbins, J.F., 1993, Kinetics and mechanism of ligand exchange of Au(III), Zn(II) and Cd(II) chlorides in aqueous solution: An NMR study from 28°–98°C: Geochimica et Cosmochimica Acta, v. 57, p. 721–732.
Shea, D., and Helz, G.R., 1988, The solubility of copper in sulfidic waters: Sulfide and polysulfide complexes in equilibrium with covellite: Geochimica et Cosmochimica Acta, v. 52, p. 1815–1826.
Shenberger, D.M., and Barnes, H.L., 1989, Solubility of gold in aqueous sulfide solutions from 150° to 350°C: Geochimica et Cosmochimica Acta, v. 53, p. 269–278.
Shikina, N.D., Zotov, A.V., and Khodakovskiy, I.L., 1982, An experimental investigation of equilibria in the α-HgS-H_2S-H_2O system at 90° and 150°C: Geochemistry International, v. 18, p. 109–117.
Shikina, N.D., Borisov, M.V., and Khodakovskiy, I.L., 1986, Applying thermodynamic methods to natural cinnabar dissolution: Geochemistry International, v. 22, n. 9, p. 21–25.
Shikina, N.D., Zotov, A.V., and Kartashova, L.F., 1988, The behavior of Sb in the Sb-H_2O-H_2 system at elevated temperatures: Geochemistry International, v. 24, p. 105–109.
Shironosova, G.P., Kolonin, G.R., Galkin, A.V., and Kopyatkevich, I.R., 1988, Estimation of the stability constants of forms of tungsten in high temperature chloride solutions: Thermodynamics in geology, Summary Proceedings of the 2nd All-Union Symposium, Akademiia Nauk SSSR, September 6–8, 1988, p. 200–201 (in Russian).
Shock, E.L., 1995, Organic acids in hydrothermal solutions: Standard molal thermodynamic properties of carboxylic acids, and estimates of dissociation constants at high temperatures and pressures: American Journal of Science, v. 295, p. 496–580.
Shock, E.L., and Helgeson, H.C., 1988, Calculation of the thermodynamic and transport properties of aqueous species at high pressures and temperatures: Correlation algorithms for ionic species and equation of state predictions to 5 kb and 1000°C: Geochimica et Cosmochimica Acta, v. 52, p. 2009–2036.
—— 1990, Calculation of the thermodynamic and transport properties of aqueous species at high pressures and temperatures: Standard partial molal properties of aqueous species: Geochimica et Cosmochimica Acta, v. 54, p. 915–945.
Shock, E.L., Helgeson, H.C., and Sverjensky, D.A., 1989, Calculation of the thermodynamic and transport properties of aqueous species at high pressures and temperatures: Standard partial molal properties of inorganic neutral species: Geochimica et Cosmochimica Acta, v. 53, p. 2157–2183.
Shock, E.L., Oelker, E.H., Johnson, J.W., Sverjensky, D.A., and Helgeson, H.C., 1992, Calculation of the thermodynamic and transport properties of aqueous species at high pressures and temperatures: Effective electrostatic radii, dissociation constants and standard partial molal properties to 1000°C and 5 kbar: Journal of the Chemical Society, Faraday Transactions, v. 88, p. 803–826.
Shock, E.L., Sassani, D.C., Willis, M., and Sverjensky, D.A., 1997, Inorganic species in geologic fluids: Correlations among standard molal thermodynamic properties of aqueous ions and hydroxide complexes: Geochimica et Cosmochimica Acta, v. 61, p. 907–950.
Sillén, L.G., and Martell, A.E., 1964, Stability constants of metal-ion complexes: London, The Chemical Society, Special Publication No. 17, 754 p.
Skibsted, L.H., and Bjerrum, J., 1974, Studies on gold complexes. II. The equilibrium between gold(I) and gold(III) in the ammonia system and the standard potentials of couples involving gold, diamminegold(I), and tetramminegold(III): Acta Chemica Scandinavica A, v. 28, p. 764–770.
Smith, R.W., Norman, D.I., and Popp, C.J., 1980, Calculated solubility of molybdenite in hydrothermal solutions [abs.]: Geological Society of America Abstracts with Programs, v. 12, p. 525.
Snellgrove, R.A., and Barnes, H.L., 1974, Low temperature solid phases and aqueous species in the copper sulfide system: EOS Transactions of the American Geophysical Union, v. 55, p. 484.

Sorokin, V.I., 1973, Solubility of mercury in water at temperatures from 300° to 500°C and pressures from 500 to 1000 atm.: Doklady Akademia Nauk SSSR, v. 213, p. 905–908.

Spycher, N.F., and Reed, M.H., 1989, As(III) and Sb(III) sulfide complexes: An evaluation of stoichiometry and stability from existing experimental data: Geochimica et Cosmochimica Acta, v. 53, p. 2185–2194.

—— 1990a, Reply to comments by R.E. Krupp on "As(III) and Sb(III) sulfide complexes: An evaluation of stoichiometry and stability from existing experimental data": Geochimica et Cosmochimica Acta, v. 54, p. 3241–3243.

—— 1990b, Response to the Response of R.E. Krupp: Geochimica et Cosmochimica Acta, v. 54, p. 3246.

Stumm, W., and Morgan, J.J., 1981, Aquatic chemistry: An introduction emphasizing chemical equilibria in natural waters, 2nd. ed.: New York, Wiley, 780 p.

Sugaki, A., Scott, S.D., Hayashi, K., and Kitakaze, A., 1987, Ag_2S solubility in sulfide solutions up to 250°C: Geochemical Journal, v. 21, p. 291–305.

Suleimenov, O.M., and Seward, T.M., 1997, A spectrophotometric study of hydrogen sulphide ionisation in aqueous solutions to 350°C: Geochimica et Cosmochimica Acta, v. 61, p. 5187–5198.

Sverjensky, D.A., Shock, E.L., and Helgeson, H.C., 1997, Prediction of the thermodynamic properties of aqueous metal complexes to 1000°C and 5 kb: Geochimica et Cosmochimica Acta, v. 61, p. 1359–1412.

Sweeton, F.H., and Baes, C.F., Jr., 1970, The solubility of magnetite and hydrolysis of ferrous ion in aqueous solutions at elevated temperatures: Journal of Chemical Thermodynamics, v. 2, p. 479–500.

Tanger, J.C., IV, and Helgeson, H.C., 1988, Calculation of the thermodynamic and transport properties of aqueous species at high pressures and temperatures: Revised equations of state for the standard partial molal properties of ions and electrolytes: American Journal of Science, v. 288, p. 19–98.

Taylor, J.R., 1997, An introduction to error analysis, 2nd ed.: Sausalito, California, University Science Books, 327 p.

Taylor, J.R., and Wall, V.J., 1993, Cassiterite solubility, tin speciation, and transport in a magmatic aqueous phase: Economic Geology, v. 88, p. 437–460.

Thompson, R.A., and Helz, G.R., 1994, Copper speciation in sulfidic solutions at low sulfur activity: Further evidence for cluster complexes?: Geochimica et Cosmochimica Acta, v. 58, p. 2971–2983.

Tingle, T.N., and Fenn, P.M., 1982, The concentration and transport of molybdenum in magmatic systems, experimental evidence [abs.]: Geological Society of America Abstracts with Programs, v. 14, p. 240.

Tossell, J.A., 1991, Calculations of the structures, stabilities, and Raman and Zn NMR spectra of $ZnCl_n(OH_2)_a^{2-n}$ species in aqueous solution: Journal of Physical Chemistry, v. 95, p. 366–371.

—— 1994, The speciation of antimony in sulfidic solutions: A theoretical study: Geochimica et Cosmochimica Acta, v. 58, p. 5093–5100.

—— 1996, The speciation of gold in aqueous solution: A theoretical study: Geochimica et Cosmochimica Acta, v. 60, p. 17–29.

—— 1997, Theoretical studies on arsenic oxide and hydroxide species in minerals and in aqueous solution: Geochimica et Cosmochimica Acta, v. 61, p. 1613–1623.

Tossell, J.A., and Vaughan, D.J., 1992, Theoretical geochemistry: applications of quantum mechanics in the earth and mineral sciences: Oxford: Oxford University Press, 514 p.

—— 1993, Bisulfide complexes of zinc and cadmium in aqueous solution: Calculation of structure, stability, vibrational and NMR spectra, and of speciation on sulfide mineral surfaces: Geochimica et Cosmochimica Acta, v. 57, p. 1935–1945.

Tremaine, P.R., and LeBlanc, J.C., 1980, The solubility of magnetite and the hydrolysis and oxidation of Fe^{2+} in water to 300°C: Journal of Solution Chemistry, v. 9, p. 415–442.

Tugarinov, I.A., Ganeyev, I.G., and Khodakovskiy, I.L., 1975, Experimental determination of hydrolysis constants of lead ions in aqueous solutions at temperatures up to 300°C: Geochemistry International, v. 12, no. 5, p. 47–55.

Uhler, A.D., and Helz, G.R., 1984, Solubility product of galena at 298°K: A possible explanation for apparent supersaturation in nature: Geochimica et Cosmochimica Acta, v. 48, p. 1155–1160.

Varekamp, J.C., and Buseck, P.R., 1984, The speciation of mercury in hydrothermal systems, with applications to ore deposition. Geochimica et Cosmochimica Acta, v. 48, p. 177–185.

Var'yash, L.N., 1992, Cu(I) complexing in NaCl solutions at 300° and 350°C: Geochemistry International, v. 29, p. 84–92.

Var'yash, L.N., and Rekharskiy, V.I., 1981, An experimental investigation of the hydrolysis of univalent copper at a temperature of 532.15 K: Geokhimiya, n. 5, p. 683–688.

—— 1982, Behavior of Cu(I) in chloride solutions: Geochemistry International, v. 19, p. 61–67.

Vlassopoulos, D., and Wood, S.A., 1990, Gold speciation in natural waters: I. Solubility and hydrolysis reactions of gold in aqueous solution: Geochimica et Cosmochimica Acta, v. 54, p. 2–12.

Webster, J., 1986, The solubility of gold and silver in the system Au-Ag-S-O_2-H_2O at 25°C and 1 atm: Geochimica et Cosmochimica Acta, v. 50, p. 1837–1845.

—— 1990, The solubility of As_2S_3 and speciation of As in dilute and sulphide-bearing fluids at 25° and 90°C: Geochimica et Cosmochimica Acta, v. 54, p. 1009–1017.

Wells, J.T., and Ghiorso, M.S., 1988, Rock alteration, mercury transport, and metal deposition at Sulphur Bank, California: Economic Geology, v. 83, p. 606–618.

Wesolowski, D.J., 1984, Geochemistry of tungsten in scheelite deposits: The skarn ores at King Island, Tasmania: Unpublished Ph.D. thesis, University Park, Pennsylvania State University, 431 p.

Wesolowski, D.J., Drummond, S.E., Mesmer, R.E., and Ohmoto, H., 1984, Hydrolysis equilibria of tungsten(VI) in aqueous sodium chloride solutions to 300°C: Inorganic Chemistry, v. 23, p. 1120–1132.

Wesolowski, D.J., Bénézeth, P., and Palmer, D.A., 1998, ZnO solubility and Zn^{2+} complexation by chloride and sulfate in acidic solutions to 290°C with in-situ pH neasurement. Geochimica et Cosmochimica Acta, v. 62, p. 971–984.

Wheat, C.G., and Carpenter, R., 1988, $MnCl^+$ and $MnSO_4$ association constants to 170°C: Journal of Solution Chemistry, v. 17, p. 467–480.

Williams-Jones, A.E., and Normand, C., 1997, Controls of mineral parageneses in the system Fe-Sb-S-O: Economic Geology, v. 92, p. 308–324.

Wilson, G.A., and Eugster, H.P., 1990, Cassiterite solubility and tin speciation in supercritical chloride solutions, in Spencer, R.J., and Chou, I.M., eds., Fluid-mineral interactions—A tribute to H.P. Eugster: The Geochemical Society, Special Publication No. 2, p.179–195.

Wolery, T.J., 1979, Calculation of chemical equilibria between aqueous solutions and minerals: the EQ3/6 software package: Livermore, California, Lawrence Livermore National Laboratory (UCRL-52658), 41 p.

—— 1983, EQ3NR, a computer program for geochemical aqueous speciation-solubility calculations: User's guide and documentation: Livermore, California, Lawrence Livermore National Laboratory (UCRL-5314) 191 p.

Wolfram, O., and Krupp, R.E., 1996, Hydrothermal solubility of rhodochrosite, Mn(II) speciation, and equilibium constants: Geochimica et Cosmochimica Acta, v. 60, p. 3983–3994.

Wood, B.J., and Fraser, D.G., 1978, Elementary thermodynamics for geologists: Oxford, Oxford University Press, 303 p.

Wood, S.A., 1989, Raman spectroscopic determination of the speciation of ore metals in hydrothermal solutions: I. Speciation of antimony in alkaline sulfide solutions at 25°C: Geochimica et Cosmochimica Acta, v. 53, p. 237–244.

—— 1990, Do tungsten chloride complexes contribute to the genesis of hydrothermal tungsten deposits? [abs.]: Second Goldschmidt Conference Abstract Volume, Baltimore, Maryland, May 2–4, 1990, p. 92.

—— 1992a, Experimental determination of the solubility of WO_3(s) and the thermodynamic properties of H_2WO_4(aq) in the range 300°–600°C at 1 kbar: Calculation of scheelite solubility: Geochimica et Cosmochimica Acta, v. 56, p. 1827–1836.

—— 1992b, Theoretical prediction of speciation and solubility of beryllium in hydrothermal solution to 300°C at saturated vapor pressure: Application to bertrandite/phenakite deposits: Ore Geology Reviews, v.7, p.249–278.

Wood, S.A., and Vlassopoulos, D., 1989, Experimental determination of the hydrothermal solubility and speciation of tungsten at 500°C and 1 kb: Geochimica et Cosmochimica Acta, v. 53, p. 303–312.

Wood, S.A., and Williams-Jones, A.E., 1994, The aqueous geochemistry of the rare earth elements and yttrium. Part Iv. Monazite solubility and REE mobility in exhalative massive sulfide-forming environments: Chemical Geology, v. 115, p. 47–60.

Wood, S.A., Crerar, D.A., and Borcsik, M.P., 1987, Solubility of the assemblage pyrite-pyrrhotite-magnetite-sphalerite-galena-Au-stibnite-bismuthinite-argentite-molybdenite in H_2O-CO_2-NaCl solutions from 200° to 350°C: Economic Geology, v. 82, p. 1864–1887.

Wood, S.A., Mountain, B.W., and Pan, P., 1992, Recent advances in the aqueous geochemistry of platinum, palladium and gold: Canadian Mineralogist, v. 30, p. 955–982.

Wood, S.A., Tait, C.D., and Janecky, D.R., 1995, Photoacoustic spectroscopic studies of sparingly soluble REE complexes: 41st International Conference on Spectroscopy and Analytical Techniques, Windsor, Ontario, Canada, August 14–16, 1995. p. 11.

Xiao, Z., Gammons, C.H., and Williams-Jones, A.E., in press An experimental study of copper chloride complexing at temperatures from 40°C to 300°C and saturated vapor pressure: Geochimica et Cosmochimica Acta.

Yefremova, V.P., Kuznetsov, V.A., and Shikina, N.D., 1982, The solubility of α-HgS in hydrosulfide solutions at elevated temperatures: Geochemistry International, v. 19, p. 55–62.

Yurchenko, E.N., Kolonin, G.R., Shironosova, G.P., and Aksenova, T.P., 1976, Determination of the formation constants for $PbCl^+$ and $PbCl_2^0$ complexes at elevated temperatures by the analysis of integral intensities of the individual Gaussian absorption bands: Zhurnal Neorganicheskoi, v. 21, p. 3050.

Ziegenbein, D., and Johannes, W., 1980, Graphite in C-H-O fluids: an unsuitable compound to buffer fluid composition at temperatures up to 700°C: Neues Jahrbuch Mineralogie Monatshefte, v. 7, p. 289–305.

Ziemniak, S.E., 1992, Metal oxide solubility behavior in high temperature aqueous solutions: Journal of Solution Chemistry, v. 21, p. 745–759.

Zotov, A.V., and Baranova, N.N., 1989, Thermodynamic features of the aurochloride solute complex, $AuCl_2^-$, at temperatures from 350° to 500°C and under pressure of from 500 to 1500 bar: Science Géologie Bulletin, v. 42, p. 335–342.

Zotov, A.V., Levin, K.A., Kotova, Z.Yu., and Volchenkova, V.A., 1982, An experimental study of the stability of silver hydroxychloride complexes in hydrothermal solutions: Geochemistry International, v. 19, p. 151–164.

Zotov, A.V., Baranova, N.N., Dar'yina, T.G., Bannykh, L.M., and Kolotov, V.P., 1985, The stability of $AuOH^0_{sol}$ in water at 300°–500°C and 500-1500 atm.: Geochemistry International, v. 22, p. 156–161.

Zotov, A.V., Levin, K.A., and Kotova, Z.Yu., 1986, The existence of Ag^0(sol) particles under hydrothermal conditions: Geochemistry International, v. 23, p. 156–158.

Zotov, A.V., Levin, K.A., Khodakovskiy, I.L., and Kozlov, Vl.K., 1987, Thermodynamic parameters of Ag(I) chloride complexes in aqueous solution at 273–623 K: Geochemistry International, v. 24, p. 103–116.

Zotov, A.V., Baranova, N.N., Dar'yina, T.G., and Bannykh, L.M., 1990, Gold(I) complexing in the KCl-HCl-H_2O system at 450°C and 500 atm.: Geochemistry International, v. 27, p. 66–75.

—— 1991, The solubility of gold in aqueous chloride fluids at 350°-500°C and 500–1500 atm: thermodynamic parameters of $AuCl_2^-$(aq) up to 750°C and 5000 atm.: Geochemistry International, v. 28, p. 63–71.

APPENDIX

Detailed Description of the Use of EQBRM in Solving Multi-component Chemical Equilibria

In the section above entitled "Simultaneous Equilibrium Calculations," we developed a model for the solubility of galena at 200°C, SWVP, pH = 3, m_{NaCl} = 1.0 molal, and $\Sigma S = 10^{-3}$ molal. We defined a system of 22 combined mass action, mass balance, and charge balance equations relating 22 unknown species concentrations, requiring a computer algorithm to solve. As mentioned above, EQBRM is one of the simplest of the codes employing such an algorithm, and can be obtained from the authors (EQBRM can be downloaded from the website www.cs.uwind:ca/users/i/ims/eqbrm). Here we demonstrate in detail the use of EQBRM in solving the galena solubility model described above. EQBRM contains an algorithm for solving n equations in n unknowns using the Newton-Raphson method (cf. Crerar, 1975) and involves expressing the mass action, mass balance, and charge balance relations in matrix form. We use the version of the code published by Anderson and Crerar (1993). This version currently is limited to equilibria involving 30 species or less. In addition, EQBRM does not contain a thermodynamic database. However, this code is particularly useful as a means of understanding how more complicated codes (SOLMINEQ.88, SOLVEQ, EQ3/6) function, and is also easily modified for tackling problems involving species or phases that are not in the current databases. For some examples of the use of EQBRM in solving geochemical problems including those involving mineralizing systems, see Wood et al. (1987), Wood and Vlassopoulos (1989), Anderson and Cermignani (1991), Wood (1992b), Wood and Williams-Jones (1994), and Wood and Samson (in prep.).

The model defined above contains 22 species, 18 mass action expressions (eq. 2.5–2.9 and 2.29–2.41), 3 mass balance expressions (eq. 2.43–2.45), and one charge balance expression (eq. 2.42). After defining the required equations relating the unknown species, the next step is to compile the necessary equilibrium constants. Obviously, if the equilibrium constant is unavailable for a particular reaction, then it is necessary to either estimate its value or omit that reaction and any species unique to that equilibrium. We illustrate several methods for accomplishing the former in this chapter. The consequences of omitting a species for lack of thermodynamic data is explored in Chapter 5. In the model we are using, the equilibrium constant is unavailable for reaction (2.40) at 200°C and we therefore have chosen to omit the species $Pb(HS)_3^-$ from the model. Because Pb^{2+} is a borderline Pearson acid, we would expect the chloride complexes of Pb^{2+} to be of similar strength as the bisulfide complexes. Therefore, because the concentration of chloride is three orders of magnitude greater than that of bisulfide in our model, we would not expect $Pb(HS)_3^-$ to be present in high concentrations relative to the lead chloride complexes. Consequently, omitting this species from the model should not greatly affect the results of the calculation. However, it is wise to reevaluate this assumption after the calculation is completed. The thermodynamic data for the remaining mass action expressions are compiled in Table 4.

After compiling the thermodynamic data, it is necessary to encode the equations relating the unknown species into matrix form in order to be read by the computer. The first step is to determine the total number of species and the total number of mass action expressions, which will be input as integers, in this case 21 and 17 respectively. Then it is necessary to express the stoichiometries of all the reactions as a matrix of stoichiometric coefficients, with the coefficients of reactants expressed as negative integers and those of the products as positive integers. It should be noted that where liquid water or solid phases appear in a reaction their stoichiometric coefficients should not appear in this matrix because we are concerned only with the concentrations of aqueous species. The matrix representing the reactions for the galena solubility model is presented in Table A1.

TABLE A1. Stoichiometric reaction coefficient matrix for the galena solubility model

	H^+	OH^-	HCl^0	Na^+	Cl^-	$NaCl^0$	$NaOH^0$	H_2S^0	HS^-	S^{2-}	Pb^{2+}	$PbOH^+$	$Pb(OH)_2^0$	$Pb(OH)_3^-$	$PbCl^+$	$PbCl_2^0$	$PbCl_3^-$	$PbCl_4^{2-}$	$Pb(HS)_2^0$	$PbS(H_2S)_2^0$	$NaHS^0$
2.5a	–2	0	0	0	0	0	0	1	0	0	1	0	0	0	0	0	0	0	0	0	0
2.6	0	0	0	0	–1	0	0	0	0	0	–1	0	0	0	1	0	0	0	0	0	0
2.7	0	0	0	0	–2	0	0	0	0	0	–1	0	0	0	0	1	0	0	0	0	0
2.8	0	0	0	0	–3	0	0	0	0	0	–1	0	0	0	0	0	1	0	0	0	0
2.9	0	0	0	0	–4	0	0	0	0	0	–1	0	0	0	0	0	0	1	0	0	0
2.29	–1	0	1	0	–1	0	0	0	0	0	0	0	0	0	0	0	0	0	0	0	0
2.30	0	0	0	–1	–1	1	0	0	0	0	0	0	0	0	0	0	0	0	0	0	0
2.31	1	1	0	0	0	0	0	0	0	0	0	0	0	0	0	0	0	0	0	0	0
2.32	0	–1	0	–1	0	0	1	0	0	0	0	0	0	0	0	0	0	0	0	0	0
2.33	1	0	0	0	0	0	0	–1	1	0	0	0	0	0	0	0	0	0	0	0	0
2.34	1	0	0	0	0	0	0	0	–1	1	0	0	0	0	0	0	0	0	0	0	0
2.35	0	0	0	–1	0	0	0	0	–1	0	0	0	0	0	0	0	0	0	0	0	1
2.36	1	0	0	0	0	0	0	0	0	0	–1	1	0	0	0	0	0	0	0	0	0
2.37	2	0	0	0	0	0	0	0	0	0	–1	0	1	0	0	0	0	0	0	0	0
2.38	3	0	0	0	0	0	0	0	0	0	–1	0	0	1	0	0	0	0	0	0	0
2.40	0	0	0	0	0	0	0	–1	0	0	0	0	0	0	0	0	0	0	1	0	0
2.41	0	0	0	0	0	0	0	–2	0	0	0	0	0	0	0	0	0	0	0	1	0

TABLE A2. Mass and charge balances for the galena solubility model

	H^+	OH^-	HCl^0	Na^+	Cl^-	$NaCl^0$	$NaOH^0$	H_2S^0	HS^-	S^{2-}	Pb^{2+}	$PbOH^+$	$Pb(OH)_2^0$	$Pb(OH)_3^-$	$PbCl^+$	$PbCl_2^0$	$PbCl_3^-$	$PbCl_4^{2-}$	$Pb(HS)_2^0$	$PbS(H_2S)_2^0$	$NaHS^0$
ΣS (2.43)	0	0	0	0	0	0	0	1	1	1	0	0	0	0	0	0	0	0	2	3	1
$[H^+]$ (2.44)	1	0	0	0	0	0	0	0	0	0	0	0	0	0	0	0	0	0	0	0	0
ΣCl (2.45)	0	0	1	0	1	1	0	0	0	0	0	0	0	0	1	2	3	4	0	0	0
(2.42)[1]	1	–1	0	1	–1	0	0	0	–1	–2	2	1	0	–1	1	0	–1	–2	0	0	0

[1]Charge balance

Appendix *(cont.)*

Data are read into EQBRM via the data file EQBRM.DAT which may be edited using any text editor. For the particular model under consideration here, this data file takes the following form:

Contents of the file EQBRM.DAT

```
21,17
-2,0,0,0,0,0,0,1,0,0,1,0,0,0,0,0,0,0,0,0,
0
0,0,0,0,-1,0,0,0,0,0,-1,0,0,0,1,0,0,0,0,0,
0
0,0,0,0,-2,0,0,0,0,0,-1,0,0,0,0,1,0,0,0,0,
0
0,0,0,0,-3,0,0,0,0,0,-1,0,0,0,0,0,1,0,0,0,
0
0,0,0,0,-4,0,0,0,0,0,-1,0,0,0,0,0,0,1,0,0,
0
-1,0,1,0,-1,0,0,0,0,0,0,0,0,0,0,0,0,0,0,0,
0
0,0,0,-1,-1,1,0,0,0,0,0,0,0,0,0,0,0,0,0,0,
0
1,1,0,0,0,0,0,0,0,0,0,0,0,0,0,0,0,0,0,0,
0
0,-1,0,-1,0,0,1,0,0,0,0,0,0,0,0,0,0,0,0,0,
0
1,0,0,0,0,0,0,-1,1,0,0,0,0,0,0,0,0,0,0,0,
0
1,0,0,0,0,0,0,0,-1,1,0,0,0,0,0,0,0,0,0,0,
0
0,0,0,-1,0,0,0,0,-1,0,0,0,0,0,0,0,0,0,0,0,
1
1,0,0,0,0,0,0,0,0,0,-1,1,0,0,0,0,0,0,0,0,
0
2,0,0,0,0,0,0,0,0,0,-1,0,1,0,0,0,0,0,0,0,
0
3,0,0,0,0,0,0,0,0,0,-1,0,0,1,0,0,0,0,0,0,
0
0,0,0,0,0,0,0,-1,0,0,0,0,0,0,0,0,0,0,1,0,
0
0,0,0,0,0,0,0,-2,0,0,0,0,0,0,0,0,0,0,0,1,
0
0.001
0,0,0,0,0,0,0,1,1,1,0,0,0,0,0,0,0,0,2,3,
1
1.00
0,0,1,0,1,1,0,0,0,0,0,0,0,0,1,2,3,4,0,0,
0
1.79E-03
1,0,0,0,0,0,0,0,0,0,0,0,0,0,0,0,0,0,0,0,
0
-3.64,2.64,3.97,3.94,3.52,-0.09,0.09,-11.28
0.09,-7.12,-10.75,0.09,-3.78,-11.37,-20.76,-4.78
-4.88
1,-1,0,1,-1,0,0,0,-1,-2,2,1,0,-1,1,0,-1,-2,0,0,
0
1.0,1.0,1.0,1.0,1.0,1.0,1.0,1.0,
1.0,1.0,1.0,1.0,1.0,1.0,1.0,1.0,
1.0,1.0,1.0,1.0,1.0
0.8099
```

The first line consists of the number of species and the number of mass action expressions entered as integers, separated by commas. Following this are the rows of the matrix shown in Table A1 expressed as integers, separated by commas. Note that only 20 entries are allowed per line of the data file in this section. Thus, the 21st coefficients of each reaction appears on a separate line. Next the mass balance expressions are entered beginning with the total concentration in question in decimal or "E" format (e.g. as 0.003 or 3.0E-3) followed by the mass balance parameters, again entered as integers separated by commas. For example, for the mass balance on ΣS, this section appears as:

0.001	*ΣS in molal units*
0,0,0,0,0,0,0,1,1,1,0,0,0,0,0,0,0,0,2,3,	*Mass balance parameters (from Table A2 above)*
1	*21st parameter (only 20 allowed to a line)*

In this model there are three mass balance constraints, ΣS, ΣCl, and $[H^+]$. The mass balance sections for ΣCl and $[H^+]$ have similar formats and appear after the ΣS expressions in EQBRM.DAT. The mass balance sections are followed by the logarithms of the equilibrium constants entered in decimal format, separated by commas, with no more than eight to a line. Next, the charge balance coefficients are listed as integers, separated by commas, again with a maximum of 20 to a line. The penultimate parameters to be listed are first guesses for the concentrations of the 21 species. These should be in decimal format with no more than eight to a line. The first guesses can be any number other than zero although the rate of convergence of the Newton-Raphson algorithm is dependent on the proximity of these first guesses to the actual concentrations. In some cases, the program will not converge unless the guesses are reasonably close to the actual values, and it is also possible to converge on a physically unrealistic or inappropriate solution (see Bethke, 1992, for a general discussion of problems of this type in geochemical modeling). However, these cases are relatively rare. Finally, the Debye-Hückel A parameter for the temperature and pressure of interest is listed in decimal format on the last line.

One minor complication in the application of EQBRM to the galena solubility model is that we have specified pH = 3 with a mass balance constraint on $[H^+]$. The pH refers to the negative log of the activity of H^+. The value of $[H^+]$ is calculated according to equation (2.44). However, the value of γ_{H^+} is not known initially and it can only be calculated after the true ionic strength is determined. Therefore for this particular case, it is necessary to run EQBRM assuming $[H^+] = 10^{-3}$, i.e. $\gamma_{H^+} = 1$ to obtain the true ionic strength and therefore a new value of γ_{H^+}. Then EQBRM is run again with the new value of $[H^+]$ calculated according to equation (2.44), and this procedure is repeated until there is no further change in $[H^+]$. In this case, the final value of $[H^+]$ is 1.79×10^{-3}.

The final values of the activity coefficients and concentrations of each of the species after a single run of EQBRM are written to a file called EQBRM.OUT, which can be read using any text editor. Any subsequent use of EQBRM will also write to this file, requiring that EQBRM.OUT be renamed prior to re-running EQBRM if one wants to retain the output from a particular run. The output from the final EQBRM run for the galena solubility model is given below, where GAMMA (*i*) refers to the activity coefficient of species *i*, and A (*i*) represents the concentration of species *i*. Each species has a designated number in EQBRM based on its position in the coefficient listing in EQBRM.DAT, i.e., the column number in Table A1.

GAMMA(1)=5.58D-01	H^+
GAMMA(2)=5.58D-01	OH^-
GAMMA(3)=1.00D+00	HCl^0
GAMMA(4)=5.58D-01	Na^+
GAMMA(5)=5.58D-01	Cl^-
GAMMA(6)=1.00D+00	$NaCl^0$
GAMMA(7)=1.00D+00	$NaOH^0$
GAMMA(8)=1.00D+00	H_2S^0
GAMMA(9)=5.58D-01	HS^-
GAMMA(10)=9.66D-02	S^{2-}
GAMMA(11)=9.66D-02	Pb^{2+}
GAMMA(12)=5.58D-01	$PbOH^+$
GAMMA(13)=1.00D+00	$Pb(OH)_2^0$
GAMMA(14)=5.58D-01	$Pb(OH)_3^-$
GAMMA(15)=5.58D-01	$PbCl^+$
GAMMA(16)=1.00D+00	$PbCl_2^0$
GAMMA(17)=5.58D-01	$PbCl_3^-$
GAMMA(18)=9.66D-02	$PbCl_4^{2-}$
GAMMA(19)=1.00D+00	$Ph(HS)_2^0$
GAMMA(20)=1.00D+00	$PbS(H_2S)_2^0$
GAMMA(21)=1.00D+00	$NaHS^0$

Appendix *(cont.)*

Note that the italicized text does not appear in the actual output file.

A(1) =1.790D-03	*H^+*
A(2) =9.433D-09	*OH^-*
A(3) =3.483D-04	*HCl^0*
A(4) =7.692D-01	*Na^+*
A(5) =7.703D-01	*Cl^-*
A(6) =2.266D-01	*$NaCl^0$*
A(7) =2.775D-09	*$NaOH^0$*
A(8) =9.998D-04	*H_2S^0*
A(9) =1.363D-07	*HS^-*
A(10)=1.000D-10	*S^{2-}*
A(11)=2.362D-06	*Pb^{2+}*
A(12)=6.807D-08	*$PbOH^+$*
A(13)=1.000D-10	*$Pb(OH)_2{}^0$*
A(14)=1.000D-10	*$Pb(OH)_3{}^-$*
A(15)=7.673D-05	*$PbCl^+$*
A(16)=3.927D-04	*$PbCl_2{}^0$*
A(17)=2.823D-04	*$PbCl_3{}^-$*
A(18)=2.660D-04	*$PbCl_4{}^{2-}$*
A(19)=1.659D-08	*$Pb(HS)_2{}^0$*
A(20)=1.000D-10	*$PbS(H_2S)_2{}^0$*
A(21)=4.010D-08	*$NaHS^0$*

Note that EQBRM assigns a value of 1.000D-10 (i.e., 1×10^{-10}) to the concentration of any species that is calculated to be a negative number. This usually happens when a species concentration is insignificant relative to those of other species.

In order to calculate the solubility of galena, it is necessary to sum the concentrations of all Pb species which, in this case, are A(11) through A(20), giving 1.020×10^{-3}.

Chapter 3

Calculation of Activity-Activity and Log f_{O_2}-pH Diagrams

SCOTT A. WOOD

Department of Geology and Geological Engineering, University of Idaho, Moscow, Idaho 83844-3022

Introduction

It is hardly possible to read a single paper in the literature on the origin of hydrothermal ore deposits without encountering activity-activity, log f_{O_2}-pH, or related diagrams. Such diagrams are immensely useful in graphically depicting phase relationships, solution speciation, mineral solubilities, and fluid evolution. Nevertheless, despite their wide usage, there are few published accounts fully illustrating construction of these diagrams. The subject is treated at various levels of detail by Holland (1959, 1965), Barnes and Kullerud (1961), Garrels and Christ (1965), Barton and Skinner (1979), Henley et al. (1984), Nesbitt (1984), Faure (1991), Anderson and Crerar (1993), Nordstrom and Munoz (1994), Krauskopf and Bird (1995), Stumm and Morgan (1996), and Drever (1997), among others. In this chapter, a step-by-step description of the methods of construction of activity-activity and log f_{O_2}-pH diagrams from tabulated thermodynamic data (Gibbs free energies of formation, equilibrium constants), as well as some of the possible pitfalls, is provided. It is assumed throughout the chapter that reliable, internally consistent thermodynamic data are available for all phases and species in the systems of interest. This will not be the case for every system of relevance to the economic geologist. Henley et al. (1984) discuss some alternatives for constraining the construction of activity-activity and log f_{O_2}-pH diagrams in the event that some of the necessary thermodynamic data are not available or reliable.

Activity-Activity Diagrams

Background

In the broadest sense, activity-activity diagrams consist of any plot of the activity of one component or species in a system versus the activity of another, and can be used to depict phase relations and aqueous speciation. However, in this chapter we consider a narrower class of diagrams that are generally employed to depict phase relations among various alumino-silicate minerals at a constant temperature and pressure. A complete activity-activity diagram consists of a series of isobarically-isothermally univariant reaction boundaries that intersect in one or more isobaric-isothermal invariant points and divide activity-activity space into isobarically-isothermally divariant phase fields. The axes of this type of diagram are the logarithms of the activities or activity ratios of various aqueous species relevant to the stability of phases in the system under investigation, and the reaction boundaries consist of straight lines. Such activity-activity diagrams are particularly helpful in visualizing wall-rock alteration processes. A useful compendium of various activity-activity diagrams over a range of pressures and temperatures has been published by Bowers et al. (1984). We first discuss some of the general principles involved in the construction of activity-activity diagrams using a single reaction boundary as an example. This is followed by two worked examples of the construction of entire activity-activity diagrams.

Consider the alteration of albite to kaolinite. To investigate geochemical controls on this and related reactions, we might desire to construct an activity-activity diagram depicting phase relations in the Na-Al-Si-O-H system. If we wish to plot the albite/kaolinite reaction boundary on such a diagram, we must first write a chemical reaction with kaolinite on one side and albite on the other, and this reaction must be balanced with aqueous species or additional phases as required. The axes of the activity-activity diagram will be some combination of the logarithm of the activities of the aqueous species employed in balancing the reaction.

One reaction that could be written to define the albite/kaolinite boundary is:

$$\underset{\text{(albite)}}{NaAlSi_3O_8} + H^+ + Al(OH)_3{}^0 + 2H_2O(l) = \underset{\text{(kaolinite)}}{Al_2Si_2O_5(OH)_4} + Na^+ + H_4SiO_4{}^0 \quad (3.1)$$

where we write dissolved Na, K, Si, and Al as the expected predominant aqueous species, i.e., Na^+, K^+, $H_4SiO_4{}^0$ and $Al(OH)_3{}^0$. Any such reaction must be balanced both with respect to the number of atoms of each element and the sum of the charges, and here we also employ H^+ and $H_2O(l)$ to balance the reaction, because these species will always be present in an aqueous solution. However, a problem in using reaction (3.1) as the basis for construction of a reaction boundary on an activity-activity diagram is that the stoichiometry shown is not unique. An equally valid balanced version of this reaction is:

$$\underset{\text{(albite)}}{3NaAlSi_3O_8} + 3H^+ + 16H_2O(l) = \underset{\text{(kaolinite)}}{Al_2Si_2O_5(OH)_4} + Al(OH)_3{}^0 + 3Na^+ + 7H_4SiO_4{}^0 \quad (3.2)$$

Reaction (3.2) obviously has a very different stoichiometry from that of reaction (3.1), i.e., the ratios of the stoichiometric coefficients of the reactants and products are different. Still another possibility is:

$$NaAlSi_3O_8 + H^+ + 19Al(OH)_3{}^0 + 17H_4SiO_4{}^0 \\ \text{(albite)} \\ = 10Al_2Si_2O_5(OH)_4 + Na^+ + 43H_2O(l) \\ \text{(kaolinite)} \quad (3.3)$$

which has yet again a different stoichiometry. In fact, there is an infinite number of possible ways to balance the reaction, which results in ambiguity in the slope of the reaction boundary in activity-activity space. In order to write a thermodynamically meaningful reaction (i.e., one with a unique stoichiometry), we must place an additional stoichiometric constraint on the reaction. A further problem with reactions (3.1–3.3) is that there are too many variables, (i.e., the activities of Na^+, H^+, $Al(OH)_3{}^0$, and $H_4SiO_4{}^0$) to plot these conveniently on a two-dimensional diagram. The resolution of this problem also requires an additional constraint.

The most commonly employed constraint is the assumption that Al is immobile during hydrothermal alteration, i.e., Al is conserved in the solid phases. In practice this simply means that we are assuming that the total activity of dissolved Al in solution is much less than the total activity of any of the other dissolved components. None of the three reactions written above conserves Al because each is written with an aqueous Al-bearing species as a reactant or product. A reaction that does conserve Al is:

$$2NaAlSi_3O_8 + 2H^+ + 9H_2O(l) = \\ \text{(albite)} \\ Al_2Si_2O_5(OH)_4 + 2Na^+ + 4H_4SiO_4{}^0 \\ \text{(kaolinite)} \quad (3.4)$$

In fact, once the assumption is made that Al is conserved, then reaction (3.4) is the only way to balance the reaction and the stoichiometry is unique (note: multiplying all stoichiometric coefficients in a reaction by a constant factor does not produce an essentially different stoichiometry). In many, but not all, situations, conservation of Al is a good assumption. If Al is demonstrated to have been mobile on the basis of geological evidence, then another element, such as Si, might have been immobile, and the reaction can be written to conserve that element. The choice of which element to conserve may be based on mass balance calculations using the isocon method (Grant, 1986), Gresen's (1967) method, the method of MacLean and Kranidiotis (1987), or some other method. Alternatively, it is possible to specify that the balanced reaction conserve the volume of the solids, e.g., if geological evidence suggests volume-for-volume replacement or pseudomorphism. The latter approach requires knowledge of the molar volumes or densities of the solid phases, and a unique stoichiometry can be found most easily using linear algebraic methods. Aside from the fact that different stoichiometries are produced for the reactions in question, there are no fundamental differences in the method of construction of activity-activity diagrams when constraints other than Al-conservation are applied. Thus, for simplicity we employ conservation of Al to constrain the stoichiometries of reactions in all subsequent calculations.

Now that we have defined a unique stoichiometry, it is possible to plot the position of the albite/kaolinite reaction boundary in log (a_{Na^+}/a_{H^+}) versus log $a_{H_4SiO_4}$ space for some specified pressure and temperature, if we know the value of the equilibrium constant of reaction (3.4). We can write the equilibrium constant for reaction (3.4) as follows (see Chap. 1 for the definition of the equilibrium constant):

$$K = \frac{a^2_{Na^+}\, a^4_{H_4SiO_4}}{a^2_{H^+}} \quad (3.5)$$

assuming that the minerals are pure end-member phases (i.e., no solid solution) and that the aqueous solution is dilute, and employing as a standard state the pure solids and liquid water at pressure and temperature; thus the activity terms for kaolinite, albite, and liquid water are unity (see Chap. 1). Taking the logarithm of both sides of the equation we then obtain:

$$\log K = 2\log a_{Na^+} + 4\log a_{H_4SiO_4} - 2\log a_{H^+} \quad (3.6)$$

which can be rearranged to give:

$$\log (a_{Na^+}/a_{H^+}) = 0.5\log K - 2\log a_{H_4SiO_4} \quad (3.7)$$

The above relation is an equation for a straight line in log (a_{Na^+}/a_{H^+}) versus log $a_{H_4SiO_4}$ space of the type $y = mx + b$, where m, the slope, is equal to –2 and b, the intercept, is equal to 0.5 log K. Thus, if we knew the value of log K at a specific pressure and temperature, we could plot the boundary for reaction (3.4) on a diagram with coordinates of log (a_{Na^+}/a_{H^+}) and log (a_{Na^+}/a_{H^+}). For the purpose of illustration, let us suppose log $K = 15.0$. Then the y-intercept will be 7.5 and the slope will be –2, as shown in Figure 1. The interpretation of the boundary in Figure 1 is that it is the locus of all points in log (a_{Na^+}/a_{H^+}) versus log $(a_{H_4SiO_4})$ space where kaolinite and albite are in equilibrium. Above the line in Figure 1, albite is the stable phase, and below the line, kaolinite is stable.

Note that the need to consider the ratio a_{Na^+}/a_{H^+} as one of the solution composition variables in plotting the boundary for reaction (3.4) on an activity-activity diagram arises owing to charge balance considerations. For every Na^+ ion there must be one H^+ ion on the opposite side of the reaction to balance the charge, so a_{Na^+} and a_{H^+} are not fully independent variables. If a divalent ion is involved in a reaction, then two hydrogen ions are required to balance the charge, and the activity of H^+ would appear in the denominator raised to the second power. For example, suppose we wish to plot a reaction boundary between Mg-chlorite and kaolinite. We would write the following reaction:

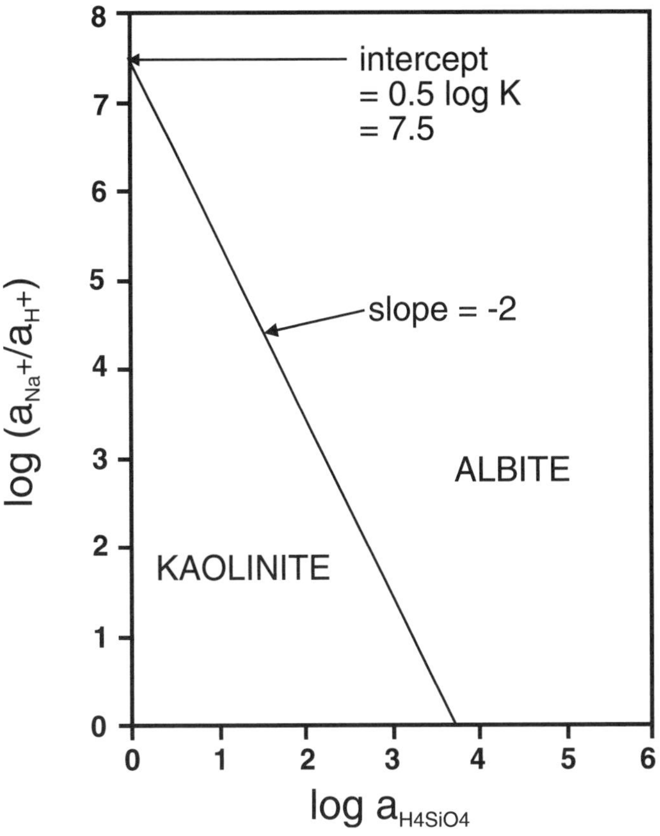

FIG. 1. Schematic plot of log (a_{Na^+}/a_{H^+}) vs. log $a_{H_4SiO_4}$ showing the kaolinite/albite boundary at some unspecified temperature and pressure, according to reaction (3.4) in the text.

$$Mg_2Al_2SiO_5(OH)_4 + H_4SiO_4^0 + 4H^+$$
(Mg-chlorite)
$$= Al_2Si_2O_5(OH)_4 + 2Mg^{2+} + 4H_2O(l) \quad (3.8)$$
(kaolinite)

which could now be plotted on a diagram where log ($a_{Mg^{2+}}/(a_{H^+})^2$) is on one of the axes and log $a_{H_4SiO_4}$ is on the other.

Finally, we note that an additional assumption that is often made in order to reduce the number of compositional variables (i.e., activities), is to assume that $a_{H_4SiO_4}$ is fixed by saturation with respect to quartz. In this case we can then substitute SiO_2(quartz) for $H_4SiO_4^0$ in the reaction and, for example, reaction (3.8) would become:

$$Mg_2Al_2SiO_5(OH)_4 + SiO_2 + 4H^+$$
(Mg-chlorite) (quartz)
$$= Al_2Si_2O_5(OH)_4 + 2Mg^{2+} + 2H_2O(l) \quad (3.9)$$
(kaolinite)

Now, using the pure solid at temperature and pressure as the standard state for quartz, $a_{SiO_2} = 1$, and there is one less compositional variable to consider. Because quartz is nearly ubiquitous in many hydrothermal environments, the assumption of quartz saturation is frequently a valid one. However, diagrams constructed based on this assumption may lead to erroneous conclusions in rare cases where alteration may have occurred under quartz-undersaturated conditions.

Activity-Activity Diagrams in the System K-Na-Al-Si-O-H

We now illustrate the construction of complete activity-activity diagrams for phases in the system K-Na-Al-Si-O-H at a pressure of 1,000 bars and temperatures of 350° and 500°C. Activity-activity diagrams for this system are particularly useful in the elucidation of silicate alteration in porphyry Cu-Mo-Au and epithermal deposits, among others. The first step in the procedure is to decide which phases to include in our calculations. In some ways this step is the most difficult, and is usually based on a combination of factors including field evidence, geologic "intuition" and the availability of thermodynamic data. For the purposes of illustration we will consider the phases paragonite [$NaAl_3Si_3O_{10}(OH)_2$], muscovite [$KAl_3Si_3O_{10}(OH)_2$], albite [$NaAlSi_3O_8$], K-feldspar (in this case, microcline) [$KAlSi_3O_8$], kaolinite [$Al_2Si_2O_5(OH)_4$], gibbsite [$Al(OH)_3$], pyrophyllite [$Al_2Si_4O_{10}(OH)_2$], and andalusite [Al_2SiO_5]. The next step is to locate reliable, internally consistent thermodynamic data for each of these phases (again, not always easy or even possible). In this case, we have used SUPCRT92 (Johnson et al., 1992) to calculate apparent Gibbs free energies of formation of each of the phases and aqueous species required for the diagrams (Table 1). Then, we define the activity ratios to be used as the axes of the diagram, which in our case will be log (a_{Na^+}/a_{H^+}) versus log (a_{K^+}/a_{H^+}). We will also need to fix the activity of silica in solution, which we will accomplish by stipulating saturation with respect to quartz.

In order to facilitate plotting phase boundaries, and to avoid calculating boundaries that ultimately will not appear on the diagram (no reason to do more work than necessary), it is useful to rank the phases of interest in order of expected stability with respect to the two variables on the axes. For example, we can order the phases with respect to increasing log (a_{Na^+}/a_{H^+}) by noting that phases with higher Na/Al ratios will plot at higher values of this parameter. Thus, gibbsite, kaolinite, pyrophyllite,

TABLE 1. Apparent standard molal Gibbs free energies (in cal/mole) from SUPCRT92 for phases and aqueous species in the K-Na-Al-Si-O-H system at 1,000 bars

Phase or species	$\Delta_f G^o$(350°C)	$\Delta_f G^o$(500°C)
paragonite	-1,356,293	-1,378,310
muscovite	-1,367,379	-1,389,954
albite	-907,635	-922,912
microcline	-917,028	-932,426
quartz	-208,990	-212,202
kaolinite	-928,279	-945,096
gibbsite	-284,419	-290,769
pyrophyllite	-1,282,662	-1,302,520
andalusite	-591,274	-599,389
Na+	-68,725	-72,339
K+ -	-75,607	-79,646
H_2O(l)	-64,011	-68,829

and andalusite would all plot at the lowest, paragonite at the next highest, and albite at the highest values of log (a_{Na^+}/a_{H^+}), respectively. Similarly, the order of increasing stability with increasing log (a_{K^+}/a_{H^+}) is gibbsite, kaolinite, pyrophyllite, and andalusite, then muscovite, then K-feldspar. Note that gibbsite, kaolinite, pyrophyllite, and andalusite contain neither Na nor K, and thus boundaries among these phases cannot be plotted on our log (a_{Na^+}/a_{H^+}) versus log (a_{K^+}/a_{H^+}) diagram. This implies that only one of the latter four phases can be stable at a given pressure, temperature and silica activity.

The next task is to use the thermodynamic data to tell us which phase of the four is most stable at each of the temperatures of interest. To do this, we first write a balanced reaction between, e.g., kaolinite and gibbsite, conserving Al and using quartz to balance silica:

$$\underset{\text{(kaolinite)}}{Al_2Si_2O_5(OH)_4} + H_2O(l) = \underset{\text{(gibbsite)}}{2Al(OH)_3} + \underset{\text{(quartz)}}{2SiO_2} \quad (3.10)$$

The standard Gibbs free energy of reaction $\Delta_r G^o$ for this reaction at each temperature is then (see Chap. 1 for the definitions of $\Delta_r G^o$ and $\Delta_f G^o$):

$$\Delta_r G^o = 2\Delta_f G^o \text{ (gibbsite)} + \Delta_f G^o \text{ (quartz)} - \Delta_f G^o \text{ (kaolinite)} - \Delta_f G^o(H_2O(l)) \quad (3.11)$$

and now inserting each of the values of $\Delta_f G^o$ at the appropriate temperature from Table 1 we obtain:

$$\Delta_r G^o(350°C) = 2(-284{,}419) + 2(-208{,}990) - (-928{,}279) - (-64{,}011) = 5{,}472 \text{ cal/mole} \quad (3.12)$$

$$\Delta_r G^o(500°C) = 2(-290{,}769) + 2(-212{,}202) - (-945{,}096) - (-68{,}829) = 7{,}983 \text{ cal/mole} \quad (3.13)$$

In both cases, $\Delta_r G^o > 0$, implying that the assemblage on the left-hand side is more stable than that on the right, and so at both temperatures, kaolinite is stable relative to gibbsite. Note that we can use $\Delta_r G^o$ (i.e., the Gibbs free energy of reaction at the standard state) to decide which way the reaction should proceed only if all reactants and products are in their standard states, i.e., have unit activities; otherwise we have to determine $\Delta_r\mu$ (i.e., the change of chemical potential of the reaction under the actual conditions of interest), which requires that we know the activities of all products and reactants (see Chap. 1). In reaction (3.10), the only reactants are solid phases and liquid water that we can assume are in their standard states, i.e., have activities equal to unity.

We now repeat the process for kaolinite and pyrophyllite and write:

$$\underset{\text{(pyrophyllite)}}{Al_2Si_4O_{10}(OH)_2} + H_2O(l) = \underset{\text{(kaolinite)}}{Al_2Si_2O_5(OH)_4} + \underset{\text{(quartz)}}{2SiO_2} \quad (3.14)$$

for which

$$\Delta_r G^o(350°C) = -928{,}279 + 2(-208{,}990) - (-1{,}282{,}662) - (-64{,}011) = 414 \text{ cal/mole} \quad (3.15)$$

$$\Delta_r G^o(500°C) = -945{,}096 + 2(-212{,}202) - (-1{,}302{,}520) - (-68{,}829) = 1{,}849 \text{ cal/mole} \quad (3.16)$$

Thus, pyrophyllite is more stable than kaolinite at both temperatures.

Finally, we compare andalusite and pyrophyllite:

$$\underset{\text{(pyrophyllite)}}{Al_2Si_4O_{10}(OH)_2} = \underset{\text{(andalusite)}}{Al_2SiO_5} + \underset{\text{(quartz)}}{3SiO_2} + H_2O(l) \quad (3.17)$$

$$\Delta_r G^o(350°C) = -591{,}274 + 3(-208{,}990) + (-64{,}011) - (-1{,}282{,}662) = 407 \text{ cal/mole} \quad (3.18)$$

$$\Delta_r G^o(500°C) = -599{,}389 + 3(-212{,}202) + (-68{,}829) - (-1{,}302{,}520) = -2{,}304 \text{ cal/mole} \quad (3.19)$$

These calculations suggest that pyrophyllite is slightly more stable at 350°C, but that andalusite is more stable at 500°C. Thus, pyrophyllite will appear as the phase at the lowest log (a_{Na^+}/a_{H^+}) versus log (a_{K^+}/a_{H^+}) values at the lower temperature, and andalusite will appear at the higher temperature.

We are now in a position to plot boundaries among the phases on our activity-activity diagram. We start with the 350°C diagram and the pyrophyllite-muscovite boundary. To calculate the boundary, we need to write a reaction with muscovite on one side and pyrophyllite on the other. We balance the reaction by conserving Al and using quartz, water, K^+, and H^+ as necessary:

$$\underset{\text{(pyrophyllite)}}{3Al_2Si_4O_{10}(OH)_2} + 2K^+ = \underset{\text{(muscovite)}}{2KAl_3Si_3O_{10}(OH)_2} + 2H^+ + \underset{\text{(quartz)}}{6SiO_2} \quad (3.20)$$

for which

$$\Delta_r G^o(350°C) = 2(-1{,}367{,}379) + 2(0) + 6(-208{,}990) - 3(-1{,}282{,}662) - 2(-75{,}607) = 10{,}502 \text{ cal/mole} \quad (3.21)$$

Note that, by convention, $\Delta_f G^o(H^+) = 0$ at all temperatures and pressures. Note also that, unlike the solid-solid reactions discussed previously, the fact that $\Delta_r G^o > 0$ does not necessarily imply that muscovite + quartz is unstable. This is because neither H^+ nor K^+ are necessarily in their standard states, i.e., their activities are not necessarily unity.

Using equation (1.131), we calculate log K:

$$\log K = \frac{-\Delta_r G^o}{2.303RT} = \frac{-10{,}502}{2.303(1.987)(623.15)} = -3.68 \quad (3.22)$$

but

$$K = \frac{a^2_{H^+}}{a^2_{K^+}} \tag{3.23}$$

so

$$\log K = \log\left(\frac{a^2_{H^+}}{a^2_{K^+}}\right) = -2\log\left(\frac{a^2_{K^+}}{a^2_{H^+}}\right) \tag{3.24}$$

Thus, we have log (a_{K^+}/a_{H^+}) = 1.84 and the pyrophyllite/muscovite boundary is a vertical line at this value with pyrophyllite stable on the left side of the boundary and muscovite stable on the right side (Fig. 2). It is therefore evident that the ratio a_{K^+}/a_{H^+}, and not $\Delta_r G^o$ alone, determines which phase is stable.

Eventually, the boundary we have just drawn must intersect the pyrophyllite/paragonite boundary, so it is logical to calculate the latter next. We begin with the reaction

$$3Al_2Si_4O_{10}(OH)_2 + 2Na^+ =$$
(pyrophyllite)

$$2NaAl_3Si_3O_{10}(OH)_2 + 2H^+ + 6SiO_2 \tag{3.25}$$
(paragonite) (quartz)

and calculate log K as follows:

$$\Delta_r G^o(350°C) = 2(-1{,}356{,}293) + 2(0) + 6(-208{,}990) - 3(-1{,}282{,}662) - 2(-68{,}725) = 18{,}910 \text{ cal/mole} \tag{3.26}$$

$$\log K = -6.63 \text{ and } \log\left(\frac{a_{Na^+}}{a_{H^+}}\right) = 3.32 \tag{3.27}$$

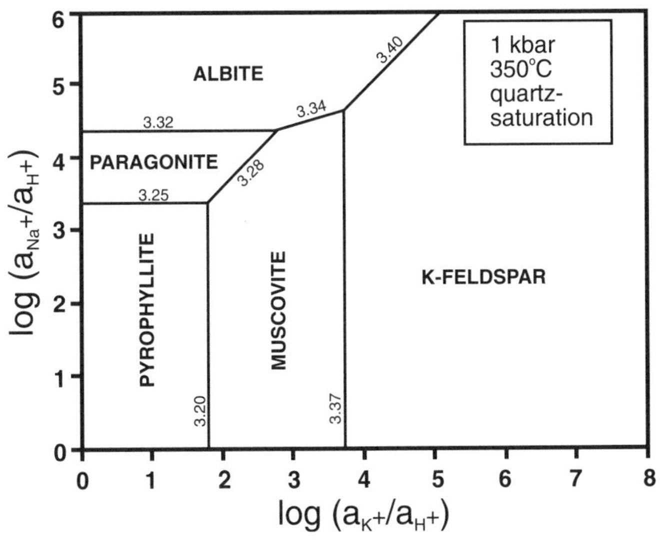

FIG. 2. Plot of log (a_{Na^+}/a_{H^+}) vs. log (a_{K^+}/a_{H^+}) for the system Na-K-Al-Si-O-H at 350°C, 1,000 bars, and quartz saturation. The small numerals labeling the boundaries refer to reaction numbers employed in the text.

which yields a horizontal line that, together with the pyrophyllite/muscovite boundary, encloses the field of pyrophyllite in the lower left hand corner of Figure 2. It is then apparent that a boundary between paragonite and muscovite must be calculated. Writing a reaction between paragonite and muscovite we obtain:

$$NaAl_3Si_3O_{10}(OH)_2 + K^+ = KAl_3Si_3O_{10}(OH)_2 + Na^+ \tag{3.28}$$
(paragonite) (muscovite)

The above reaction does not contain H^+ and we must modify it to plot it on Figure 2. This problem is solved simply by adding H^+ to both sides of the equation to get:

$$NaAl_3Si_3O_{10}(OH)_2 + K^+ + H^+ =$$
(paragonite)

$$KAl_3Si_3O_{10}(OH)_2 + Na^+ + H^+ \tag{3.29}$$
(muscovite)

for which

$$\Delta_r G^o(350°C) = -1{,}367{,}379 + (-68{,}725)(0) - (-1{,}356{,}293) - (-75{,}607) - (0) = -4{,}204 \text{ cal/mole} \tag{3.30}$$

and log K = 1.47. However,

$$\log K = \log\left(\frac{a_{Na^+}a_{H^+}}{a_{H^+}a_{K^+}}\right), \text{ so } \log\left(\frac{a_{Na^+}}{a_{H^+}}\right) = 1.47 + \log\left(\frac{a_{K^+}}{a_{H^+}}\right) \tag{3.31}$$

and this boundary plots as a straight line with slope = +1 and intercept = 1.47. Note that the intercept value for this reaction boundary is not really required because we know that the paragonite/muscovite boundary must pass through the intersection of the pyrophyllite/muscovite and pyrophyllite/paragonite boundaries, and we can draw the paragonite/muscovite boundary as a line of slope 1 emanating from this intersection. However, it is a good check of the calculations to use the full form of equation (3.31) and demonstrate that indeed the three boundaries do intersect at more or less the same point.

In calculating the next boundary, we do not know at this point whether the paragonite/muscovite boundary will intersect the paragonite/albite or the muscovite/K-feldspar boundary first. We arbitrarily choose to calculate the former boundary first.

$$3NaAlSi_3O_8 + 2H^+ = NaAl_3Si_3O_{10}(OH)_2 + 2Na^+ + 6SiO_2 \tag{3.32}$$
(albite) (paragonite) (quartz)

$$\Delta_r G^o(350°C) = -1{,}356{,}293 + 2(-68{,}725) + 6(-208{,}990) - 3(-907{,}635) - 2(0) = -24{,}778 \text{ cal/mole} \tag{3.33a}$$

$$\log K = 8.69 = 2\log\left(\frac{a_{Na^+}}{a_{H^+}}\right) \text{ and } \log\left(\frac{a_{Na^+}}{a_{H^+}}\right) = 4.35 \tag{3.33b}$$

When this horizontal line is plotted it is apparent that it truncates the paragonite/muscovite boundary, suggesting that the next boundary to be calculated should be the albite/muscovite boundary, defined by the relationships

$$\underset{\text{(albite)}}{3NaAlSi_3O_8} + K^+ + 3H^+ = \underset{\text{(muscovite)}}{KAl_3Si_3O_{10}(OH)_2} + 3Na^+ + H^+ + \underset{\text{(quartz)}}{6SiO_2} \quad (3.34)$$

$$\Delta_r G^o(350°C) = -1{,}367{,}379 + 3(-68{,}725) + (0) + 6(-208{,}990) - 3(-907{,}635) - (-75{,}607) = -28{,}982 \text{ cal/mole} \quad (3.35)$$

$$\log K = 10.16 = 3\log\left(\frac{a_{Na^+}}{a_{H^+}}\right) - \log\left(\frac{a_{K^+}}{a_{H^+}}\right) \text{ and } \log\left(\frac{a_{Na^+}}{a_{H^+}}\right) = \frac{1}{3}\log\left(\frac{a_{K^+}}{a_{H^+}}\right) + 3.39 \quad (3.36)$$

Note that, in reaction (3.34), an extra H^+ has been added to both sides of the equation to facilitate plotting. It is now apparent that the albite/muscovite boundary should intersect the muscovite/K-feldspar boundary and so we calculate the latter:

$$\underset{\text{(K–feldspar)}}{3KAlSi_3O_8} + 2H^+ = \underset{\text{(muscovite)}}{KAl_3Si_3O_{10}(OH)_2} + 2K^+ + \underset{\text{(quartz)}}{6SiO_2} \quad (3.37)$$

$$\Delta_r G^o(350°C) = -1{,}367{,}379 + 2(-75{,}607) + 6(-208{,}990) - 3(-917{,}028) - 2(0) = -21{,}449 \text{ cal/mole} \quad (3.38)$$

$$\log K = 7.52 = 2\log\left(\frac{a_{K^+}}{a_{H^+}}\right) \text{ and } \log\left(\frac{a_{K^+}}{a_{H^+}}\right) = 3.76 \quad (3.39)$$

The remaining boundary required to complete the diagram is the albite/K-feldspar boundary that we calculate as follows:

$$\underset{\text{(albite)}}{NaAlSi_3O_8} + K^+ + H^+ = \underset{\text{(K-feldspar)}}{KAlSi_3O_8} + Na^+ + H^+ \quad (3.40)$$

Once again we find it necessary to add H^+ to both sides of the reaction to facilitate plotting.

$$\Delta_r G^o(350°C) = -917{,}028 + (-68{,}725) + (0) - (-907{,}635) - (-75{,}607) - (0) = -2{,}511 \quad (3.41)$$

$$\log K = 0.881 = \log\left(\frac{a_{Na^+}}{a_{H^+}}\right) - \log\left(\frac{a_{K^+}}{a_{H^+}}\right) \text{ and } \log\left(\frac{a_{Na^+}}{a_{H^+}}\right) = \log\left(\frac{a_{K^+}}{a_{H^+}}\right) + 0.88 \quad (3.42)$$

Now, with appropriate labeling, our activity-activity diagram is complete (Fig. 2).

The calculation of the 500°C diagram presents a new situation, not encountered in the construction of Figure 2, but nevertheless quite commonly encountered in general. We start by calculating the andalusite/paragonite boundary:

$$\underset{\text{(andalusite)}}{3Al_2SiO_5} + \underset{\text{(quartz)}}{3SiO_2} + 3H_2O(l) + 2Na^+ = \underset{\text{(paragonite)}}{2NaAl_3Si_3O_{10}(OH)_2} + 2H^+ \quad (3.43)$$

$$\Delta_r G^o(500°C) = 2(-1{,}378{,}310) + 2(0) - 3(-599{,}389) - 2(-72{,}339) - 3(-68{,}829) - 3(-212{,}202) = 29{,}318 \text{ cal/mole} \quad (3.44)$$

$$\log K = -8.287 = -2\log\left(\frac{a_{Na^+}}{a_{H^+}}\right) \text{ and } \log\left(\frac{a_{Na^+}}{a_{H^+}}\right) = 4.14 \quad (3.45)$$

Then we calculate the paragonite/albite boundary at 500°C:

$$\underset{\text{(albite)}}{3NaAlSi_3O_8} + 2H^+ = \underset{\text{(paragonite)}}{NaAl_3Si_3O_{10}(OH)_2} + 2Na^+ + \underset{\text{(quartz)}}{6SiO_2} \quad (3.46)$$

$$\Delta_r G^o(500°C) = -1{,}378{,}310 + 2(-72{,}339) + 6(-212{,}202) - 3(-922{,}912) - 2(0) = -27{,}464 \text{ cal/mole} \quad (3.47)$$

$$\log K = 7.76 = 2\log\left(\frac{a_{Na^+}}{a_{H^+}}\right) \text{ and } \log\left(\frac{a_{Na^+}}{a_{H^+}}\right) = 3.88 \quad (3.48)$$

The problem we encounter (Fig. 3) is that the albite/paragonite boundary plots at a lower log (a_{Na^+}/a_{H^+}) value (3.88) than the paragonite/andalusite boundary (4.14), which is logically inconsistent. This indicates that paragonite does not have a stability field, i.e., it is metastable, on the log (a_{Na^+}/a_{H^+}) versus log (a_{K^+}/a_{H^+}) diagram at 500°C. We therefore must calculate the stable andalusite/albite boundary:

$$\underset{\text{(albite)}}{2NaAlSi_3O_8} + 2H^+ = \underset{\text{(andalusite)}}{Al_2SiO_5} + 2Na^+ + \underset{\text{(quartz)}}{5SiO_2} + H_2O(l) \quad (3.49)$$

which, as the reader should verify occurs at log (a_{Na^+}/a_{H^+}) = 3.97.

The calculation of the remainder of the log (a_{Na^+}/a_{H^+}) versus log (a_{K^+}/a_{H^+}) diagram at 500°C is straightforward, and using the calculations above for 350°C as a template, the reader should verify that Figure 4 is the result. In

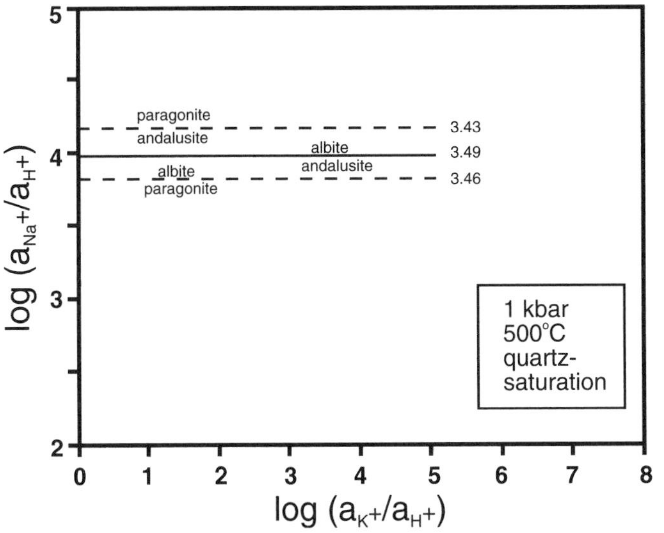

FIG. 3. Plot of log (a_{Na^+}/a_{H^+}) vs. log (a_{K^+}/a_{H^+}) for selected boundaries in the system Na-K-Al-Si-O-H at 500°C, 1,000 bars, and quartz saturation. This plot illustrates the metastability of paragonite under these conditions. The small numerals labeling the boundaries refer to reaction numbers employed in the text.

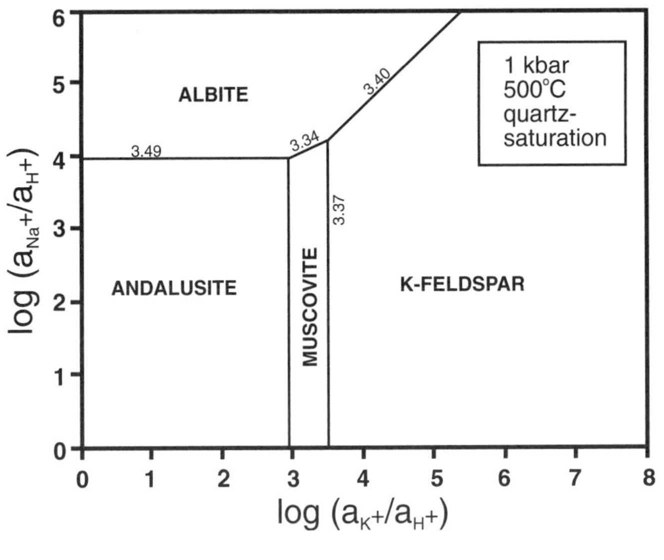

FIG. 4. Plot of log (a_{Na^+}/a_{H^+}) vs. log (a_{K^+}/a_{H^+}) for the system Na-K-Al-Si-O-H at 500°C, 1,000 bars, and quartz saturation. The small numerals labeling some of the boundaries refer to reaction numbers employed in the text.

comparing Figures 2 and 4 it is apparent that, as would be expected, an increase from 350° to 500°C favors completely dehydrated phases (i.e., pyrophyllite gives way to andalusite, paragonite becomes metastable, and the stability field of muscovite shrinks).

In applying Figures 2 and 4 (or any similar activity-activity diagrams) to problems in economic geology, it must be kept in mind that they have been constructed in terms of *activities* of the free ions, and not the total stoichiometric *concentrations* of the ions. Therefore, to plot rigorously an actual fluid composition on the diagram, the concentrations of the free ions of interest must be determined from the total stoichiometric concentrations of each ion using multicomponent equilibrium calculations (i.e., a correction must be made for complexation; see Chap. 2 for a primer on multi-component equilibrium calculations), and activity coefficients (see Chap. 1) must be known. However, in relatively dilute solutions these complications often can be ignored as a first approximation. It is relatively straightforward to modify the calculation procedures and construct the diagrams in terms of total stoichiometric concentrations of the various ions, but this does not avoid the need to calculate activity coefficient and complex formation corrections; this approach merely shifts the applications of these corrections from the plotting of the actual fluid composition to the construction of the diagram, and does not result in any savings of effort. However, for some people total concentrations may be easier to visualize than activities of free ions. Either approach is equally valid and either type of diagram will show the same general trends.

Log f_{O_2}-pH Diagrams

Log f_{O_2}-pH diagrams are used to depict a variety of relationships among solid phases and aqueous species that are dependent on solution pH and/or redox state. We will calculate and plot a number of types of boundaries on log f_{O_2}-pH diagrams in order to illustrate how such diagrams are constructed. The construction of these diagrams follows similar principles to those employed in the calculation of activity-activity diagrams to which they are closely related. By definition, pH = $-\log a_{H^+}$ and $a_{O_2} = f_{O_2}/f_{O_2}^{\circ}$ (Chap. 1), and if we choose our standard state for $O_2(g)$ to be the ideal gas at temperature and one bar, then $f_{O_2}^{\circ}$ = 1 bar and $a_{O_2} = f_{O_2}$. Often, the parameter a_{O_2} is used instead of f_{O_2} in plotting the diagrams, but with the standard state we have chosen, the resulting diagrams are identical. The parameter a_{O_2} is more logical in that it is a unitless quantity (getting around the sticky mathematical problem of taking the logarithm of a dimensioned quantity). However, the use of f_{O_2} is entrenched and many people find it easier to deal with fugacity because it is an analogue of pressure (and indeed pressure and fugacity converge at low pressures; Chap. 1). Thus, we continue to use it here. However, it should be remembered that throughout this chapter, fugacity has the units of bars.

It has been suggested that, because the variable f_{O_2} can take on very small values and cannot be directly measured in geothermal systems, a more meaningful variable to use as an indicator of redox conditions is f_{H_2} (Giggenbach, 1987, 1992, 1997). However, we continue to use f_{O_2} as a variable for the following reasons: (1) the vast majority of the literature continues to use f_{O_2} as a redox variable, (2) f_{O_2}, although typically a very small number, remains a perfectly valid indicator of oxidation potential, even if it has no physical significance (cf. discussion by Anderson and Crerar, 1993), (3) through the use of solid-state electrodes, e.g., yttria-stabilized zirconia electrodes (Bourcier et al., 1987; Anderson and Crerar, 1993), f_{O_2} can be measured directly, at least at high-temperatures, and (4) log f_{O_2} is simply and linearly related to log f_{H_2} through the water dissociation reaction:

$$H_2O(l) = H_2(g) + 1/2O_2(g) \qquad (3.50)$$

such that: log f_{H_2} = log K_w – 1/2log f_{O_2} – log a_{H_2O}. From the latter equation it can be seen that at constant pressure and temperature (i.e., constant K_w) and assuming that $a_{H_2O} \approx 1$ (usually an excellent assumption unless salinity is very high or there are significant quantities of other gases such as CO_2), a log f_{O_2}-pH diagram can be easily changed to a log f_{H_2}-pH diagram simply by relabeling the log f_{O_2} axis. All diagrams depicted in this chapter are shown with both oxygen and hydrogen fugacity scales. Note that once again we are employing a standard state of the pure ideal gas at temperature and one bar for H_2. The same type of criticism has been leveled at pH as a variable (Giggenbach, 1997). However, we retain pH for reasons similar to those for retaining f_{O_2}.

Note that writing a reaction such as (3.50) above in terms of gaseous H_2 and O_2 does not imply the presence of a separate gas phase. Whether or not a separate gas phase exists, chemical potentials for $O_2(g)$ and $H_2(g)$ can be defined for any system containing O_2 or H_2 as components. Because fugacity is directly related to chemical potential, then such a system will also have fugacities for these components, even if there is no separate gas phase.

We will first produce a log f_{O_2}-pH diagram for the system Fe-S-O-H at 200°C and saturated water vapor pressure (SWVP) which will depict Fe mineral phase relations and fields of predominance of aqueous S species. In order to depict phase relations involving Fe sulfide minerals, the boundaries among the aqueous S species must be determined first. The thermodynamic data required are given in Table 2.

TABLE 2. Apparent standard molal Gibbs free energies (in cal/mole) from SUPCRT92 for phases and aqueous species shown in Figures 5, 6, 7, and 8 (200°C, SWVP).

Phase or species	$\Delta_f G^o$	Phase or species	$\Delta_f G^o$
pyrite	-41,186	HS^-	919
pyrrhotite	-27,319	SO_4^{2-}	-176,326
magnetite	-250,344	$O_2(g)$	-8,892
hematite	-182,987	HSO_4^-	-186,000
barite	-332,239	Ca^{2+}	-129,369
graphite	-357	Ba^{2+}	-133,920
$H_2O(l)$	-60,395	$H_2CO_3^0$	-159,633
chalcopyrite	-51,388	HCO_3^-	-144,052
bornite	-106,698	CO_3^{2-}	-121,396
calcite	-274,685	CH_4^0	-14,300
H_2S^0	-13,550		

Aqueous Sulfur Species

The aqueous species we wish to plot on our diagram are H_2S^0, HS^-, HSO_4^-, and SO_4^{2-}. Thermodynamic data for the species S^{2-} are highly uncertain, but it appears that this species is not predominant under any geologically relevant conditions (Seward and Barnes, 1997). It can be shown via thermodynamic calculations (cf. Barnes and Kullerud, 1961), that other sulfur species, such as thiosulfate ($S_2O_3^{2-}$), sulfite (SO_3^{2-}), tetrathionate ($S_4O_6^{2-}$), and polysulfide (S_x^{2-}), although present, are also never predominant under any reasonable geological conditions.

The species H_2S^0 and HS^- are reduced species and will therefore plot at low log f_{O_2} values. We will calculate their boundary first by writing the reaction:

$$H_2S^0 = HS^- + H^+ \qquad (3.51)$$

for which $\Delta_r G^o$ = 14,469 cal/mole and log K = –6.68. The equilibrium constant K for the above reaction may be written as:

$$K = \frac{a_{HS^-} a_{H^+}}{a_{H_2S^0}} .$$

The boundary we wish to calculate is called a predominance boundary (also known as an isoactivity boundary) because it separates the region of log f_{O_2}-pH space where H_2S^0 is the highest activity species (i.e., the predominant species) from that where HS^- is the predominant species. At the boundary itself the activities of the two species are equal. Hence, to plot this boundary on the diagram we set $a_{H_2S^0} = a_{HS^-}$ so that now pH = –log K = 6.68. Thus, the boundary is a vertical line on Figure 5 with H_2S^0 predominant on the left and HS^- predominant on the right.

The species HSO_4^- and SO_4^{2-} are oxidized and will plot at high log f_{O_2} values on our diagram. We can calculate the boundary between HSO_4^- and SO_4^{2-} in a similar manner. We write

$$HSO_4^- = SO_4^{2-} + H^+ \qquad (3.52)$$

for which $\Delta_r G^o$ = 9,674 cal/mole and log K = –4.47. Following similar reasoning as for the H_2S^0/HS^- boundary we set $a_{HSO_4^-} = a_{SO_4^{2-}}$, which leads to pH = –log K= 4.47. This boundary is also a vertical line on Figure 5 with HSO_4^- predominant on the left and SO_4^{2-} predominant on the right.

The next logical boundary to calculate is the HSO_4^-/H_2S^0 boundary. We need to write a reaction with one of the sulfur species on either side of the reaction, and use $O_2(g)$, H^+, and/or $H_2O(l)$ to balance the reaction as necessary, e.g.:

$$H_2S^0 + 2O_2(g) = HSO_4^- + H^+ \qquad (3.53)$$

for which $\Delta_r G^o$ = –154,666 and log K = 71.43. The equilibrium constant for this reaction may be written:

$$K = \frac{a_{HSO_4^-} a_{H^+}}{a_{H_2S^0} f_{O_2}^2} .$$

Setting the activities of the two sulfur species to be equal, they cancel, leaving, in log form: log K = –pH – 2log f_{O_2}.

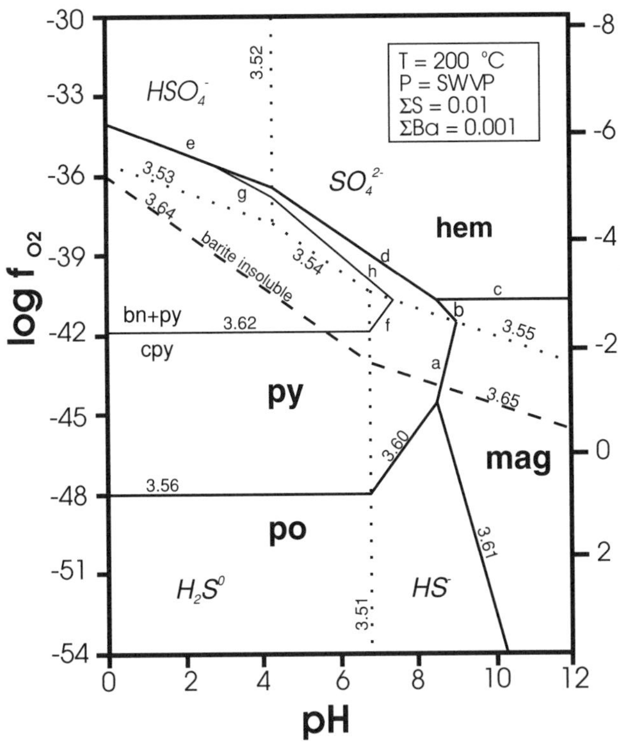

FIG 5. Log f_{O_2}-pH diagram for the system Fe-S-O-H (including the solubility of barite) at 200°C, saturated water vapor pressure, $\Sigma S = 0.01$, and $\Sigma Ba = 0.001$. Dotted lines separate fields of predominance of aqueous sulfur species and heavy solid lines separate the stability fields of iron minerals. The lighter solid line separates the bornite + pyrite from the chalcopyrite stability field. The dashed line separates the area in which barite is supersaturated (above) from the area in which it is undersaturated (below). The small numerals labeling some of the boundaries refer to reaction numbers employed in the text; the small letters refer to reactions in Table 3. Abbreviations: py - pyrite; mag - magnetite; po - pyrrhotite; hem - hematite.

The equation of the boundary then becomes: log f_{O_2} = –35.7 – 0.5pH. This boundary truncates the HSO_4^-/SO_4^{2-} boundary as shown in Figure 5.

The H_2S^0/SO_4^{2-} boundary is given by:

$$H_2S^0 + 2O_2(g) = SO_4^{2-} + 2H^+ \qquad (3.54)$$

and log f_{O_2} = –pH – 33.48. Finally, the $HS^-/SO4^{2-}$ boundary is given by:

$$HS^- + 2O_2(g) = SO_4^{2-} + H^+ \qquad (3.55)$$

and log f_{O_2} = –0.5pH – 36.8. Thus, Figure 5 is divided into four predominance regions, one for each of the four aqueous sulfur species, by the dotted boundaries just calculated. Note that none of the boundaries calculated depend on the actual total activity or concentration of sulfur in solution.

The predominance boundaries calculated for the aqueous sulfur species differ from the phase boundaries calculated above for the activity-activity diagrams and those calculated below for iron minerals. On crossing a phase boundary, one phase reacts to form another phase. On either side of the boundary either one phase or the other is stable, and only at the boundary itself can the two phases coexist. However, predominance boundaries between aqueous species merely separate regions of the diagram where one of the aqueous species is predominant over the rest. For example, in the H_2S^0 field, the other aqueous sulfur species are still present, but at much lower activities or concentrations than H_2S^0. Similarly, H_2S^0 does not completely disappear when crossing the boundaries that enclose its field of predominance, but its concentration falls rapidly with distance from its predominance field. It is important to keep this fundamental difference in mind when constructing and interpreting activity-activity, log f_{O_2}-pH or related diagrams.

It is also important to keep in mind the difference between isoactivity predominance boundaries and isoconcentration boundaries. We have thus far constructed isoactivity boundaries where it is assumed that, for example, for the H_2S^0/SO_4^{2-} boundary, $a_{H_2S^0} = a_{SO_4^{2-}}$. In dilute solutions the position of this isoactivity boundary is nearly identical to that of the analogous isoconcentration boundary where $m_{H_2S^0} = m_{SO_4^{2-}}$, because $\gamma_{H_2S^0} = \gamma_{SO_4^{2-}} \approx 1$. However, in concentrated solutions, the activity coefficients can be significantly different from unity, and in general, $\gamma_{SO_4^{2-}} \ll \gamma_{H_2S^0}$. Thus, the positions of the isoactivity and isoconcentration predominance boundaries could be significantly different. However, given the uncertainty in both the calculation of activity coefficients and the thermodynamic data required to calculate either type of boundary, this difference is usually a secondary consideration.

Iron Minerals

We will now plot stability fields for pyrite, pyrrhotite, magnetite, and hematite. Other potential phases such as wüstite are metastable under the conditions chosen, except possibly native iron. It would be an interesting exercise for the reader to determine whether or not native iron has a stability field on any of the log f_{O_2}-pH diagrams constructed below. This should be relatively straightfoward once the principles outlined below are understood (don't forget to calculate apparent Gibbs free energies of formation for native iron using SUPCRT92!).

To plot the phase boundaries for the iron minerals on the diagram, it is necessary to choose the first two solids, for example, pyrite and pyrrhotite. Then we must specify the sulfur species with which we will balance the chemical reaction corresponding to the chosen phase boundary. The sulfur species to choose is the species anticipated to be predominant in the portion of log f_{O_2}-pH space where we expect the boundary to be located. For example, we can calculate the pyrite-pyrrhotite boundary in the predominance field of H_2S^0 by first balancing the reaction:

$$\underset{\text{(pyrrhotite)}}{FeS} + 0.5O_2(g) + H_2S^0 = \underset{\text{(pyrite)}}{FeS_2} + H_2O(l) \qquad (3.56)$$

Note that we attempt to balance the reaction using only the expected predominant aqueous sulfur species, gaseous oxygen, liquid water, and/or H^+ as needed. For the above reaction, log K = 25.99 and

$$K = \frac{1}{a_{FeS} a_{H_2S^0} \cdot f_{O_2}^{1/2}} .$$

In general, a_{FeS} is not equal to unity owing to non-stoichiometry in pyrrhotite (cf. Barton and Skinner, 1979). However, for simplicity we assume a_{FeS} = 1.0. We then have:

$$\log K = -\log a_{H_2S^0} - 0.5 \log f_{O_2} \quad (3.57)$$

In order to plot this boundary, we must define the value of $a_{H_2S^0}$. Because this boundary lies in the predominance field of H_2S^0, the latter species accounts for nearly 100 percent of the total dissolved sulfur in solution. Thus, if we use the symbol ΣS to denote the total activity of dissolved sulfur in solution, then $a_{H_2S^0}$ = ΣS in the H_2S^0 field (note that, in dilute solutions, activity coefficients approximate unity, so in this case it is also true that $m_{H_2S^0} \approx \Sigma S$, where $m_{H_2S^0}$ is the molal concentration of H_2S^0). We will use ΣS = 0.01 (note the lack of units; activity is a dimensionless quantity!) to complete Figure 5, although it should be noted that such a high ΣS is geologically unusual at 200°C. We will investigate the effect of varying ΣS below. When ΣS is set equal to 0.01, equation (3.57) becomes:

$$25.99 = -(-2.0) - 0.5 \log f_{O_2} \text{ and } \log f_{O_2} = -47.98 \quad (3.58)$$

and the pyrite/pyrrhotite boundary (reaction 3.56) plots as a horizontal line in the H_2S^0 field (Fig. 5).

An obvious question that now arises is: How do we know that the pyrite/pyrrhotite boundary will lie in the H_2S^0 field so that we can write reaction (3.56) in terms of this species? The answer is, we won't necessarily know this a priori, unless we have calculated a similar diagram before. However, this is not a cause for concern. If we make the wrong initial decision, eventually it will be obvious, although we may have to do a little more work. For example, let's suppose that we had chosen to try to plot the pyrite/pyrrhotite boundary in the HSO_4^- field. As we can see from Figure 5, the pyrite/pyrrhotite boundary does not appear in the HSO_4^- field (it is metastable in this field). We would discover this fact in the same way that we discovered that paragonite was metastable at 500°C and 1,000 bars earlier i.e., a logical inconsistency would appear on our diagram. However, in most cases we can find diagrams in the literature similar to the diagram we desire to construct that we can use as a guide, thus eliminating, or at least minimizing, the effort of calculating boundaries that may ultimately turn out to be metastable.

The astute reader will also notice that we have written reaction (3.56) so as to conserve iron. However, we could have written it to conserve sulfur, which would result in the stoichiometry:

$$\underset{\text{(pyrrhotite)}}{2FeS} + 2H^+ + 0.5O_2(g) = \underset{\text{(pyrite)}}{FeS_2} + H_2O(l) + Fe^{2+} \quad (3.59)$$

and ΣFe instead of ΣS would have to be specified. The above boundary obviously has a quite different slope in log f_{O_2}-pH space than reaction (3.56); the boundary for reaction (3.59) involves pH whereas that for reaction (3.56) does not. However, under an assumption of conservation of sulfur, only the pyrite/pyrrhotite and hematite/magnetite boundaries can be plotted. A pyrite/magnetite boundary, for example, cannot be plotted under an assumption of sulfur conservation because sulfur cannot be balanced in a chemical reaction involving only pyrite and magnetite without introducing another sulfur-bearing phase, such as S(l). Thus, conservation of Fe is the logical choice of constraint in this system.

As the pyrite/pyrrhotite boundary intersects the H_2S^0/HS^- boundary, the predominant species changes from H_2S^0 to HS^-. Thus, we now need to rewrite the pyrite/pyrrhotite boundary reaction in terms of the new predominant species, HS^-:

$$\underset{\text{(pyrrhotite)}}{FeS} + 0.5O_2(g) + HS^- + H^+ = \underset{\text{(pyrite)}}{FeS_2} + H_2O(l) \quad (3.60)$$

From this reaction we see that the pyrite/pyrrhotite boundary should change slope as it enters the HS^- field, because reaction (3.56) does not involve H^+, but reaction (3.60) does. For reaction (3.60), log K = 32.67 and

$$K = \frac{1}{a_{FeS} a_{HS^-} a_{H^+} f_{O_2}^{1/2}} .$$

Assuming a_{FeS} = 1 and a_{HS^-} = ΣS = 0.01, we obtain for the equation of the reaction boundary: log f_{O_2} = 2pH − 61.34. It is a general rule that, every time a solid-solid phase boundary involving sulfur-bearing minerals crosses a predominance boundary between aqueous sulfur species, there must be a change in slope of the former.

It should be noted that, although in Figure 5 the pyrite/pyrrhotite boundary is depicted as changing slope abruptly at a sharp angle as it intersects the H_2S^0/HS^- boundary, the boundary is actually curved at this point (cf. Henley et al., 1984). The reason for this is that as the H_2S^0/HS^- boundary is approached, the activity of H_2S^0 begins to decrease from 0.01 until at the boundary, $a_{H_2S^0} = a_{HS^-}$ = 0.5(ΣS) = 0.005. Then, on the other side of the boundary, the activity of HS^- increases from 0.005 to 0.01 upon moving away from the H_2S^0/HS^- boundary. However, this curvature is a relatively small effect and is difficult to sketch accurately on the diagram, so it is often not represented. For simplicity, we shall follow this practice.

Within the HS^- predominance field, the pyrite/pyrrhotite boundary will continue until it either intersects the

HS^-/SO_4^{2-} boundary, where it would change slope once again, or until it intersects another solid-solid phase boundary to form an invariant point where either pyrrhotite or pyrite react out. In the case of Figure 5, the pyrite/pyrrhotite boundary intersects the pyrrhotite/magnetite boundary in the HS^- predominance field. The latter boundary is calculated by first writing the following equation:

$$\underset{\text{(pyrrhotite)}}{3FeS} + 3H_2O(l) + 0.5O_2(g) = \underset{\text{(magnetite)}}{Fe_3O_4} + 3HS^- + 3H^+ \quad (3.61)$$

The reader should be able to verify that the equation used to plot this reaction boundary is: $\log f_{O_2} = 6.47 - 6pH$.

The pyrite/magnetite boundary must then intersect the pyrite/pyrrhotite and pyrrhotite/magnetite boundaries in an invariant point where all three phases coexist. The reaction and equation for the pyrite/magnetite boundary are given in Table 3. Three points should be made about the invariant point just plotted. First, the three univariant boundaries intersect as straight lines without any curvature such as when the pyrite/pyrrhotite boundary crosses the H_2S^0/HS^- boundary. This is because the invariant point is located entirely within the HS^- predominance field so that activity of HS^- remains approximately constant and equal to ΣS. Second, the three univariant reaction boundaries divide log f_{O_2}-pH space into three sectors, one containing pyrite, one containing pyrrhotite, and one containing magnetite. The rules of phase diagrams as enumerated by Schreinemaker (Zen, 1966) dictate that each of these sectors subtend an angle less than or equal to 180°. This rule applies to any invariant point on any phase diagram and can be used as a check on the construction of these diagrams. Third, if the thermodynamic data used to construct the diagram are all internally consistent (which should be the case for SUPCRT92), then the three phase boundaries should all intersect at a single point. If this does not happen, then there are two possible explanations: an error has been made in either the calculation or plotting of one or more of the boundaries; or the thermodynamic data are not internally consistent. The latter situation usually arises

TABLE 3. Reactions and equations for selected boundaries on log f_{O_2}-pH diagrams shown in Figures 5, 6, 7, and 8

Boundary	Reaction	Equation
a) py/mag (HS^- field)	$3FeS_2 + 6H_2O = Fe_3O_4 + 6HS^- + 6H^+ + O_2$	$\log f_{O_2} = -95.25 + 6pH$
b) py/mag (SO_4^{2-} field)	$3FeS_2 + 6H_2O + 11O_2 = Fe_3O_4 + 6SO_4^{2-} + 12H^+$	$\log f_{O_2} = -31.51 + (12/11)pH$
c) hem/mag	$1/3Fe_3O_4 + 1/12O_2 = 1/2Fe_2O_3$	$\log f_{O_2} = -40.48$
d) hem/py (SO_4^{2-} field)	$2FeS_2 + 4H_2O + 15/2O_2 = Fe_2O_3 + 4SO_4^{2-} + 8H^+$	$\log f_{O_2} = -31.7 - (16/15)pH$
e) hem/py (HSO_4^- field)	$2FeS_2 + 4H_2O + 15/2O_2 = Fe_2O_3 + 4HSO_4^- + 4H^+$	$\log f_{O_2} = -34.1 - (8/15)pH$
f) bn/cpy (HS^- field)	$5CuFeS_2 + 2HS^- + 2H^+ + O_2 = Cu_5FeS_4 + 4FeS_2 + 2H_2O$	$\log f_{O_2} = -55.23 + 2pH$
g) bn/cpy (HSO_4^- field)	$5CuFeS_2 + 2HSO_4^- + 2H^+ = Cu_5FeS_4 + 4FeS_2 + 2H_2O + 3O_2$	$\log f_{O_2} = -33.67 - (2/3)pH$
h) bn/cpy (SO_4^{2-} field)	$5CuFeS_2 + 2SO_4^{2-} + 4H^+ = Cu_5FeS_4 + 4FeS_2 + 2H_2O + 3O_2$	$\log f_{O_2} = -30.69 - (4/3)pH$
i) $H_2CO_3^0/HCO_3^-$	$H_2CO_3^0 = HCO_3^- + H^+$	pH = 7.2
j) HCO_3^-/CO_3^{2-}	$HCO_3^- = CO_3^{2-} + H^+$	pH = 10.46
k) $H_2CO_3^0$/graphite	$C(s) + H_2O + O_2 = H_2CO_3^0$	$\log f_{O_2} = -42.56$
l) HCO_3^-/ graphite	$C(s) + H_2O + O_2 = HCO_3^- + H^+$	$\log f_{O_2} = -35.37 - pH$
m) CH_4^0/graphite	$C(s) + 2H_2O = CH_4^0 + O_2$	$\log f_{O_2} = -44.24$
n) CH_4^0/ HCO_3^-	$CH_4^0 + 2O_2 = HCO_3^- + H^+ + H_2O$	$\log f_{O_2} = -39.8 - (1/2)pH$
o) CH_4^0/CO_3^{2-}	$CH_4^0 + 2O_2 = CO_3^{2-} + 2H^+ + H_2O$	$\log f_{O_2} = -34.57 - pH$
p) $H_2CO_3^0$/calcite	$CaCO_3(s) + 2H^+ = Ca^{2+} + H_2CO_3^0$	pH = 4.31
q) graphite/calcite	$CaCO_3(s) + 2H^+ = Ca^{2+} + C(s) + H_2O + O_2$	$\log f_{O_2} = -33.95 - 2pH$
r) CH_4^0/calcite	$CaCO_3(s) + 2H^+ + H_2O = Ca^{2+} + CH_4^0 + 2O_2$	$\log f_{O_2} = -39.1 - pH$

when data have been taken from a variety of different sources, some of which may be employing mutually incompatible standard states. The best course of action to remedy this situation is to attempt to discover which piece(s) of data are not consistent (not always a job for those with weak stomachs!) and replace them. However, if the mismatch in the boundary intersections is not too large (a judgment call), then it is reasonable to adjust one or more of the boundaries slightly to force the intersection. This is permissible because as pointed out below, there is some uncertainty in the location of the boundaries anyway owing to uncertainty in the thermodynamic data used in their construction.

The remaining phase boundaries among the iron minerals are calculated in a similar manner. The reactions and equations for each of the boundaries are summarized in Table 3 and the reader should confirm these results. It can be seen that the field of pyrite stability occurs as a wedge pinching out with increasing pH (Fig. 5). The size of this field (and that of pyrrhotite) is dependent on the value of S employed, the sulfides naturally becoming more stable with increasing ΣS. With a decrease in ΣS, the pyrite and pyrrhotite fields decrease in size until the pyrite-pyrrhotite-magnetite triple point plots on the H_2S^0/HS^- boundary. At even lower ΣS values, pyrite and pyrrhotite can no longer coexist because a narrow strip of magnetite stability interposes itself between the pyrite and pyrrhotite fields. These changes in the log f_{O_2}-pH diagram with decreasing ΣS for the Fe-S-O system are illustrated in Figures 6 and 7. In addition, at sufficiently high ΣS and/or low temperature, a field of stability of solid or liquid sulfur appears as a wedge along the aqueous sulfide/sulfate boundaries, pinching out with increasing pH. However, the predominance boundaries for the aqueous sulfur species do not change with ΣS, because the activity terms for the aqueous sulfur species on each side of the equation cancel. It is a useful exercise for the reader to repeat the calculation of Figure 5 at various values of ΣS and compare the results to the diagrams shown in Figures 6 and 7.

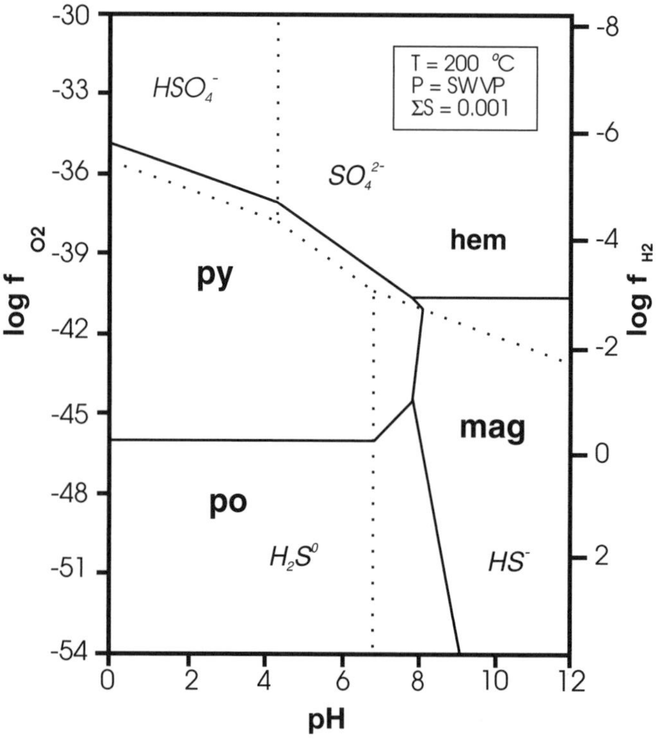

FIG. 6. Log f_{O_2}-pH diagram for the system Fe-S-O-H at 200°C, saturated water vapor pressure, and $\Sigma S = 0.001$. All lines and abbreviations have the same significance as in Fig. 5.

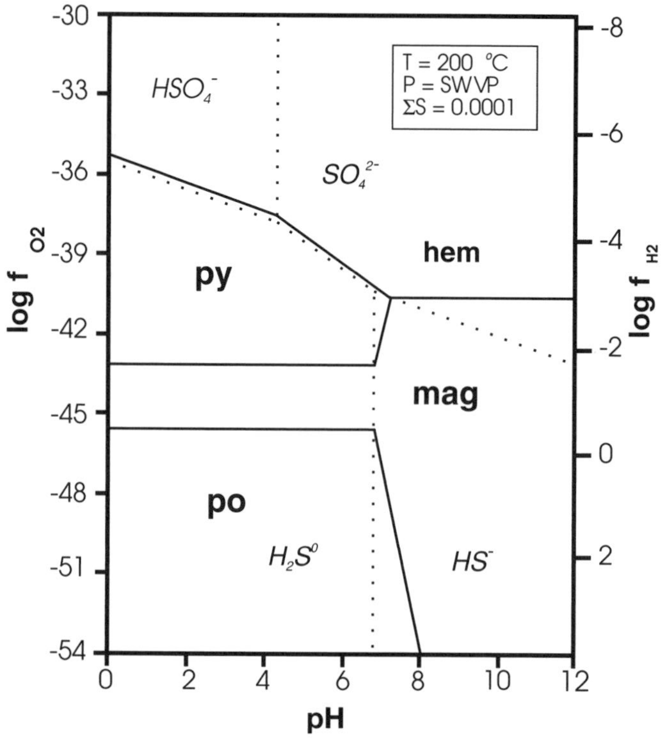

FIG. 7. Log f_{O_2}-pH diagram for the system Fe-S-O-H at 200°C, saturated water vapor pressure, and $\Sigma S = 0.0001$. All lines and abbreviations have the same significance as in Fig. 5.

From a comparison of Figures 5, 6, and 7, it is evident that the choice of values of fixed activities, such as ΣS, can have a significant impact on the topology of the diagram, and any conclusions drawn therefrom. For example, Figure 5 suggests that pyrite can coexist with magnetite only at geologically unusual pH values (>8.5). However, this is misleading because, as mentioned above, $\Sigma S = 0.01$ is unusually high. At lower values of ΣS, pyrite and magnetite can coexist over the entire pH range from less than 0 to almost 8, and pyrite and pyrrhotite cannot coexist at any pH (Fig. 7). This discussion illustrates the danger of making generalized conclusions about phase relations from a single log f_{O_2}-pH diagram constructed at a single ΣS, and emphasizes the importance of expressly constructing a diagram at conditions appropriate to the problem at hand, rather than simply depending on a previously published diagram.

Copper-Iron Sulfides

A number of other types of boundaries may be plotted on the basic diagram in Figure 5. For example, we can now superimpose the bornite + pyrite/chalcopyrite boundary. Starting with this boundary in the H_2S^0 field, we write:

$$\underset{\text{(chalcopyrite)}}{5CuFeS_2} + 2H_2S^0 + O_2(g) = \underset{\text{(bornite)}}{Cu_5FeS_4} + \underset{\text{(pyrite)}}{4FeS_2} + 2H_2O(l) \quad (3.62)$$

The equation for this boundary is log f_{O_2} = –41.86, assuming ΣS = 0.01. Note that we have assumed conservation of both Cu and Fe. The reactions and equations for the branches of this boundary in the HS^-, SO_4^{2-} and HSO_4^- fields are given in Table 3. As shown in Figure 5, the bornite + pyrite/chalcopyrite boundary curves around, enclosing a field of bornite + pyrite, similar to the field of pyrite alone. The field of stability of bornite + pyrite will shrink as ΣS decreases.

Barite Solubility

It is also possible to plot solubility contours on log f_{O_2}-pH diagrams. A solubility contour is the locus of all points in log f_{O_2}-pH space where the total concentration (or in this case, activity) of the metal in question is constant (see earlier in this chapter for the definition of solubility). As an example, we will plot the solubility contour for barite at ΣBa = 0.001 (where ΣBa is the sum of the activities of all aqueous Ba species). As with the iron-bearing mineral phase boundaries, the barite solubility contours will change slope each time they cross a boundary involving aqueous sulfur species. Let us start by calculating the contour in the HSO_4^- predominance field. We write the reaction:

$$BaSO_4(s) + H^+ = Ba^{2+} + HSO_4^- \quad (3.63)$$

for which

$$K = 10^{-5.69} = \frac{a_{Ba^{2+}} a_{HSO_4^-}}{a_{H^+}}$$

and $\log K = \log a_{Ba^{2+}} + \log a_{HSO_4^-} + pH$

but assuming $a_{Ba^{2+}} = \Sigma Ba$ = 0.001 and $a_{HSO_4^-} = \Sigma S$ = 0.01, the equation for this boundary is: pH = –0.69. This contour obviously plots off the pH scale of Figure 5, suggesting that barite is insoluble at the chosen ΣBa and ΣS over the entire HSO_4^- and SO_4^{2-} predominance fields. We now turn to calculation of the solubility contour in the H_2S^0 field for which the reaction is:

$$BaSO_4(s) + 2H^+ = Ba^{2+} + H_2S^0 + 2O_2(g) \quad (3.64)$$

Assuming once again that $a_{Ba^{2+}} = \Sigma Ba$ = 0.001 and $a_{H_2S^0} = \Sigma S$ = 0.01, the equation for this contour is: log f_{O_2} = –36.06 – pH. This boundary plots in the H_2S^0 field (Fig. 5) and so it is stable. Upon intersection with the H_2S^0/HS^- boundary, the reaction of the contour changes to:

$$BaSO_4(s) + H^+ = Ba^{2+} + HS^- + 2O_2(g) \quad (3.65)$$

and its equation is: log f_{O_2} = –39.40 – 0.5pH. Barite is insoluble under the chosen conditions everywhere above the plotted contour (Fig. 5), and is soluble everywhere below it. In essence, there is a flat barite solubility basin corresponding to the sulfate predominance field, where barite solubility is fixed by the solubility product of barite at a given value of ΣS, and is independent of pH and f_{O_2}:

$$BaSO_4(s) = Ba^{2+} + SO_4^{2-} \quad (3.66)$$

$$\bar{K}_{S0} = a_{Ba^{2+}} a_{SO_4^{2-}}$$

For example, at 200°C, log $K_{3.66}$ = –10.16, and so, at ΣS = 0.01, $\Sigma Ba = 10^{-8.16}$ throughout the sulfate predominance field. Barite solubility increases upon moving out of the SO_4^{2-} predominance field in any direction. It is possible to plot a series of barite solubility contours at various values of ΣBa on Figure 5. Contours for $\Sigma Ba < 0.001$ would plot above and parallel to the ΣBa = 0.001 contour, and those for $\Sigma Ba > 0.001$ would plot below and parallel to the ΣBa = 0.001 contour.

The N-O-H and Ca-C-O-H Systems

The N-O-H system provides another example of how to plot boundaries on a log f_{O_2}-pH diagram. In this case, boundaries must be calculated between pairs of the species N_2^0, NH_3^0, and NH_4^+. Note that N_2^0 refers to dissolved nitrogen. The NH_3^0/NH_4^+ boundary is straightforward. We write:

$$NH_3^0 + H^+ = NH_4^+ \quad (3.68)$$

Setting $a_{NH_3^0} = a_{NH_4^+}$, we obtain pH = 5.80 as the equation for this boundary (see Table 4 for the necessary thermodynamic data). For the NH_3^0/N_2^0 boundary we obtain:

$$N_2^0 + 3H_2O(l) = 2NH_3^0 + 1.5O_2(g) \quad (3.69)$$

The equilibrium constant for this reaction (Table 4) is:

$$K = 10^{-67.46} = \frac{a^2_{NH_3^0} \cdot f^{3/2}_{O_2}}{a_{N_2^0}}$$

To plot this boundary it is necessary to assign a value to the total activity of dissolved nitrogen. We choose ΣN = 0.001, and thus obtain the equation: log f_{O_2} = –42.97. Finally, the NH_4^+/N_2^0 boundary is obtained from the reaction:

$$N_2^0 + 3H_2O(l) + 2H^+ = 2NH_4^+ + 1.5O_2(g) \quad (3.70)$$

for which: log f_{O_2} = –35.24 – (4/3)pH. Note that log $K_{3.70}$ = log $K_{3.69}$ + 2log $K_{3.68}$ = –67.46 + 2(5.80) = –55.86. The three boundaries for this system are shown in Figure 8.

TABLE 4. Equilibrium constants at 200°C and SWVP for selected reactions used in the text

Reaction	log K(200°C)	Source
$H^+ + NH_3^0 = NH_4^+$	5.80	SUPCRT92
$N_2^0 + 3H_2O(l) = 2NH_3^0 + 1.5O_2(g)$	–67.46	SUPCRT92
$Au(s) + H_2S^0 + HS^- = Au(HS)_2^- + 0.5H_2(g)$	–1.07	Benning and Seward (1996)
$H_2O(l) = H_2(g) + 0.5O_2(g)$	–23.18	SUPCRT92

The reactions and equations for log f_{O_2}-pH boundaries in the Ca-C-O-H system are given in Table 3 and plotted in Figure 8. These include boundaries between aqueous carbon species and solid graphite, and solubility contours for calcite. For additional practice, the reader is encouraged to calculate the equations for the boundaries (using thermodynamic data from Table 2) and compare them with those given in Table 3. It is worth mentioning that we are following the convention (Stumm and Morgan, 1996) that $H_2CO_3^0$ is equivalent to $CO_2(aq)$ so that the latter does not appear as a separate species in Figure 8.

Solubility of Gold as $Au(HS)_2^-$

Some of the most commonly encountered log f_{O_2}-pH diagrams in the literature on ore deposits are those depicting the solubility of gold. As a final example, we will add solubility contours for gold as the bisulfide complex, $Au(HS)_2^-$, to a log f_{O_2}-pH diagram (Fig. 5) already containing predominance boundaries for aqueous sulfur species and stability fields for iron-bearing minerals. Predominance boundaries for the sulfur species must be calculated and plotted first before attempting to plot the gold solubility contours. Plotting of the iron-mineral stability fields is optional.

We will commence by writing the reaction for the Au solubility contour in the H_2S^0 predominance field:

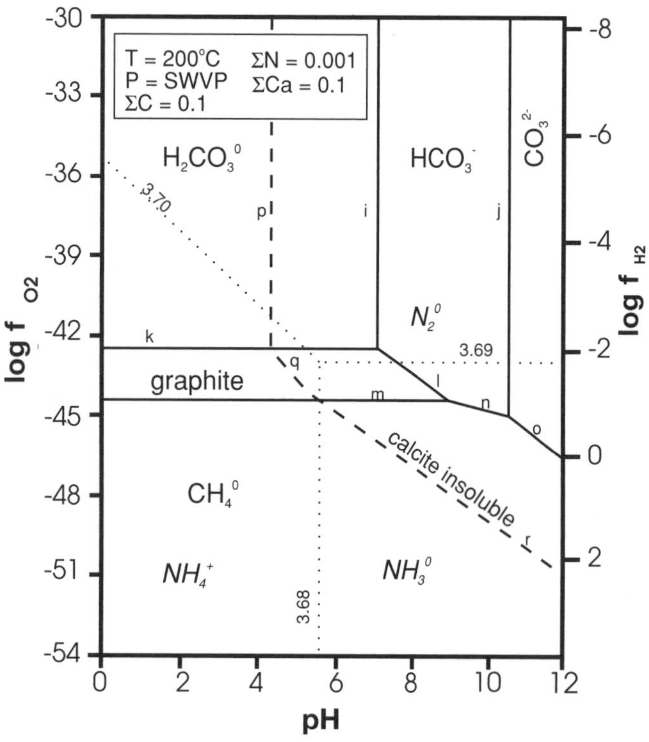

FIG. 8. Log f_{O_2}-pH diagram for the systems Ca-C-O-H and N-O-H at 200°C, saturated water vapor pressure, ΣCa = 0.1, ΣC = 0.1, and ΣN = 0.001. Dotted lines separate fields of predominance of nitrogen species and heavy solid lines separate the fields of predominance of carbon species. The dashed line separates the area in which calcite is supersaturated (above) from the area in which it is undersaturated (below). The small numerals labeling some of the boundaries refer to reaction numbers employed in the text; the small letters refer to reactions in Table 3.

$$Au(s) + 2H_2S^0 + 1/4O_2(g) = Au(HS)_2^- + 1/2H_2O(l) + H^+ \quad (3.71)$$

However, we encounter the difficulty that SUPCRT92 does not contain thermodynamic data for the gold complex, $Au(HS)_2^-$. As pointed out in Chapter 2, the most reliable thermodynamic data for this species comes in the form of the equilibrium constant for the following reaction given by Benning and Seward (1996):

$$Au(s) + H_2S^0 + HS^- = Au(HS)_2^- + 1/2H_2(g) \quad (3.72)$$

To convert this to the form required, we need the equilibrium constant for the reaction:

$$H_2O(l) = H_2(g) + 1/2O_2(g) \quad (3.73)$$

Thus, to obtain reaction (3.71), we need to take reaction (3.72), subtract 1/2 reaction (3.73) and add reaction (3.51). Thus, $\log K_{3.71} = \log K_{3.72} - 0.5(\log K_{3.73}) + \log K_{3.51} = -1.07 - 0.5(-23.18) + (-6.68) = 3.84$. Then we write:

$$K_{3.71} = \frac{a_{H^+} a_{Au(HS)_2^-}}{a_{H_2S^0}^2 f_{O_2}^{1/4}} \quad (3.74)$$

As before, we set $a_{H_2S^0} = \Sigma S = 0.01$, but in order to plot the solubility contour, we need to define the activity of the gold species. As a simplification we will set the activity coefficients for the gold species equal to unity so that activity equals concentration. Suppose we wish to plot the 1 ppb Au solubility contour. We must first convert this value to molality units, whereby $\Sigma Au = m_{Au(HS)_2^-} = (10^{-6}$g Au/kg H_2O)/(197g Au/mole) = 5.08×10^{-9} molal. Under these conditions, the equation for the solubility contour becomes: $\log f_{O_2} = -32.52 - 4pH$. If we repeat the calculations for 100 ppb and 10 ppm Au we obtain: $\log f_{O_2} = -24.52 - 4pH$ and $\log f_{O_2} = -16.52 - 4pH$, respectively.

The Au solubility contours in the HS^- field are calculated based on the reaction:

$$Au(s) + 2HS^- + H^+ + 1/4O_2(g) = Au(HS)_2^- + 1/2H_2O(l) \quad (3.75)$$

The equilibrium constant for this reaction is: $\log K_{3.75} = \log K_{3.71} - 2(\log K_{3.51}) = 3.84 - 2(-6.68) = 17.20$. The equations for the contours at 1 ppb, 100 ppb, and 10 ppm, respectively, are: $\log f_{O_2} = -85.96 + 4pH$, $\log f_{O_2} = -77.96 + 4pH$, and $\log f_{O_2} = -69.96 + 4pH$.

In the SO_4^{2-} field, the contours are governed by the reaction:

$$Au(s) + 2SO_4^{2-} + 3H^+ = Au(HS)_2^- + 1/2H_2O(l) + 15/4O_2(g) \quad (3.76)$$

for which $\log K_{3.76} = \log K_{3.71} - 2(\log K_{3.54}) = 3.84 - 2(66.966) = -130.1$. The resulting contours are: $\log f_{O_2} = -33.54 - (4/5)pH$, $\log f_{O_2} = -34.08 - (4/5)pH$, and $\log f_{O_2} = -34.61 - (4/5)pH$ for 1 ppb, 100 ppb, and 10 ppm, respectively.

Finally, in the HSO_4^- field we have:

$$Au(s) + 2HSO_4^- + H^+ = Au(HS)_2^- + 1/2H_2O(l) + 15/4O_2(g) \quad (3.77)$$

and log $K_{3.77}$ = log $K_{3.76}$ + 2(log $K_{3.52}$) = –130.1 + 2(–4.47) = –139.0. Now the contours can be expressed as: log f_{O_2} = –35.9 – (4/15)pH, log f_{O_2} = –36.5 – (4/15)pH, and log f_{O_2} = –37.0 – (4/15)pH for 1 ppb, 100 ppb, and 10 ppm, respectively.

The solubility contours resulting from the above calculations are depicted in Figure 9, where the familiar "bull's eye" pattern for the solubility of gold as the $Au(HS)_2^-$ complex is seen. An obvious solubility maximum exists at the point where H_2S^0, HS^-, and SO_4^{2-} are present with equal activities. Solubility contours are analogous to elevation contours on a topographic map; the more closely spaced the contours in log f_{O_2}-pH space, the steeper the solubility gradient. Thus, in Figure 9 it can be seen that gold solubility decreases at a much faster rate moving away from the solubility maximum towards higher f_{O_2} than towards lower f_{O_2}. This means that oxidation of a solution bearing gold in the form of bisulfide complexes is a more efficient means of deposition than reduction.

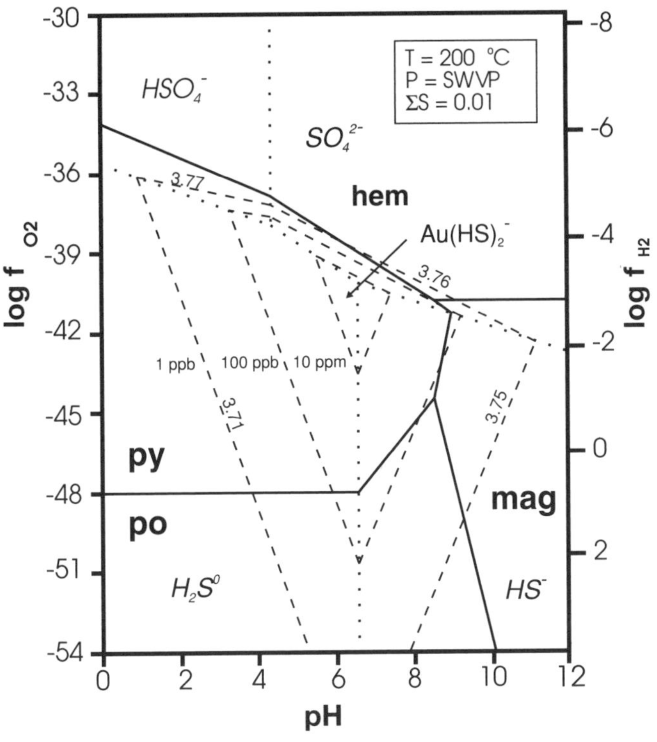

FIG. 9. Log f_{O_2}-pH diagram showing the solubility of gold as the complex $Au(HS)_2^-$ at 200°C, saturated water vapor pressure and ΣS = 0.01. Dotted lines separate fields of predominance of sulfur species and heavy solid lines separate the stability fields of iron minerals. The dashed lines represent gold solubility contours in parts per billion (ppb) and parts per million (ppm). The small numerals labeling some of the boundaries refer to reaction numbers employed in the text; the small letters refer to reactions in Table 3.

Concluding Remarks

Using the general methods outlined above, the reader is now in a position to construct any type of speciation or phase diagram that may be useful in the study of hydrothermal ore deposits. Some examples include diagrams depicting relationships among combinations of variables such as: log a_{Cl^-}-pH, log f_{S_2}-log f_{O_2}, log (a_{K^+}/a_{H^+})-temperature, log f_{H_2}-log ΣS, etc. The only real limitations are the imagination of the user and the availability of thermodynamic data for the required species and phases. The main steps in the construction of any such type of diagram are: (1) decide which chemical system and the corresponding species and phases you want to depict; (2) decide on the variables for the X- and Y-axes; (3) collect the required thermodynamic data; (4) write chemical reactions for each boundary, using, first, H_2O and the chemical species on the X- and Y-axes, and then any other species required; (5) algebraically rearrange the equilibrium constant expressions so that they are in the form of an equation of a straight line in the variables chosen for the X- and Y-axes; (6) fix the activities of any species that do not appear on the X- and Y-axes of the chosen diagram; and (7) plot the straight lines carefully on the diagram, eliminating any and all boundaries that may turn out to be metastable. There has been some development of computer calculation/graphics packages to facilitate the construction of these diagrams, e.g., the programs THERMODATA (Turnbull and Wadsley, 1987), The Geochemist's Workbench® (Bethke, 1994), f_{O_2}-pH (Zhang and Spry, 1994) and PHOX (Polya, 1998). However, the diagrams will only be as good as the thermodynamic data on which they are based. Thus, some critical assessment of the portion of the thermodynamic database relevant to the particular system of interest should precede use of these or any other such programs.

It should also be realized that there is a certain amount of uncertainty in even the most carefully determined thermodynamic data. A small percentage uncertainty in the Gibbs free energy of formation can lead to a much larger percentage uncertainty in the Gibbs free energy change for a given reaction because the absolute value of the latter is often much smaller than the absolute values of the Gibbs free energies of formation of some of the phases and/or species involved. Thus, instead of plotting boundaries as thin lines, they should be represented as bands, the thickness of which is a reflection of the overall uncertainty (cf. Barnes and Kullerud, 1961). However, this would often lead to an illegible diagram and is rarely done. Nevertheless, these uncertainties should always be kept in mind when making conclusions based on diagrams constructed from tabulated thermodynamic data.

Acknowledgments

This chapter benefited from the detailed comments of Chris Gammons, Tom Giordano, Jeremy Richards, and Iain Samson.

REFERENCES

Anderson, G.M., and Crerar, D.A., 1993, Thermodynamics in geochemistry: The equilibrium model: New York, Oxford University Press, 588 p.

Barnes, H.L., and Kullerud, G., 1961, Equilibria in sulfur-containing aqueous solutions in the system Fe-S-O, and their correlation during ore deposition: Economic Geology, v. 56, p. 648–688.

Barton, P.B., Jr., and Skinner, B.J., 1979, Sulfide mineral stabilities, *in* Barnes, H.L., ed., Geochemistry of hydrothermal ore deposits, 2nd ed.: New York, Wiley-Interscience, p. 278–403.

Benning, L.G., and Seward, T.M., 1996, Hydrosulphide complexing of Au(I) in hydrothermal solutions from 150–400°C and 500–1500 bar: Geochimica et Cosmochimica Acta, v. 60, p. 1849–1872.

Bethke, C.M., 1994, The Geochemist's Workbench®, Version 2.0, A Users Guide to Rxn, Act2, Tact, React, and Gtplot: Urbana, University of Illinois, 213 p.

Bourcier, W.L., Ulmer, G.C., and Barnes, H.L., 1987, Hydrothermal pH sensors of ZrO_2, Pd hydrides, and Ir oxides, *in* Ulmer, G.C., and Barnes, H.L., eds., Hydrothermal experimental techniques: New York, Wiley, p. 157–188.

Bowers, T.S., Jackson, K.J., and Helgeson, H.C., 1984, Equilibrium activity diagrams for coexisting minerals and aqueous solutions at pressures and temperatures to 5 kb and 600°C: New York, Springer-Verlag, 397 p.

Drever, J.I., 1997, The Geochemistry of natural waters: Surface and groundwater environments, 3rd. ed.: Upper Saddle River, New Jersey, Prentice-Hall, 436 p.

Faure, G., 1991, Principles and applications of inorganic geochemistry: New York, Macmillan, 626 p.

Garrels, R.M., and Christ, C.L., 1965, Solutions, minerals, and equilibria: New York, Harper and Row, 450 p.

Giggenbach, W.F., 1987, Redox processes governing the chemistry of fumarolic gas discharges from White Island, New Zealand: Applied Geochemistry, v. 2, p. 143–161.

—— 1992, Magma degassing and mineral deposition in hydrothermal systems along convergent plate boundaries: Economic Geology, v. 87, p. 1927–1944.

—— 1997, The origin and evolution of fluids in magmatic-hydrothermal systems, *in* Barnes, H.L., ed., Geochemistry of hydrothermal ore deposits, 3rd ed.: New York, Wiley-Interscience, p. 737–796.

Grant, J.A., 1986, The isocon diagram—A simple solution to Gresens' equation for metasomatic alteration: Economic Geology, v. 81, p. 1976–1982.

Gresens, R.L., 1967, Composition-volume relationships of metasomatism: Chemical Geology, v. 2, p. 47–55.

Henley, R.W., Truesdell, A.H., Barton, P.B., Jr., and Whitney, J.A., 1984, Fluid-mineral equilibria in hydrothermal systems: Reviews in Economic Geology, v. 1, 267 p.

Holland, H.D., 1959, Some applications of thermochemical data to problems of ore deposits: I. Stability relations among the oxides, sulfides, sulfates and carbonates of ore and gangue minerals: Economic Geology, v. 54, p. 184–233.

—— 1965, Some applications of thermochemical data to problems of ore deposits: II. Mineral assemblages and the composition of ore-forming fluids: Economic Geology, v. 60, p. 1101–1166.

Johnson, J.W., Oelkers, E.H., and Helgeson, H.C., 1992, SUPCRT92: A software package for calculating the standard molal thermodynamic properties of minerals, gases, aqueous species, and reactions from 1-5000 bars and 0-1000°C: Computers and Geosciences, v. 18, p. 899–947.

Krauskopf, K.B., and Bird, D.K., 1995, Introduction to Geochemistry, 3rd ed.: New York, McGraw-Hill, 647 p.

MacLean, W.H., and Kranidiotis, P., 1987, Immobile elements as monitors of mass transfer in hydrothermal alteration: Phelps Dodge massive sulfide deposit, Matagami, Quebec: Economic Geology, v. 82, p. 951–962.

Nesbitt, H.W., 1984, Equilibrium diagrams displaying chemical speciation and mineral stabilities in aqueous solutions, *in* Fleet, M.E., ed., Short Course in Environmental Geochemistry: Mineralogical Association of Canada Short Course Notes, v. 10, p. 15–44.

Nordstrom, D.K., and Munoz, J.L., 1994, Geochemical thermodynamics, 2nd ed.: Boston, Blackwell Scientific Publications, 493 p.

Polya, D.A., 1998, PHOX: Automated calculation of mineral stability and aqueous species predominance fields in Eh (or log (f_{O_2}) or pε)–pH space, *in* Arehart, G.B. and Hulston, J.R., eds., Water-Rock Interaction: Proceedings of the 9th International Symposium on Water-Rock Interaction–WRI-9/Taupo, New Zealand, March 30–April 2, 1998, Rotterdam, A.A. Balkema, p. 897–900.

Seward, T.M., and Barnes, H.L., 1997, Metal transport by hydrothermal ore fluids, *in* Barnes, H.L., ed., Geochemistry of hydrothermal ore deposits, 3rd ed.: New York, Wiley-Interscience, p. 435–486.

Stumm, W., and Morgan, J.J., 1996, Aquatic chemistry: Chemical equilibria and rates in natural waters, 3rd ed.: New York, Wiley-Interscience, 1022 p.

Turnbull, A.G., and Wadsley, M.W. 1987, The CSIRO-SGTE THERMODATA system (version V): Division of Mineral Chemistry, Institute of Energy and Earth Resources, CSIRO, P.O. Box 124, Port Melbourne, Victoria, 3207, Australia.

Zen, E., 1966, Construction of pressure-temperature diagrams for multicomponent systems after the method of Schreinemakers—A geometric approach. U.S. Geological Survey Bulletin 1225, 56 p.

Zhang, X., and Spry, P.G., 1994, f_{O_2}-pH: A quickBasic program to calculate mineral stabilities and sulphur isotope contours in log f_{O_2}-pH space: Mineralogy and Petrology, v. 50, p. 287–291.

Chapter 4

Magmatic Contributions to Hydrothermal Ore Deposits: An Algorithm (MVPart) for Calculating the Composition of the Magmatic Volatile Phase

P.A. CANDELA
Department of Geology, University of Maryland, College Park, Maryland 20742

AND P.M. PICCOLI
Department of Geology, University of Maryland, College Park, Maryland 20742

Introduction

Examination of igneous rocks and/or alteration products associated with geothermal systems, ore deposits, and volcanism suggests that magmatic volatiles may be active agents of acid alteration, ore-metal transport, magma ascent, and volcanic eruption. Thus, an understanding of the magmatic volatile phase (MVP) is critical to pure and applied geology. However, because of its fugitive nature, the magmatic volatile phase is difficult to sample or study. Therefore, experimental and theoretical modeling plays an important role in our attempt to understand magmatic-hydrothermal processes such as those thought to be active in the generation of granite-related ore deposits. Geologic studies of past magmatic-hydrothermal activity include a combination of experimental and field-based methods of analysis. However, the relationship between static, microscale, equilibrium experiments (e.g., studies of element partitioning, phase equilibria, etc.), and the complex, time-integrated natural world is a tenuous one. Without models, the deductive consequences of experiments cannot be tested against field observations.

Candela and Piccoli (1995) refined a model (now called MVPart) that can be used to predict the concentration of ore metals in successive aliquots of a (Rayleigh) fractionating aqueous phase during second boiling. Here the term "second boiling" indicates volatile exsolution from a melt due to crystallization of the melt at a constant pressure. This model is available in the form of a DOS/PC executable file (see Appendix 1). The model requires several different types of input, such as the estimation of intensive parameters (e.g., temperature, pressure, the initial ratio of chlorine to water in the melt), and the determination of relevant thermodynamic data (e.g., equilibrium constants). To preserve generality, we present a chemical model that is independent of any physical model of devolatilization; however, specific physical models of devolatilization can place severe restrictions on how predictions of the MVP chemistry can be compared to fluid inclusion or other field-based data (cf. Candela, 1991, 1994, 1997; Candela and Blevin, 1995; Shinohara and Kazahaya, 1995).

The algorithm discussed in this paper can be used by researchers and explorationists to test how variations in certain geological parameters can affect the probability of orthomagmatic-hydrothermal ore formation. For example, by varying the pressure of volatile exsolution in the model, the effect of the depth of emplacement of the granitic magma on the efficiency of ore metal removal from the melt can be evaluated. In turn, the level of emplacement of granites exposed in a particular region is related to the level of erosion. For magmas of a given bulk composition, wetter magmas saturate earlier with respect to hornblende. The model can be used to evaluate the extent to which wetter magmas can more efficiently partition ore metals into "ore fluids" relative to the crystallizing phases. Similarly, the effect of magmatic pyrrhotite (po) crystallization on the removal of copper from the magma-ore system can be evaluated. By using the information presented in this paper and elsewhere (Piccoli and Candela, 1994), a model chlorine concentration for any sub- to peraluminous apatite-bearing granite (s.l.) magma can be estimated, and the resulting concentration of magmatic chlorine can be used in the model to evaluate its effect on ore-metal partitioning during magmatic volatile exsolution. Assuming that the efficiency of ore-metal removal from the melt by the MVP is related, in part, to the probability of ore formation, then sensitivity analyses can be performed. For example, the explorationist can evaluate how variations in the Cl concentration in apatite, or variations in depth of emplacement, may affect the probability of ore formation. Further, the program can be used to determine: the maximum concentration of an ore metal in aliquots of vapor or brine evolved from the magma, corresponding possibly to the maximum likely concentration of an ore metal that might be detected in a fluid inclusion; the average concentration (averaged over reaction progress) of any element in the evolving volatile phases, which may be more indicative of the concentration of the ore metal in the fluid that actually gains egress from a crystallizing pluton; the proportion of vapor to brine evolved, that may be related to the probability of trapping vapor versus brine inclusions in the ore; how magma, and in turn, vapor or brine composition (e.g., concentrations of other cations) can affect the ore metal concentrations in the ore fluids; and whether or not brine is formed.

MVPart

The algorithm MVPart (Magmatic Volatile Phase partitioning) can be used to simulate a simplified, model composition of the magmatic volatile phase(s), vapor or vapor + brine, that are exsolved isobarically from granitic (s.l.) magmas. This phenomenon of crystallization-driven volatile exsolution in plutonic environments has been referred to as second boiling (e.g., Bowen, 1928). Strictly speaking, second boiling is the exsolution of a volatile phase during isobaric cooling (hence the term "second" boiling) of a subliquidus multicomponent liquid. If the sum of the vapor pressures of the volatile constituents rises to the total load (magmatic) pressure during cooling and crystallization, then a state of vapor saturation is reached. The vapor pressure of a volatile constituent would normally decrease with decreasing temperature according to the Clausius-Clapeyron equation. However, in a magma, the activity or vapor pressure of a volatile constituent increases upon cooling due to the increase in the mole fraction of the volatile constituent during the crystallization of anhydrous minerals. "First boiling" occurs when the total load pressure is reduced to the sum of the vapor pressures of the liquid solution (melt); first boiling is not treated explicitly in this model. Of course, in nature, second boiling may occur non-isobarically; decreasing pressure can drive second boiling due to the crystallization that accompanies an increase in solidus temperature. Indeed, the quench textures found in many ore-related porphyries attest to the non-equilibrium, polybaric volatile exsolution that occurs in these systems as magma rises toward the Earth's surface. However, in the "equilibrium limit," the components of the system will distribute themselves according to the conditions of chemical equilibrium as represented by equilibrium constants or, under restricted conditions, as Nernst partition coefficients (see Candela, 1990, for details).

The MVPart algorithm can be used to model volatile saturation of a melt of a given bulk composition and initial water concentration, and at a specified temperature and pressure. Crystallization is modeled implicitly through the use of bulk crystal/melt partition coefficients for each element. Once the composition of the melt is calculated at volatile saturation (which is equivalent to water saturation in this algorithm), the composition of successive aliquots of vapor or vapor + brine is calculated, until the volatile-saturated melt has crystallized. In this model, the MVP is fractionated according to a Rayleigh law—that is, it is removed as it is formed. This, of course, is a limiting case—in reality, a finite amount of the MVP may remain in equilibrium with the melt; this modification has been considered by Candela (1994), but is not treated here. Further, the reader may wish to consult Lowenstern (1994) and Webster (1997) for conditions of volatile saturation with activities of water (significantly) below unity. Sufficient data do not yet exist to allow the concentration of a full complement of the components of the brine to be calculated accurately. However, until such data are procured, we suggest that the results presented here represent the most rigorous treatment possible at this time, and are broadly illustrative of the effects of brine saturation. A noteworthy point, however, is that data do exist to allow the concentrations of Na, K, H, Cu, and Cl to be calculated in the brine phase. As more data are obtained from laboratory investigations, they can be added to the database. The end product of this modeling includes (1) the elucidation of general trends in the calculated efficiencies with which metals are removed from crystallizing magmas into evolving aqueous/saline ore fluids; and (2) estimates of the concentrations of ore-metals in the volatile phases.

Immiscibility in the Magmatic Aqueous Phase

Shallow felsic magmatic systems exist in a P-T regime wherein vapor and brine can coexist in the subcritical region of salt-water systems (as exemplified by the simple system NaCl-H_2O). At temperatures of 700° to 850°C and pressures of approximately 30 to 150 MPa, magmas may be saturated with respect to a two-phase mixture of low-salinity aqueous vapor and a hydrosaline liquid (brine; Sourirajan and Kennedy, 1962; Bodnar et al., 1985). The presence of carbon dioxide can extend the field of immiscibility to higher pressures. Thus, at the pressures and temperatures of interest here, the equilibria are written to include the phases: aqueous vapor + silicate melt ± brine ± crystals. The vapor + brine assemblage defined by tie-lines in P-T-(NaCl/H_2O) space is isobarically and isothermally invariant (see Chap. 7). Changes in the ratio of Cl/H_2O are reflected by shifts in the mass proportion of vapor relative to brine. The experimental data from Williams et al. (1997) can be used to calculate the concentration of NaCl, KCl, and HCl in a magmatic volatile phase for a given melt composition, temperature, pressure, and total chloride concentration in the volatile phase. However, the salinities of the coexisting vapor and brine can vary widely over rather small regions of P-T-X space, especially for bulk MVP compositions that are near-critical at pressures and temperatures close to the water-saturated granite solidus. If a magma is brine and vapor saturated, there is a unique weight ratio of Cl to H_2O in the melt at a given T and P. For example, at 800°C and 100 MPa, a brine-saturated vapor in the NaCl-H_2O system has 10,800 ppm Cl (Bodnar et al., 1985). Under these conditions, the melt has approximately 4.2 wt percent water, and the Nernst-type vapor/melt (v/melt) partition coefficient for Cl is approximately 5 ($D_{Cl}^{V/melt} \approx$ 5; see Candela and Piccoli, 1995), yielding Cl/H_2O (melt) $\approx$ 0.05. A melt with Cl/H_2O < 0.05 at 800°C and 100 MPa saturates initially with respect to a vapor (brine-undersaturated), and the chloride concentration increases in the melt (ignoring the incorporation of Cl into crystalline phases) until brine + vapor saturation is reached. For melts that become vapor-saturated at low pressures, the usual course of evolution will be from a state of vapor saturation to one of vapor + brine saturation, unless crystallization of the system is complete prior to brine saturation. It certainly is possible, however, for a melt to become saturated with respect to brine only (i.e., the melt saturates with respect to a hydrous molten salt mixture; Webster, 1997), but the sum of the vapor pressures of the volatile constituents of the melt (NaCl, KCl, H_2O, etc.) has not yet reached the load pressure. For melts with Cl/H_2O > 0.05 at 800°C and 100 MPa, crystallization leads first to brine saturation. Given that these melts would be saturated with brine only, we consider them to be vapor-undersaturated. According to the data summarized in Webster (1992) and Metrich and Rutherford (1992), metaluminous melts saturated with NaCl have chloride concentrations that are not very different from melts saturated with respect to a vapor + brine mixture. Because only melts that saturate with respect to vapor or vapor + brine are considered in this paper, we will limit our discussion to melts with Cl/H_2O ratios at or below the ratio on the vapor + brine cotectic at a given pressure. At 100 MPa and 800°C, the critical concentration of chlorine on the vapor-brine cotectic is approximately 2,200 ppm given a vapor/melt partition coefficient for Cl equal to 5. At 50 MPa, the critical chloride concentration (for water concentration ≈ 2.7 wt %) is just under 500 ppm.

Introduction to the Algorithm

Using this algorithm, saturation of a melt with a CO_2-free vapor or a CO_2-free vapor + brine mixture can be modeled. Implicitly, the melt composition is modeled as near minimum, and does not change in major element composition with crystallization. In reality, the crystallization of even a "minimum melt" is polythermal when the activity of water is less than unity (i.e., when the melt is undersaturated with water). However, here we will ignore the effect of temperature on the partitioning of ore-metals between melt and crystals prior to MVP saturation; this simplification is made to reduce unnecessary complexity in the algorithm. Also, it should be pointed out that this is an equilibrium model, and as such, represents a limiting case in the modeling of natural processes. The algorithm routinely considers Cu, Mn, Zn, Ca, Mg, Yb, Ce, K, Na, Eu (exchange partitioning), and Cl, Mo, W, F, and B (Nernst-type behavior). It can be modified easily to include other elements. In the current version of the algorithm, constant bulk crystal/melt partition coefficients are used. However, the partition coefficients can be changed to reflect different values before and after vapor saturation. Based on published data from our laboratory, we can calculate melt/brine equilibria for Cu, K, Na, and HCl (Williams et al., 1995, 1997). For other metals we assume that the metal-Na vapor/melt exchange is constant and can be used as an estimate of the brine/melt exchange constant, as was demonstrated for Cu by Williams et al. (1995). Elements treated as partitioning according to a Nernst-type law (e.g., Cl, Mo, W, F, and B) are modeled as partitioning into brine in proportion to the ratio of water in the brine relative to the vapor; this approach is highly tentative (and should be taken only as an approximation at this time). Therefore, in this communication, we emphasize the behavior of Cu in melt-vapor-brine systems; the consideration of other elements is needed so that a reasonable estimate of Cl-cation balance in the brine can be made (given that the concentration of any given element is dependent upon all other elements in the vapor and/or brine).

Given that magmatic volatile phases are complex, multi-component phases (with many cations complexed by Cl), it is reasonable to assume that the concentration of any given Cl-complexed element in the MVP is a function not only of the Cl concentration, but also of the concentration of all other elements that compete with it for Cl or "charge" balance. In the case of Cu, its concentration in the MVP is dependent upon both the Cl concentration in the MVP and the concentrations of Na, K, Ca, Fe, etc. (present as NaCl, KCl, $CaCl_2$, $FeCl_2$, respectively) in the MVP. Therefore, other approaches that model the partitioning of single cations only in the MVP (e.g., Cline and Bodnar, 1991) cannot be used to model accurately the effects of variations in bulk composition of the melt on the composition of the volatile phase.

Our computations have a number of consequences for the evaluation of the behavior of chloride-complexed cations in magmatic hydrothermal processes (Table 1 shows the initial concentrations and bulk crystal/melt partition coefficients for elements that were used in the computations). The general mathematical principles of these calculations are discussed in Candela (1986, 1989); however, some modifications have been made since then (including the incorporation of brine into the model) and have been discussed in Candela and Piccoli (1995).

TABLE 1. Bulk crystal/melt partition coefficients,

$$\overline{D_i} = \Sigma x_j D_i^{xl_j/melt}$$

before/after volatile saturation at NNO (nickel nickel-oxide) and GM (graphite-methane)), and average composition (in ppm) of Lachlan Fold Belt I-type granite used in the calculations

	$\overline{D}$ before volatile saturation: NNO (GM)	$\overline{D}$ after volatile saturation: NNO (GM)	Concentration (ppm)
Cu	2(2)	0.2(0.2)	10
Mn	0.5(0.5)	0.5(0.5)	550
Zn	1(1)	1(1)	49
Ca	1(1)	1(1)	22500
Mg	1(1)	1(1)	8900
Yb	0.27(0.27)	0.27(0.27)	8.3
Ce	1.53(1.53)	1.53(1.53)	66
K	1(1)	1(1)	28700
Na	1(1)	1(1)	23400
B	0.1(0.1)	0.1(0.1)	20
Mo	0.2(0.4)	0.2(0.4)	1
W	0.5(0.4)	0.5(0.4)	5
Cl	0(0)	0(0)	*
Eu	1.61(2.48)	1.61(2.48)	1.2

* indicates that the concentration of Cl was varied in individual runs.

Estimation of Geological Parameters

To calculate the composition of an aliquot of the magmatic vapor or brine, a number of geological parameters must be estimated, and then used in MVPart. While it is beyond the scope of this contribution to discuss the many methods for the estimation of all input parameters, we present here an outline of some methods that can be used to estimate initial water concentrations, total pressure, and Cl/H_2O ratios.

The parameters needed to perform an MVPart calculation for a given granite/ore system are: composition of devolatilizing melt (considered to be constant over devolatilization); pressure of magma emplacement and devolatilization; oxygen fugacity; and initial chlorine and water contents of the melt.

A crude estimate of the composition of the devolatilizing melt is given by the bulk composition of the granite rock itself. In the absence of other data, this composition may be used; however, one should attempt to use the composition of the least altered granite, and if any fine-grained, relatively unaltered, quenched phases are present (e.g., a groundmass or cogenetic aplite dike), they may yield a better estimate of the melt composition during devolatilization. Alternatively, the composition of associated volcanic rocks or melt inclusions may provide an estimate of the composition of the devolatilized melt. This discussion has not considered important issues such as the role of cumulates in the generation of granitic rocks, but that issue is beyond the scope of this communication.

Pressure and Initial Water Concentrations

The determination of the pressure of emplacement and devolatilization has generated lively debate in the recent geological literature (see reviews of thermobarometry in granitic batholiths by Anderson, 1996; Ague, 1997; Candela, 1997). Stratigraphic reconstructions and phase equilibria-based estimates from fluid inclusions have been the mainstays of pressure estimates for ore-forming systems. Here we will review some of the latest research on the use of hornblende to estimate pressure. As with any method of pressure estimation for magmatic hydrothermal systems, it must be noted whether the pressure estimate is for the ore zone, or for the intrusion. Note that the average pressure of volatile exsolution in the magma may be significantly greater than even the "lithostatic" pressure prevailing at the site of ore deposition.

Hornblende barometry is based on the observed increase in the Al concentration in hornblende with increasing pressure. The critical pressures needed to run the program MVPart are not the pressures of ore formation, but the average pressure prevailing at the site of MVP exsolution in the magmatic system. Anderson (1996) gives the equation:

$$P(\text{MPa}) = [4.76Al - 3.01 - [(T - 675)85] \\ [0.530Al + 0.005294\ (T - 675)]] \cdot 100 \qquad (4.1)$$

(where T is in °C) for the estimation of pressure in granitic rocks; see the discussion therein for the rather strict mineralogical requirements that need to be satisfied for this method to yield reasonable estimates of pressure. In this equation, the concentration of aluminum (Al in the above equation) is given by the sum of $Al^{IV} + Al^{VI}$ per 13 cations. The temperatures used in the barometric estimate may be plagioclase-amphibole equilibrium temperatures (Anderson, 1996) or estimates of the temperature range of amphibole growth in the granitic liquid (Candela, 1997, and references therein). This method yields, at best, pressures with uncertainties on the order of ±100 MPa (1,000 bars); however, note that the analyzed amphiboles may have equilibrated at or below the level of emplacement.

Comparison between the composition of leucocratic granite dikes and the ternary minima from Tuttle and Bowen (1928) can also yield estimates of pressure (Ratajeski, 1995; Kistler and Swanson, 1981). Alternatively, if suitable mineral assemblages are present in the country rocks, pressure may be estimated from contact metamorphic relationships. As with any type of geobarometry, the significance of the pressure estimated by these techniques is problematic. Pressure is only defined in an isotropic (hydrostatic, in the fluid dynamic sense) stress field. Pressures estimated from contact metamorphic relationships probably reflect a combination of the last fluid pressure with which the rocks equilibrated, and the response of mineral chemistry to later changes in intensive parameters. Further, if the minerals were subjected to an anisotropic stress field during equilibration with the fluid phase, then the free energy of the phases will not be those assumed in geobarometric models, and pressures calculated may be problematic. This is a continually overlooked problem in metamorphic petrology, and it becomes more severe at lower pressures where the uncertainty in the estimation of total pressure approaches the pressure itself. The pressure in a magma may be taken as the vertical normal component of stress due to the weight of overlying rock. Note, however, that the pressure in the overlying hydrothermal system (including part of the contact aureole), that may only be in transient, episodic (and possibly catastrophic) communication with the magma, may be due to the weight of the overlying water column. In general, if amphibole barometry consistently yields pressures on the order of 100 MPa, then one can reasonably assume that the granite is epizonal, and a provisional estimate of P on the order of 100 MPa, but with rather large uncertainties, can be assigned to the granite in question.

The initial water concentration in the intermediate igneous rocks found associated with many porphyry ore deposits can be estimated from the relative position of hornblende in the crystallization sequence. For granodioritic rocks of a given bulk composition, higher initial water concentrations should correlate with the earlier appearance of hornblende. Near-liquidus amphibole indicates that a melt had at least 4 to 5 wt percent water initially (Johnson et al., 1994). Such a magma would saturate almost instantaneously with respect to a water-rich vapor (assuming it is nearly CO_2 free) upon commencement of crystallization at depths on the order of 4 km. On the other hand, an otherwise similar but drier granodiorite, with only 1 wt percent initial water, could not crystallize hornblende until at least 75 percent of the melt crystallized, if at all. For further discussion of amphibole geobarometry, and also the role played by hornblende in the estimation of initial water concentrations in granite magmas related to ore deposits, see Candela (1997).

Chlorine

Many metals in granite- or diorite-related hydrothermal ore deposits are chloride complexed in high temperature aqueous systems. Therefore, the ability of a magmatic volatile phase to transport ore metals into a high temperature hydrothermal system will be partly dependent upon the Cl concentration in the melt at the onset of devolatilization. The ratio of Cl to H_2O in the melt is entered at the beginning of an MVP calculation. Piccoli and Candela (1994) developed a routine for the estimation of a model initial concentration of chloride in a melt for a given granitic rock that contains accessory apatite.

First, the solubility of apatite and the temperature of apatite saturation must be calculated for the melt of interest. Temperature and SiO_2 concentrations in the melt are the two most important parameters needed to calculate the solubility of apatite in cooling metaluminous magmas. Therefore, the solubility of apatite in the magma can be calculated for magma compositions of interest, given estimates of how melt SiO_2 and P_2O_5 concentrations change as the magma crystallizes. In this way, the apatite saturation temperature (AST) and the amount of apatite crystallized for a given cooling interval (ΔT) can be calculated. Second, apatite crystals are analyzed by electron microprobe (or an alternative appropriate technique) for Cl and F, and the mole fractions of chlorapatite (ClAp), fluorapatite (FAp) and hydroxyapatite (HAp) are calculated. The third step is to calculate the HCl to H_2O ratio of the magmatic volatile phase that would be in equilibrium with the apatites analyzed in the second step, at the respective AST value given in step one. Please note that apatite composition does not yield a salinity, but a measure of Cl/OH. The calculation is performed by using published thermodynamic data on the pertinent apatite and magmatic volatile phase components. The fourth step is to estimate the total Cl in the magmatic volatile phase from the relationship between HCl and total chloride ($\Sigma Cl_{aq} = HCl_{aq} + NaCl_{aq} + KCl_{aq} + 2FeCl_{2\ aq}$, etc.) for the given melt composition (see Williams et al., 1997). The final step in the analysis is to calculate the melt chloride and fluoride concentrations, by using magmatic volatile phase/melt partitioning data and the chloride concentration in the model aqueous phase. Additionally, initial halogen concentrations in the melt can be obtained using estimates of melt crystallization preceding apatite saturation assuming incompatible behavior of the halogens. These steps are condensed into the following equations taken from Piccoli and Candela (1994).

Estimations of apatite crystallization temperature can be obtained by comparing natural and experimental systems. Harrison and Watson (1984) found that for metaluminous melts with initial (0) concentrations of SiO_2 and H_2O of

$$C_{SiO_2}^{melt,o} = 0.45 \text{ to } 0.75 \quad C_{H_2O}^{melt,o}$$

= 0 to 0.10 (expressed as weight fractions: wt %/100) and at pressures exhibited in the crust, the solubility of apatite could be expressed as a function of temperature, and the instantaneous

$$C_{SiO_2}^{melt,AST} \text{ and } C_{P205}^{melt,AST}$$

at which the apatite crystallizes (apatite saturation temperature, AST).

Piccoli and Candela (1994) recast the results of Harrison and Watson (1984) as an empirical solubility expression (see discussion therein for limitations on this equation):

$$T = \frac{[26{,}400 \cdot C_{SiO_2}^{melt,\,AST} - 4{,}800]}{[12.4 \cdot C_{SiO_2}^{melt,\,AST} - \ln(C_{P_2O_5}^{melt,\,AST}) - 3.97]} \qquad (4.2)$$

where T is the apatite saturation temperature, AST (in Kelvin). Generally these values will not be the whole rock concentrations

$$C_{SiO_2}^{melt,o} \text{ and } C_{P205}^{melt,o},$$

except in those cases where apatite is a liquidus or near-liquidus phase. If apatite is the liquidus phase, the calculation of the temperature at which apatite begins to crystallize is straightforward, given whole rock phosphorus and silica concentration as estimators of

$$C_{SiO_2}^{melt,AST} \text{ and } C_{P205}^{melt,AST}$$

Whereas this is not an unusual case in felsic melts, it is not true universally. The solubility of apatite is higher in more mafic magmas (e.g., in a tonalite melt) and apatite may not appear until 1:3 of the melt has crystallized. For granites, sensu stricto,

$$C_{SiO_2}^{melt,AST} = \text{whole rock } SiO_2 \text{ concentration},$$

and the same is true for P_2O_5. For treatment of other felsic rocks, see Piccoli and Candela (1994).

The concentration of Cl in the melt (in ppm) at the AST is computed from

$$C_{Cl}^{melt} = \frac{\dfrac{X_{ClAp}^{Ap}}{X_{HAp}^{Ap}} \cdot \dfrac{3.54\times10^7}{18} \cdot \dfrac{1}{10^{\left[0.04661 + \frac{2535.8 - 0.0303 \cdot (P-1)}{T} - \frac{}{T}\right]}}}{D_{Cl}^{v/melt} \cdot 10^{(-0.63 - 0.00035 \cdot P)}} \qquad (4.3)$$

where

$$X_{ClAp}^{Ap}, X_{HAp}^{Ap}$$

are the mole fractions of chlorapatite and hydroxyapatite, respectively (calculated following the method defined in Piccoli and Candela, 1994), $D_{Cl}^{v/melt}$ is the vapor melt partition coefficient for Cl, P is in kbar, and T is in Kelvin.

Calculation of Initial Cl Concentration in a Plutonic Suite

Applying these calculations to the Tuolumne Intrusive Suite (California), and accounting for melt composition as a function of crystallinity, yields the following AST values: Kuna Crest (KC) 928°C, Half Dome Equigranular (HDE) 901°C, Half Dome Porphyry (HDP) 915°C, Cathedral Peak (CP) 925°C, and Johnson Porphyry (JP) 795°C. These temperatures, which mark the beginning of apatite crystallization, are all below the respective liquidus temperatures for reasonable water contents. The proportion of the melt that crystallizes before apatite saturation has also been estimated: KC (35%), HDE (9%), HDP (9%), CP (9%), and JP (16%). The ratio of the mole fraction of chlorapatite to hydroxyapatite

$$X_{ClAp}^{Ap}, X_{HAp}^{Ap}$$

decreases, and fluorapatite to hydroxyapatite

$$X_{FAp}^{Ap}/X_{HAp}^{Ap}$$

increases within the host rocks from the outer to the inner units of the Tuolumne Intrusive Suite: KC (0.08, 1.7), HDE (0.06, 4.6), HDP (0.02, 2.7), CP (0.03, 5.0) and JP (0.02, 8.0). The calculated initial Cl and F concentrations (in ppm) for the Tuolumne Intrusive Suite units are, respectively: KC (400; 100–150), HDE (400; 320–430), HDP (130; 210–290), CP (210; 400–590) and JP (58; 240–290).

The equigranular Half Dome granodiorite (HDE), that is similar in composition and mineralogy to many ore-related granites, serves as a useful example for demonstration of these calculations (details can be found in Piccoli and Candela, 1994). The granodiorite has an average SiO_2 and P_2O_5 concentration of 66.7 and 0.156 wt percent (n = 7), respectively, in the rock at present. Following the rationale discussed in Piccoli and Candela (1994), the present composition need not be representative of the magma during the crystallization of apatite; however, assumptions can be made to back-correct whole rock SiO_2 and P_2O_5 to approach those in the melt as apatite began to crystallize. Following this rationale, the HDE melt had 68.9 wt percent SiO_2 and 0.170 wt percent P_2O_5 as apatite began to precipitate; under these conditions, the model suggests the melt crystallized about 8 percent (Piccoli and Candela, 1994) and was at a temperature of 948°C (from eq. 4.2 above). Apatite from the granodiorite contains

$$0.08 \text{ wt \% Cl } (X^{Ap}_{ClAp} = 0.12) \text{ and } 3.05 \text{ wt \% F } (X^{Ap}_{FAp} = 0.810),$$

on average. From this, assuming stoichiometry is preserved in the halogen site in apatite (which is consistent with the experimental data), a value of 0.32 wt percent OH in apatite can be calculated, in which OH = 1.79 [1 – (wt % F/3.767) – (wt % Cl/6.809)], which corresponds to

$$X^{Ap}_{HAp} = 1.79.$$

Given the apatite saturation temperature of 948°C calculated above, a melt with approximately 440 ppm Cl (calculated using eq. 4.3 above) would be in equilibrium with the measured apatite composition.

Oxygen Fugacity, Crystal/Melt Partitioning, and ASI

Many authors have suggested, based on field observations, thermodynamic calculations, and experimentation, that oxygen fugacity can exert a strong control on the efficiency with which some ore metals may be partitioned among crystalline, melt, and volatile phases (e.g., Burnham and Ohmoto; 1980; Candela and Bouton, 1990; Blevin and Chappell, 1992). Oxygen fugacity may affect partitioning directly, through f_{O_2} dependence of crystal/melt and/or MVP/melt partition coefficients, or indirectly, by affecting the availability of Cl for complexation with ore metals. Candela and Bouton (1990) showed that the partitioning of both W and Mo is dependent upon oxygen fugacity, with crystal/melt partitioning of Mo decreasing with increasing oxygen fugacity (i.e., molybdenum becomes more crystal incompatible with increasing f_{O_2}), and W exhibiting an increasing crystal/melt partition coefficient with increasing f_{O_2}. However, Nernst-type (D) partition coefficients do not always model the partitioning of metals between melt and crystalline phases accurately. For example, equilibria in the subsystem Cu-Fe-S-O between pyrrhotite (po) and melt can be represented as:

$$\mu^{po}_{CuFeS_2} + \mu^{melt}_{FeO} = 2\mu^{po}_{FeS} + \mu^{melt}_{CuO_{0.5}} + (0.25)\mu^{system}_{O_2}$$

$$\mu^{po}_{FeS} + (0.5)\mu^{system}_{O_2} = \mu^{melt}_{FeO} + (0.5)\mu^{system}_{S_2}$$

$$\mu^{po}_{S_2} = \mu^{system}_{S_2} \tag{4.4}$$

where all components of the phases are independently variable, as dictated by the definition of chemical potential, μ (see Appendix 2 and Chap.1). In equation (4.4), μ^{ϕ}_{i} is the chemical potential of component i in phase ϕ, or in the system. The first equilibrium shows that the partitioning of copper between melt and pyrrhotite (a function of the concentration of $CuFeS_2$ in po divided by the concentration of $CuO_{0.5}$ in the melt) will be dependent upon the oxygen fugacity of the system and the Fe(II) concentration in the granitic melt (or, at a given oxygen fugacity, the concentration of total iron in the melt). Alternatively, within the confines of the linearly independent system of chemical equilibria shown in equation (4.4), the first and second equations of the set can be combined so as to show that the partition coefficient for copper is dependent upon the fugacities of sulfur and oxygen in the system, rather than the oxygen fugacity and Fe(II) concentration in the melt. Note that these two alternatives are entirely equivalent, because the second equilibrium relates the concentration of Fe(II) in the melt to the activity of FeS in po, and the fugacities of oxygen and sulfur. These relationships could not be discerned if equilibria involving independently variable components of the phases (phase components) were not considered.

Bulk partition coefficients are treated as constant (subject to the thermodynamic constraints we have just discussed) throughout crystallization for most elements. However, as discussed by Candela and Holland (1986) and Lynton et al. (1993), the bulk D for Cu should change from greater than one (which models "compatible" behavior), to a value much less than one (which models incompatible behavior) at water saturation. This is merited because of (1) the importance of small amounts of magmatic sulfide in the sequestering of copper (Lynton et al., 1993), and (2) the fact that felsic melts seem to be saturated with a magmatic sulfide phase early in their history, but not at the later stages of crystallization (i.e., sulfides are not uncommon as inclusions in early formed minerals, but glass/sulfide contacts are rare in volcanic rocks; see Stimac and Hickmott (1995).

For metals that have a demonstrated affinity for magmatic sulfides (e.g., Cu and Au), increasing oxygen fugacity can destabilize the host crystalline phase, causing a compatible element to become incompatible, regardless of the f_{O_2}-dependence of the partition coefficient. That is, the bulk partition coefficient for ore metal i, expressed as the weighted sum of the individual mineral/melt (xl/melt) partition coefficients for i, (the weighting factor is the weight fraction x_j of the mineral j in the instantaneous crystalline assemblage) defined by:

$$\overline{D_i} = \Sigma x_j D_i^{xl_j/melt} \quad (4.5)$$

can vary with oxygen fugacity due to variations in x_j or the individual mineral/melt partition coefficient(s). For example, if a magma crystallizes 1 percent magnetite (mt) and 0.1 percent pyrrhotite, the bulk partition coefficient for an element with magnetite/melt and pyrrhotite/melt partition coefficients of 5 and 500 respectively would be equal to $(0.01 \times 5) + (0.001 \times 500) = 0.55$.

Here we outline a few methods for making rough approximations of magmatic f_{O_2}. First, there are the qualitative indicators of magmatic oxygen fugacity. In quartz-saturated systems such as many high level felsic magmas, magnetite coexists with quartz at the solidus. This is only possible at oxygen fugacities above QFM; hence magnetite-bearing granites are at an oxygen fugacity equal to or above QFM. Many fresh, pink granites (i.e., granites that have glassy pink K-feldspar) with amphibole, sphene, and magnetite probably crystallized at oxygen fugacities of ca. NNO or higher. Blevin and Chappell (1992) discuss "reduced I-type granites" that correspond to some of Ishihara's (1977) ilmenite series granites. These granites may contain amphibole and ilmenite, but lack magnetite and sphene. Their oxygen fugacities are in the vicinity of QFM. Most S-type granites appear to have oxygen fugacities below QFM. The presence of stable pyrrhotite (see Whalen and Chappell, 1988) probably limits the oxygen fugacity to approximately NNO +1 or +2 or below, whereas high sulfate in apatite probably is indicative of oxygen fugacities in the vicinity of NNO +1 or +2 or above.

Candela (1989) modified an equation from Ague and Brimhall (1988) that can be used to estimate the f_{O_2} of a granite magma given the hematite component of ilmenite, the annite component of biotite, and assumed activities of water and the K-feldspar component in the alkali feldspar solid solution at given P and T. Further, Blevin and Candela (1997) have shown that internally consistent results can be obtained from consideration of bulk rock Fe^{3+}/Fe^{2+} by using the equation from Kress and Carmichael (1991), designed for estimating the oxygen fugacity of lavas at magmatic P and T given the bulk composition of glassy volcanic rocks. Blevin and Candela (1997) show the following trends for log f_{O_2} for granitic rock suites: peraluminous S-type granites have calculated ΔQFM in the range 0 to –2, whereas metaluminous to mildly peraluminous I-types range from ΔQFM = –1 to +2.

Modeling the Partitioning of Cu: An Overview

We first present a specific example of the calculation of the efficiency of copper removal from a crystallizing magma, and of the concentration of copper and chloride in the MVPs for successive aliquots of the MVP exsolved from a given homogeneous aliquot of melt. The homogeneous aliquot of melt will generally not represent the whole magma chamber. Rather, it is probably a relatively small segment of the crystallization interval in an inwardly crystallizing chamber (Candela, 1991); the homogeneous aliquot of melt could represent a larger portion of the chamber in the case where a magma devolatilizes polybarically (Candela and Piccoli, 1995). Table 2 shows an example of selected results for Cu and Cl from a typical run of the MVPart algorithm. In this example, a metaluminous oxidized I-type granite melt (composition is listed in Table 1), with approximately 2 wt percent H_2O and 530 ppm Cl (a reasonable Cl concentration for a Sierran granite; Piccoli and Candela, 1994) is crystallized at 100 MPa. Vapor saturation occurs at 50 percent crystallization, and brine saturation occurs at 80 percent crystallization (see Fig. 1). The calculated efficiency of removal of Cu from the magma into the magmatic volatile phase is approximately 16 percent (Fig. 2).

A number of authors (e.g., Candela, 1989; Candela and Piccoli, 1995; Shinohara and Kazahaya, 1995) have pointed out that because the magma may have undergone different degrees of crystallization and devolatilization at different places at any one time, the volatile phase that gains egress from the melt will in fact have an averaged composition; investigators should not expect to see the exact compositions of aliquots of magmatic vapor/brine calculated by many workers (e.g., Candela, 1989; Cline and Bodnar, 1991) represented commonly in fluid inclusions in ore. However, each aliquot of devolatilizing melt

TABLE 2. Example of isothermal crystallization of hydrous, felsic, low-CO_2 magma, with exsolution of volatiles. See also (See also Figs. 1 and 2)

Initial melt: magma = (100% melt as a limiting case), major element composition = average Lachlan Fold Belt I-type granite (see Table 4.1); also, ASI=1.01, f_{O_2} = NNO, and 2.1 wt % water in the melt, at a temperature of 800°C at volatile saturation:

Concentration (ppm)

	melt		melt	vapor	brine		melt	vapor	brine
water	21,000	Cl	530			Cu	100		

At 50% crystallization, the melt saturates with respect to vapor:

Concentration (ppm)

	melt		melt	vapor	brine		melt	vapor	brine
water	42,400	Cl	1,070	5,350		Cu	50	625	

At 75% crystallization (50% of water exsolved), the volatile phase is still "vapor only":

Concentration (ppm)

	melt		melt	vapor	brine		melt	vapor	brine
water	42,400	Cl	1,850	9,240		Cu	45	950	

At 80% crystallization (60% of water exsolved), the melt saturates with respect to brine (system is now vapor + brine saturated). The variance of the system drops by 1, and the concentration of Cl in the melt is now constant. A constant Cl/H_2O ratio in the melt at vapor + brine saturation fixes the vapor/brine weight ratio in the exsolved product:

Concentration (ppm)

	melt		melt	vapor	brine		melt	vapor	brine
water	42,400	Cl	2,180	10,900	368,000	Cu	40	990	22,400

The concentrations of Cl and water are constant in the melt, vapor (10,900 ppm; 1.8 wt % NaCl eq.), and brine (368,000 ppm; 60.8 wt % NaCl eq.) from 80% to 100% crystallization (in most magmas, this interval of crystallization is nearly isothermal). The weight ratio brine/(vapor + brine) is also constant (0.11). However, other unbuffered concentrations (e.g., Cu) can vary freely.

In the above simulation, the concentration of Cu in the initial melt was 100 ppm. At brine saturation, the Cu concentration in the 20% melt remaining was 40 ppm (mainly the effect of prolonged crystal fractionation before volatile exsolution, together with vapor-only exsolution prior to brine saturation). The concentration of Cu in the vapor and brine at that point = 990 and 22,400 ppm, respectively. The Cu concentration in all three phases plummets after brine saturation. The overall efficiency of removal of Cu by vapor and brine is 16%.

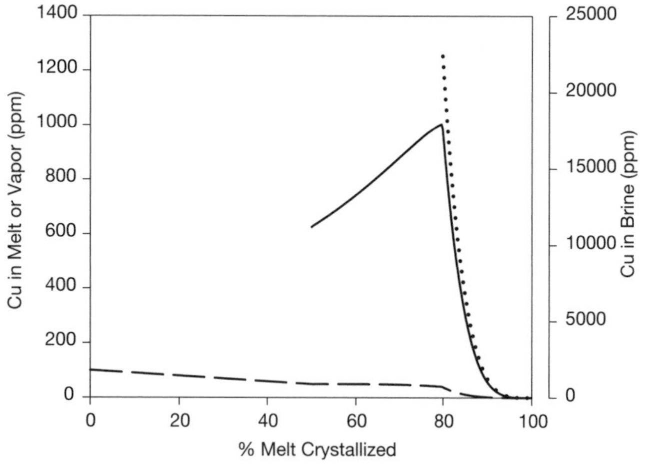

FIG. 1. Concentration of copper in MVPs exsolved from successive aliquots of crystallizing melt (also shown) as a function of the proportion of melt crystallized. Conditions: calculations were performed to simulate a magma with an ASI of 1.01, emplaced at a pressure of 100 MPa, with 2.1 wt % initial magmatic water, at an of NNO, at 800°C. Composition of the initial melt, and the bulk partition coefficients are listed in Table 1.

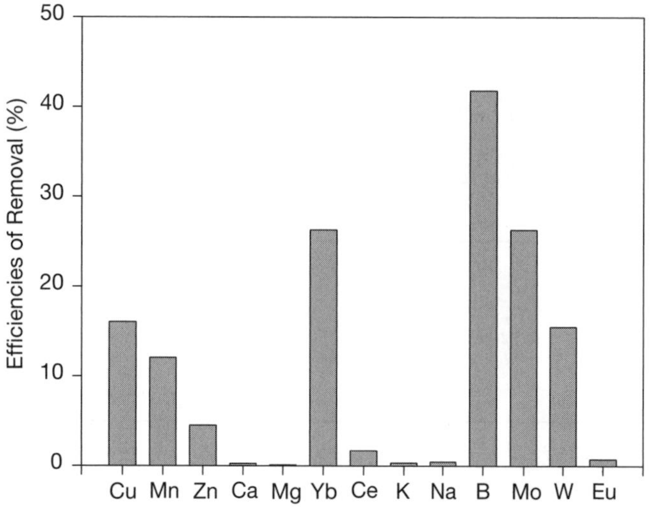

FIG. 2. Histogram showing the efficiency of ore-metal removal from a crystallizing magma undergoing second boiling. Metals not removed into the MVP have been sequestered into crystallizing phases that are removed from contact with the MVP. Conditions: same as Figure 1. Composition of the initial melt, and the bulk partition coefficients are listed in Table 1.

probably approaches equilibrium with an MVP of these compositions, and one might expect that quartz phenocrysts could trap primary magmatic fluid inclusions of the MVP with compositions of this type. The best estimate of cation concentrations in the magmatic volatile phase are probably obtained by multiplying the efficiency function output (E(Cu)) by the ratio of the initial copper concentration in the melt to the quantity: initial water content of the melt minus the water content of the final rock. For example, given E(Cu) = 0.43, initial concentration of copper in the melt = 65 ppm, initial water concentration in the melt = 3 wt percent, and water content of the rock = 0.4 wt percent present in hydrous, supersolidus minerals (e.g., primary biotite, amphibole, apatite, but not sericite, chlorite, or secondary epidote or biotite); then, the concentration of Cu in the averaged MVP (Candela, 1989) is given by [E(Cu)](100)(initial copper concentration in the melt (in mg/kg))/(initial wt percent water in the melt – wt percent water in the final rock) = (0.43)(100)(65 mg/kg Cu)/(3 wt % – 0.4 wt %) = 1,075 mg Cu/kg of water evolved. This calculation yields the concentration of Cu in the combined vapor and brine (if brine was stable at any time during volatile exsolution), in parts copper per million parts water (not per million parts of the vapor + brine mass).

This number accounts for copper lost by partitioning into magmatic crystalline phases during fractional crystallization before and after volatile exsolution, and copper partitioning into either vapor alone and/or vapor + brine. In the limit where no Cu is sequestered into crystallizing phases, the calculated Cu concentration in the averaged magmatic volatile phase in this example would be 2,500 ppm. To determine the size of pluton needed to produce a given tonnage of ore metal (for a given initial ore metal concentration in the magma), the efficiency of removal (percent divided by 100) is multiplied by the initial concentration of ore metal in the magma (grams of metal/megagram of magma) and by the mass of magma tapped by the magma-hydrothermal system. Figure 3 shows the total tonnage of ore metal in a deposit as a function of the quantity of magma degassed (presented in this figure as width of an equidimensional magma (granite) of density 2,700 kg/m^3) for an initial concentration of the ore metal of interest in the magma equal to 50 ppm. The calculation has been performed at three different values of the efficiency.

Additional results based on a large number of runs of the program are as follows:

Effect of varying the initial water concentration. At a given pressure, all other parameters being equal, a higher initial

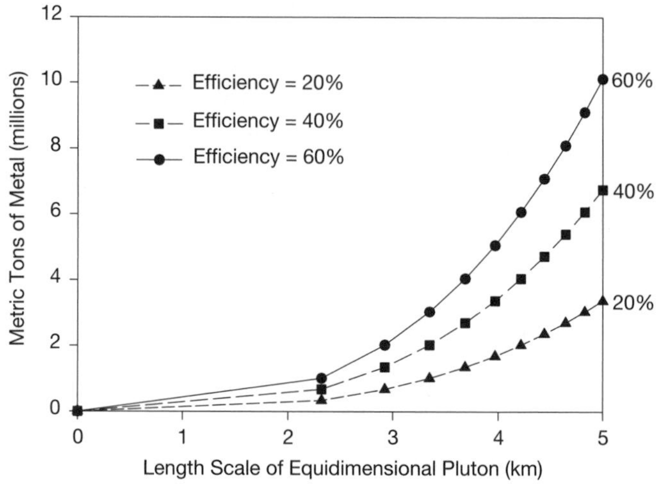

FIG. 3. Total tonnage (metric) of ore metal in a hypothetical mineral deposit, formed by partitioning of metals from a crystallizing magma into an evolving MVP, where the initial concentration of the ore metal in the magma is 50 ppm, for efficiencies of removal of 20, 40 and 60%, plotted as a function of the width in kilometers of an equidimensional (cubic) pluton. The largest pluton considered in this plot has a volume of 125 km^3. Doubling the initial ore metal concentration in the melt would double the total tonnage of metal in the deposit.

water concentration (i.e., earlier saturation with respect to a vapor phase) promotes a higher efficiency of removal for compatible elements. Further, given the same initial Cl concentration in the melt, brine exsolution accompanies vapor exsolution over a broader range of reaction progress as the initial water concentration decreases. Therefore, the probability of trapping brine inclusions increases with decreasing initial water concentration of the melt (for a given chlorine concentration in the melt). However, the efficiency of removal of compatible elements (e.g., Cu and Au) decreases sharply under these same conditions. Our modeling shows clearly that the initial water concentration in the melt is one of two main controls on compatible ore metal removal: the wetter the magma, the greater the potential for ore formation.

Effects of pressure on the ratio of the Cu concentration in the brine to the Cu concentration in the vapor, Cu(b)/Cu(v). Cu(b)/Cu(v) varies by approximately one order of magnitude, from over 100 to less than 10. This ratio is controlled primarily by the Cu-Na exchange constants and the initial bulk composition of the system; further, it decreases with increasing pressure. However, for devolatilization of a given melt, the ratio Cu(b)/Cu(v) is largely independent of the reaction progress variable (Z). Therefore, one should not expect the ratio of the concentration of copper (or other ore metals) in brine-rich fluid inclusions relative to vapor-rich inclusions, to be constant.

Effect of initial Cl. For a given wet magma (4 wt percent initial H_2O) emplaced at shallow levels in the crust (100 MPa), reducing the initial melt Cl from 2,000 to 400 ppm (five-fold) reduces the efficiency of removal of copper from 64 to 51 percent; this would reduce the tonnage of a deposit by 20 percent (i.e., by 13/64).

Effect of pressure of magmatic crystallization. Given equivalent initial water concentrations and Cl contents, the higher the pressure of crystallization, the later volatile saturation occurs. Under these conditions, compatible elements such as copper (given fugacities of sulfur and oxygen sufficient to stabilize pyrrhotite as a magmatic phase) are lost to crystallizing phases. Gold may be similarly affected. Further, the partitioning of copper into the MVP from a melt is optimized near 100 MPa (Williams et al., 1995; see a discussion of other pressure-related effects in Candela, 1997). Along with the initial water concentration in the melt, the pressure at which the magma crystallizes exerts a strong control on the efficiency of compatible ore metal partitioning into the MVP.

Effect of the magnitude of the Cl partition coefficient. The magnitude of the Cl partition coefficient has no effect of the efficiency of removal of Cu (assuming all other variables are constant). However, the concentration of Cu and all chloride-complexed metals are enriched in earlier aliquots of the volatile phase (evolved from an homogeneous aliquot of melt), relative to later aliquots of the MVP, at higher values of the Cl partition coefficient. Note, however, that if some of the MVP is trapped in the subsolidus pluton, then elements partitioning into late aliquots of the MVP may be removed from the magma chamber into the magmatic-hydrothermal ore-fluid; these elements would be removed from the chamber only during later cracking and hydrothermal alteration (Candela, 1991).

Summary

In summary, the efficiency with which ore metals and other elements can be removed from a crystallizing and devolatilizing magma into the magmatic volatile phases can be modeled by using MVPart. The model can elucidate effects on metal partitioning due to variations in initial water and chloride concentrations in the melt, pressure of emplacement and devolatilization, ore metal sequestration in crystallizing phases, inter-element effects (the effect of the concentrations of one element, e.g., iron or manganese, on the partitioning of another element, e.g., copper or gold), and more. MVPart is unique in its ability to model inter-element effects, which in the case of multivalent elements in the brine, can be large. Further, the effect of oxygen fugacity and melt ASI can be accounted for. Lastly, modeling of the type presented in this paper is an ongoing concern; in our opinion, all modeling of combined crystallization-devolatilization in ore-metal-bearing granite systems is still at a relatively primitive stage. The model is best used for predicting general trends, rather than specific concentrations of ore metals in ore fluids, although such predictions can be made with caution.

Our latest experiments show that fluid inclusions that trapped vapor (saturated with melt, brine, and Cu-Fe sulfides), have inferred masses of Cu-sulfide daughter minerals that are higher than the corresponding inferred masses of Cu-sulfides in coexisting inclusions of brine. If these daughter mineral populations reflect copper concentrations in the synthetic fluid inclusions, then, at least at low to moderate oxygen fugacities, the partitioning of copper in the presence of sulfide may favor the vapor over the brine in some cases. Further developments supporting or modifying these tentative results can be found at: http://www.geol.umd.edu/pages/facilities/lmdr/cu98.html.

REFERENCES

Ague, J.J., 1997, Thermodynamic calculation of emplacement pressures for batholithic rocks, California: Implications for the aluminum-in-hornblende barometer: Geology, v. 25, p. 563–566.

Ague, J.J., and Brimhall, G.H., 1988, Regional variations in bulk chemistry, mineralogy, and the compositions of mafic and accessory minerals in the batholiths of California: Geological Society of America Bulletin, v. 100, p. 891–911.

Anderson, J.L., 1996, Status of thermobarometry in granitic batholiths: Transactions of the Royal Society of Edinburgh, Earth Sciences, v. 87, p. 125–138.

Blevin, P.L., and Candela, P.A., 1997, The ferric-ferrous ratio in granitic rocks and the interpretation of the relative oxidation states: European Union of Geosciences, Terra Nova, Abstracts, v. 9, p. 434.

Blevin, P.L., and Chappell, B.W., 1992, The role of magma sources, oxidation states and fractionation in determining the granite metallogeny of eastern Australia: Transactions of the Royal Society of Edinburgh, v. 83, p. 305–316.

Bodnar, R.J., Burnham, C.W., and Sterner, S.M., 1985, Synthetic fluid inclusions in natural quartz: III. Determination of phase equilibrium properties in the system H_2O-NaCl to 1000° C and 1500 bars: Geochimica et Cosmochimica Acta, v. 49, p. 1861–1873.

Bowen, N.L., 1928, The evolution of igneous rocks: New York, Dover Publications, 332 p.

Burnham, C.W., and Ohmoto, H., 1980, Late-stage processes of felsic magmatism: Mining Geology Special Issue 8, p. 1–11.

Candela, P.A., 1986, Generalized mathematical models for the fractional evolution of vapor from magmas in terrestrial planetary crusts, *in* Saxena, S.K., ed., Advances in Physical Geochemistry 6: Chemistry and Physics of the Terrestrial Planets: New York, Springer-Verlag, p. 362–396.

—— 1989, Magmatic ore-forming fluids: Thermodynamic and mass transfer calculations of metal concentrations: Reviews in Economic Geology, v. 4, p. 302–321.

—— 1990, Theoretical constraints on the chemistry of the magmatic aqueous phase: Geological Society of America Special Paper 246, p. 11–20.

—— 1991, Physics of aqueous phase exsolution in plutonic environments: American Mineralogist, v. 76, p. 1081–1091.

—— 1994, Combined chemical and physical model for plutonic devolatilization: A non-rayleigh fractionation algorithm: Geochimica et Cosmochimica Acta, v. 58, p. 2157–2167.

—— 1997, Shallow, ore-related granites: textures, volatiles and ore metals: Journal of Petrology, v. 38, p. 1619–1633.

Candela, P.A., and Blevin, P.L., 1995, Do some miarolitic granites preserve evidence of magmatic volatile phase permeability?: Economic Geology, v. 90, p. 2310–2316.

Candela, P.A., and Bouton, S.L., 1990, The influence of oxygen fugacity on tungsten and molybdenum between silicate melts and ilmenite: Economic Geology, v. 85, p. 633–640.

Candela, P.A., and Holland, H.D., 1986, A mass transfer model for copper and molybdenum in magmatic hydrothermal systems: The origin of porphyry-type ore deposits: Economic Geology, v. 81, p. 1–19.

Candela, P.A., and Piccoli, P.M., 1995, Model ore-metal partitioning from melts into vapor and vapor/brine mixtures, *in* Thompson, J.F.H., ed., Magmas, fluids and ore-deposits: Mineralogical Association of Canada Short Course, v. 23, p. 101–128.

Cline, J.S., and Bodnar, R.J., 1991, Can economic porphyry copper mineralizations be generated by a typical calc-alkaline melt?: Journal of Geophysical Research, v. 95, p. 8113–8126.

Harrison, T.M., and Watson, E.W., 1984, The behavior of apatite during crustal anatexis: Equilibrium and kinetic considerations: Geochimica et Cosmochimica Acta, v. 48, p. 1467–1477.

Ishihara, S., 1977, The magnetite-series and ilmenite-series granitic rocks: Mining Geology, v. 27, p. 293–305.

Johnson, M.C., Anderson, A.T., Jr., and Rutherford, M.J., 1994, Pre-eruptive volatile contents of magma, *in* Carroll, M.R,. and Holloway, J.R., eds., Volatiles in magmas: Reviews in Mineralogy, v. 30, p. 281–330.

Kistler, R.W., and Swanson, S.E., 1981, Petrology and geochronology of metamorphosed volcanic rocks and a Middle Cretaceous volcanic rock in the east-central Sierra Nevada, California: Journal of Geophysical Research, v. 86, p. 10489–10501.

Kress, V.C., and Carmichael, I.S.E., 1991, Effects of pressure, temperature, f(O2), and composition on iron redox equilibrium in basic magmas. EOS-Transactions of the American Geophysical Union, v. 71, p. 647.

Lowenstern, J.B., 1994, Dissolved volatile concentrations in an ore forming magma: Geology, v. 22, p. 893–896.

Lynton, S.J., Candela, P.A., and Piccoli, P.M., 1993, An experimental study of the partitioning of copper between pyrrhotite and a high silica rhyolite melt: Economic Geology, v. 88, p. 901–915.

Metrich, N., and Rutherford, M.J., 1992, Experimental study of chlorine behavior in hydrous silicate melts: Geochemica et Cosmochimica Acta, v. 56, p. 607–616.

Piccoli, P.M., 1992, Apatite chemistry in felsic magmatic systems: Unpublished Ph.D. dissertation, University of Maryland at College Park, 293 p.

Piccoli, P.M., and Candela, P.A., 1994, Apatite in felsic rocks: A model for the estimation of initial halogen concentrations in the Bishop Tuff (Long Valley) and Tuolumne intrusive suite (Sierra Nevada batholith) magmas: American Journal of Science, v. 294, p. 92–135.

Ratajeski, K., 1995, Estimation of initial and saturation water concentrations for three granitic plutons in the north-central Great Basin, Nevada: Unpublished M.Sc.Thesis, University of Maryland at College Park, 299 p.

Shinohara, H., and Kazahaya, K., 1995, Degassing processes related to magma chamber crystallization, *in* Thompson, J.F.H., ed., Magmas, fluids and ore-deposits: Mineralogical Association of Canada Short Course, v. 23, p. 47–70.

Sourirajan, S., and Kennedy, G.C., 1962, The system H_2O-NaCl at elevated temperatures and pressures: American Journal of Science, v. 260, p. 115–141.

Stimac, J., and Hickmott, D., 1995, Ore metal partitioning in intermediate-to-silicic magmas: PIXE results on natural mineral/melt assemblages, *in* Clark, A.H., ed., Giant ore deposits, II: Kingston, Queens University, p. 182–220.

Thompson, J.B., Jr., 1982, Compositional space: An algebraic and geometric approach, *in* Ferry, J.M., ed., Characterization of metamorphism through mineral equilibrium: Reviews in Mineralogy, v. 10, p. 1–31.

Tuttle, O.F., and Bowen, N.L., 1958, Origin of granite in light of experimental studies in the system $KAlSi_3O_8$-$NaAlSi_3O_8$-SiO_2-H_2O: Geological Society of America Memoir 74, p. 153.

Webster, J.D., 1992, Water solubility and chlorine partitioning in Cl-rich granitic systems: Effects of melt composition at 2 kbar and 800°C: Geochimica et Cosmochimica Acta, v. 56, p. 659–678.

—— 1997, Degassing of H_2O-undersaturated Cl– ±F–, B–, P–, C-bearing felsic magmas: IAVCEI Abstracts, p. 80.

Whalen, J.B., and Chappell, B.W., 1988, Opaque mineralogy and mafic mineral chemistry of I- and S-type granites of the Lachlan fold belt: American Mineralogist, v. 73, p. 281–296.

Williams, T.J., Candela, P.A., and Piccoli, P.M., 1995, The partitioning of copper between silicate melts and two-phase aqueous fluids: An experimental investigation at 1 kbar, 800°C and 0.5 kbar, 850°C: Contributions to Mineralogy and Petrology, v. 121, p. 388–399.

—— 1997, Hydrogen-alkali exchange between silicate melts and two-phase aqueous mixtures: An experimental investigation: Contributions to Mineralogy and Petrology, v. 128, p. 114–126.

APPENDIX 1

How to Run the Program MVPart

MVPart calculates the composition of the magmatic aqueous phase for a variety of Nernst-type and "mass-balanced" elements, and the concentrations of these elements in the melt, in systems that exsolve an aqueous phase (vapor or vapor + brine) due to second boiling. The program models the concentrations of Cu, Mn, Zn, Ca, Mg, Yb, Ce, K, Na, B, Mo, Cl, Eu, HCl, Fe, K, HCl, and W. The requirements to run MVPart consist of an IBM-type computer (286 or better processor) with VGA or equivalent graphics capabilities.

Steps to Acquire/Copy the MVPart Program

To obtain a copy of the program through the Laboratory for Mineral Deposits Research Home Page at the University of Maryland at College Park, please use the following address:

URL:http://www.geol.umd.edu/pages/facilities/lmdr/mvpart.html

1. Copy the file MVPARTZ.EXE to a PC. This can be obtained on disk, or through the Laboratory for Mineral Deposits Research Home Page.

From a floppy disk, type the following (a hard return follows each line):

```
c:
cd\
md mvpart
cd mvpart
copy a:mvpartz.exe
```

Steps to Extract the MVPart Program

1. The file MVPARTZ.EXE is a self extracting ZIP file (this is the only file that you should have received through the LMDR Home Page). To decompress the file, go to the directory that contains the file MVPARTZ.EXE (on your DOS/WINDOWS machine), and type MVPARTZ (this can be performed alternatively through Windows File Manager using the RUN function: be sure to copy the file to the hard disk prior to having it expand). When this is complete, nine additional files should be present:

MVPART.EXE	The executable code for the MVP algorithm
MVPART.DOC	On line help for the program
LI.COM	Help file viewer
MVPART.HTM	Help file for viewing in Netscape or Mosaic
MVPART.WPD	Help file in Word Perfect 6.1 format.

COMP.DAT	Composition of Representative I-Type Granite
COMP.BAK	Backup copy of the composition file.
BULKD.DAT	Partition Coefficient Data File.
BULKD.BAK	Backup copy of the partition coefficient data file.

Running MVPart

Calculations, graphing, and accessing help files can all be completed through the main MVPart executable file (MVPART.EXE). The basic outline that you should follow when attempting to perform the calculations is to: (1) execute the calculations; (2) plot the data files or incorporate data into a spreadsheet. Upon executing the calculations, you have the option to list (but not graph) the output to the screen. The reason for not plotting these data is that the iteration is performed thousands of times for each element, in all three phases (melt, vapor, and brine), and simultaneously plotting them would greatly increase the run time.

Step by Step:

(1) To run the program from the directory in which the executable program resides, type MVPART (followed by the enter key). Do not run this program from within Windows or Windows 95 (it has not been thoroughly tested to run through these operating systems). The program will generate (output) data files: (1) a file containing information about the composition of aliquots of fractionally removed magmatic volatile phase; and (2) data about the efficiencies of removal. These files can be rather large, and may not fit onto a diskette. The program should be run from a hard drive due to the space requirements for the generated data files. Once MVPART is typed, the opening menu should appear:

```
M(magmatic)   V(olatile)   P(hase)   (p)ART(itioning)
          P.A. Candela and P.M. Piccoli
      Laboratory for Mineral Deposits Research
       University of Maryland at College Park
              College Park, MD 20742
1. Run MVPart
2. Plot Output Files
3. View the Help File
4. Exit the Program
```

If you have not run the program previously and saved data files, you will need to enter either 1, 3, or 4.

Calculating the Composition of the Magmatic Volatile Phase

(2) from the opening menu, enter the number 1 to run the program.

(3) ENTER THE OUTPUT MELT/VAPOR/BRINE DATA FILE NAME.
You must enter a name for the file. The name of this file must conform to the standard DOS file naming rules: no more than 8 characters, possibly followed by a period, possibly followed by an extension of 3 additional characters. The name can be of the form OUTPUT or OUTPUT.DAT or A:OUTPUT.DAT. This file will contain some information about initial conditions (initial water, pressure, vapor/(vapor + brine) weight ratio, oxygen fugacity), and a representative selection of output (vapor, brine, and melt) for each element at various values (approximately 250) of Z (reaction progress). The data will be stored as a continuous string. This file can be read by the plotting algorithm, which is accessible through the opening menu.

(4) ENTER THE OUTPUT EFFICIENCY DATA FILE NAME.
This file contains information about the initial conditions for the calculation, in addition to the efficiencies of removal for various elements. The efficiencies of removal can also be graphed using the plotting algorithm from the main opening menu.

(5) ENTER THE INITIAL WATER CONCENTRATION IN THE MELT (WEIGHT FRACTION)?
Enter a value for the initial water in the melt as a weight fraction. For example, for a melt with 4 wt percent water, you would enter 0.04.

(6) ENTER THE PRESSURE OF EMPLACEMENT (IN BARS).
Enter a pressure of emplacement that corresponds to a particular depth of interest, in bars. For example, if you want to simulate a magma emplaced at a level 1.5 km below the surface, enter a value of 500 bars. Note that the pressure entered (i.e. level of emplacement) must be such that the water solubility at a given pressure is not less than the initial water concentration listed above. If this is the case, the program will request that you reenter the values. The formalism for the water solubility equation used is from Piccoli (1992; eq. 8.12)

(7) ENTER THE CL/WATER RATIO IN THE INITIAL MELT.
Enter a value for the ratio of Cl to water in the initial melt. Values for metaluminous to slightly peraluminous silicic melts usually range from 0.01 to 0.1 (see the Appendix in Candela and Piccoli, 1995).

(8) ENTER THE [CL (VAPOR, OR SUPERCRITICAL GAS)/MELT] PARTITION COEFFICIENT.
Note: A limitation of the model is that D is fixed and not variable. D(Cl) is being modeled as a simple Nernst-type partition coefficient and does not fluctuate as melt composition (i.e., Cl) changes. We suggest using a value of 5 at 500 or 1,000 bars (see Candela and Piccoli, 1995, p. 104).

(9) ENTER THE OXYGEN FUGACITY OF THE CALCULATION.
The algorithm at present can handle the following oxygen fugacities: enter the number corresponding to the oxygen fugacity, [1] $SiO_2 - Fe_2SiO_4 - Fe_3O_4$ (QFM), [2] Ni–NiO (NNO), and [3] Fe_2O_3–Fe_3O_4 (HM).

(10) WOULD YOU LIKE TO MAKE ANY CHANGES TO THE DATA?
At this point, a summary of input parameters will appear on the screen. Notice that some information presented was not input, but is calculated and/or recorded for documentation purposes only (for example, the number of nodes and the limit of the calculation). If you would like a copy of this information, you will need to print it out at this point using the page-print function (Shift-Print Screen; this may have to be followed by a page feed on the printer). NOTE: not all laser and ink-jet printers can print this information. If you would like to make any changes to the data, press y for yes. If not, press n for no.

(11) DO YOU WANT TO HAVE INTERMEDIATE CALCULATIONS PRINTED TO THE SCREEN?
Printing the intermediate calculations to the screen adds considerable time to performing the calculation. All of the pertinent data will be stored in a series of data files. Recommendation: no.

(12) DO YOU WANT TO HAVE THE EFFICIENCIES PRINTED TO THE SCREEN?
Printing the efficiencies to the screen will not change the run time of the program significantly. Also, the efficiency calculation represents the last portion of the main MVP algorithm. When efficiency calculations are printed to the screen, it signifies to the user that the calculations are complete (the only other indication being a beep). Recommendation: yes.

(13) DO YOU WANT TO VIEW/EDIT THE BULK D FILE?
This information will be read from a data file, BULKD.DAT. This file contains 12 sets of data, the bulk D for 12 elements both before and after volatile saturation. Note that there are no data for Cl. Also, the bulk D for Eu is modeled (as denoted by the * in the listing) as being dependent upon f_{O_2} (after Candela, 1987), and the value can't be changed. Note that this information will not be stored in an output file. If you wish to retain this information, print a copy of it now.

(14) DO YOU WANT TO VIEW/EDIT THE MELT COMPOSITION FILE?
This information will be read from a file COMP.DAT. This file contains 13 concentrations. The default values are those of an "average" I-type granite from the Lachlan Fold Belt. Note that if you choose to edit the composition of the melt of interest, you will be unable to modify the value for Cl. Cl is calculated based on the previously entered value for Cl/H_2O and initial H_2O. Note that this information will not be stored in the output file. If you wish to retain a copy, print a copy at this point.

Plotting the Data in the Data Files

The plotting algorithm included with MVPart is rather crude, and is to be used for rudimentary plotting only. Higher quality plots can be made by importing data files as text into spreadsheets like Quattro Pro or Excel. However, the algorithm included is sufficient to infer trends in the data. Information about both absolute concentrations of elements in the vapor/brine and melt can be obtained, in addition to efficiencies of removal.

You will be unable to run the plotting portion of this program in a minimized mode. The program has also not been tested to run with Windows 95.

To plot the data, type MVPART in the directory that the MVPART executable file is in (assuming that you are not already in the program. When you have the opening menu on the screen, press 2 to plot the data.

Plots of the Composition of Aliquots of Magmatic Volatile Phase

(1) WHAT WOULD YOU LIKE TO PLOT (1) MELT/VAPOR + –BRINE DATA, (2) EFFICIENCIES?
Press 1.

(2) ENTER THE NAME OF THE DATA FILE.
Enter the name of the file exactly as it appeared in the step described above.

(3) WHAT ELEMENT WOULD YOU LIKE TO PLOT.
Enter the number corresponding to the element.

(4) WOULD YOU LIKE TO PLOT THE ELEMENT IN THE (1) VAPOR, (2) BRINE OR, (3) MELT?
Enter the appropriate number. At this point, the computer will generate the plot on the screen. If you wish to have a rough copy of the plot sent to your printer, and you have run the GRAPHICS program, press the shift and PrintScreen keys.

Generating Efficiency Plots

From the opening menu of the plotting algorithm (accessed by pressing 2 from the main menu), press 2 to enter the efficiency function.

(1) WHAT IS THE NAME OF THE EFFICIENCY FILE?
Enter the name of the file. A graph of the efficiencies will appear on the screen.

APPENDIX 2

This is a discussion of chemical equilibria treated using the "phase component" formalism. It has been included here because aqueous geochemists are generally unfamiliar with this treatment, and it is necessary for the proper formulation of equilibria involving solid solutions. Phase components are the independently variable constituents of phases. Only chemical equilibria written in terms of phase components are valid equilibrium expressions, because "balanced reactions," used as representations of conditions of chemical equilibria, are linear relations among chemical potentials of components of phases. Because the chemical potential of a component of a phase is the partial derivative of internal energy with respect to number of moles of the given component at a constant entropy, volume, and a constant number of moles of all other components, the given component must be capable of independent variation in the solution. Therefore, this treatment is not optional.

Definitions:

System Components: The number of system components, CS, is the minimum number of independent chemical variables necessary to define the chemical variability of the system. The number of components may be thought of as defining a "composition space": a two component system can be represented by a line (two points, or one point and a vector), a four component system defines a volume (four points, or one point and three vectors).

Phase Components: The number of phase components, Cϕ, in a phase ϕ, is the minimum number of independent chemical variables necessary to define the chemical variability of the phase with respect to the possible variations in composition of the phase. Components such as $CuFe_{-1}$ are referred to as exchange components (Thompson, 1982), whereas components such as $CuFeS_2$ are referred to as additive components. An exchange component formally contains both positive and negative units of quantity, (e.g., $CuFe_{-1}$ contains one Cu and a negative Fe); we can therefore define a (Cu,Fe) S solid solution as occurring along the line defined by the point FeS, and the direction in composition space defined by $CuFe_{-1}$, i.e., removal of Fe and substitution of Cu.

In order to model the partitioning of, for example, Cu between pyrrhotite and melt, we need to determine: (1) the number of phase components in each phase; and (2) the number of system components. We can account for the partitioning of Cu between Po and melt within the system Cu–Fe–S–O (number of system components is 4). We can choose any four points in the composition space, e.g., the elements, or the metal oxides plus S_2 and O_2, as the components of the system (so long as the four points are not coplanar, and no combination of three or more points are collinear as are, for example, O_2, FeO, and Fe_2O_3).

Here, we will choose $CuO_{0.5}$, FeO, S_2, and O_2 as system components, because oxide components are the simplest to deal with in the melt, and the system components S_2 and O_2 are commonly used in geology as indices of sulfidation and oxidation, respectively. As components of the phases we shall choose $CuFeS_2$, FeS, and S_2 for pyrrhotite, Fe_3O_4 for magnetite, and $CuO_{0.5}$, FeO, and $FeO_{1.5}$ for the melt. We could have chosen sulfide components in the melt; however, in natural silicate melts, the concentration of Fe is greater than the concentration of S; for Cu we choose an oxide component. If later studies suggest that Cu is complexed in melts by S rather than by O, the component may be changed, although thermodynamics carries no requirement that components match species; however, thermodynamic excess functions, commonly expressed as activity coefficients, will be minimized and simplified when components have stoichiometries close to those of the species present in the solution. Because SiO_2 and other melt components will not appear in the equilibria we choose to write, we do not have to consider them here explicitly.

Pyrrhotite

For the pyrrhotite solid solution, there are three phase components as we have defined the problem. We express the chemical potentials of the phase components as linear combinations of the chemical potentials of the system components:

$$\mu^{po}_{S_2} = \mu^{system}_{S_2}$$

$$\mu^{po}_{FeS} = \mu^{system}_{FeO} + 0.5\,\mu^{system}_{S_2} - 0.5\,\mu^{system}_{O_2}$$

$$\mu^{po}_{CuFeS_2} = \mu^{system}_{CuO_{0.5}} + \mu^{system}_{FeO} + \mu^{system}_{S_2} - 0.75\,\mu^{system}_{O_2} \quad \text{(A1)}$$

Given that there are three phase components for pyrrhotite and four for the melt the total number of phase components is seven (Cϕ. = 7). Given that the number of system components = 4 (CS = 4) we can calculate the number of linearly independent chemical equilibria in the system (regardless of the actual choice of components) from:

$$\left(\sum_{i=1}^{\phi} c_\phi\right) - C_s = 7 - 4 = 3 \quad \text{(A2)}$$

In this case, there are three independent conditions of chemical equilibrium (these are usually called "reactions"). These statements of chemical equilibrium can be derived from the set of seven equations that expresses the phase components (for the melt and pyrrhotite) as a function of the system components (the set of three equations for the phase components of pyrrhotite are shown in equation A4.2). This set of equations is reduced (solved) so as to eliminate the chemical potentials of the system components, yielding the three conditions for equilibrium:

$$S_2^{po} = S_2^{melt} \quad \text{(A3)}$$

$$FeS^{po} = FeS^{melt} \quad \text{(A4)}$$

$$CuO_{0.5}^{melt} + FeS^{po} + 0.5S_2^{system} = CuFeS_2^{po} + 0.25O_2^{system} \quad \text{(A5)}$$

Equation (A4.5) yields the equilibrium constant:

$$K = \frac{a^{po}_{CuFeS_2} \cdot (f^{system}_{O_2})^{0.25}}{(f^{system}_{S_2})^{0.5} \cdot a^{melt}_{CuO_{0.5}} \cdot a^{po}_{FeS}} \quad \text{(A6)}$$

and, in terms of the Nernst partition coefficient $D^{po/melt}_{Cu}$, the equilibrium can be expressed as:

$$D^{po/melt}_{Cu} = K' \frac{(f^{system}_{S_2})^{0.5} \cdot a^{po}_{FeS}}{(f^{system}_{O_2})^{0.25}} \quad \text{(A7)}$$

where

$$K = K' \cdot \frac{\gamma^{melt}_{CuO_{0.5}}}{\gamma^{po}_{CuFe_2S_2}} \quad \text{(A8).}$$

Chapter 5

Calculation of Simultaneous Chemical Equilibria in Aqueous-Mineral-Gas Systems and its Application to Modeling Hydrothermal Processes

MARK H. REED
Department of Geological Sciences, University of Oregon, Eugene, Oregon 97403-1272

Introduction

Geochemical processes in hydrothermal systems are complexly interconnected. Quantitative, whole-system modeling is one of the most effective ways to untangle the interdependent and counterposing chemical effects to determine what the actual natural processes may be. Examples of basic processes include precipitation of ore and gangue minerals in open space to form veins, metasomatic replacement of wall rock by alteration minerals, boiling of an ascending fluid, mixing of ascending and descending fluids, and condensation of boiled gases into cold ground water or into aerated fractures. The course of attendant chemical reactions depends on the combined effects of several of the processes, and the linkages among processes may be subtle. The quantitative details of species concentrations, as determined from chemical reactions, make the difference between whether a mineral precipitates or not.

As an example of a linked reaction series, consider what determines whether gold precipitates where ascending, slightly acidic, epithermal waters boil (Fig. 1). In such systems, aqueous gold is transported in a bisulfide complex such as $Au(HS)_2^-$. Gold precipitates when the bisulfide separates from the gold ion by some process that drives the following reaction:

$$8Au(HS)_2^- + 6H^+ + 4H_2O \longrightarrow 8Au^\circ + 15H_2S + SO_4^{2-}$$
$$\text{(aq)} \quad \text{(aq)} \quad \text{(aq)} \quad \text{(el)} \quad \text{(aq)} \quad \text{(aq)} \qquad (5.1)$$

Inspection of the reaction shows that acidification (pH decrease) or H_2S removal (into a gas phase or into minerals) would drive the reaction towards gold precipitation. The temperature dependence of this reaction is small. Boiling of waters that are initially acidic acidifies them further (Reed, 1992a, b), an effect that combines with H_2S removal to the gas to drive gold precipitation from such waters. In waters with an initial pH in the slightly acidic to neutral range, pH increases upon boiling, which tends to dissolve gold, while the loss of H_2S to the gas phase upon boiling tends to precipitate gold. Whether the H_2S loss is sufficient to drive gold precipitation depends on the H_2S concentration: if H_2S is abundant, its removal to the gas phase is not necessarily sufficient to drive the reaction, as illustrated below. For a sulfide-deficient system with a slightly acidic initial pH, boiling causes first gold, then sulfides, to precipitate by the following series of linked reactions (Fig. 1a):

1. Boiling removes H_2S and CO_2 to the gas phase.

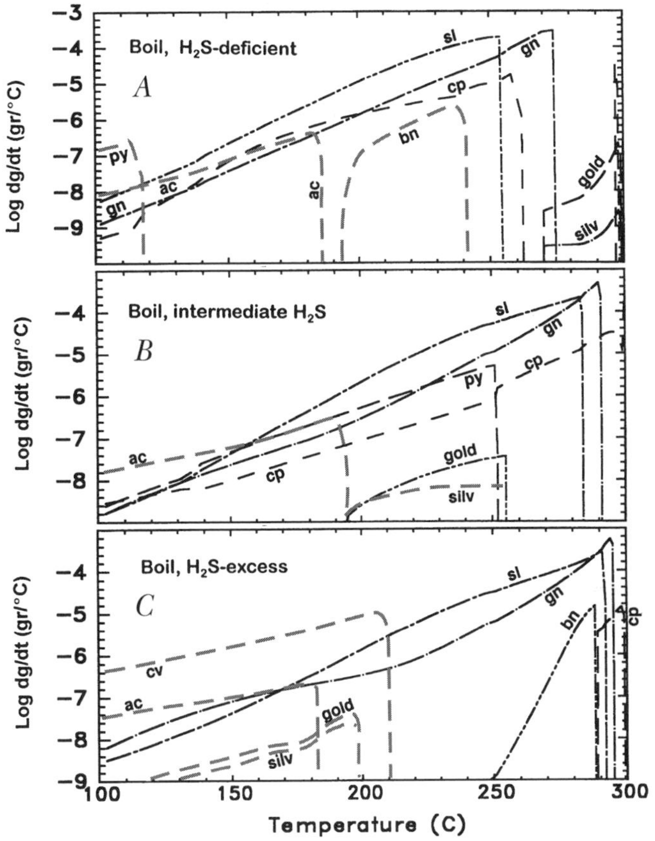

FIG. 1. Ore minerals precipitated from boiling epithermal fluids containing different concentrations of H_2S. In each case, the fluid composition is the same except for H_2S concentration, which is 0.00274m in (A), 0.00874m in (B) and 0.03274m in (C). Boiling proceeds with decreasing temperature, thus progress in the boiling is read from right to left. The rate of mineral precipitation (grams/°C per kg of initial liquid) is given by the vertical axis as log dg/dt, which is actually computed as a finite difference derivative by dividing the mass of mineral precipitated on a given temperature step by the size of the step. Mineral abbreviations are as follows: ac, acanthite; bn, bornite; cp, chalcopyrite; cv, covellite; gn, galena; py, pyrite; silv, silver; sl, sphalerite.

Graph (A) depicts a sulfide-deficient condition, wherein gold (in electrum) precipitates early in the boiling process (300°C) as the gold-complexing aqueous sulfide is depleted by removal of H_2S to the gas phase. The depletion is not sufficient to prevent sulfide mineral precipitation at lower temperature.

Graph (B) is an intermediate case, where electrum and the base metal sulfides are intimately mixed, but electrum precipitation begins at a much lower temperature (255°C) than in the case of (A).

Graph (C) shows a sulfide-excess condition, wherein electrum precipitation is delayed to 200°C, well after essentially all base metals have precipitated as sulfides.

2. CO_2 escape consumes H^+, driving pH increase (reaction 5.36, below).

3. H_2S escape consumes aqueous sulfide in sufficient quantity to drive gold precipitation by reaction (1), despite the increased pH.

4. Continued boiling causes temperature to decrease, which destabilizes metal chloride complexes; boiling also drives further increase in pH owing to CO_2 escape.

5. The pH increase and destabilized metal complexes cause galena, chalcopyrite, and sphalerite to precipitate.

The metal zoning produced by the above series of processes places gold deposition at high temperature and base metals at a lower temperature, which would typically be shallower than gold. The sequence is reversed in a sulfide-excess fluid, such as that depicted in Figure 1c, wherein the same reactions outlined above occur, but the gold precipitation reaction (5.1) occurs at the much lower temperature of 200°C, and the sulfides begin precipitating at a much higher temperature, 300°C, owing to the plentiful supply of sulfide. Figure 1b shows an intermediate case with an intermediate amount of aqueous sulfide.

Whole-System Geochemistry and Process Modeling

To understand the course of a linked reaction series, such as that outlined above for gold precipitation, it is necessary to specify the chemical system completely, including its temperature, pressure, bulk composition, and the thermodynamic stability of every chemical species in every possible phase (solids, aqueous, gas) that contains the chemical components of the system (Fig. 2). In practice, we are never able to specify all of the thermodynamic stabilities, but we hope to have enough of them to get by. In following sections, the basics of whole-system treatment are laid out.

The gold and sulfide precipitation example (above and Fig. 1), illustrates the interconnectedness of critical equilibria and the necessity for a whole-system treatment. The qualitative conclusions about the controls on the zoning of gold relative to base metals would not be possible if we were not able to account simultaneously for the behavior of pH, HS^-, H_2S_{gas}, $CO_{2\,gas}$, and sulfide solubility as a function of chloride complexing and temperature. Similarly, if the thermodynamic data for base metal and gold complexes were in error by very much, we would not be able to model the process. The gold example also illustrates how it may be better for the model to use approximate thermodynamic data for a given reaction than to omit the reaction entirely; e.g., it is better to use approximate stability constants for aqueous gold bisulfide than to exclude it from the calculation entirely. Excluding it is equivalent to stating that the complex is completely unstable, which introduces more error than including it with approximate stability data.

In the modeling approach outlined in this chapter, equilibrium thermodynamics is applied to constrain model approximations of the real world, representing a limiting condition that the real world approaches fairly closely, as argued elsewhere (Reed, 1997). The application of equilibrium formulations does not mean that the models apply only to systems at overall thermodynamic equilibrium. Overall equilibrium essentially never prevails in natural systems, but local equilibrium is common. Minerals and hydrothermal waters closely approach local equilibrium on spatial scales of centimeters to meters (e.g., in alteration envelopes) and on time scales of weeks or months (Reed and Spycher, 1984; Reed, 1997). Even in instances where equilibrium with the thermodynamically most stable mineral fails on the time scale of the process of interest, metastable minerals often do equilibrate quickly, and equilibrium methods can appropriately be applied with the metastable mineral (see Chap. 1). For example, quartz fails to equilibrate on a time scale of days to weeks in an ascending, cooling hydrothermal fluid, but amorphous silica does equilibrate on that time scale, so meaningful equilibrium calculations can be executed using amorphous silica instead of quartz. This example illuminates a basic principle of construction of useful equilibrium-based models: the time scale of the process

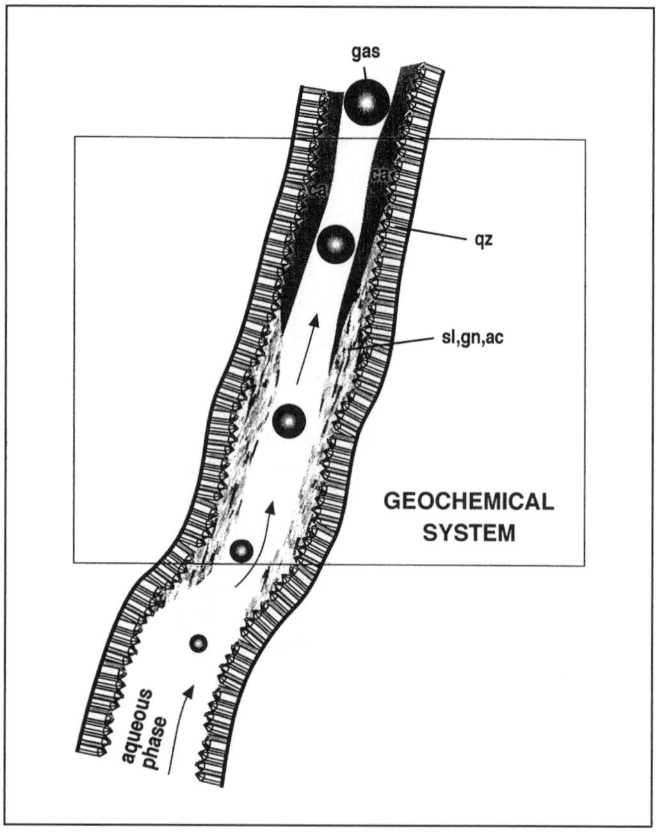

FIG. 2. A fluid-filled fracture in a boiling hydrothermal system, representing a complex multicomponent, multiphase geochemical system of the kind that whole-system geochemical modeling calculations are intended to address. This example shows an ascending aqueous phase that is boiling as it rises, yielding gas phase bubbles and precipitating minerals on the walls of the fracture, including acanthite (ac), calcite (ca), galena (gn), quartz (qz), and sphalerite (sl). Mass balance equations such as (5.19) and mass action equations such as (5.6) and (5.9) are written to account for the location and stability of species and phases in a system such as this.

being modeled should be matched to the kinetics of aqueous and mineral reactions. Excellent models can be developed simply by excluding reactions that are too slow for the time scale of the process.

Introduction to the Computational Approach

Envision a hydrothermal vein setting (Fig. 2) consisting of a fracture filled with an ascending hydrothermal fluid. As the fluid ascends, fluid pressure decreases, resulting in boiling that causes temperature to decrease and pH to increase, thereby inducing mineral precipitation. Making a geochemical model of such a geologic system requires that it be cast in terms of a chemical system that includes the aqueous phase (hydrothermal water), gas phase (steam plus CO_2, H_2S, etc.), and several solid phases (quartz, galena . . .) that precipitate on the vein walls. The goal is to compute the identities, quantities, and compositions of all phases that form as a consequence of the ascent (cooling and boiling) of the fluid. Such a computation requires that we keep an account of the location of all chemical elements in the system, which we do using mass balance equations, and that we compute the thermodynamic stability of all chemical species in the system, plus all potential additional phases that could be in the system but that are not present at any given stage. The thermodynamic stabilities are computed using mass action equations (equilibrium constant expressions; see Chap. 2). For a boiling system (Fig. 2), we also need to keep track of the partitioning of heat between the gas and liquid phases, using an enthalpy balance equation.

The boiling fluid setting shown in Figure 2 is one example of a geochemical system that can be treated using some computer programs for multicomponent, multiphase chemical equilibrium calculations. A simpler problem, for which the earliest programs were written, is a "mass transfer" calculation, consisting of the titration of a specific rock into water, simulating some aspects of hydrothermal wall-rock alteration. Since the development of the first computer program for calculation of mass transfer, PATHCALC (Helgeson, 1968), there have been improvements in numerical methods, the quality of the thermochemical database, and the formulation of the system of equations. Several computer programs that incorporate the improved methods and high quality thermochemical data bases are now available for computing multicomponent equilibria, including CHEMIX (Turnbull and Wadsley, 1986), EQ3/6 (Wolery, 1992a), REACT (Bethke, 1994), CHILLER (Reed, 1982), and others, reviewed by Bethke (1996) and by Bassett and Melchior (1990). Most of these programs can be readily applied to hydrothermal geochemistry problems and to a range of other problems from weathering of sulfide-bearing mine waste to disposal of waste H_2S gas by injection into deep formations. Much of the development of CHILLER has been focused on problems in hydrothermal geochemistry, including boiling systems, and it is the program used for calculations presented in this chapter. As for most such programs, CHILLER contains capabilities beyond simple mass transfer (rock titration into water), providing for modeling of complex chemical processes, including combinations of boiling, condensation, fluid-fluid mixing, oxidation, and variations on water-rock reactions in hydrothermal systems.

The fundamentals of the geochemical equation formulations are independent of the computer program implementation; all involve computing simultaneous multicomponent, multiphase equilibria. The following discussion is structured according to the CHILLER formulation, but it applies fundamentally to all such programs. The discussion includes examination of important issues, such as finding the stable mineral assemblage, determining when a gas phase saturates, determining when minerals that have been saturated in a model calculation become undersaturated, and problems with numerical convergence of the system of equations.

CHILLER's sister program, SOLVEQ (Reed, 1982), addresses the aqueous phase with limited capability for computing solid-aqueous equilibria. Analogous programs include EQ3NR (Wolery, 1992b), SOLMINEQ88 (Kharaka et al., 1988), WATEQ4F (Ball and Nordstrom, 1991), WATCH (Arnorrsson et al., 1982; Bjarnason, 1994), and PHREEQC (Parkhurst, 1995), all of which compute a distribution of species (homogeneous equilibrium) in an aqueous phase from a raw water analysis, and some of which compute equilibrations with selected minerals. These programs are useful for simple hydrothermal geochemistry problems, such as calculating how temperature change affects metal complexing and mineral solubility, or for determining the mineral saturation characteristics of geothermal waters. SOLVEQ calculates partial heterogeneous equilibrium, wherein equilibration of a given water with specified minerals or gas fugacities can be forced. The forced equilibria fix the total concentrations of specified component species. For example, an unknown total concentration of aluminum in a given natural water can be computed by assuming equilibrium with kaolinite ($Al_2Si_2O_5(OH)_4$). This capability, combined with one for calculating pH at high temperature from a low-T pH measurement (Reed and Spycher, 1984), is useful for processing hydrothermal experimental run products (e.g., Mottl et al., 1979; Spycher and Reed, 1989b) and for determining geothermal water properties, such as the temperature at depth and history of degassing and mixing (Reed and Spycher, 1984; Pang and Reed, 1998).

CHILLER and SOLVEQ use the database SOLTHERM (Reed and Palandri, 1998), which contains the compositions, equilibrium constants, and stoichiometries of complexes, minerals, and gases, as well as the various parameters for computing activity coefficients for aqueous species and fugacity coefficients for mixed gases. SOLTHERM is external to the main programs, so new species can be added to a chemical model simply by adding a few lines describing stoichiometry and equilibrium constants to the database. This makes it straightforward to expand or change the database and to experiment with various stability constants. Most of the constants for equilibrium between the aqueous phase and minerals or gases in SOLTHERM are calculated using SUPCRT (Johnson et al., 1992), drawing on basic mineral data from Holland and Powell (1998), and Helgeson et al. (1978; updated in SUPCRT, Johnson et al., 1992) and applying data for water and aqueous species from Helgeson and co-workers, as documented in Johnson et al. (1992), but also including new data by Shock and Koretsky (1995), and Pokrovski and Helgeson (1995). Additional data for mineral solubilities and complex stability constants are drawn from a wide range of sources referenced in SOLTHERM.

The Core System of Equations

For a chemical system consisting of an aqueous phase with dissolved salts, minerals, and a gas phase, the approach to modeling hydrothermal processes (e.g., cooling, mixing, water-rock reaction) is to set up a series of mass action and mass balance equations, then solve them simultaneously and repeatedly, as the system is changed by the hydrothermal process (cooling, rock reaction, etc.). The system of equations is solved by the Newton-Raphson technique (e.g., Van Zeggren and Storey, 1970).

Component Species

To describe the compositions of all species in all phases in a geochemical system, it is necessary to define a set of component species that are the basic units for stating composition. The choice is arbitrary. One common choice for components is the chemical elements, but a much more convenient choice is species that actually exist in the system, including ions such as H^+, SO_4^2, and neutral species like H_2O (Reed, 1982). These can be used both for description of composition in mass balance equations and for reaction stoichiometries in mass action equations. The component species constitute a set of thermodynamic components, in the strict sense (Wall, 1965, p. 211 ff.; Pitzer and Brewer, 1961). CHILLER and SOLVEQ use the following selection of species: H^+, H_2O, Cl^-, SO_4^{2-}, HS^-, HCO_3^-, SiO_2, Al^{3+}, Na^+, Ca^{2+}, Fe^{2+}, Cu^+, etc., which provides for describing the compositions of chemical species and minerals with exactly the same coefficients that describe chemical equilibria (i.e., reaction coefficients). Relative to schemes that use chemical elements for thermodynamic components, this scheme halves the number of descriptive arrays in the program and similarly reduces the number of program steps needed to set up equations.

As an example, one mole of aqueous carbonic acid, H_2CO_3, which dissociates as follows,

$$H_2CO_3 = H^+ + HCO_3^- \qquad (5.2)$$

is described as containing one mole of H^+ and one mole of HCO_3^-, rather than two H, one C, and three O. The same one H^+ and one HCO_3^- also describe the fundamental chemical equilibrium stoichiometry for carbonic acid. The carbonate species, CO_3^{2-}, is described as containing one HCO_3^- and negative one H^+. The negative coefficient for H^+ is consistent with its appearing on the left side of the equilibrium expression that relates CO_3^{2-} to its component species, H^+ and HCO_3^-:

$$CO_3^{2-} + H^+ = HCO_3^- \qquad (5.3)$$

Compared to formulations in early multicomponent equilibrium programs, this system of component species improves computational speed, increases numerical stability, and provides for a robust treatment of redox reactions (using SO_4^{2-} and HS^-, or O_2 and H_2O), and complete accounting for hydrogen ion and water. The complete mass balance treatments of H^+ ion and water (Reed, 1982; Reed and Spycher, 1984) enable correct calculation of pH at all temperatures and make possible the calculation of water-loss processes such as boiling, evaporation, and dehydration of the aqueous phase by precipitation of hydrous minerals. The difference in this treatment relative to earlier approaches and several current programs used for environmental geochemistry, is in representing both H^+ and H_2O as true thermodynamic components, and strictly adhering to this formalism. This requires negative values for masses of H^+ ion under some circumstances, for example, in describing the bulk composition of high-pH waters, wherein negative H^+ arises because $OH^- = H_2O - H^+$ and $CO_3^{2-} = HCO_3^- - H^+$. The implications of this system of component species choices for the form of the mass balance equations for HCO_3^- and H^+ are explored below in the section on mass balance equations.

A similar twist applies to redox equilibria, wherein the additional thermodynamic component may be regarded as an electron. Rather than using an electron, redox equilibria and mass balance can be accommodated completely by using two thermodynamic component species that contain the same element in different oxidation states, e.g., HS^- and SO_4^{2-}, which contain S in the −2 and +6 oxidation states, respectively, or the pair O_2-H_2O, in which oxygen is in the zero and −2 oxidation states, respectively. This scheme results in negative quantities of O_2 or SO_4^{2-} to describe the composition of reduced systems, or negative HS^- to describe the composition of oxidized systems, but such negative values introduce no computational difficulties.

Mass Action Equations

The equations for simultaneous solution for overall heterogeneous equilibrium include the basic equations of mass action, mass balance, and, in some systems, enthalpy balance. The formulations of the mass action and mass balance equations used in CHILLER are given below; the derivations of some of them are more completely presented by Reed (1982). Equations in SOLVEQ are mostly as for CHILLER, except that mineral and gas masses are omitted from the mass balance equations given below. The equations are written for a gas-solid-aqueous system at overall equilibrium, such as that depicted in Figure 2; thus, for purposes of writing the equations, we assume that the phase identities are known. The procedure for determining the phase selection is discussed separately below.

Aqueous species such as metal-ligand complexes (e.g., $AgCl_3^{2-}$), ion pairs (e.g., $NaHCO_3$, NaCl), or the associated form of acids, e.g., H_2CO_3, equation (5.2), can be assembled from the component species defined above. Such combinations of component species are referred to as “derived” species, for each of which an equilibrium expression can be written like equation (5.2) for H_2CO_3 or (5.3) for CO_3^{2-}, or the following for $AgCl_3^-$:

$$AgCl_3^{2-} = Ag^+ + 3Cl^- \quad (5.4)$$

Such equilibrium expressions determine the form of equilibrium constant expressions or mass action equations, in which the concentration, m_j, of derived species, j, is related to concentration of component species, i. Mass action equations for derived species are as follows:

$$K_j = \frac{\prod_i m_i^{\nu_{ij}} \gamma_i^{\nu_{ij}}}{m_j \gamma_j} \quad (5.5)$$

in which Kj is the equilibrium constant, m is molality, γ is the activity coefficient, and ν_{ij} are stoichiometric coefficients referring to the number of moles of component species i, in one mole of derived species j; ν_{ij} are negative for species appearing on the left hand side of the equilibrium expression (e.g., 5.4). The symbol m_i, here and below, refers specifically to the molality of component species, as distinguished from derived species molality, m_j.

For the $AgCl_3$ example (5.4), equation (5.5) is as follows:

$$K_{AgCl_3^{2-}} = \frac{m_{Ag^+}\gamma_{Ag^+} m_{Cl^-}^3 \gamma_{Cl^-}^3}{m_{AgCl_3^{2-}} \gamma_{AgCl_3^{2-}}} \quad (5.6)$$

For each mineral, or mineral solid solution end member, indexed as k below, there is a reaction that relates it to the molalities of the component species. For that reaction, written with the mineral on the left side, a mass action equation is written:

$$K_k = \frac{\prod_i m_{ik}^{\nu_{ik}} \gamma_{ik}^{\nu_{ik}}}{a_k} = \frac{Q_k}{a_k} \quad (5.7)$$

in which the stoichiometric coefficient ν_{ik} is negative for component species that appear on the left side of the reaction; a_k refers to the activity of the solid solution end member k; and Q_k equals the product in the numerator of the mass action equation, defined here for use below. For the mineral acanthite (Ag_2S), the equilibrium expression and mass action equation are as follows:

$$Ag_2S + H^+ = 2Ag^+ + HS^- \quad (5.8)$$

$$Kacanthite = \frac{m_{Ag^+}^2 \gamma_{Ag^+}^2 m_{HS^-} \gamma_{HS^-}}{a_{Ag_2S} m_{H^+} \gamma_{H^+}} \quad (5.9)$$

For pure minerals $a_k = 1$, but for solid solutions the following equation is substituted for a_k in equation (5.7):

$$a_k = (\lambda_k x_k)^b = (\lambda_k n_k / \Sigma n_l)^b$$

in which λ_k is the activity coefficient for solid solution end member k; x_k is the mole fraction of end member k; n is the number of moles of solid solution end members k and l; and the summation in the denominator is over all end members in the solid solution. The exponent b is unity for solid solutions exhibiting “molecular mixing” or where atoms mix on a single site per formula unit, but for crystals where there are multiple energetically equivalent sites of a given crystallographic type per formula unit (e.g., three octahedral sites in talc), b takes a value greater than one. For example, for the ideal mixing of clinochlore [$Mg_5Al_2Si_3O_{10}(OH)_8$] and daphnite [$Fe_5Al_2Si_3O_{10}(OH)_8$], b is set to 5 in the mass action equation for each of these end members.

Substitution of (5.10) into (5.7) yields:

$$K_k = \frac{\prod_i m_{ik}^{\nu_{ik}} \gamma_{ik}^{\nu_{ik}} (\Sigma n_l)^b}{(\lambda_k n_k)^b} \quad (5.11)$$

There is one mass action equation such as (5.11) for each currently saturated pure mineral or solid solution end member. Recall that for pure minerals, equation (5.11) reduces to equation (5.7), with the a_k in the denominator of (5.7) set to unity.

The mass action equation for gas species g in a mixed gas is:

$$K_g = \frac{\prod_i m_{ig}^{\nu_{ig}} \gamma_{ig}^{\nu_{ig}}}{f_g} = \frac{Q_g}{f_g} \quad (5.12)$$

in which f_g is the fugacity of gas species g, and Q_g is the product in the numerator of the equation, defined here for use below. The fugacity f_g in equation (5.12) can be expressed:

$$f_g = \phi_g P n_g / \Sigma n_l \quad (5.13)$$

in which ϕ_g is the fugacity coefficient for gas species g, n_g is the number of moles of species g in the gas phase, P is fluid pressure, and the summation in the denominator is over all components in the gas phase. Substitution of (5.13) into (5.12) yields the gas mass action equation that is central to boiling calculations:

$$K_g P = \frac{\prod_i m_{ig}^{\nu_{ig}} \gamma_{ig}^{\nu_{ig}} \Sigma n_l}{\phi_g n_g} \quad (5.14)$$

For a gas phase consisting of H_2O, CO_2, and H_2S, the equilibrium and mass action expressions (5.14) for CO_2 are as follows:

$$CO_2 + H_2O = HCO_3^- + H^+ \quad (5.15)$$

$$K_{CO_2} P = \frac{m_{HCO_3^-} \gamma_{HCO_3^-} m_{H^+} \gamma_{H^+} \left(n_{H_2O} + n_{CO_2} + n_{H_2S}\right)}{\phi_{CO_2} n_{CO_2} a_{H_2O}} \quad (5.16)$$

Equation (5.14) is identical in form to the mass action equation for solid solutions (5.11), except that the pressure, P, is multiplied by K. By this formulation, the gas phase is treated nearly identically to solid solutions, both using the same computer algorithms except for the routines for computing fugacity and activity coefficients. There is one equation (5.14) for each gas species in the gas phase. Because the gas equilibrium is computed as part of an overall heterogeneous equilibrium among gases, solids, and the aqueous phase, the pH dependence and the Henry's Law solubility behavior of gases are implicitly accommodated in the simultaneous equations for equilibrium in the total system. Further, the salinity and temperature dependence of the gas solubilities are implicitly accounted for in the activity coefficients for the dissolved gas species that appear in other equations, e.g., equation (5.20), rendering unnecessary any explicit use of Henry's Law constants or gas volatility ratios (cf. Drummond and Ohmoto, 1985).

Mass Balance Equations

The location of all thermodynamic components in the system (Fig. 2) must be specifically tracked using mass balance equations. For each thermodynamic component there is one mass balance equation:

$$M_i^t = n_w \left[m_i + \sum_j m_j \right] + \sum_k \nu_{ik} n_{ik} + \sum_g \nu_{ig} n_{ig} \tag{5.17}$$

In this equation, M_i^t is the total number of moles of component i, and n_w represents the mass of solvent water, in kilograms. Other symbols are as previously defined. The multiplication by n_w in equation (5.17) converts molalities to moles so that all mass balance equations are expressed simply in total moles. This substantially simplifies many complex calculations in which the mass of the total system changes owing to mineral fractionation, evaporation, or mixing of separate waters.

For component HCO_3^-, assuming that calcite and a gas phase are in the phase assemblage, mass balance equation (5.17) is as follows:

$$M^t_{HCO_3^-} = n_w \begin{bmatrix} m_{HCO_3^-} + m_{H_2CO_3} + m_{CO_3^{2-}} + m_{CaHCO_3^+} \\ + m_{CaCO_3} + m_{MgHCO_3^+} + m_{MgCO_3} + \ldots \end{bmatrix} + n_{calcite} + n_{CO_2} \tag{5.18}$$

In this equation, the first molality term within the brackets, $m(HCO_3^-)$, corresponds to the m_i term in equation (5.17); the others within the brackets are the summation over derived species, m_j, indicated in equation (5.17); the n(calcite) and $n(CO_2)$ terms refer to the number of moles of calcite and CO_2 gas, respectively. Notice that the equation includes terms for CO_3^{2-} and other carbonate ion pairs even though the mass balance is for the specific component HCO_3^-. The CO_3^{2-} species must be included because CO_3^{2-} is itself a derived species composed of HCO_3^- and negative H^+.

For component H^+, assuming that calcite and a gas phase are in the phase assemblage, the mass balance equation (5.17) is as follows:

$$M^t_{H^+} = n_w \begin{bmatrix} m_{H^+} + m_{H_2CO_3} + m_{HCl} + m_{H_2S} - m_{CO_3^{2-}} \\ - m_{OH^-} - m_{MgOH^+} - 4m_{Al(OH)_4^-} + \ldots \end{bmatrix} - n_{calcite} + n_{CO_2} \tag{5.19}$$

In this example, the terms for all derived species that contain hydroxide are negative, because $OH^- = H_2O - H^+$, as explained above. Similarly, the mineral calcite contains negative H^+ that balances out the H in its HCO_3^- component, in accordance with the relationship:

$$CaCO_3 + H^+ = Ca^{2+} + HCO_3^-$$

Equation (5.5) can be rearranged to express molality (m_j) of derived species, j, in terms of the molalities and activity coefficients of component species, etc., and the result substituted into equation (5.17) to yield a substituted mass balance equation:

$$M_i^t = n_w \left[m_i + \sum_j \frac{\prod_i (m_{ij}\gamma_{ij})^{\nu_{ij}}}{\gamma_j K_j} \right] + \sum_k \nu_{ik} n_{ik} + \sum_g \nu_{ig} n_{ig} \tag{5.20}$$

Equations such as this one, the number of which is equal to the number of thermodynamic components, exemplify the master mass balance equations for solving the simultaneous heterogeneous equilibrium system. A slight variation on this equation is used for the solvent, water (Reed, 1982).

Enthalpy Balance

For calculations of boiling in geothermal systems, constraining the temperature and enthalpy of the gas-liquid system instead of constraining temperature and pressure not only provides a rational model of the natural process (discussed below), but it also simplifies numerical aspects of computing boiling. Numerical treatment is simpler because enthalpy and temperature or enthalpy and pressure provide a much more sensitive constraint on the gas/liquid ratio than do temperature and pressure, thus avoiding blundering into pure vapor or pure liquid stability fields in the course of a boiling calculation. The latter is a problem because the exact P-T position of the boiling curve for a natural water depends on its particular dissolved gas content and salinity; it is impossible to predict, a priori, exactly where its boiling curve lies in P-T space.

The enthalpy equation is solved simultaneously with the mass action and mass balance equations, above, to compute the pressure that satisfies the enthalpy balance constraint. For a total enthalpy H_{tot} distributed among the species i and j of the aqueous phase, the species g of the gas phase, and in solid phases k, the enthalpy balance is given by:

$$H_{tot} = H_{init} + \Delta H = \sum_i n_i \overline{H}_i + \sum_j n_j \overline{H}_j + \sum_g n_g \overline{H}_g + \sum_k n_k \overline{H}_k \quad (5.21)$$

where $\overline{H}$ indicates the partial molal enthalpy of the subscripted species (i,j,g,k), and n refers to the mass in moles of the various species. ΔH represents heat transferred to or from the surroundings, thereby changing the initial enthalpy H_{init} by ΔH. Boiling is isoenthalpic if ΔH is zero. Non-isoenthalpic paths can be computed by setting ΔH to non-zero positive or negative values (see below).

Equation (5.21) is the complete form of the enthalpy balance. In most calculations of boiling hydrothermal systems, the heat terms for the gas phase and the liquid water component of the aqueous phase are much larger than the heat of the other aqueous components (e.g., NaCl) or of the small quantities of minerals that precipitate. Thus, a good approximation of equation (5.21) is obtained by including only the terms for the gas components and for the liquid water. The gas species enthalpies can be computed using virial equation expressions from Spycher and Reed (1988).

Simultaneous Equations

Among the preceding equations, (5.11), (5.14), (5.20), and (5.21) constitute the core set that CHILLER solves simultaneously by a Newton-Raphson technique to compute overall heterogeneous equilibrium for any given incremental step in a model calculation. The primary unknowns are: m_i, n_w, n_k, n_g, and P. Pressure, P, is an unknown quantity only in calculations of boiling where the enthalpy balance equation (5.21) is used. For a typical large model calculation for a boiling system, the number of simultaneous equations might be 50, of which 25 are mass balance, 15 are mineral mass action, nine are gas mass action, and one is enthalpy balance. Representing the mineral and gas mass action equations (5.11) and (5.14) in logarithmic form improves convergence rates in most cases. As explained by Reed (1982), a charge balance equation is unnecessary. Nevertheless, it is useful to compute for each equilibration the net charge on the aqueous phase and minerals as a backup check for stoichiometry errors in the data compilations. If a charge imbalance appears (within a very small tolerance), it must be due to an error in some reaction stoichiometry, which can then be corrected.

Program SOLVEQ and its analogs (see above) solve only the substituted mass balance equation (5.20), truncated after the first term (that is, excluding the gas and mineral mass terms) for homogeneous equilibrium, yielding values for each of the N_i unknown molalities (m_i) of component species. For forced equilibrium of a given water with an arbitrary number (N_k) of minerals, SOLVEQ solves for all unknown molalities (m_i) using N_i-N_k of the mass balance equations (5.20) along with N_k mineral mass action equations (5.7), one for each mineral in the assemblage. In equation (5.7), the activity factor, a_k, is set to unity or to another desired value. When computing forced mineral equilibration, for each of the N_k minerals in the assemblage, we solve in an external loop for the unknown mass (total moles, M_i^t) of a specified component using equation (5.17) truncated after the first term. To buffer a gas fugacity, SOLVEQ may also use an equation such as (5.28); see below. To use titration alkalinity as an input quantity, an equation for alkalinity distribution resembling equation (5.20) with the aqueous term only, is used in place of a mass balance on carbonate.

Although the mass action equations (5.5) for derived species are implicitly solved for m_j, as part of equation (5.20), these, as well as the various equations for fugacity and activity coefficients and the equations for the enthalpy of the various phases, are solved explicitly in an "external" loop following each Newton iteration (see below).

Solving the System of Equations

Newton Raphson Method

The basic Newton-Raphson method (e.g., VanZeggren and Storey, 1970) is applied in CHILLER with variations (Reed, 1982, and below; see also Bethke, 1996) to solve the system of simultaneous, non-linear equations defined above. The method is not explained here, except to point out that it requires taking partial derivatives of equations (5.11), (5.14), (5.20), and (5.21) with respect to variables m_i, n_w, n_k, n_g, and P, then setting up the derivatives in a matrix that is repeatedly solved for incremental adjustments, δx_i to the unknowns (where x_i refers to m_i, n_w, n_k, n_g, and P). After each iteration, an improved estimate, $x_{i,new}$, of each unknown variable is computed from $x_{i,new} = x_{i,old} + \delta x_i$. The new values of x_i are then substituted into the equations and the process is repeated. The values of δx_i converge on zero through the Newton iterative process. In some instances, the iteration diverges, most commonly because the initial trial values of the unknowns are not sufficiently close to the ultimate solution value.

Inasmuch as negative molality of an individual aqueous component species (as distinguished from a negative total molality of a component species) cannot prevail at equilibrium, if a negative value of m_i is produced in the iterative process (when δm_i is negative and its absolute value exceeds m_i), it is arbitrarily reset to a small positive value. An analogous procedure specifically is not applied to mineral masses, n_k, for reasons explained below in the section pertaining to selection of the phase assemblage.

Trial Values

To begin the Newton-Raphson iterative solution process, trial values of the unknowns, m_i, n_w, n_k, n_g, and P are supplied. Typically, these need to be within five or six orders of magnitude of their correct values. For m_i, initial trial values that are smaller than the final values work better than larger ones; but for n_k, larger values work better, except for solid solution end members, where very small trial values (e.g., 10^{-12}) are better. For SOLVEQ calculations of forced mineral equilibria (see above), very small trial values for the m_i corresponding to the unknown M_is are most effective.

As explained further below, CHILLER calculations always involve solving the set of simultaneous equations repeatedly with incremental changes in composition or temperature, for example, between repeat calculations. Trial values for successive increments are the solutions from the previous increment, thus the change in the values of the unknowns (m_i, n_k, etc.) are small if the step is small (e.g., a small temperature change or titration of a small bit of rock). Consequently, the trial values on successive increments can be optimized by cutting the step size between increments. Of course, very small steps require added computing time and storage capacity, so there is reason to use large steps. In practice, steps are cut to small values where needed to aid convergence, but are otherwise set at relatively large values. The meaning of "small values" and "large values" varies depending on the details of the calculation. For temperature change calculations, a small step is 0.1° and a large step is 16°. For rock titration calculations, the difference between "small" and "large" would typically be one or two orders of magnitude. For example, if convergence problems arise as basalt is titrated into 1 kg of seawater, the step size might be cut from 1 g to 0.1 or 0.01 g for 10 steps, then the larger step size would be resumed.

Convergence Test and Convergence Forcing

To solve the system of simultaneous equations by the Newton-Raphson method, equations (5.11), (5.14), (5.20), and (5.21) are rearranged by subtracting their left sides from both sides of the equations, defining residual functions, F, whose value is zero when the system of equations is solved. The numerical solution is judged to have converged when the value of F for every equation is less than 10^{-12} times the largest term in the equation. If every function is not tested, it is possible to compute an apparent convergence in which most of the equations are solved, but those with very small terms (e.g., mass balance on trace elements like gold) are not.

Rarely, the Newton iterative process fails to converge, most commonly in large systems when the number of phases approaches the number components and some of the phases are solid solutions. Under these circumstances, convergence sometimes can be forced (Prausnitz et al., 1980) by multiplying the value of F (above) by a factor, t, between 0 and 1 (e.g., 0.9). The value of t is decreased by small steps (e.g., 0.1) on any Newton iterations for which F fails to decrease by the normal Newton process or until t becomes too small (e.g., 0.1).

Component Swapping

Most current FORTRAN compilers allow for accurate representation of numbers, x, in the range of $10^{-200} < x < 10^{+200}$, thus it is not necessary, as it was in the past, to use separate choices of component species depending on the oxidation range of the system under consideration. Nevertheless, it is convenient to choose component species for redox systems that are appropriate to the range of oxidation of interest. For example, the exceedingly small concentration ($<10^{-60}$) of sulfide in a system in contact with the atmosphere renders HS^- less meaningful and less convenient than O_2 as the principal redox component. For reduced systems (e.g., log $f(O_2) < -54$ at 25°C), component species SO_4^{2-} and HS^- provide well for treatment of redox equilibria (Reed, 1982). In oxidizing systems, O_2 can be substituted for HS^-, so that redox equilibria are expressed in terms of O_2 and H_2O. For calculations that cross the transition oxidation state between redox buffers, for example, the oxidation of an H_2S-bearing gas condensate above a boiling hydrothermal system (Reed, 1994), we can change from one set of component species to the other, and overlap the calculation at the transition $f(O_2)$ to verify that the calculated concentrations match. We commonly find in calculations that traverse a sharp redox boundary that the Newton-Raphson process diverges at the boundary, making it necessary to cut step size to very small values to complete the transition between redox buffers. For example, in a model for the origin of a metal-bearing brine in the Olympic Dam system wherein oxygen is removed from 1 kg of oxidized brine, cutting titration increments to 10^{-5} grams of O_2 is necessary (e.g., Haynes et al., 1994).

Activity Coefficients

The equations outlined above constitute the core system that must be solved for the unknown molalities and phase masses (m_i, n_k, n_g). These are the unknowns that are specifically computed by the Newton-Raphson procedure, but the equations rely on some numerical values that are computed in equations that are external to the core system, particularly values for activity coefficients of aqueous species and mineral solid solution end members and fugacity coefficients for gas species. These are the variables γ, λ, and ϕ in equations (5.5), (5.11), (5.14), and (5.20), which are computed in an external loop after each Newton iteration loop.

Non-ideality of H_2, H_2O, CO_2, and CH_4 gases and non-ideal mixing of the latter three is treated in CHILLER using a virial equation representation of their mixing properties (Spycher and Reed, 1988). This entails accounting for both the non-ideality of the individual gas components and their non-ideal mixing, through the appropriate application of a virial equation in pressure (as opposed to the customary equation in volume) containing cross-coefficients for mixing as well as the normal coefficients for gas non-ideality. This treatment facilitates a fast and efficient computation of non-ideal gas mixing in calculations of hydrothermal boiling, phase separation in hydrocarbon reservoirs, or gas production by reaction of acidic water with limestone, for example.

There are two formulations for computing aqueous activity coefficients (γ_i, γ_j, above) currently in common use in geochemical modeling programs. One applies a virial equation form, initially developed by Pitzer and co-workers (e.g., reviews by Pitzer, 1987, and Bethke, 1996, p. 115ff) which, when applied with existing fit coefficients (e.g., Harvie et al., 1984), provides for accurate activity coefficients for common electrolytes at high ionic strengths at low temperatures. Although the Pitzer equations yield accurate coefficients, they currently are limited to major solutes, excluding most ore metals and major rock-forming elements such as Al and Si. The second common formulation is an extended Debye-Hückel equation by Helgeson et al. (Helgeson et al., 1981; see also Chaps. 1 and 2), which yields good approximations for activity coefficients for nearly all species over a range of true ionic strengths up to about three molal and temperatures up to at least 300°C. The Helgeson et al. formulation entails computing a true ionic strength from the distribution of aqueous species, then applying that ionic strength in the HKF equation to compute activity coefficients.

For solid solutions, CHILLER and other programs such as EQ6 accommodate ideal mixing, as discussed above, and are equipped to compute activity coefficients (λ_k) for non-ideal mixing in any minerals for which the necessary mixing properties are programmed into subroutines. The broad range of different mixing models for various minerals precludes a general algorithm analogous to that for the aqueous phase; thus each non-ideal solid solution requires a different subroutine. In CHILLER, the only currently programmed non-ideal solid solution is electrum. This is not a serious limitation to modeling, however, because the ideal mixing approximation with site mixing is quite adequate for many alteration minerals of interest (e.g., chlorite, amphiboles).

Phase Assemblage Selection and Gas Buffering

Selection of the Phase Assemblage

Any chemical system at equilibrium at T and P is in a state of minimum Gibbs Free Energy (G) for some particular phase assemblage (see Chap.1). In a system that includes an aqueous phase, it is convenient to determine the mineral and gas assemblage by referring to the state of saturation of potential phases in the aqueous phase. This is executed after each incremental step in a model calculation, by scanning all possible previously undersaturated phases (pure minerals, solid solutions, gas) to determine whether any have become supersaturated as a consequence of the incremental change (of T, P, H, or M_i^t) leading to the current step. If any supersaturated phases are found, a selection of them is incorporated in the system, and the equilibration step is repeated.

Addition of supersaturated pure minerals. For pure minerals (k) a scaled (Wolery, 1979) saturation index, $\log(Q/K)_{k,s}$ (or $S'_{k,s}$) is computed after each equilibration step for each mineral that is not already saturated:

$$S'_{k,s} = \log Q/K)_{k,s} = \frac{\log Q_k - \log K_k}{s_k} \qquad (5.22)$$

In this equation, Q_k is the equilibrium quotient defined in equation (5.7), K_k is the equilibrium constant for mineral k, and s_k is a scaling factor equal to the sum of the absolute values of the reaction coefficients:

$$s_k = \sum_i \left|\nu_{ik}\right| \qquad (5.23)$$

The mineral with the largest positive scaled saturation index is included in a repeat equilibration calculation. This process is continued until no supersaturated phases remain. In some instances, a mineral that is selected by this process is determined to be undersaturated once the total phase assemblage is approached, in which case the procedure for removing undersaturated minerals (below) corrects the assemblage.

Scaling the saturation indices puts all minerals, regardless of the number of components in a formula unit, on a normalized basis for comparison. Without scaling, the absolute value of the saturation index for minerals that have a large number of component species in a single formula unit is disproportionately large compared to minerals with simple formulae, thereby skewing the phase selection process in favor of minerals with large formulae, which slows the process of finding the correct assemblage.

Addition of solid solutions. The basic approach (Reed, 1982) used for ideal gases and solid solutions requires computing a summation, Σ_ϕ, of hypothetical mole fractions, x_k, for solid solution end members. If Σ_ϕ exceeds one, the solid solution is supersaturated. The value of x_k depends on the corresponding activity, a_k required for saturation of the aqueous phase. The latter are computed for ideal solid solutions from the current composition of the aqueous phase, using equation (5.10) (with λ_k set to 1.0) and a rearrangement of equation (5.7):

$$a_k = Q_k/K_k \qquad (5.24)$$

Although this sum-of-mole-fractions method also works for non-ideal solid solutions, it is more convenient to constrain the sum of mole fractions to unity ($\Sigma_\phi = 1$) and compute a saturation index for the solid solution (Bourcier, 1985):

$$S'_{ss} = \sum_k x_k \log \frac{Q_k}{K_k a_k} \qquad (5.25)$$

The summation is over all end members in the solid solution. The solid solution is supersaturated if S'_{ss} is greater than zero for any values of x_k. Further, the composition of the most stable solid solution is the one that maximizes S'_{ss}.

To determine whether S'_{ss} exceeds zero for any x_k and to approximate the most stable composition for use in trial values for the next equilibration, we simply step through values of x_k in 0.1 increments and find the composition that gives the maximum S'_{ss}. By using a relatively coarse step interval (0.1) to speed the computation we risk stepping over an interval where the solid solution is barely supersaturated. This is inconsequential because the quantity of solid would be quite small and it is likely that on the next incremental step in the calculation, the solid will saturate for several of the discrete values of x.

Addition of a gas phase. The fugacity in the aqueous phase of any gas can be computed from a re-arrangement of equation (5.12):

$$f_g = Q_g/K_g \tag{5.26}$$

Further (Spycher and Reed, 1988),

$$f_g = \phi_g p_g = \phi_g x_g P \tag{5.27}$$

in which p_g is the partial pressure of gas species g, and other symbols are as defined above. The fugacity coefficient, ϕ_g is a function of T, P, and x_g (Spycher and Reed, 1988). Next, we substitute equation (5.26) into (5.27), use the constraint that the sum of all x_g is unity, and include the fugacity coefficient functions for ϕ_g, thereby defining a set of simultaneous non-linear equations that are solved using a Newton-Raphson algorithm to yield values for p_g. The sum of the p_g's is then compared to the total pressure, P, to determine whether a gas phase is supersaturated.

Removal of undersaturated minerals. When a given mineral that is already part of the phase assemblage undersaturates, this is indicated by a negative computed mass for the mineral at the end of an equilibration step. Thereupon, the corresponding mass action equation (5.11) is removed from the matrix and the calculation is repeated.

An improved approach eliminates the repeat calculation by testing for negative mineral masses after just five Newton iterations and throwing out the undersaturated minerals, if any, at that point, then continuing the iterative process. If, in any such instance, a mineral is incorrectly eliminated because its fifth-iteration computed mass is negative, even though it would have become positive again at true equilibrium, that mineral will have a positive scaled saturation index and will be replaced on a repeat equilibration. The latter is rare; when it occurs, the fifth-iteration procedure is temporarily skipped.

Solid solution removal. The fifth-iteration assemblage check, described above, can be used to detect undersaturation of solid solutions by the negative mass method (Reed, 1982), previously used only for pure minerals. Unlike pure minerals, the mass of one or another end member of a solid solution cannot be allowed to be less than zero because the mass action equations (5.11) cannot be solved at all if n_k is negative. As a solid solution end member dissolves out, its mole fraction becomes infinitesimal, but it is always positive at equilibrium.

The fifth-iteration negative mass method can still be applied, however, if the test for negative mass ($n_k < 0$) is executed immediately after the latest Newton-Raphson corrections (δn_k) are applied to the current values of mineral mass, n_k. At this point, if δn_k is negative but its absolute value exceeds the very small current value of n_k, the new n_k (= $n_{k,old} + \delta n_k$) will be negative, and the end member is thrown out. If this occurs before the fifth Newton iteration, n_k is just reset to a small positive value so that equation (5.11) can be used. By this test, CHILLER sometimes throws out one end member of a solid solution (e.g., typically when its mass approaches 10^{-13} moles or less and its mole fraction is less than 10^{-6}), while keeping the others. This results in improved computation efficiency since the small mass of end member is of no consequence but it does contribute to numerical instabilities.

Buffering Gas Fugacity

Gas fugacity can be buffered by equilibrating the system with a hypothetical gas phase at a set fugacity (cf. Delany and Wolery, 1984). To set the fugacity of gas g at a value f_g, we equilibrate with an arbitrary, large quantity (e.g., one mole) n_g of a hypothetical gas phase whose governing equation is a rearrangement of equation (5.12), as follows:

$$K_g f_g = \prod_i m_{ig}^{\nu_{ig}} \gamma_{ig}^{\nu_{ig}} \tag{5.28}$$

where K_g is the ordinary equilibrium constant for the gas and f_g is set at the desired buffer fugacity. For example, to set CO_2 fugacity at $10^{-3.5}$ (atmospheric), equation (5.28) takes the form:

$$10^{-3.5} K_{CO_2} = \frac{m_{HCO_3^-} \gamma_{HCO_3^-} m_{H^+} \gamma_{H^+}}{a_{H_2O}} \tag{5.29}$$

This method can be applied, for example, to set buffers for CO_2 and O_2 at atmospheric levels to model the weathering of basalt and granite by saline brines in an arid environment (Haynes et al., 1994). This approach is much more efficient and informative than the alternative approach of titrating oxygen and CO_2 into the system after equilibrating water and rock at a given ratio.

Process Models

A geochemical "process" model refers to a geologically based hypothesis for how a particular mineral assemblage or mineral zoning pattern might have formed. "Processes" involve specific sequences of cooling, boiling, fluid-rock reaction, mixing of two fluids, etc. In each such process, the variables that change as the process unfolds are temperature, pressure, bulk composition, enthalpy, or some combination of these. In the formulation of equations, above, all of these variables are present either explicitly, or in functions that yield constants that appear in the equations (e.g., K_j, K_k, γ_i), but which are computed externally from the core system of equations (see above). The modeling of "processes" consists of changing the temperature, pressure, enthalpy, and (or) total moles (M_i^t), then computing overall heterogeneous equilibrium by solving equations (5.11), (5.14), (5.20), and (5.21) simultaneously, then repeating the process over and over through a series of stepwise changes of the variables. By this simple procedure, one can compute a tremendous variety of processes, such as water-rock reactions, boiling, fluid-fluid mixing, evaporation, etc., some of which involve simultaneous changes in several variables, such as temperature and composition. Such process models are appropriately termed "reaction path" models, although this term is especially applied to rock titrations (see below). For each process, depending on the physical model being investigated, it is possible to manipulate the changes in M_i^t in specifically defined ways to fractionate minerals or gases, for example.

In a complete process model for the origin of a particular ore type, e.g., epithermal adularia-silica-gold, the overall process is broken down into stages pertaining to the metal and fluid sources, fluid evolution along a flow path, and various possibilities for metal trapping (e.g., Plumlee et al., 1994; Reed, 1997). The stages can be further divided into a sequence of "unit processes," each one of which can be addressed with a single series of calculations, such as a rock titration or cooling or fluid-fluid mixing. A series of simple "unit process" methods is explained below.

Rock Titration ("Mass Transfer")

One of the most common unit processes of interest in hydrothermal systems is the reaction of a hydrothermal fluid with its wall rock, yielding alteration minerals. Such calculations have been called "mass transfer" models, but the term "rock titration" more directly describes the model process. In studies of hydrothermal systems, rock titrations are most useful for studying hydrothermal alteration of wall rock along a fluid flow path, where they illuminate the reactions responsible for forming the zoned alteration envelopes bordering veins. The change in the composition of the bulk system is most conveniently expressed as a function of the water/rock ratio, *w/r*, which is simply the ratio of the total amount of initial water to the total amount of rock titrated. The use and meaning of *w/r* is further discussed by Reed (1997) and is distinct from the usage in stable isotope studies (see Chap. 8).

In a rock titration, we start with a single aqueous phase of specified mass and composition (both specified in M_i^t, commonly summing to 1 kg) at internal equilibrium and not supersaturated with any other phase. Rock of specific composition, expressed in wt percent oxides or wt percent minerals, is titrated into the water in small bits (usually in gram units), and overall equilibrium is computed after addition of each bit (Fig. 3). The bit size depends on the water salinity and pH, but is typically in the range of 10^{-4} grams (per kilogram of initial water) to begin with, then increasing to tens or hundreds of grams as the total amount of titrated rock ranges through hundreds, then thousands of grams. The maximum amount of titrated rock is limited in titrations of aluminosilicate rocks by alteration "dry up," that occurs in the range of 30 or 40 kg of rock per kilogram of initial water because the precipitation of hydrous minerals consumes all of the water in the aqueous phase (Reed, 1997).

Computationally, rock titrations are executed by changing M_i^t as follows:

$$M^t_{i,s+1} = M^t_{i,s} + \Delta M^{rock}_i \qquad (5.30)$$

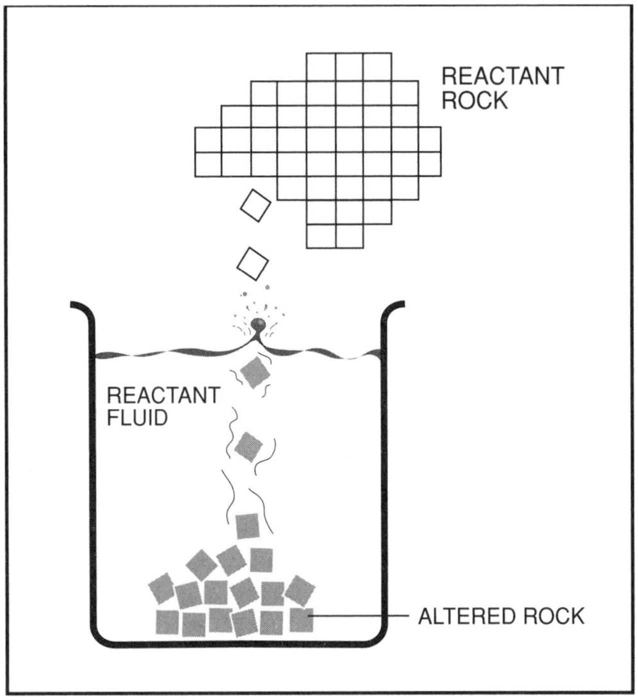

FIG. 3. Rock titration. In rock titrations, small bits of the reactant rock (granite, limestone, orthoclase) are titrated into the aqueous phase one after the other; each addition changes the bulk composition of the system according to equation (5.30). After each titration increment, the system of equilibrium equations is solved to identify the equilibrium mineral assemblage and distribution of aqueous species.

wherein M_i^t is the number of moles of component i (eq. 5.17), $s + 1$ refers to the titration step following step s, and ΔM_i^{rock} is the amount of component i added in an increment of titrated rock.

Flow-through and Flush

Two variations on rock titrations can best be understood with reference to a one-dimensional flow system, such as that depicted in Figure 4, wherein fluid enters a permeable rock pathway on the left, then passes from one rock segment to the next, reacting with the rock as it flows. In a flow-through model, the leading fluid parcel reacts with fresh rock in each incremental advance down the flow path, and, in each increment, it moves out of contact with the minerals formed in the immediately preceding segment. A flow-through calculation is useful for modeling the evolution of a potential ore fluid as it traverses a source rock (e.g., seawater reaction with basalt) or for modeling precipitation of ore minerals where they react with an appropriate trap rock (e.g., reaction of an oxidized fluid with an organic carbon-bearing shale). The computational process is the same as a rock titration, except that minerals are fractionated from the system in each titration step, in accordance with the following:

$$M^t_{i,s+1} = M^t_{i,s} - M^{min}_{i,s} + \Delta M^{rock}_i \qquad (5.31)$$

wherein $M_{i,s}^{min}$ refers to the composition of the fractionated minerals that precipitated in step s. Except for conditions

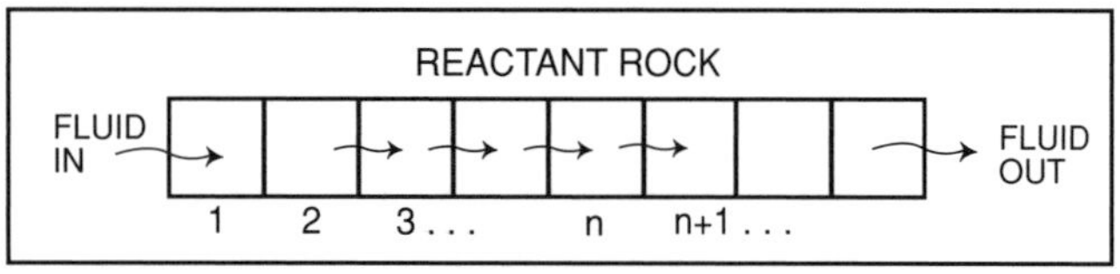

FIG. 4. One dimensional fluid flow: flow-through and flush systems. Fresh fluid enters the flow path from the left and moves successively through the series of rock-filled boxes. A flow-through calculation tracks the behavior of the leading bit of fluid as it progresses along the flow path, changing composition according to equation (5.31). A flush calculation models the changes in the first box, changing composition according to equation (5.32); in each increment of the calculation, fresh fluid enters, reacts with the rock, then moves out, leaving behind a changed mineral assemblage.

of unusually large porosity, the calculation begins to resemble a realistic model of a flow-through system when the throughput w/r (w/r computed from initial fluid mass divided by the summation of titrated rock increments) is less than 0.16, corresponding to porosities of less than 30 percent.

A flush calculation can be understood with reference to the first rock segment in the flow pathway (Fig. 4), where fresh input fluid enters the segment, equilibrates with the rock mass, then leaves. The first segment is repeatedly flushed with previously unreacted fluid. This process is calculated by the following manipulation of bulk composition:

$$M^{t}_{i,s+1} = M^{t}_{i,s} - M^{aq}_{i,s} + \Delta M^{aq}_{i} \qquad (5.32)$$

The composition of the already-reacted aqueous phase is given by $M^{aq}_{i,s}$, and the next increment of fresh fluid is given by ΔM_i^{aq}. In a flush calculation, the volume available in the rock mass for the incoming fluid is limited by the porosity, which determines the size of ΔM_i^{aq}. Porosity is computed at each step by converting mineral masses to volume, then subtracting the total mineral volume from the volume of the segment as initially defined. See Reed (1997) for an example of a flush calculation applied to reaction of an acidic magmatic volatile phase with andesite.

Temperature Change

Decreasing temperature of a hydrothermal fluid is one of the most commonly expected processes that promotes precipitation of ore minerals. Because temperature decrease unaccompanied by boiling or by mixing with a cold fluid can only take place by conduction of heat away from the hydrothermal fluid, simple temperature decrease is likely to be limited to initial or transient stages of fluid advance through propagating fractures or to circumstances of natural heat exchange, where a physically isolated cold fluid convects heat away from a conduit carrying hot fluid. Although simple temperature decrease is probably uncommon, it is useful to be able to model temperature change in isolation to understand its effects. A temperature change process model is carried out by incrementally changing temperature by recomputing the equilibrium constants (see Chap.1) in equations (5.11), (5.14), and (5.20), as well as the temperature dependent parameters in the activity coefficient equations. Temperature change with fractionation of minerals is executed by coupling a bulk composition change with each temperature change:

$$M^{t}_{i,s+1} = M^{t}_{i,s} - M^{min}_{i,s} \qquad (5.33)$$

Fluid-Fluid Mixing

Mixing of a metal-bearing hydrothermal fluid with a dilute or cold water is one likely process that precipitates ore in many settings, ranging from sea floor hot springs to epithermal fissures (e.g., Plumlee, 1994). Such a calculation can be executed by adding either fluid to the other in small increments, as indicated in Figure 5. Isothermal mixing involves only a manipulation of composition, as follows:

$$M^{t}_{i,s+1} = M^{t}_{i,s} + \Delta M^{aq_c}_{i} \qquad (5.34)$$

$\Delta M_i^{aq_c}$ refers to the added increment of the second fluid, designated by subscript *c*.

If the two fluids are different in temperature, the temperature change must be computed for each step in addition to the composition change explained above. Because the heat capacity of water is not independent of temperature between 25° and 300°C, the temperature of the mixed fluids is not a linear function of the mixing ratio, and the heat capacity must be used to calculate the temperature of the mixture. For this purpose steam table enthalpy data are regressed to produce two power functions: (1) enthalpy of water as a function of temperature, and (2) temperature as a function of enthalpy. The effects of salinity on the enthalpy of water can generally be ignored because they are small. Using the first of the power functions, the enthalpy of one kilogram of each of the hot and cold waters is calculated. The enthalpy per

$$H_{mixture,s+1} = \frac{n_s H_s + \Delta w\, n_c H_c}{n_s + \Delta w\, n_c} \qquad (5.35)$$

kilogram of a mixed fluid is then:
in which H is the enthalpy per kilogram and n is the number of kilograms; subscript s refers to the previous incremental step, and c refers to the added fluid on the new incremental addition given by $\Delta w n_c$, wherein Δw is a unitless incremental titration factor. Because the total mass of precipitated minerals is small in most cases, their heat contributions can be neglected, although for systems at very low w/r, the mineral heat effects are likely to be important. Once $H_{mixture}$ is calculated for a new titration increment, the corresponding temperature is calculated using the second power function mentioned above, which expresses temperature as a function of enthalpy. The new temperature of the mixture is used to calculate a full set of equilibrium constants for use in equations (5.11), (5.14), and (5.20).

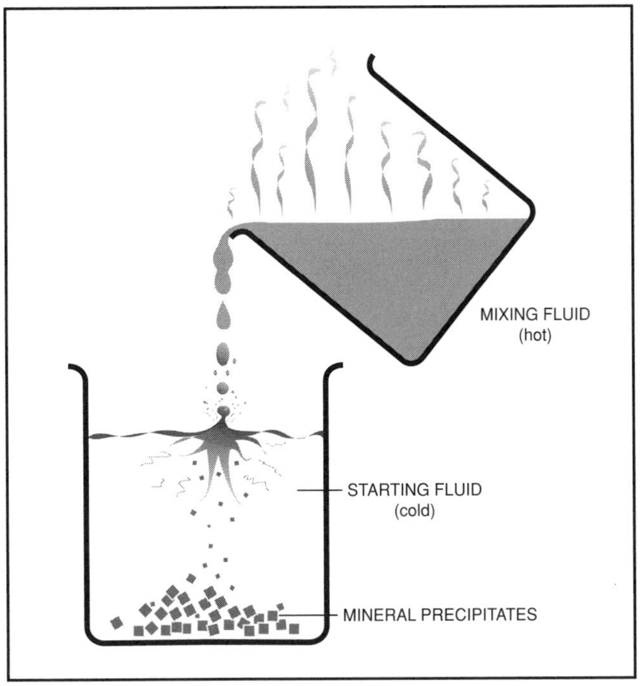

FIG. 5. Fluid-fluid mixing. In a mixing calculation, we start with a specific amount of one fluid at a specified temperature, represented here in the lower beaker, then add a second fluid of different temperature and composition to the first in small increments, recalculating overall equilibrium after each incremental addition, according to equation (5.34). The temperature of the mixture is also recalculated, using enthalpy relations explained in text.

Boiling

An enthalpy constraint provides a rational means of modeling natural boiling systems, but it also substantially simplifies the numerical treatment, as discussed above. Typical hydrostatic, steady-state boiling conditions in hydrothermal systems necessarily approach isoenthalpic conditions because the wall-rock temperature along a fluid ascent path matches the temperature of the boiling water itself, at steady state. Consequently, there can be no heat transfer to or from the wall rock, and boiling is isoenthalpic. Departures from steady state isoenthalpic boiling into super- or sub-isoenthalpic conditions might result from changes in pressure due to variations in the permeability (silica plugging) of the outlet system (Spycher and Reed, 1989a). Such non-isoenthalpic boiling paths can be readily computed using the ΔH term in equation (5.21).

The constraints of heat transfer in boiling, near-neutral-pH geothermal systems actually control the precipitating mineral assemblage through the relationship of gas fraction to CO_2 partitioning, and the effect of the latter on pH:

1. Heat budget controls the fraction of boiled gas (that is, the transfer of heat between the wall rock and the boiling fluid, whether into or out of the fluid, controls the proportion of gas phase to form at the prevailing pressure at a given depth).

2. The consequent gas fraction controls the amount of CO_2 partitioned into the gas phase.

3. The CO_2 partitioning controls the pH of the aqueous phase by way of:

$$HCO_3^-(aq) + H^+(aq) = H_2O(aq) + CO_2(g) \quad (5.36)$$

4. The pH controls the mineral assemblage that precipitates (i.e., the identity and abundance of sulfides, carbonates, silicates, etc.). Thus, overall, the heat budget controls the mineral assemblage.

To compute isoenthalpic boiling, we first compute the total enthalpy of a given mass of the pure liquid phase (H_{tot} in eq. 5.21) at a specified temperature and at the pressure of exact gas saturation, corresponding to the depth in the system where boiling begins. As this parcel of liquid ascends into a lower-pressure environment, it boils, partitioning its heat between the liquid and gas. The heat absorbed by vaporization causes temperature to decrease. This process is computed by stepwise decreases in temperature while holding enthalpy constant at the initial value and solving for the pressure at each step that produces the ratio of gas to liquid necessary to satisfy equation (5.21). Of course, this constraint is met simultaneously with the other chemical equilibrium constraints (eq. 5.11, 5.14, 5.20) so changes in the composition of the aqueous phase and gas phase and in the abundances of minerals are computed too. Non-isoenthalpic paths, either super- or sub-isoenthalpic, are computed by adding or subtracting heat on successive model steps using ΔH in equation (5.21). This simulates heat transfer into or out of the fluid as it ascends in the boiling system, as illustrated by Spycher and Reed (1989a). Boiling with mineral fractionation or gas fractionation can be accomplished by applying equation (5.33), for minerals, or the same equation with an additional term ($M_{i,s}^{gas}$) for subtracting the gas composition on each step.

Cold Water Mixing in a Boiling System

In natural hydrothermal systems, there are places where the boiling zone may be intruded by descending cold meteoric ground waters or by cold waters that migrate in laterally through an aquifer. One such place is the Fushime geothermal system, Japan, where 100°C seawater appears to be mixing with the gas-liquid mixture in the reservoir (Reed et al., 1988). Mixing of such cold waters with the gas-liquid mixture in the boiling zone must result in partial or complete condensation of the steam phase into the cold water, which is heated as a consequence. Such processes can be modeled using CHILLER by titrating cold water of specified composition and temperature (T_c) into the two-phase hot mixture (at T_h). For each increment (Δn_c) of cold water, we set ΔH (eq. 5.21) to the enthalpy of that increment at temperature T_c. Each such increment of cold mixing water increases H_{tot} (eq. 5.21), but the total enthalpy must then be distributed over more water; furthermore, the cold water must be heated to the temperature of the existing gas-liquid mixture. Thus heat is absorbed from the steam, causing it to condense. The quantity, n_c, of cold water of temperature T_c

needed to resorb fully the n_g moles of steam at temperature T_h is given by:

$$n_c \int_{T_c}^{T_h} C_p dT = n_g \Delta H_{vap} \tag{5.37}$$

where ΔH_{vap} refers to the heat of vaporization of the water at T_h, and C_p is the heat capacity of water. This equation is solved implicitly in CHILLER by way of equation (5.21).

As long as steam is condensing at a fixed pressure, the temperature remains constant. This temperature plateau during steam resorption is illustrated in Figure 6a. Once the steam is fully resorbed, the temperature decreases owing to the dilution of hot water by cold. An additional consequence of gas phase resorption as in the Fushime example is the sharp decrease in pH (increase in a (H^+), Fig. 6c), as CO_2 (gas) enters the aqueous phase. The pH decrease causes sulfide minerals to dissolve (etch) temporarily, until further dilution and cooling cause them to re-precipitate (Reed, 1992a). This Fushime model illustrates the simultaneous changing of temperature, pressure, and bulk composition in a complex aqueous-solid-gas system where two fluids of different compositions and temperatures mix.

Concluding Statement

Models of hydrothermal processes are based on field observations and laboratory studies. Whether models are thermodynamically permissible can be evaluated by stepwise computing of simultaneous multicomponent equilibria with changes of temperature, pressure, composition, or a combination of these between steps. Valid models must be consistent with the field constraints and must satisfy thermodynamic constraints, but a numerical model that reproduces the observations is not necessarily a model of what actually happens because more than one different model may yield the same results. In such instances, more detailed observations and more sophisticated models are necessary.

Acknowledgments

Nicolas Spycher played an indispensable role in developing and improving many aspects of computing methods in general, and in the formulation and computation of processes pertaining to aqueous-gas systems. I am most appreciative of his very substantial contributions. The

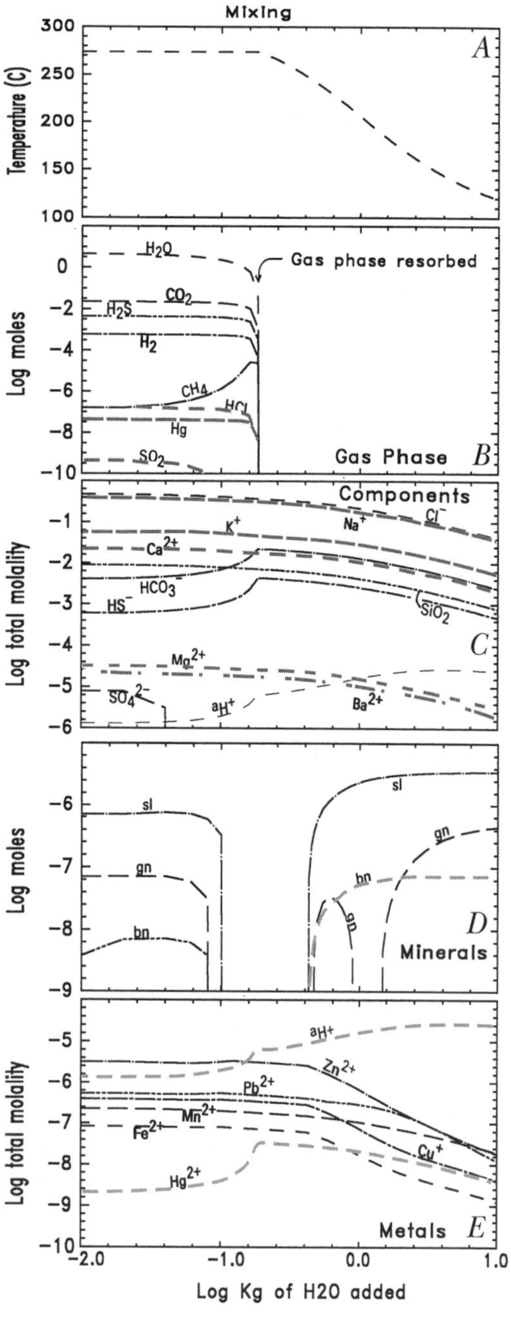

←

FIG. 6. Mixing and gas resorption. A 100°C pure water is added to a partly boiled 274°C water containing metals and sulfide. The abscissa shows the number of kilograms of pure water titrated into an initial one kilogram of boiled water plus gas. (A) Temperature of mixture. The temperature remains constant until all of the gas phase is resorbed. (B) Composition of the gas phase, originally produced by boiling of the hot fluid. The gas is fully resorbed by (condensed into) the cooler fluid after a sufficient amount of the cooler fluid is added to meet the constraints of equation (5.37). (C) Total molalities of major component species. Any components that enter the gas phase, such as HCO_3^- or HS^-, respond to the gas resorption process with an upswing their concentrations. The concentrations of other species, such as K^+, are simply diluted. pH decreases as gas is resorbed, as described by reaction (5.36). (D) Sulfide minerals, sphalerite (sl), galena (gn) and bornite (bn) that were initially present owing to the boiling process are resorbed (etched) as the gas condenses into the aqueous phase because the fluid becomes more acidic. After a sufficient amount of added cool fluid, the sulfides reprecipitate owing to dilution of the ligand, Cl^-, that is complexing the metals, and to the cooler temperature, which causes chloride complexes to dissociate. The precipitation of base metal sulfides after gas resorption follows the simple pattern expected for precipitating ore sulfides by cold water mixing. (E) Total concentrations of metals. Base metals, Cu^+, Pb^{2+}, and Zn^{2+}, initially increase in concentration as their respective sulfides dissolve, then decrease once the sulfides reprecipitate. Hg does not follow this pattern because it is part of the gas phase initially; its concentration increases, then follows a simple dilution path.

manuscript has benefited from critiques by Tom Wolery and Ian Ridley, both of whom provided excellent, thoughtful criticisms, which I appreciate. Anne Blanchard drafted many of the figures.

REFERENCES

Arnorrsson, S., Sigurdsson, S., and Svavarsson, H., 1982, The chemistry of geothermal waters in Iceland: I. Calculation of aqueous speciation from 0° to 370°C: Geochimica et Cosmochimica Acta, v. 46, p. 1513–1432.

Ball, J.W., and Nordstrom, D.K., 1991, User's manual for WATEQ4F, with revised thermodynamic data base and test cases for calculating speciation of major, trace, and redox elements in natural waters: U.S. Geological Survey Open File Report, p. 91–183.

Bassett, R.L., and Melchior, D.C., 1990, Chemical modeling of aqueous systems: An overview, *in* Melchior, D.C., and Bassett, R.L., eds., Chemical modeling of aqueous systems, American Chemical Society Symposium Series 416, p. 1–14.

Bethke, C.M., 1994, The geochemist's workbench, version 2.0, A user's guide to Rxn, Act2, Tact, React, and Gtplot: hydrogeology program, University of Illinois.

—— 1996, Geochemical reaction modeling, concepts and applications: Oxford University Press, 397 p.

Bjarnason, J.O., 1994, The speciation programme WATCH: version 2.1: Reykjavik, Orkustofnun, 7 p.

Bourcier, W.L., 1985, Improvements in the solid solution modeling capabilities of the EQ3/6 geochemical code: UCID-20587, Lawrence Livermore National Laboratory.

Delany, J.M., and Wolery, T.J., 1984, Fixed fugacity option for the EQ6 geochemical reaction path code, Lawrence Livermore National Laboratory, University of California Research Laboratories, 20 p.

Drummond S.E., and Ohmoto, H., 1985, Chemical evolution and mineral deposition in boiling hydrothermal systems: Economic Geology, v. 80, p. 126–147.

Harvie, C.E, Moller, N., and Weare, J.H., 1984, The prediction of mineral solubilities in natural waters: The Na-K-Mg-Ca-H-Cl-SO_4- OH^--HCO_3^--CO_3^{2-}-CO_2-H_2O system to high ionic strengths at 25°C: Geochimica et Cosmochimica Acta, v. 48, p. 723–751.

Haynes, D.W., Cross, K.C., Bills, R.T., and Reed, M.H., 1994, Olympic Dam ore genesis: A fluid mixing model: Economic Geology, v. 90, p. 281–307.

Helgeson, H.C., 1968, Evaluation of irreversible reactions in geochemical processes involving minerals and aqueous solutions: I. Thermodynamic relations: Geochimica et Cosmochimica Acta, v. 32, p. 853–877.

Helgeson, H.C., Delany, J.M., Nesbitt, H.W., and Bird, D.K., 1978, Summary and critique of the thermodynamic properties of rock-forming minerals: American Journal of Science, v. 278-A, 229 p.

Helgeson, H.C., Kirkham, D.H., and Flowers, G.C., 1981, Theoretical prediction of the thermodynamic behavior of aqueous electrolytes at high pressures and temperatures: IV. Calculation of activity coefficients, osmotic coefficients, and apparent molal and standard and relative partial molal properties to 600°C and 5 kb: American Journal of Science, v. 281, p. 1249–1516.

Holland, T.J.B., and Powell, R., 1998, An internally consistent thermodynamic data set for phases of petrologic interest: Journal of Metamorphic Geology, vol. 6, p. 309–343.

Johnson, J.W., Oelkers, E.H., and Helgeson, H.C., 1992, SUPCRT92: A software package for calculating the standard molal thermodynamic properties of minerals, gases, aqueous species and reactions from 1 to 5000 bars and 0° to 1000°C: Computers and Geosciences, v.18, p. 899–947.

Kharaka, Y.K., Gunter, W.D., Aggarwal, P.K, Perkins, E.H., and DeBraal, J.D., 1988, SOLMINEQ.88, a computer program for geochemical modeling of water-rock interactions: U.S. Geological Survey Water Resources Investigation Report 88-4227.

Mottl, M.J., Holland, H.D., and Corr, R.F., 1979, Chemical exchange during hydrothermal alteration of basalt by seawater, II. Experimental results for Fe, Mn and sulfur species: Geochimica et Cosmochimica Acta, v. 45, p. 868–884.

Pang, Z.H., and Reed, M.H., 1998, Theoretical chemical thermometry on geothermal waters: Problems and method: Geochimica et Cosmochimica Acta, v. 62, p. 1083–1091.

Parkhurst, D.L., 1995, User's guide to PHREEQC, a computer model for speciation, reaction-path, advective transport and inverse geochemical calculations: U.S. Geological Survey Water Resources Investigation Report 95-4227, 143 p.

Pitzer, K.S., 1987, A thermodynamic model for aqueous solutions of liquid-like density, *in* Carmichael, I.S.E., and Eugster, H.P., eds., Thermodynamic modeling of geological materials: Minerals, fluids and melts: Reviews in Mineralogy, v. 17, p. 97–142.

Pitzer, K.S., and Brewer, L., 1961, Thermodynamics, 2nd ed., revised: New York, MacGraw-Hill, 723 p.

Plumlee, G.S, 1994, Fluid chemistry evolution and mineral deposition in the Main-Stage Creede epithermal system: Economic Geology, v. 89, p. 1860–1882.

Plumlee, G.S, Leach, D.L., Hofstra, A.H., Landis, G.P., Rowan, E.L., and Viets, J.G., 1994, Chemical reaction path modeling of ore deposition in Mississippi Valley-Type Pb-Zn deposits of the Ozark Region, U.S. Midcontinent: Economic Geology, v. 89, p. 1361–1383.

Pokrovskii, V.A., and Helgeson, H.C., 1995, Thermodynamic properties of aqueous species and the solubilities of minerals at high pressures and temperatures: The system Al_2O_3-H_2O-NaCl: American Journal of Science, v. 295, p. 1255–1342.

Prausnitz, J.M., Anderson, T.F., Grens, E.A., Eckert, C.A. and O'Connell, J.P., 1980, Computer calculations for multicomponent vapor-liquid equilibria: Englewood Cliffs, New Jersey, Prentice-Hall, 351 p.

Reed, M.H., 1982, Calculation of multicomponent chemical equilibria and reaction processes in systems involving minerals, gases, and an aqueous phase: Geochimica et Cosmochimica Acta, v. 46, p. 513–528.

—— 1992a, Computer modeling of chemical processes in geothermal systems: Examples of water-rock reaction, boiling and mixing, *in* D'Amore, F., ed., Applications of geochemistry in geothermal reservoir development: New York, United Nations Institute for Training and Research, United Nations Development Program, p. 275–298.

—— 1992b, Origin of diverse hydrothermal fluids by reaction of magmatic volatiles with wall rock, *in* Hedenquist, J.W., ed., Magmatic contributions to hydrothermal systems: Reports of the Geological Survey of Japan, no. 279, p. 135–140.

—— 1994, Hydrothermal alteration in active continental hydrothermal systems, *in* Lentz, D.R., ed., Alteration and alteration processes associated with ore-forming systems: Geological Association of Canada, Short Course Notes, v. 11, p. 315–337.

—— 1997, Hydrothermal alteration and its relationship to ore fluid composition, *in* Barnes, H.L., ed., Geochemistry of hydrothermal ore deposits, 3rd ed.: New York, Wiley, p. 303–366.

Reed, M.H. and Palandri, J., 1998, SOLTHERM data base: A compilation of thermodynamic data from 25 to 300 C for aqueous species, minerals and gases: Unpublished report, available upon request to the authors.

Reed, M.H. and Spycher, N.F., 1984, Calculation of pH and mineral equilibria in hydrothermal waters with application to geothermometry and studies of boiling and dilution: Geochimica et Cosmochimica Acta, v. 48, p. 1479–1492.

Reed, M.H., Spycher, N., and Akaku, K., 1988, Numerical models of boiling and mixing in geothermal waters: International Symposium on Geothermal Energy, Kumamoto and Beppu, Japan, November 10–14, 1988, International Heat Flow Commission of I.A.S.P.E.I., I.U.G.G. and the Geothermal Research Society of Japan, Extended Abstracts, p. 51–54.

Shock, E.L. and Koretsky, C.M., 1995, Metal-organic complexes in geochemical processes: Estimation of standard partial molal thermodynamic properties of aqueous complexes between metal cations and monovalent organic acid ligands at high pressures and temperatures: Geochimica et Cosmochimica Acta, v. 59, p. 1497–1532.

Spycher, N.F., and Reed, M.H., 1988, Fugacity coefficients of H_2, CO_2, CH_4, H_2O and of H_2O-CO_2-CH_4 mixtures: A virial equation treatment for moderate pressures applicable to calculations of hydrothermal boiling: Geochimica et Cosmochimica Acta, v. 52, p. 739–749.

—— 1989a, Evolution of a Broadlands-type epithermal ore fluid along alternative P-T paths: Implications for the transport and deposition of base, precious, and volatile metals: Economic Geology, v. 84, p. 328–359.

—— 1989b, As(III) and Sb(III) sulfide complexes: An evaluation of the stoichiometry and stability from existing experimental data. Geochimica et Cosmochimica Acta, v. 53, p. 2185–2194.

Turnbull, A.G., and Wadsley, M.W., 1986, The CSIRO-SGTE THERMODATA system, version V: Melbourne, CSIRO Division of Mineral Chemistry Communication, v. 1–7, 413 p.

Van Zeggren, F., and Storey S.H., 1970, The computation of chemical equilibria: Cambridge University Press. 176 p.

Wall, F.T., 1965, Chemical thermodynamics: San Francisco, W.H. Freeman, 451 p.

Wolery, T.J., 1979, Calculation of chemical equilibrium between aqueous solution and minerals: The EQ3/6 software package: Lawrence Livermore National Laboratory, University of California Research Laboratories-52658.

—— 1992a, EQ3/6, a software package for geochemical modeling of aqueous systems, package overview and installation guide (version 7.0), Lawrence Livermore National Laboratory Report, University of California Research Laboratories, MA-110662 (1).

—— 1992b, EQ3NR, a computer program for geochemical aqueous speciation-solubility calculations: Theoretical manual, user's guide, and related documentation (version 7.0), Lawrence Livermore National Laboratory Report, University of California Research Laboratories, MA-110662 (3).

Chapter 6

Fluid Inclusion Techniques of Analysis

T.J. SHEPHERD

British Geological Survey, Keyworth, Nottingham, United Kingdom NG12 SGG

AND A.H. RANKIN

School of Geological Sciences, Kingston University, Penrhyn Road, Kingston Upon Thames, Surrey, United Kingdom KT1 2EE

Introduction

Few areas of geochemistry have challenged the ingenuity and patience of researchers as much as the analysis of fluid inclusions (see reviews by Roedder, 1972, 1984, 1990; Hollister, 1981; Shepherd et al., 1985; Boiron and Dubessy, 1994). From simple optical techniques to the use of particle accelerators, no stone has been left unturned in the search for analytical perfection. Progress has been painfully slow and, by comparison with methods for the analysis of rocks and minerals, we are still in the rudimentary stages of development. The last five years, however, have seen a quantum leap in progress, largely as a result of rapid advances in microbeam technology that have established new standards in sensitivity, precision, and accuracy. Though rooted historically in the study of ore deposits, many of the recent breakthroughs have been pioneered by analysts in the petroleum and materials science industries. As in the wider field of chemistry, techniques tend to fall into two categories: those for organic and those for inorganic constituents. The situation is very similar with regard to elemental and isotope analysis. This has tended to polarize studies of the composition of fluid inclusions much to the detriment of all concerned, in particular those geologists concerned with the genesis of low-temperature, sediment-hosted hydrothermal deposits where organic material plays an important role in the distribution of ore minerals. Fortunately, technology transfer is now resulting in hybrid instruments that offer multiple capabilities and should lead to a substantial broadening of opportunities and applications.

In this chapter we describe and critically evaluate, for the non-specialist user or novice, the principal techniques currently employed for the quantitative and semiquantitative analysis of fluid inclusions. Our aim is to provide clear guidelines for choosing the most appropriate technique based upon the type of inclusion and analytical data required, together with advice on sample preparation, advantages and disadvantages of the methodology, and the time and cost of analysis.

A compromise has to be reached in arriving at an appropriate method for the quality and quantity of data required and fitness-for-purpose. It should always be borne in mind that even the most precise and accurate data are of little value if the sample analyzed cannot be placed within a well-defined paragenetic sequence and geologic framework.

With over 35 methods proposed or tested, we have had to be selective, giving priority to those techniques that stand up to chemometric validation or show the greatest potential for further development. Methods for stable and radiogenic isotope analysis of inclusions are described in Chapters 8 and 9, though many of the pre-analysis criteria listed here apply equally to other types of analysis. No a priori geochemical knowledge is assumed other than a basic understanding of the principles of fluid inclusion analysis and the ability to identify and recognize the main types of inclusion. We hope that in taking this pragmatic approach to fluid inclusion analysis we shall satisfy those who wish to take advantage of proven techniques while at the same time stimulating continued research. Because this volume is concerned primarily with inorganic hydrothermal processes, we have restricted our discussion of methods for analyzing organic components in inclusions to those that may be applied to ore environments. Before reading on, the reader should stop and ask one very important question: "Are the data really needed?" Extending databases is fine, but they are really only of value if they can be applied to the modeling of hydrothermal processes such as those described in the previous chapter.

What is so Special about Fluid Inclusions?

Hydrothermal processes, like many other geological processes, ancient and modern, involve a fluid phase (Fig. 1). The role may be chemical, as in the case of mineral deposition, or physical, as in the case of hydraulic fracturing. To model satisfactorily ancient hydrothermal systems, information is needed on the chemical and physical properties of both the fluid and solid phases. Automated rock and mineral analysis has buried us beneath mountains of data, and in general, this aspect is more than adequately covered. By comparison, virtually nothing is known directly about the fluid phase except from what little we know about the composition of fluid inclusions. Even for present day hydrothermal fluids, our observations and measurements are restricted to near-surface environments, be they hot springs, ocean ridge geothermal vents, or subsurface reservoirs penetrated by deep drilling. It is well established that the chemistry of modern hydrothermal

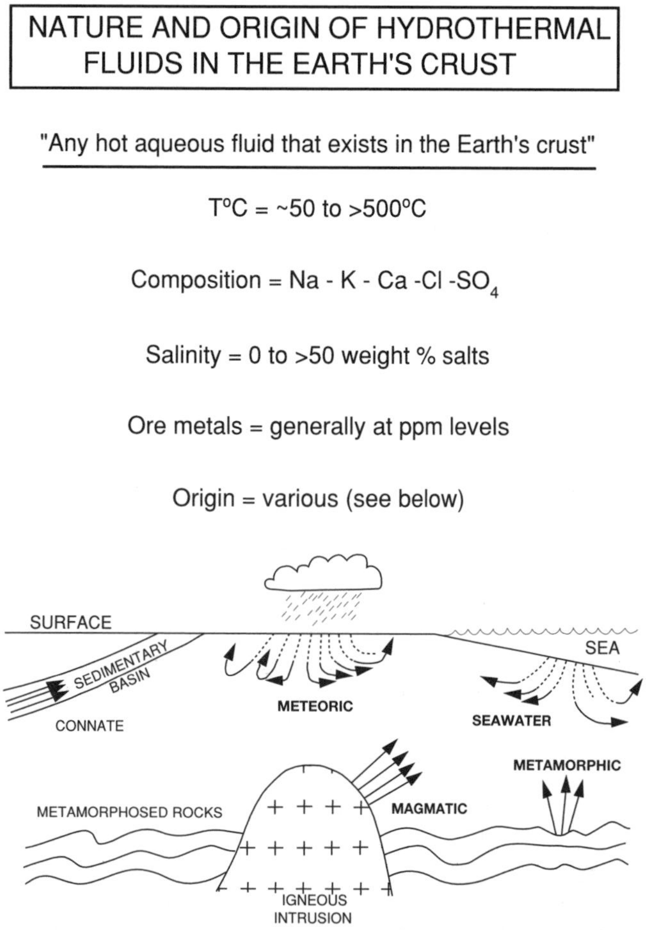

FIG. 1. Schematic diagram illustrating diverse origins and compositions of hydrothermal fluids in the Earth's crust. Note: Mantle-derived fluids not shown; connate waters may be substituted by formational waters or basinal brines.

fluids is controlled primarily by mineral-fluid interactions at elevated temperatures, and mirrors the composition of the reactive phases. For example, the pronounced enrichments in Ca and Fe for the Mid-Atlantic Ridge vents compared to the Broadlands geothermal field are a direct consequence of differences in the mineralogy of the reservoir rocks: oceanic basalts versus silicic volcanic rocks. Thus, depending upon the rock type, source of water, pressure, and temperature, we can expect large natural variations in hydrothermal fluid chemistry just as we can observe diverse styles of mineralization. One only need consider the exotic mineralogy of rare earth element pegmatites to realize the dangers of gross oversimplification. The only generalization that can be made is that hydrothermal fluids are normally aqueous solutions containing, as major constituents, Na, K, Ca, Fe, Al, Si, Cl, and CO_2 with salinities that vary from 0 to 70 wt percent total dissolved solids. Other constituents have concentrations <1,000 ppm except where there is a significant component of magmatic water which tends to raise the level of silicate-incompatible elements. It is to the credit of the imagination of nineteenth-century geologists that hot fluids were linked to the formation of mineral deposits.

Indirect estimates of palaeofluid composition can be obtained from thermodynamic consideration of the coexisting mineral phases (Chap. 3). Certain hydrothermal systems, for example, the porphyries or epithermal systems with their extensive wall-rock alteration envelopes, lend themselves very well to this approach. In general, however, the chemical complexity of natural fluids is too great to reconstruct from the limited mineral assemblages found in most rocks. Moreover, this approach is relatively insensitive to variations in the conservative elements (e.g., the halogens) that are now finding increasing use as source indicators for hydrothermal fluids. To our knowledge, the compositions of secondary inclusions that are universally associated with the microfracturing and rehealing of ore and gangue minerals cannot be used to model the conditions relating to the crystallization of the host mineral. They can, however, provide a valuable insight into the chemistry of post-deposition fluids and their relationship to late-stage alteration and mineral assemblages.

Thus, in order to access the composition of hydrothermal fluids, the most direct and least equivocal route is through the analysis of fluid inclusions. If this is true, then why are there so few published analyses of inclusion fluids?

The Analytical Challenge

Even the simplest fluid inclusions, formed by hydrothermal processes, constitute extremely small aqueous systems of variable composition enclosed within a solid matrix, often itself of variable composition. Depending upon the geological environment, the inclusions may also contain silicate glass, mineral salts, compressed gases, or liquid hydrocarbons (Table 1). These factors (small size, variable chemistry, multi-phase systems, host matrix variability) present difficult analytical problems that cannot be resolved using one technique alone. Most of the well established instrumental methods (e.g., electron microprobe analysis (EMPA), secondary ion mass spectrometry

TABLE 1. List of major phases reported in fluid inclusions from a range of hydrothermal ore deposits

Liquid	Vapor phase components	Solids
Water (brines)	H_2O	Halite (NaCl)
Carbon dioxide (often impure)	CO_2	Sylvite (KCl)
"Oil" (mixture)	N_2	Gypsum/Anhydrite $CaSO_4$)
Silicate glass	CH_4	Hematite (Fe_2O_3)
	Ar	Various Fe-Cl-(K) phases
	H_2S	Nahcolite ($NaHCO_3$)

Note 1: All observations at room temperature
Note 2: Different phases are present in different types of ore deposits; e.g., CO_2-liquid inclusions are typical of mesothermal gold deposits, oil-inclusions are typical of MVT deposits, and inclusions rich in daughter minerals are most common in magmatic/hydrothermal deposits.

(SIMS)) have been designed for surface analysis and, with the exception of silicate glass inclusions and daughter minerals, are of limited value for the analysis of subsurface fluid inclusions. Where adequate depth of penetration can be achieved, as in micro-laser Raman spectroscopy (μLRS), synchrotron X-ray fluorescence microanalysis (SXFMA) and proton induced X-ray emission spectroscopy (PIXE), complications arise due to host mineral interferences. It is not surprising, therefore, that analysts have not yet found the universal tool. Ideally, the perfect technique would be one that permits sub-picogram ($<10^{-12}$ g), non-destructive, multi-element, multi-component analysis of individual inclusions in a wide variety of mineral matrices. The best techniques currently available yield partial analyses. This is not as restrictive as it may first appear because many geological problems can be addressed using specific information. For example, there is little gain in painstakingly determining the absolute abundances of the major cations and anions in aqueous inclusions if element ratios are all that are required. Similarly, for a mixed hydrocarbon-aqueous inclusion, chemical characterization of the organics may suffice.

Another feature that complicates the analysis of inclusion-bearing material is the presence of multiple generations of inclusions (primary and secondary). This a natural consequence of the duration of hydrothermal activity and mechanisms of fluid entrapment. It is rare in our experience to find samples that contain only one generation or compositional type of inclusion. Thus the choice of technique depends upon: (1) a proper understanding of the types of inclusions present in the sample; (2) the relationship of the host crystal to mineral-forming events under investigaton; (3) the phases to be analyzed; (4) a clear idea of the way in which the analysis will help solve the problem.

Analysis of fluid inclusions in opaque minerals is quite feasible. However, with few exceptions, it is usually necessary to carry out an appropriate optical and thermometric study to satisfy the first requirement above. In most instances this is not possible. But exceptions do occur. For example, with wolframite, pyrite, and enargite that are transparent in the infrared, IR microscopy can be used (Campbell and Panter, 1990; Richards and Kerrich, 1993; Mancano and Campbell, 1995).

Technique Overview

For those fortunate enough to work with macroscopic inclusions (>200 μm), novel puncturing techniques can be used to open the inclusions and extract the contents for quantitative analysis (e.g., Lazar and Holland, 1988). If this can be achieved without loss or addition of material, then there are an unlimited number of methods available for analyzing the extracts. Such large inclusions are rare in hydrothermal minerals. The method works best with soft minerals (e.g., halite and galena) but has proven difficult to apply to quartz, fluorite, and other hard to moderately hard minerals. The typical fluid inclusion sample, however, is very different and normally comprises several generations of inclusions that rarely exceed 30μm in diameter. To handle this type of material and the quantities of fluid involved (Fig. 2), two strategies have been adopted: bulk sample techniques and single inclusion techniques.

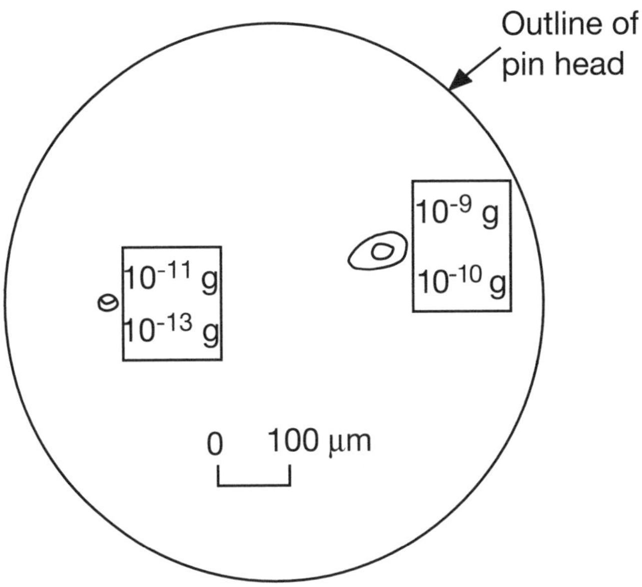

FIG. 2. Typical fluid inclusion volumes in relation to the size of a pinhead, at 1% and 100 ppm levels for 10 and 100 μm inclusions.

Bulk sample techniques. These rely on the ability to release the contents of from thousands to millions of individual inclusions by crushing or thermal decrepitation in order to separate the contents from the host mineral, and then perform various analyses on the extracts. The techniques are by necessity destructive, and interpretation of the data must take into account more than one generation of inclusions, if present. In combination with mass spectrometry or gas chromatography, this approach has been widely used for the analysis of inclusion volatiles (H_2O, CO_2, CH_4, N_2, H_2, and the noble gases). For solute analysis, the preferred technique is crush-leach extraction and analysis. This has proven invaluable for determining the cation-anion composition of aqueous inclusions, a mark of quality being the ability to achieve charge-balanced analyses where the sum of cation charges is close to the sum of anion charges. It must be remembered that this type of analysis does not give absolute ion concentrations for the inclusion fluid. These are derived by normalization to bulk salinity estimates obtained from complementary microthermometric studies or in direct combination with volatile analyses (Channer and Spooner, 1994). The solute chemistry can also be looked at semi-quantitatively using a combination of decrepitation and one or more instrumental methods. One technique, decrepitation-linked inductively coupled plasma emission spectroscopy, D-ICP, analyzes the nebulized inclusion material "vapor" released from the inclusions, while another (EMPA) deals with the residual salts precipitated on the sample surface. Neither is inclusion specific and little control can be exercised on the completeness of fluid expulsion. Despite the many potential problems of sample contamination, chemical fractionation, and changes in chemical speciation during extraction, bulk techniques have a very important role to play in the analysis of inclusion fluids. They are able to generate data quite rapidly for inclusions that are too small to examine using single inclusion techniques (<2 μm) and are an excellent means of screening samples for more detailed follow-up studies, or even mineral exploration purposes (e.g., Alderton et al., 1992).

The vagaries of inclusion abundance, size, and type are such, however, that in order to understand and model multi-stage hydrothermal systems one must acquire data for well defined generations of inclusions. Physically separating the different generations of inclusions is, for most situations, impractical. Unless a single inclusion population predominates, one must resort to single inclusion techniques.

Single inclusion techniques. Recent advances in microbeam technology have transformed the point analysis of single inclusions (elemental and molecular) and, with the availability of synthetic fluid inclusions as standards, has resulted in the development of several new, high spatial resolution, high sensitivity techniques capable of beam resolutions, in some cases, down to a few microns. These fall into two categories, non-destructive and destructive, which may be quantitative or qualitative depending upon the ease or otherwise of calibration. Most are under continuing development, and the state-of-the-art expressed in this chapter is true as of publication.

Of the non-destructive techniques, micro-laser Raman spectroscopy (μLRS) holds the center ground for the detection and measurement of the polyatomic gas species, and to a more limited extent, daughter minerals and polynuclear species in solution. Fourier transform infrared spectroscopy (FTIR) and UV fluorescence spectroscopy (UVFS) perform best with organic compounds and, though not yet as advanced as μLRS, have tremendous potential for providing semi-quantitative information for hydrocarbon inclusions (liquid and solid). For elemental analysis, PIXE (proton induced X-ray emission), PIGE (proton induced gamma-ray emission) and SXFMA (synchrotron X-ray fluorescence microanalysis) are the most widely used and tested techniques. PIXE and PIGE are best suited for the analysis of high and low atomic number elements respectively. SXFMA is equally versatile, with detection limits for metals in the 10 to 100 ppm range. Of the three techniques, the latter shows the greatest promise though all are subject to complex fluorescence absorption corrections when applied to inclusions located well below the surface of a mineral. A practical disadvantage of using proton-and synchrotron-based techniques is that these facilities are rare, very costly, and normally operated and managed by national research centers. Access for routine analysis is not always supported.

The second major group of single inclusion techniques are those that require the inclusions to be opened for analysis, either by mechanical, thermal, or laser-induced methods. This disturbs the chemical equilibrium of the inclusion and there is little opportunity for replicate analysis. It is all or nothing, and because the total mass of material is so small (typically $<10^{-12}$ g) the technique selected for analysis is usually phase specific (volatile components, non-volatile solute components plus daughter minerals, or daughter minerals). One of the simplest and most frequently used of these techniques is scanning electron microscopy-electron microprobe analysis (SEM-EMPA). This is used principally for the chemical characterization of daughter minerals and only requires that the inclusions are exposed on a mechanically broken surface, and carbon or gold coated for analysis. The selection of inclusions, however, is more or less random.

A more rigorous use of SEM-EMPA is for the quantitative analysis of brine inclusions. In this case the inclusions are frozen in liquid nitrogen before breaking the sample.

Mechanical and thermally-induced methods of opening inclusions are now being replaced by laser ablation techniques. This approach has proven particularly useful for the rapid multi-element analysis of non-volatile components. The laser is used initially as a microdrill but on entering the inclusion the contents are energetically volatilized. The resultant vapor is then analyzed by ICP-atomic emission spectroscopy (ICP-AES) or ICP-mass spectrometry (ICP-MS). Both methods show tremendous potential as routine analytical tools and afford simplicity of operation and data reduction. Not all elements are amenable to analysis, and detection limits vary from element to element. Analysis of the volatile constituents utilizes the same techniques as for bulk sample analysis, appropriately down-scaled. The volatiles are released either thermally or by laser ablation, and the gas species analyzed by mass spectrometry. Calibration is far from straightforward and analyses are best regarded as semi-quantitative.

Pre-analysis Checks

To make best use of the techniques available we have drawn together a list of pre-analysis checks that should be adopted as part of good laboratory practice. Failure to carry these out may result in meaningless or equivocal analyses, and considerable wasted time and effort. All too frequently, insufficient attention is given to this basic requirement and it is at this stage that the user must decide whether: (1) the samples contain inclusions relevant to the problem under investigation; (2) the amount of material available and the proportion of primary to secondary inclusions favor a bulk technique (i.e., analysis of an extract isolated from an unknown number of inclusions), or one which requires single inclusion analysis; (3) the sample matrix is compatible with the technique selected; and (4) the specifications of the technique match the type and quality of data required.

Before selecting or proceeding with any type of analysis, an optical and preferably thermometric examination of the material should be carried out to document the abundance, size, type, and generations of inclusions present.

This is best done on conventional fluid inclusion wafers, but grain mounts and thin sections may be adequate for some applications.

Inclusion abundance and diversity. Even for the experienced inclusionist, there are no hard and fast rules that can be used to predict the abundance, size, or type of inclusion in any one sample. Primary quartz from hydrothermally altered rocks may contain up to 1 to 2 vol percent inclusion fluids. Milky white quartz from a mesothermal vein may carry up to 10^{-3} vol percent inclusions varying from <1 to 30 µm in size, whereas late stage glassy quartz from an epithermal vein may have less than 10^{-8} wt percent inclusions no larger than 5 µm in diameter. Several orders of magnitude variation can be routinely expected. There are also differences between host minerals. Table 2 lists the 10 most commonly used hydrothermal minerals for fluid inclusion observation and analysis. Inclusion abundance is usually more critical for bulk techniques, whereas inclusion size influences the choice of single inclusion technique. Optical examination should be used, in the first instance, to check that a particular group or groups of inclusion are present and suitable for analysis. Microthermometric study of the samples (see Chap. 7) is, however, advisable to check for variations in gross compositions that may reflect different generations of inclusions.

Primary versus secondary inclusions. Bulk techniques rely upon a predominance of one type of inclusion or several closely related types of inclusions that represent a discrete hydrothermal event. These may be primary (P) but more often include a proportion of secondary (S) inclusions. If there is a high P:S ratio, analysis of the extract will yield a close estimate of the primary fluid composition. However, if the P:S ratio is low and the S inclusions have a composition that is significantly different from the P inclusions, then the resultant analysis will always be a weighted average of the two types. There are certain situations where the latter approach can be justified, but normally this is to be avoided. Densely clustered, multiple generations of P and S inclusions of variable composition, as in the case of porphyry copper deposits, can be so intermixed intimately as to make bulk analytical data very difficult to interpret.

TABLE 2. The top ten minerals from hydrothermal ore deposits in which fluid inclusions are most commonly reported

1.	Quartz
2.	Fluorite
3.	Calcite
4.	Dolomite
5.	Topaz
6.	Barite
7.	Sphalerite
8.	Cassiterite
9.	Garnet
10.	Pyroxene

Note 1: Opaque minerals, except cinnabar, chromite, wolframite, enargite, and pyrite, that are transparent in the infra-red, are not generally suitable for study.
Note 2: Most feldspars from most ore deposits are too turbid to study.

Having established the overall fluid inclusion characteristics of the sample(s), it should be considered whether the host matrix is likely to interfere with the analysis. Sometimes this question may be difficult to answer prior to analysis. In chemically complex silicates (garnets, pyroxenes), apatite, carbonates, and fluorite, the inclusion analysis will be unavoidably contaminated by the host mineral. For this reason—because of its chemical simplicity—quartz is generally the preferred host mineral for analysis.

Choosing the right technique. Choosing the most appropriate technique for fluid inclusion analysis is a matter of identifying the types of information required, determining how much material is available, and establishing accessibility to available equipment. There is no shortcut. Perfectly adequate results may be obtained for the major components of most inclusions using one of the simple methods described below.

The current trend in research is to consider microbeam as the only appropriate way forward, but meaningful data for the major solutes can be acquired from bulk methods, provided one particular population or type of inclusion predominates. Material released by crushing or heating can be analyzed using standard, low-cost methods such as atomic absorption or emission spectroscopy (cations), colorimetry, or specific ion electrodes (for anions). If data for trace and minor components are needed, for example, Br/Cl/I ratios and ore metal contents (Cu, Pb, etc.), more sensitive methods such as ion chromatography or ICP-MS are required. Nowadays, analyses of inclusion volatiles in bulk samples can be carried out using relatively simple gas chromatographic and mass spectrometric methods at very low levels of detection. But, if all that is needed is an estimate of the water content, simpler volumetric/absorption (Roedder, 1958) or colorimetric methods (e.g., Behr and Gerler, 1987) may be adequate. Specialist techniques are required for the analysis of hydrocarbon liquids and "oil" inclusions. Particularly appropriate is the combination of gas chromatography and mass spectrometry (GC-MS) where components of complex mixtures may be resolved and characterized.

Microbeam analysis provides the only sensible solution if: (1) complex or multiple generations of inclusions are present, or (2) little sample material is available (<0.5 g), or (3) the material is too fine grained (<2 mm) and difficult to separate from the matrix. Contaminant grains inside coarse crystals (e.g., carbonates and/or sulfides in quartz) can cause particular problems with some bulk methods.

Host mineral matrix effects can severely limit the choice of method as discussed above. Quartz is usually the preferred host because of its natural abundance, transparency, mechanical and chemical stability, and excellence as a host for inclusions. Even so, it can prove problematic for certain applications. For example, its strong infrared (IR) absorption means that it is not a suitable host for IR studies. Similarly, lattice-bound aluminum may cause interference with determination of the aluminum contents of inclusion fluids.

Bulk Methods for Volatile Analysis

Bulk methods fall into three categories: gas mass spectrometry (MS), gas chromatography (GC), and classical volumetric/manometric and gas absorption methods. Few analysts nowadays consider classical methods as a viable option for fluid inclusion volatile analysis because of the relatively low costs, widespread availability, greater sensitivity, and increased simplicity of modern mass spectrometers and gas chromatographs. For both GC and MS, the volatiles may be released either by grinding, heating, or crushing.

Grinding (in vacuo for MS) is very efficient at releasing the contents of all but the smallest inclusion, but a major drawback is that it creates a very large surface area on which released gases may be readily and even preferentially adsorbed (Piperov and Penchev, 1973). There is also the danger of gas reactions taking place during grinding and thus modifying the composition of the released volatiles. Typically, 20 g of sample is required. It is therefore the least preferred method of extraction although it has been used quite successfully for rare gas analysis (D. Norman, pers. commun., 1998).

Thermal decrepitation involves rapid heating (>20°C/min) of the sample to the temperature where the build-up of internal fluid pressure in an inclusion exceeds the confining strength of the host mineral (e.g., Shepherd and Miller, 1985; Kesler et al., 1986; Norman and Sawkins, 1987). A number of variables influence the decrepitation temperature. These include inclusion density, composition, size, shape and position within the sample, and the nature of the host mineral (Chryssoulis and Rankin, 1988). For these reasons the commonly held belief that stepwise heating and analysis can resolve different generations of inclusions in a sample is simplistic. In quartz, decrepitation usually starts at around 350°C with bulk decrepitation taking place over the interval 400° to 550°C. For softer, easily cleaved minerals such as fluorite and calcite, bulk decrepitation temperatures will be significantly lower. Above 600°C gas reactions producing CO and H_2 become increasingly significant and may substantially modify the original gas composition (Shepherd et al., 1985; Zimmermann and Veeken, 1997). It is most unlikely, however, that significant numbers of inclusions survive the α–β quartz transition at 573°C so there is no advantage in thermal decrepitation at higher temperatures. Of greater concern is the release of volatiles from non-inclusion sources (lattice sites in the host mineral) and minor contaminant minerals. The latter include the thermal degradation of hydrocarbons, carbonates, sulfates (e.g., alunite, anhydrite), and hydrated minerals (e.g., gypsum, sericite). When working with inclusion-poor epithermal quartz samples one must be especially aware of the dehydration of chalcedony and opaline phases which swamp the inclusion water. For carbonates, decomposition of the host mineral above 250°C generally precludes accurate measurement of inclusion CO_2. Great care must be taken at all times to prepare samples that are as free of surface and mineral contamination as possible (Shepherd et al., 1985), and that potential non-inclusion sources are recognized (Norman and Sawkins, 1987; Table 3). Typically, 100 to 500 mg of sample is required for decrepitation.

Crushing (in vacuo for MS) is less effective than thermal decrepitation and grinding but because the surface area of the crushed fragments is smaller, it is less prone to gas adsorption. Similarly, there is little danger in generating gases from non-inclusion sources. Sample weights (2–5 g) are greater than for thermal decrepitation but much depends upon the abundance and size of inclusions. Graney and Kesler (1995) report a procedure for analysis of inclusion gases evolved from sample sizes of less than 1 mg. To ensure optimum release of the inclusion volatiles while at the same time preserving the larger inclusions, a grain size of 1 to 2 mm is recommended. A number of imaginative and simple crushing devices have been used. These include small 10- to 20-cm lengths of copper or steel tubing that may be crushed in a vice or hydraulic press, and solenoid-operated metal plungers that systematically pulverize the sample. By carrying out the extraction at about 110°C (e.g., Bray and Spooner, 1992), problems due to water adsorption on mineral fragments and the walls of the crusher are minimized.

Laser-induced decrepitation provides an alternative means of opening inclusions, especially for small samples, but has not yet found general application except in the field of noble gas and isotope ratio mass spectrometry.

TABLE 3. Conditions under which volatiles released on heating and determined by MS methods are likely to be spurious, and unrelated to inclusion composition or simply at background levels (modified from Norman and Sawkins, 1987)

Gas	Conditions
CO_2	T_d>500°C and admixed carbonate minerals
H_2S	>1% admixed phyllosilicate minerals; T_d>700°C and admixed sulfide minerals
N_2	Admixed phyllosilicate or amphibole minerals containing ammonium ions
Ar	K-bearing minerals
SO_2, SO_3, CS_2	Admixed sulfide minerals; H_2S or sulfate in inclusion fluids; admixed sulfate minerals
C_nH_n	Pyrolysis of bituminous organic compounds
H_2, CO	T_d>500°C; amount <10^{-8} mol; C_nH_n in inclusion fluids
CH_4	T_d>400°C; amount <10^{-8} mol; C_nH_n in inclusion fluids
NH_3	Admixed minerals containing ammonium ions
H_2O	Amount <5 (10^{-7} mol; admixed water-bearing minerals)

Note 1: T_d= decrepitation temperature
Note 2: The table is also appropriate to decrepitation analysis by GC methods
Note 3: CH_4, H_2, and CO may be generated at high temperature on reactive surfaces by catalytic reaction, involving CO_2 and H_2O

This is a rather specialized area and is based upon the analysis of Ar, Kr, and Xe isotopes produced by neutron irradiation of Cl, K, Ca, Br, Se, I, Ba, Te, and U contained within inclusions. The reader is referred to the works of Bohlke and Irwin (1992), Turner and Bannon (1992), Irwin and Reynolds (1995), and Irwin and Roedder (1995) for further details.

All of the above procedures utilize an on-line volatile extraction/preparation system (in glass or metal) interfaced to a mass spectrometer or gas chromatograph. This allows the volatiles to be separated if necessary and/or their volumes to be measured to give absolute quantities per gram of sample. For aqueous inclusions, the measurement of water is clearly needed to estimate the mole proportions of the various gas species. Different methods have been adopted to measure water. These include measuring the vapor pressure of water in a calibrated volume, freezing it into a capillary and weighing it (Norman et al., 1991), conversion to H_2 gas and measuring its pressure in a known volume (Shepherd et al., 1985), or direct measurement by gas chromatography (Bray and Spooner, 1992).

Gas Mass Spectrometry (MS)

In gas mass spectrometry, the volatiles released from the inclusions are bombarded with electrons that ionize the molecules, producing positively charged ion fragments. Each ionized fragment has a particular mass to charge (m/e) ratio. For CH_4, the dominant fragments are CH_4^+, CH_3^+, CH_2^+, C^+, and H_2^+, with m/e ratios of 16, 15, 14, 12, and 2, respectively. By recording the intensities of each mass fragment over a m/e range of 2 to 100, a mass spectrum is obtained that can be used to identify and quantify the gas species present within a gas mixture (Fig. 3). Where there is overlap between major ion fragments (e.g., m/e 28 N_2^+ and CO^+), minor ion fragments can be used to characterize most simple gas mixtures (H_2O, CO_2, CH_4, C_2H_6, N_2, Ar, He, CO, H_2S, and H_2). If the volatiles contain higher order hydrocarbons, the ion fragmentation patterns are too complex to be interpreted uniquely and in such cases the volatiles must be separated into fractions prior to analysis. This is best achieved using GC-MS methods. Quadrupole gas mass spectrometers are favored for fluid inclusion volatile analysis because of their rapid mass scanning capability on extremely small samples, their low cost, and their relative ease of operation.

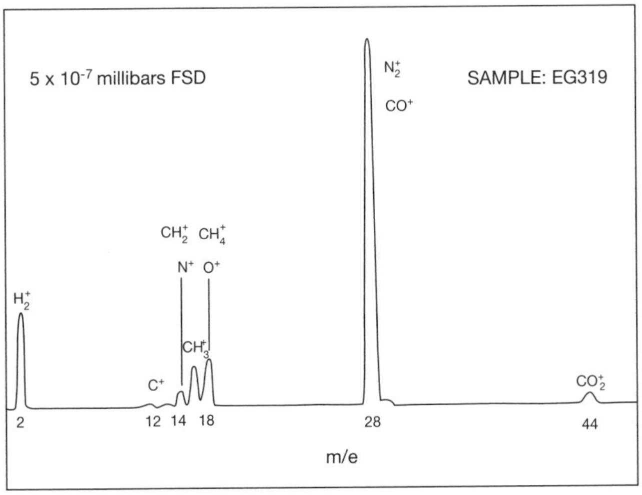

FIG. 3. Mass spectrum of a mixture of CH_4, N_2, and CO_2 showing fragmentation patterns of gas molecules and peak overlap for CO^+ and N_2^+ at m/e = 28 (Shepherd et al., 1985).

For quantitative analysis it is essential to use standard gases to establish relative gas sensitivities and cracking patterns.

As described above, most exponents of the method have until recently (e.g., Norman and Moore, 1997) carried out extraction, some form of cryogenic separation, and volumetric measurement prior to analysis. This permits absolute and relative mole concentrations to be calculated for each volatile component. Volumetric measurements for each gas fraction are accurate to within ±3 percent. Analytical precision is generally <5 percent for thermal decrepitation and 10 to 20 percent for crushing (Norman and Moore, 1997). Detection limits are the order of 1×10^{-9} μmoles.

However, ingenious designs have been developed in which the sample is decrepitated directly in the ion source of the mass spectrometer (e.g., Barker and Smith, 1986; Hoffmann et al., 1988; Guha et al., 1990; Jones and Kesler, 1992; Graney and Kesler, 1995; Williams-Jones, 1997), and/or using crush-freeze-scan (CFS) methods (Newman et al., 1997; Norman and Moore, 1997). In this way the sample size can be reduced to 0.03 mg or even introduced as a fragment of a fluid inclusion wafer. With this type of geometry and fast scanning capabilities it is possible to detect individual fluid inclusion bursts. However, it has yet to be demonstrated that the signals can be truly calibrated. Non-inclusion gases are still a problem, but the information obtained is quite remarkable and the method approaches the sensitivity of microbeam analysis on good samples (Table 4).

Gas Chromatography (GC)

Gas chromatography involves the separation of a mixture of gases based on their differing rates of movement through a porous medium: the chromatography column. Small variations in the absorption properties of each gas are sufficient to bring about marked differences in the time it takes for species to pass through the column (the "retardation" or retention time). An inert carrier gas (usually He or N_2) transports the samples through the column. Detectors monitor the emergence of each component gas within the sample as a function of time. Various detectors may be used depending on the volatiles to be analyzed, but photoionization and micro-thermal conductivity detectors connected in series are favored (e.g., Bray and Spooner, 1992). For a given set of operating conditions (column length and diameter, types of column packing, gas flow, and temperature) and suitable calibration, the retention time is characteristic of each

TABLE 4. Summary of main advantages and disadvantages of gas mass spectrometry for fluid inclusion analysis

Good Features	Poor Features
Equipment readily available	Unsuitable for complex hydrocarbon mixtures (unless attached to a GC)
Capable of analyzing a wide range of volatiles	High vacuum extraction line required unless the inclusion volatiles are released within the ion source.
Absolute and relative concentrations of simple gas species easily measured. Good overall level of precision (5-20%).	Extraction lines not available commercially
Very high sensitivities (typically 10^{-15} moles)	Potential release of non-inclusion volatiles during thermal decrepitation.
Calibration using simple gas mixtures	Calibration difficult for volatiles released within the ion source.
Small sample sizes (mg range)	Time consuming sample preparation. Samples must be thoroughly cleaned and free from most mineral impurities.

gas. The method is much less sensitive than mass spectrometry—typically 10^{-5} (moles), so sample sizes need to be slightly larger (1–5 g).

Considerable advances were made in the development and application of the GC method to fluid inclusion analysis in the 1970s (Andrawes and Gibson, 1979). One major drawback was the inability to analyze water and the need for two separate columns for permanent gases and low molecular weight hydrocarbons (see review by Roedder, 1984). These problems have now been largely overcome (Fig. 4). Single PoroPlot Q columns, for example, can now be used and the amounts of water determined directly. The method developed by Bray and Spooner (1992) and then modified by Salvi and Williams-Jones (1997a, b), is challenging mass spectrometry for "pole position" among fluid inclusionists as an effective quantitative method for volatile analyses. Reported reproducibility of GC analyses is now better than 15 percent.

On-line crushing using a hydraulic press is the preferred method for opening the inclusions, rather than thermal decrepitation or "off-line crushing." To reduce adsorption of gases on to freshly exposed mineral surfaces, it is also advisable to crush the sample at ~110°C (Bray and Spooner, 1992). As with MS analyses, the sample fragments need to be about 1 to 2 mm in size and scrupulously cleaned.

An impressive range of inclusion volatiles (H_2O, N_2, CO_2, CO, COS, H_2, Ar, CH_4, CH_3SH, C_2H_4, C_2H_6, and a range of higher order hydrocarbons) have now been quantitatively determined (Table 5). Analysis of H_2S, SO_2, and CS_2 has proved more difficult to achieve due to peak overlaps and adsorption on the chromatographic columns. GC and GC-MS methods for the analysis of hydrocarbon liquids are outlined briefly below.

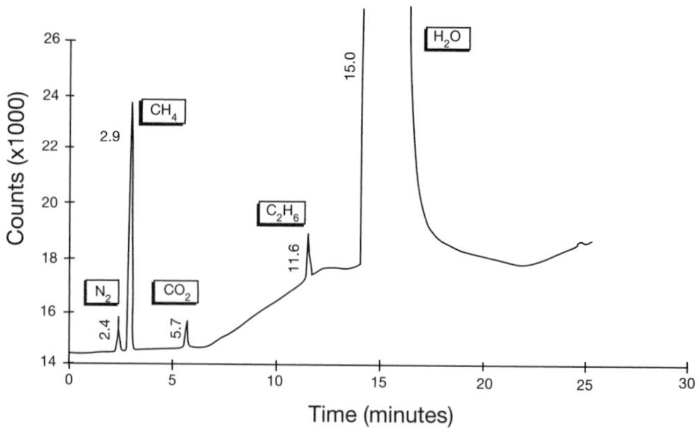

FIG. 4. Typical gas chromatogram (He carrier gas and thermal conductivity detector) showing broad peak for H_2O and smaller peaks for other volatiles (after Salvi and Williams-Jones, 1997b). Retention time shown in minutes on x-axis.

MS and GC Methods for the Analysis of High Molecular Weight Hydrocarbons

The basic GC and MS methods described above are effective for analyzing low molecular weight hydrocarbons in fluid inclusions. For higher order hydrocarbons (C5 and above) and complex mixtures present in "oil" inclusions, a different approach is required. In its simplest form, this involves the use of organic solvents to extract the liquid and waxy hydrocarbons. The extract is then passed through a chromatography column where separation takes place. Although the method is often referred to as gas-liquid-chromatography (GLC) it is essentially similar in principle to the GC method. The main differences are that (1) components are separated using hydrocarbon

TABLE 5. Summary of main advantages and disadvantages of gas chromatography for fluid inclusion analysis

Good Features	Poor Features
Equipment widely available	Detection limits typically 10^{-5} mmoles. $10^3 \times$ less sensitive than MS
Capable of analyzing a wide range of volatiles with a single column (including H_2O)	Sample size typically 1–5g but data have been acquired for 50 mg fluid inclusion wafer fragments
No high vacuum extration line required	Use of N_2, Ar, or He carrier gases precludes analysis of these gases in a single run
Complex organic compounds can be separated and analyzed; especially effective when combined with MS	High retention time limits throughput rate to about 5 analyses per hour

liquid eluants rather than inert gas carriers; (2) linear heating rates up to about 300°C are used to enhance movement of components through the column; and (3) chromatograms can be shown as plots against temperature rather than retention time. Peaks related to simple hydrocarbons can be recognized and quantified using suitable standard oil mixtures.

The technique is even more powerful when coupled to the inlet system of an MS (combined GC-MS). Separated components are recognized by their cracking patterns and characteristic m/e peaks. Kvenvolden and Roedder (1971) were the first to use a combined GLC and GC-MS approach on exceptionally large (>100 µm) oil-bearing inclusions in quartz. They successfully determined a full range of n-alkanes from C_{10} to C_{33}, in addition to isoprenoid hydrocarbons. Three separate columns were needed with n-hexane as the carrier. Another landmark paper was by Perin (1973) who used GLC (alumina columns) to detect a similar range of alkanes (up to C_{30}) in much smaller inclusions in fluorite from an MVT deposit in the United Kingdom. Large sample sizes (approximately 500 g) were needed.

More recently a GC-MS method has been developed and applied to the analysis of "biomarker" organic molecules in inclusion fluids associated with MVT deposits (Etminan and Hoffmann, 1989), and also higher temperature hydrothermal veins (Hoffmann et al., 1988). Extraction was carried out on approximately 10 g samples using chloroform-methanol mixtures eluted through alumina columns. Thermal decrepitation mass spectrometry (TD-MS) was used to determine low order alkanes (C_1-C_4) and other gases such as CO_2, N_2, and H_2O. By decrepitating the samples directly within the ion source of the mass spectrometer and monitoring the characteristic biomarker fragments (peak at m/e = 43), the authors reasoned that the biomarker fragments were trapped in the inclusions.

Surprisingly, there has been little follow-up work on the method outlined above by ore geochemists interested in the link between oil and ore. However, petroleum geochemists are acutely aware of the value of such data in providing information on the sources and timing of oil migration. For example, Karlsen et al. (1993) provide a detailed account of GC-MS methods applied to fluid inclusion analysis related to petroleum studies (Fig. 5). They also provide full details of the cleaning and extraction methods used, information somewhat lacking in earlier publications. The gaseous components of the inclusions (C_1-C_5) were liberated by crushing, and analyzed by conventional GC methods. GC and GC-MS analyses were carried out on 10-100 g samples extracted in an agate pestle and mortar using dichloromethane. Reproducibility of measurements was better than ±10 percent for gases (C_1-C_5); for GC and GC-MS analyses of steranes and hopanes, reproducibility was better than ±5 percent. Carbon isotope analyses were also determined but with low precision because of the poor yields (e.g., $\delta^{13}C = 39\% \pm 3$).

Barker and Smith (1986) have demonstrated the possibility of acquiring data on the composition of individual oil-bearing inclusions using mass spectrometry alone. The technique is similar to that described under MS above. Although the method cannot readily distinguish between different hydrocarbon components in a complex mixture, it does provide useful information on the association between hydrocarbons and other components (e.g., H_2O and H_2S) in individual inclusions in 10 mg samples.

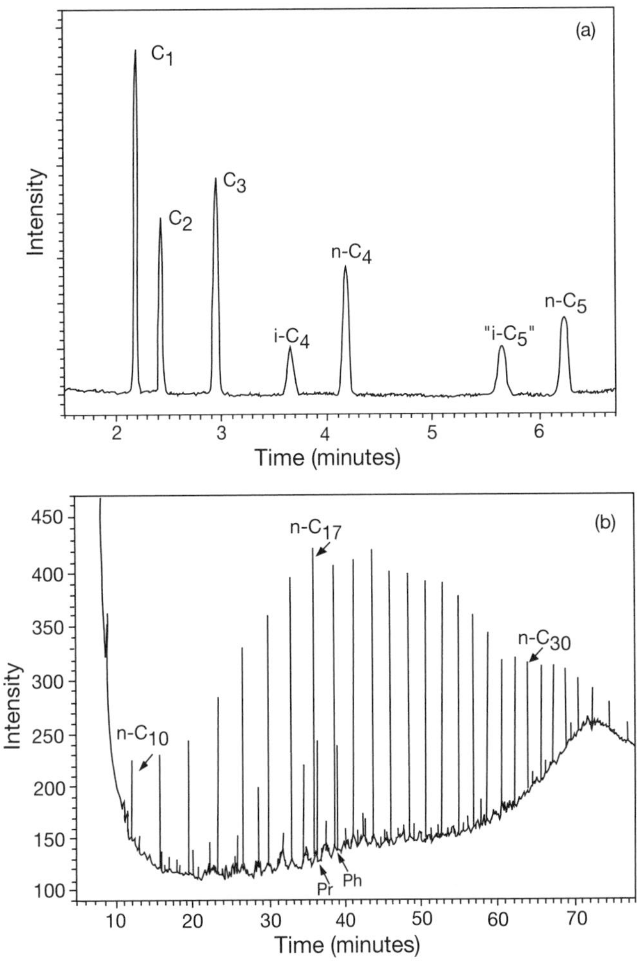

FIG. 5. Gas chromatograms of petroleum inclusions in quartz from the North Sea oil fields (after Karlsen et al., 1993):
(a) volatiles released by "on-line" crushing;
(b) extracts from opened petroleum inclusions.

Bulk Methods for Solute Analysis

Bulk methods have remained a favored means of determining ionic species in fluid inclusions since the pioneering early work of Roedder (1958) and Roedder et al. (1963). This may seem somewhat surprising in view of the inherent problems already discussed. However, through sensible choice of material and scrupulous care during sample preparation, good data can be obtained. Water is seldom determined together with the ionic species in most recent studies. This presents an immediate problem if truly quantitative data are required because only relative concentrations may be obtained (usually reported as ratios, K/Na, Cl/SO_4, etc.). The problem may be overcome to some extent by using knowledge of the total salinity or total dissolved salt content of the inclusion population based on microthermometry. The approach and methodology have been discussed in some detail by Shepherd et al. (1985). It is based on a priori knowledge (or reasonable assumption) that the inclusion fluids are essentially chloride brines. The problem has recently been overcome by the integrated SC/IC approach of Channer and Spooner (1994).

Bulk destructive methods for solute analysis fall into two main categories: (1) analysis of leachates based on release of inclusion contents by crushing (the crush-leach method) or decrepitation, and (2) direct analysis by various means of material released by decrepitation, usually by inductively coupled plasma emission spectroscopy (the D-ICP method). Total analysis of the bulk sample (inclusions plus host) might seem like a viable option. Nevertheless, unless the inclusions make up a significant proportion of the host (>2%) and one can be sure that interferences from trace elements in the host mineral, or contaminant grains, are negligible, the approach is ill-advised for routine applications. However, for the non-destructive bulk analysis of fluid inclusions, one is left with little choice. The only practical method for this purpose is instrumental neutron activation analysis (INAA). For example, Luckscheiter and Parekh (1979) used this technique for the non-destructive analysis of Na, K, Mn, As, Cl, and Br for inclusions in a few grams of quartz. The potential problems of contamination from lattice-bound Na were overcome by demonstrating a correlation between Na and Cl. Comparison with crush-leach results provided additional validation. Wilkinson (1990) and Rankin et al. (1993b) also used this method to detect gold in natural and synthetic fluid inclusions, although the results were difficult to validate.

Leachate Analysis

Leachate methods have been used extensively to analyze fluid inclusions for well over 100 years. With the recent development of high sensitivity analytical methods such as ICP-MS and ion chromatography, the method has received new impetus and is now capable of analyzing a large range of cations and anions in inclusion fluids. In earlier studies, sample weights of several tens or even hundreds of grams were required. These have now been routinely reduced to a few grams (Poty et al., 1974) and, in some instances, even down to the milligram level (e.g., Banks and Yardley, 1992). The method can be described in terms of four successive stages: sample preparation; opening of inclusions; separation of leachate; analysis of leachate.

Sample preparation is the most crucial stage. This begins with careful handpicking of a few grams of a coarsely crushed sample (typically 1–3 mm in size) under a binocular microscope. The objective is simply to avoid contaminant or composite grains rather than to select grains with predominant types of inclusions. A variety of methods can be used to clean the samples prior to crushing and leaching. Simple washing in warm HNO_3 overnight, followed by repeated washing in doubly-distilled water (DDW) may be quite acceptable for some applications, e.g., where very large, abundant, and saline inclusions are present in large crystals (Rankin et al., 1992). However, for optimum cleanliness the sample is normally washed with HNO_3/H_2O_2/DDW followed by electrolytic cleaning in DDW until the conductivity of the water has fallen to background levels (e.g., Norman et al., 1989; Channer and Spooner, 1992). This is based on the procedure originally described by Roedder (1958).

Opening of inclusions may be achieved by milling, crushing, or decrepitation. Crushing is most commonly employed using either copper or stainless steel tubes, or hand-held pestles and mortars. Agate pestles and mortars occasionally can give unacceptably high blanks; those composed of sintered alumina are better, whereas Kesler et al. (1996) preferred ones composed of diamonite. Whatever crushing method is used, careful monitoring of possible sources of contamination during abrasion is necessary by repeated analysis of suitable blanks. Clearly, the use of copper or stainless steel tubes precludes the analysis of the component metals within the inclusions. The crushed material is then leached with a small volume (~2–3 ml) of DDW.

Separation of the leachate can then be carried out using a combination of centrifuging, millipore filtration, and washing. If the sample is crushed too finely, adsorption problems can occur due to the large surface areas of newly exposed surfaces. Gentle crushing, rather than excessive grinding, can reduce the problem. It can also be alleviated, to some extent, by the addition of NH_4^+ (Kozlowski, 1978) or La^{3+} (Bottrell and Yardley, 1988) to the leachate solution, which are preferentially adsorbed thus inhibiting adsorption of other ions. A modification of the latter method involves two leachates: DDW for anions and an acidified $LaCl_3$ solution for cations (Yardley et al., 1993).

Analysis of leachate. This can be achieved by using a variety of modern instrumental methods. Ion chromatography is best suited to the analysis of anions (such as Cl^-, Br^-, SO_4^{2-}, F^-, NO_3^-), although the method can also be applied to alkali, alkaline earth, and ammonium cations (Channer and Spooner, 1992). Minimum detection limits in leachate solutions are reported to be typically in the range 1 to 30 ppb for most ions. Selective ion electrodes may have similar sensitivity ranges, but larger sample volumes (~10 ml) are usually required (Shepherd et al., 1985). INAA is also an option (Norman et al., 1989; Bennett et al., 1992), but availability is somewhat limited (Behr and Gerler, 1987). The multi-element capability and sensitivity of ICP-AES and ICP-MS methods makes them ideally suited to analysis of a very wide range of minor and trace cations (and possibly some anion species such as P as PO_4^{2-}, or B as $B_2O_3^-$). Usually, a combination of ICP and AAS methods are employed. A typical range of elements that can now be routinely determined by crush-leach methods includes Na, K, Li, Rb, Ca, Mg, Fe, Mn, Zn, Cu, Pb, (Al), Ba, Sr, Cl, Br, F, B, and SO_4^{2-} (Yardley et al., 1993). For some samples, REE analyses have also been reported (Norman et al., 1989; Banks et al., 1994). A crucial final stage in crush-leach analysis is to ensure that total cation to total anion charge balance is close to unity, otherwise contamination is to be suspected (Table 6). Alternatively, if there is an excess of cations, bicarbonate or bisulfide ions may be present. Unfortunately, these are too difficult to determine by crush-leach methods because loss of CO_2 and H_2S on crushing will upset the ionic balance. See Table 7 for a summary of advantages and disadvantages of this method.

ICP-Decrepitation—The (D-ICP) Method

In the late 1970s, a simple and rapid method was proposed for the qualitative and semi-quantitative analysis of metals in fluid inclusions using a combination of thermal decrepitation and ICP spectroscopy (Thompson et al., 1980; Alderton et al., 1982; Thompson and Walsh, 1983). A small (0.2–0.5 g) sample of 1- to-2-mm-sized fragments, previously hand-picked and separated, is heated in a small pyrex tube to the point at which bulk decrepitation occurs (for quartz, between 350° and 550°C) over an approximately one-minute interval. The sample tube is connected to the inlet of the ICP by a short length of silicone tubing. A stream of argon carrier gas is passed over the sample during decrepitation. The flow rate is carefully controlled so that only small (<20 μm) fragments of host minerals and material released from the inclusions during decrepitation are transferred into the plasma source. The scanning or integration time of the ICP is set to coincide with the onset, and diminution to background levels, of the decrepitation signal. Using this approach, up to 40 elements may be detected simultaneously over the space of a few minutes. These include Na, K, Li, Mg, Fe, (Si), (Al), S, B, Ca, Zn, Sr, Ba, Be, Sb, Bi, Cd, P, Mo, Sn, As, Cu, W, and Rb. Not all of these elements are necessarily derived from inclusion fluids. Small fragments of host mineral (e.g., quartz, hence brackets for Si and Al above), or admixed solid contaminants (including sublimates from sulfides giving rise to Pb, As, S, Sb, etc.) can cause problems. However, with care and appropriate use of time-temperature-ICP response profiles these effects can be minimized or at least recognized (Chryssoulis, 1983; Rankin et al., 1993). The effects of spectral line interferences also need to be recognized and evaluated (Thompson and Walsh, 1983). A recent development of the method (Coles et al., 1996) allows an improvement in the detection limits by up to an order of magnitude, taking into account fluctuations in the background plasma intensity. High salinity inclusions, with daughter minerals, are not suitable for analysis by the D-ICP method because the liquid component of the inclusions is likely to be preferentially released into the plasma. Similar concerns have been expressed (Roedder, 1990) about the possibility of incomplete transfer of material into the plasma, leaving behind a residue either inside the inclusion or on the surface of decrepitated grains. However, for moderate to low salinity inclusions the effects for major cations appear minimal (e.g., Coles et al., 1996).

For the alkali metal ratios, in particular Na, K, and Li, the results are often in excellent agreement with data obtained from other independent methods (Rankin and Graham, 1988; Rankin et al., 1993a). However, the method is only really semi-quantitative in the sense that elements cannot be determined in terms of absolute concentration units. All results are, therefore, expressed as element ratios (normalized to sodium). What the method lacks in terms of rigor and certainty compared to the crush-leach method, it makes up for in terms of speed of analysis and preparation, and sample sizes required. For

TABLE 6. Crush-leach results for two samples of vein quartz from SW England, based on raw data normalized against a given salinity value. Sample 54150 shows a poor charge balance, while sample 54154 shows a good charge balance (modified from Smith et al., 1996).

Sample No.	**54150**	**54154**
Mean salinity (wt % NaCl eq.)	**6.9**	**8.7**
Na	16310	24065
K	4186	3843
Li	58	352
Ca	4411	6534
Mg	598	564
Fe	9130	3190
Mn	834	427
Ba	29	61
Cu	837	151
Zn	192	104
B	623	1947
F	1540	1785
Cl	28119	43116
Br	80	38
SO4	2051	823
Σ +ve/Σ -ve	1.37	0.92

TABLE 7. Summary of main advantages and disadvantages of leachate analysis for fluid inclusion analysis

Good Features	**Poor Features**
Anion and cation analyses permit estimates of charge balance, and hence possible identification of contamination	Relatively large sample sizes (usually 3–5g) required
Good sensitivity and low detection limits with ICP-MS, ICP-AES, and ion chromatography	Even small contaminant grains can affect results (especially for ore metals)
Materials for cleaning, extraction, and leaching readily available	Insoluble daughter minerals may not be taken into the leachate
	Quantification of data relies on a knowledge of the salinity (usually by microthermometry)
	Suitable standards or reference materials not currently available in bulk
	Complicated (and time-consuming) procedures of sample preparation, cleaning, and leaching required prior to analysis

certain applications (e.g., a routine application of geothermometry) it has proven most effective (see Table 8).

Single Inclusion Techniques

Synchrotron X-ray Fluorescence Microanalysis (SXFMA)

Synchrotron X-ray fluorescence microanalysis (SXFMA) is undoubtedly the single most powerful analytical technique available to Earth scientists. It combines the non-destructive capability of X-ray fluorescence with high resolution diffraction and absorption spectroscopy to give valuable information on the valency state and chemical coordination of elements. This incredible power is due to the extreme intensity of the X-ray source, the "synchrotron storage ring" that is 10^6 times more brilliant than a conventional hot cathode source. For microanalysis, beam focusing and simple pinhole techniques produce spot sizes of a few microns—well within the size range of most inclusions. A second characteristic of SXFMA is the very low background continuum from Rayleigh and Compton scattering which means that sensitivities (peak to background ratios) are generally high and uniform across the whole periodic table. This is especially advantageous for the measurement of low atomic number elements ($Z < 20$). In theory, therefore, SXFMA satisfies all the requirements of single inclusion analysis (non-destructive, multi-element, ppm detection limits, with micro spatial resolution). In practice, however, the quantitative chemical analysis of inclusions has proven extremely difficult to achieve. In part this is due to very limited access to synchrotron sources, and the XRF instrumentation required; only about seven facilities exist worldwide at the time of writing. The main problems relate, however, to the irregular geometry of inclusions and their variable depth beneath the surface of the sample. This produces differences in the path length of the incident beam and makes corrections for self absorption and secondary fluorescence difficult to quantify except for near surface, regular shaped inclusions. Thus, to convert X-ray intensities to element concentrations, ZAF corrections must include functions that describe the depth distribution of X-ray production in the sample (Pouchou and Pichoir, 1988). None of these problems is unique to SXFMA, and all techniques (PIXE, EMPA, etc.) where fluorescence X-rays are generated from within thick samples require comparable absorption corrections. The net effect, as shown in Figure 6, is to markedly reduce the scope of elemental analysis for inclusions that are greater than five microns below the surface of the sample, particularly for S, P, Mg, and Na. For the lighter elements, uncertainties of ± 1 µm in the measured depth of an inclusion can lead to analytical uncertainties of ± 30 percent (Vanko et al., 1993). A good rule of thumb is to exclude elements with $Z < 14$ for fluid inclusion analysis.

Detection limits and precision are difficult to estimate, but relative standard deviations (RSD) are between 10 and 25 percent and detection limits are of the order 10 to 1,000 ppm depending on the element, host matrix, and various instrumental factors (Mavrogenes et al., 1995). Accuracy is dependent upon the use of matrix-matched standards, and many workers use synthetic fluid inclusions in quartz or silica microcapillaries containing standard solutions. Others have successfully used thin film standards from the U.S. National Institute of Standards and Technology (NIST). By adopting one or more of these strategies, quantitative and semi-quantitative data have been obtained for a variety of synthetic inclusions (Frantz et al., 1988; Vanko et al., 1993), aqueous hypersaline, and silicate melt inclusions (Rankin et al., 1992; Bodnar, 1993; Vanko et al., 1993; Mavrogenes et al., 1995). Because the

TABLE 8. Summary of main advantages and disadvantages of ICP-decrepitation for fluid inclusion analysis

Good Features	Poor Features
Small sample sizes required (0.2–0.5 g typically)	
No dilution of inclusion fluids	Chloride ions cannot be analyzed. Therefore, cation/anion charge balance calculations not possible
Simple sample preparation procedures and sample introduction system; contamination from these sources minimized	Method not really applicable to samples containing large daughter minerals; these may not be released into the plasma during decrepitation
Rapid "turn-around" time for samples; over 100 analyses/day possible	
Contamination problems from admixed grains readily identified and avoided through ease of peforming time-resolved or replicate D-ICP analysis	Ineffective decrepitation can result in partial leakage of contents and subsequent selective volatilization of elements; may be minimized by very rapid heating and restricting technique to moderately dilute (<20 wt % TDS) inclusions

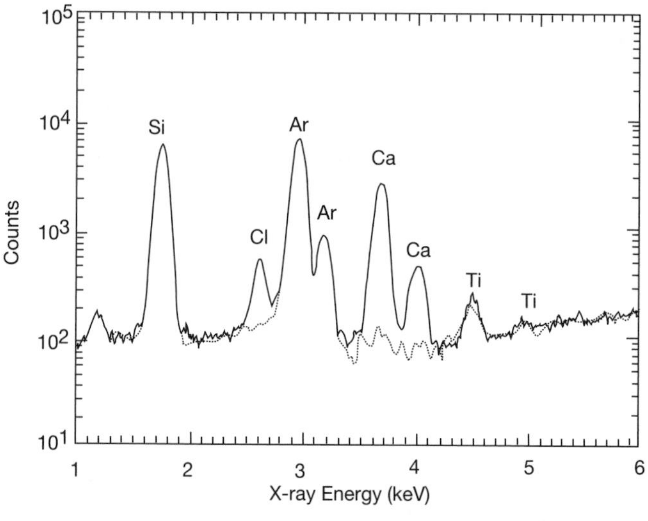

FIG. 6. SXFMA spectrum of a synthetic $NaCl\text{-}CaCl_2\text{-}H_2O$ fluid inclusion in quartz. Solid line shows results from the fluid inclusion, dotted line represents background quartz. Ar is from air; Si and Ti are from quartz host. The peak for Na is absent because of strong X-ray absorption effects (after Vanko et al., 1993).

transition metals and heavier elements have relatively high X-ray energies, SXFMA has proven very effective at determining the metal content of ore forming fluids. Most programs developed for synchrotron XRF analysis generate relative fluorescence intensities, and the data are conveniently expressed as element ratios. To determine the composition of the inclusion, the concentration of at least one element must be established by an independent technique. In practice this is seldom possible and most researchers resort to fluid inclusion salinity measurements to estimate the concentrations of Na or Cl. Because Na is difficult to measure by SXFMA, normalization is very dependent upon the quality of the chlorine analyses. This does not appear to be a problem for hypersaline inclusions but it remains to be seen whether SXFMA can handle more dilute fluids (<10 wt % TDS).

Concerning other uses of synchrotron radiation, the work by Anderson et al. (1995) deserves special mention. Using synchrotron X-ray absorption fine structure spectroscopy (SXAFS) they were able to identify the dominant complex of zinc in hypersaline inclusions in quartz at room temperature. This approach can be applied to other elements and eliminates some of the uncertainties about fluid chemistry that are inherent in hydrothermal experiments of simple model solutions. Furthermore, by acquiring SXAFS data from inclusions at different temperatures, conditions could be optimized to reproduce fluid speciation at the time of trapping. This is an extremely exciting area of research and more studies of this type should be encouraged.

What does the future hold? Work has now started on the construction of third generation synchrotron sources (undulator sources) which promise to deliver $10^4 \times$ more power with 0.01 to 0.1 ppm detection limits and 1 micron spot sizes for elements up to Z = 92 (J.V. Smith, pers. commun., 1997). These conditions also favor the application of SXAFS to solutes at lower concentrations (<100 ppm) and to smaller inclusions. With the emergence of brighter synchrotron X-ray sources it is hoped that serious attention will also be given to the problems imposed by inclusion geometry, fluid composition, and pathlength. Novel methods have been devised to minimize these problems, one of which involves rotating the sample within the beam and measuring changes in X-ray yield with respect to inclusion orientation (Mavrogenes and Bodnar, 1994). This works well for inclusions that lie parallel to the upper polished surface but is unsuited to inclusions whose long axes do not lie in the axis of rotation. Of all the techniques currently under investigation, SXFMA probably commands the greatest potential for non-destructive elemental and molecular analysis, although, for reasons of access to synchrotron facilities, it is unlikely to become a routine method (Table 9).

TABLE 9. Summary of main advantages and disadvantages of synchotron X-ray fluorescence microanalysis for fluid inclusion analysis

Good features	Poor features
Non-destructive, multi-element analysis	Limited number of suitable microprobe beamlines at synchrotron centers (7 sites worldwide); not appropriate for routine analysis
10–1,000 ppm detection limits	Depth of inclusion very critical. Inclusions must be within 5–10μm of the surface for realistic detection of the light elements and major solutes (Z <20). Detection of Li, Be, and B impossible for unopened inclusions
Applicable to +5 μm inclusions	Absorption corrections difficult to apply to inclusions of irregular geometry. Quantitative analysis requires considerable data reduction
No special sample preparation required—uncoated, free-standing fluid inclusion wafers are ideal. If mounted, glass slides should be replaced by silica slides to avoid interference from X-rays generated within the borosilicate glass	Difficult to analyze large inclusions containing daughter minerals. The beam must be broader than the diameter of the inclusion to ensure total irradiation, unless separate analyses of daughters and solutes is attempted
Analysis does not require a vacuum sample chamber	Selected inclusions must not overlap with adjacent inclusions within the beam path (i.e., multiple signals)
Allows or has the potential for complementary work on the chemical coordination and speciation of elements (aqueous solution or daughter minerals)	Matrix-matched standards required for quantitative analysis

Proton Induced X-ray Emission Analysis (PIXE)

Proton induced X-ray emission analysis (PIXE) is aptly described as the proton analog of electron microprobe analysis (EMPA). One of several nuclear microprobe techniques, it utilizes a highly focused beam of 2 to 3 MeV protons to generate characteristic secondary X-rays from the sample, which are then analyzed using energy dispersive detectors. Due to the higher mass of the proton compared to the electron, the beam is less scattered than for EMPA, giving higher spatial resolution and lower X-ray backgrounds (Rayleigh and Compton scattering). Depending upon the chemistry of the sample matrix, trace elements can be measured to less than 1 ppm for a 1 μm spot (Fig. 7). Thus, PIXE detection limits are comparable to SXFMA. Unfortunately, the technique suffers from the same absorption problems and many of the problems described for SXFMA apply equally to PIXE. Nevertheless, the relatively deep penetration of the proton beam is well suited to inclusion analysis. For 3 MeV protons the depth of penetration in a silicate matrix is about 100 μm. However, this also means that for inclusion-rich samples, secondary X-rays may be generated by more than one inclusion and hence it is important to have a good prior three-dimensional knowledge of the distribution of inclusions. Given the irregular geometry of inclusions and their orientation with respect to the proton beam, calculation of X-ray yields is far from straightforward. The two main complications are energy loss by the protons on penetrating the sample, and absorption of the secondary X-rays.

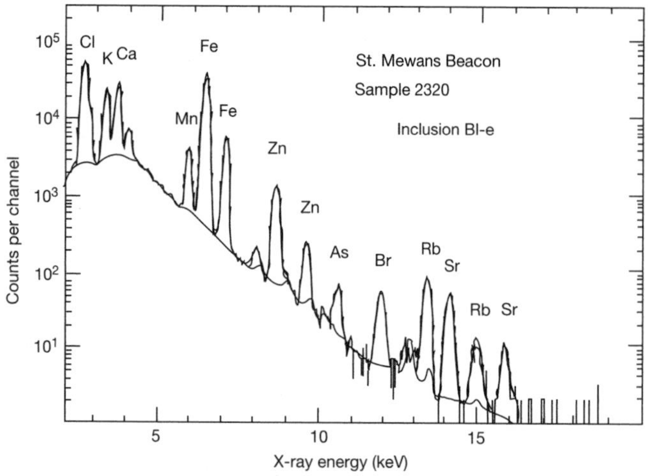

FIG. 7. PIXE spectrum of fluid inclusion in quartz showing X-ray peaks for a range of elements (Z >25). Note the broad shoulder at lower keV values affecting determination of the lighter elements (after Ryan et al., 1991).

Ryan et al. (1991) and Campbell et al. (1993) calculated the yields using a layered model in which the inclusion is treated as a layer of unknown composition within a quartz (or mineral) sandwich. This is currently the best theoretical model for processing fluid inclusion PIXE data and results compare favorably with independent analyses for test samples. For optimum conditions the beam should bathe the entire inclusion in protons. The practicalities of achieving this goal for inclusions of variable size and geometry are formidable and, like SXFMA, analysis is dependent upon the sophistication of the correction software.

The first comprehensive accounts of PIXE applied to fluid inclusions were those of Horn and Traxel (1987), and Anderson et al. (1989). More recently, Ryan et al. (1991, 1993) and Heinrich et al. (1992) have extended the methodology and provided a useful assessment of the pros and cons of PIXE. Detection limits and analytical uncertainties vary according to the depth of the inclusion, its volume, nature of the matrix, and beam profile. Low energy X-rays (K lines for Z <20 and L lines for Z <50) are very depth sensitive. For example, a depth uncertainty ±1.5 μm can lead to concentration errors of ±50 percent for chlorine (Heinrich et al., 1992), and it has proved impracticable to measure elements lighter than Si in inclusions deeper than 10 μm (Anderson et al., 1989). By comparison, the higher energy X-rays (K lines for Z >25 and L lines for Z >60) are less affected. Overall, the lower limits of detection for Z >25 appear to be 100 to 200 ppm for inclusions 10 to 50 μm in diameter. Published values for analytical reproducibility (RSD) are scant but are generally around ± 20 to 30 percent for the more sensitive elements. Inclusions containing daughter minerals or large vapor bubbles (i.e., vapor-rich inclusions) pose a special problem. Such inclusions invalidate the assumption of beam path-inclusion homogeneity and require careful modification of the correction procedures (Heinrich et al., 1992). As yet, no systematic attempt has been made to convert X-ray yields to concentrations using synthetic fluid inclusions of known composition and geometry. Presumably, the problem lies in producing the requisite synthetic inclusions. See Table 10 for a summary of the advantages and disadvantages of this method.

An attractive feature of proton microprobe analysis is the ability to carry out proton induced gamma-ray spectroscopy (PIGE). Proton interactions with atomic nuclei induce nuclear reactions that yield gamma-rays from the very light elements (Z <14). Depending upon the design of the specimen chamber, these gamma-rays can be measured simultaneously with PIXE and thereby complement the range of elements amenable to XRF analysis. This approach was used by Anderson et al. (1989) to examine aqueous inclusions in quartz and spodumene for Li, B, F, Na, and Al. The methodology is less well developed than for PIXE but warrants further development because of its specificity for the lighter elements.

Laser Ablation Microanalysis

Three laser-based destructive techniques have now been developed for the elemental analysis of single fluid inclusions: laser ablation inductively coupled plasma mass spectrometry (LA-ICP-MS), laser ablation inductively coupled plasma atomic emission spectroscopy (LA-ICP-AES), and laser ablation atomic emission spectroscopy (LA-AES). Note: in the literature, the terms atomic and optical are used interchangeably to describe the spectroscopy of photon emissions. Each technique utilizes a laser to penetrate the inclusion; thereafter analysis of the

TABLE 10. Summary of main advantages and disadvantages of proton induced X-ray emission analysis for fluid inclusion analysis

Good features	Poor features
Non-destructive, multi-element analysis	Greater availability of proton microbeam facilities than for SXFMA but cannot be regarded as routine analysis
100–1,000 ppm detection limits	Depth of inclusion very critical for multi-element analysis. Inclusions must be within 5–10 μm of the surface for realistic detection of Z <20 by PIXE
Applicable to +5 μm inclusions	Absorption corrections difficult to apply to inclusions of irregular geometry. Quantitative analysis requires sophisticated data reduction
Excellent depth of beam penetration (up to 100 μm)	Difficult to analyze large inclusions containing daughter minerals. The beam must be broader than the diameter of the inclusion to ensure total irradiation
Provides complementary proton induced gamma-ray emission spectroscopy (PIGE) for analysis of the light elements (Z <14)	Selected inclusions must not overlap with adjacent inclusions within the beam path

ablated material differs according to the method of detection employed (ion mass spectrometry or photon emission spectrometry). Unlike SXFMA and PIXE, these techniques are totally destructive and cannot provide information on the molecular nature of the elements detected. However, they all provide rapid multi-element analysis with equipment that can be purchased and maintained by any well resourced laboratory. Laser ablation microanalysis is now one of the fastest growing areas of inclusion research, stimulated by the decreasing cost of lasers, the use of proven analytical instrumentation, and the availability of suitable standards.

Method application has developed more or less in parallel with the design and availability of ultraviolet and excimer lasers which operate at 266 nm and shorter wavelengths. Having the right type of laser is crucial for single inclusion analysis, and the following guidelines are intended to help those wishing to use or acquire laser ablation equipment.

Choice of laser. Until the late 1980s, the standard laser in most laboratories was a pulsed infrared Nd-YAG (1064 nm) or ruby (694 nm) laser. These performed extremely well for the ablation of metals and metal oxides but were found to be erratic and inefficient in their ablation of silicate matrices. When tested on fluid inclusions in quartz, the laser would often produce a large 100 μm crater at the surface with little or no depth, or fail to interact with the sample except at very high power densities. In the latter case the effect was to blast a large diameter hole through the specimen, considerably in excess of the theoretical beam diameter. The best results were obtained for 30 to 100 μm inclusions using a beam diameter of 50 μm (Ramsey et al., 1992; Wilkinson et al., 1994). It became apparent that the answer was to go to shorter wavelengths (<266 nm) to ensure better energy coupling between the laser and sample (silicate or non-silicate) and facilitate finer focusing of the beam to <2 μm. This greatly improved the ablation of inclusions in quartz (Shepherd and Chenery, 1995) and most laboratories now use UV lasers for this type of analysis. The rate of ablation varies from mineral to mineral depending upon the position of the absorption edge with respect to the UV wavelength and the vaporization temperature of the mineral. Compared to the poor performance of the Nd-YAG laser, it is now possible to drill clean holes into 10 to 100 μm diameter inclusions up to 60 μm below the surface in minerals that are transparent in the infrared (quartz, fluorite; Moissette et al., 1996). Research is also under way to explore the benefits of ArF excimer lasers (193 nm) that have the potential for creating perfectly formed, flat-bottomed, cylindrical holes to depths of 100 μm (Gunther et al., 1997). Whatever the choice, it is important to bear in mind the need for research quality optics for the laser microscope. When working at 1,064 nm (Nd-YAG) one can use normal, high magnification, compound-type optical glass lenses. Image resolution is excellent. However, at 266 nm and shorter wavelengths the laser energy is absorbed by such lenses, often with explosive consequences! For work in the UV one must use specially coated Cassegrain reflecting objective lenses for beam focusing. Image quality is not as good as for glass refracting objectives but is generally acceptable.

Laser Ablation Inductively Coupled Plasma Atomic Emission Spectroscopy (LA-ICP-AES)

This was the first laser-based ICP configuration to be rigorously applied to the analysis of fluid inclusions, and is described fully by Rankin et al. (1992), Ramsey et al. (1992), and Wilkinson et al. (1994). The sample (thin section, fluid inclusion wafer, or cleavage fragment) is contained within a small cell attached to the stage of an optical microscope. By focusing the laser onto the surface of the sample, ablation holes can be drilled into selected sub-surface inclusions. After penetration of the inclusion, the volatilized material is transported by an argon carrier gas into an inductively coupled plasma (7,000°K) where it is totally ionized. The light emitted during ionization is resolved into its component wavelengths and the intensity of each wavelength is converted into mass units by reference to suitable calibration standards. Spectral interferences are well documented and automatic correction procedures are incorporated into most ICP-AES systems. Where there is significant spectral overlap, interferences can be avoided by choosing one of many other emission wavelengths. For conventional laser ablation analysis of minerals, precision is better than 5 percent and detection limits are 10 to 100 ppm for most elements.

Due to uncertainties in the mass of inclusion material volatilized and the absence of an internal standard, absolute element concentrations cannot be determined. However, the technique provides quantitative, relative element concentrations with a precision of 20 to 45 percent (Table 11). Detection limits are a function of the mass of analyte released and are therefore controlled by the size of the inclusion and the concentration of analyte within the inclusion. Estimated detection limits for >30 μm inclusions containing >20 wt percent salts are of the order of several 100 to 1,000 ppm. Calibration is carried out by laser ablation of synthetic fluid inclusions or the nebulization of standard solutions, the latter giving higher precision (Ramsey et al., 1992).

Laser Ablation Atomic Emission Spectroscopy (LA-AES)

An elegant simplification of LA-ICP-AES, this technique utilizes the light emitted in situ during laser interaction with the sample. During ablation, the air immediately above the specimen surface becomes intensely ionized. This creates a microplasma that interacts with the volatilized material to produce a highly efficient source of photons. By focusing the plasma onto the entrance slit of a monochromator, the emission lines of elements present in the plasma (200 to 800 nm) can be analyzed using a multichannel detector (Boiron et al., 1995). With the laser and detector suitably synchronized, time-resolved analysis permits chemical discrimination between the inclusion and its host matrix. For fluid inclusion studies, absolute line intensities are poorly reproducible

TABLE 11. Summary of main advantages and disadvantages of laser ablation inductively coupled plasma atomic emission spectroscopy for fluid inclusion analysis

Good features	Poor features
Instrumentation readily available	
Rapid, multi-element technique	Destructive analysis
Quantitative measurement of element ratios; precision 20–45%	Analysis restricted to cation species
Detection limits controlled by size and salinity of inclusion; generally >1,000 ppm	Not applicable to low salinity inclusions <50–60 µm
Good for moderate to highly saline inclusions >30 µm	Variable sensitivities for different elements; generally lower than for ICP-MS
Applicable to inclusions up to 100 µm below the specimen surface	Does not provide absolute element abundances
Calibration using synthetic fluid inclusions or standard solutions	
No special sample preparation required. Ideal for fluid inclusion wafers	

(45–50%) due to problems of accurate laser focusing and variations in the amount of material ablated by each laser pulse. However, emission line ratio reproducibility is much better (10–15%) allowing element ratios to be estimated with some degree of confidence. Calibration curves can be established using either NIST reference glasses or synthetic fluid inclusions. Detection limits for a 10-µm aqueous inclusion are typically 10 to 20 ppm for Ca, Sr, Mg, Li, and Na, and 200 ppm for K (Moissette et al., 1997). No special sample preparation is required and standard fluid inclusion wafers are perfectly adequate. In all other respects the method is subject to the same limitations as for conventional ICP-AES (Thompson and Walsh, 1983). Compared to other single inclusion ion techniques, laser ablation atomic emission spectroscopy requires minimal equipment, is very simple to operate, and has the potential for becoming a low-cost, rapid analysis, bench top technique (Table 12). A logical development of this technology would be the integration of laser ablation optical emission and ICP-mass spectrometry to maximize the advantages of both methodologies.

Laser Ablation Inductively Coupled Plasma Mass Spectrometry (LA-ICP-MS)

Compared to LA-ICP-AES, this technique provides higher sensitivity and lower detection limits for most elements—at least two to 10 times lower, especially for the heavier elements (Z >50). Except for the detector system (quadrupole mass spectrometer) the ICP and laser ablation configuration are the same as for atomic emission spectroscopy. The first substantive study using LA-ICP-MS was by Deloule and Eloy (1982) who obtained

TABLE 12. Summary of main advantages and disadvantages of laser ablation atomic emission spectroscopy for fluid inclusion analysis

Good features	Poor features
Instrumentation readily available	
Rapid, multi-element analysis	Destructive analysis
Quantitative measurement of element ratios; precision 10–15%	Analysis restricted to cation species. Technique not appropriate for chlorine and sulfur
Detection limits (10–200 ppm) for alkali and alkali earth elements	Validated for alkali and alkaline earth elements only. Not tested yet for daughter mineral-rich inclusions
Applicable to +10 µm inclusions up to 50 µm below the surface	Spot size dependent upon wavelength of laser
Calibration using synthetic fluid inclusions or reference glasses	Does not provide absolute element abundances
No special sample preparation required. Ideal for fluid inclusion wafers	

semi-quantitative Na/K ratios for aqueous inclusions using a Nd-YAG laser. Shepherd and Chenery (1995) described improvements in laser ablation using a UV laser and calibration methods for the routine, quantitative, multi-element analysis of inclusions in quartz and fluorite (Fig. 8). Subsequent papers have reported calibration strategies and an extension of the technique for the analysis of Cl and Br (Ghazi et al., 1996; Moissette et al., 1996). For the reasons discussed above, the technique does not give absolute element concentrations. However, it does permit relative ratios to be measured with moderate to high precision (5–32%) for a wide range of alkali, alkaline earth, and transition elements. Detection limits are dependent upon the size of the inclusion and concentration of the analyte to be measured, but are about 5 to 10 ppm for Ag, Cu, Li, Rb, Sr, Pb, and Zn, and 1,000 ppm for Ca and K in a 20-µm inclusion. Polyatomic ions created within the ICP cause considerable interferences for elements Z <25 (e.g., the $^{38}Ar\text{-}H^+$ dimer interferes with ^{39}K; ^{56}Fe is masked by $^{40}Ar^{16}O^+$). Usually another isotope can be selected but for ^{32}S and ^{34}S severe interferences with $^{16}O_2$ and $^{16}O^{18}O$ are unavoidable. When Z >25 or Z <6, polyatomic problems are minimal, background levels are very low, and thus detection limits are excellent (Table 13). Several methods are currently under investigation to reduce the effect of polyatomic species which, if successful, should then permit determination of the SO_4^{2-} and CO_3^{2-} anions.

At least four different methods of calibration have been tested (synthetic fluid inclusions, standard solutions, reference glasses, and microcapillaries). LA-ICP-MS is relatively matrix-insensitive compared to other methods, and for analysis of most inclusions the choice is not critical. Overall, the standard solution method (Moissette et al., 1996) presents greater freedom in the selection of elements and range of working concentrations. Finally, if the

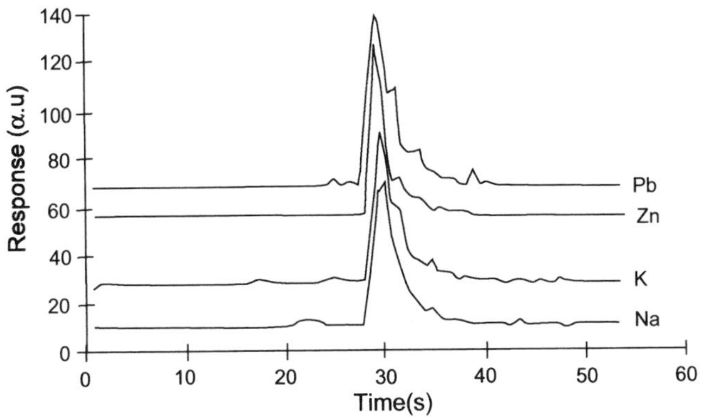

FIG. 8. Time resolved LA-ICP-MS spectrum for Na, K, Pb, Zn for a discrete pulse of fluid released from a small inclusion in quartz (after Shepherd and Chenery 1995).

TABLE 13. Summary of main advantages and disadvantages of laser ablation inductively coupled plasma mass spectrometry for fluid inclusion analysis

Good features	Poor features
Increasingly available and accurate instrumentation	
Rapid multi-element analysis	Destructive analysis. Cannot determine molecular species
Quantitative, high precision ratios for a wide range of alkali, alkaline earth and transition elements including the halogens. Precision typically 10–35%	Does not provide absolute element abundances (ratios only)
High spatial resolution: 2μm for UV laser (266 nm); 20-50 μm for Nd-YAG laser (1,064 nm)	Nd-YAG laser unsuitable for inclusions in quartz or other minerals transparent in the infrared
Applicable to all types of aqueous inclusions >5 μm (liquid-gas-solids) up to 60 μm beneath the sample surface	Quantitative data only obtained for high salinity inclusions >20 μm
Detection limits from 10–1,000 ppm	Polyatomic interferences restrict detection and measurement of elements Z <25 >6 at low concentrations. Cannot determine carbon or sulfur
Easy to calibrate; several alternative methods tested	
No special sample preparation required; perfect for fluid inclusion wafers	

amount of ablated material (volume of inclusion fluid) can be calculated or estimated (Ghazi et al., 1996) there is no reason why LA-ICP-MS should not also yield absolute element concentrations.

Secondary Ion Mass Spectrometry (SIMS)

With the introduction of secondary ion mass spectrometry into the Earth sciences, it was anticipated that it could be adapted to provide a routine method for the elemental and isotope analysis of fluid inclusions. Secondary ion mass spectrometry is based upon the analysis of charged ions (+ve and –ve) emitted or "sputtered" from the surface layers of a sample during bombardment by energetic particles. For the analysis of geological materials the primary beam consists of O^- or Cs^+ ions, the latter providing a minimum spot size of 0.1 to 0.2 μm. The combination of sub-micron resolution, stable ion beams, zero background noise, and multi-element capability make it ideally suited for the analysis of trace elements at low ppm or ppb levels (MacRae, 1995). Its application to fluid inclusions exploits the fact that if the primary beam is continuously focused at the same position, erosion of the sample leads to the formation of a deep crater. Nambu et al. (1977) used this method to obtain semi-quantitative data for 11 elements in individual frozen fluid inclusions located 5 to 20 μm below the surface. More recent studies by Diamond et al. (1990) and Boiron et al. (1992) have shown that, although alkali element ratios can be obtained for unfrozen liquid inclusions, analytical reproducibility is very poor (50–200%). Both conclude that the analysis of frozen inclusions as pioneered by Nambu et al. (1977) is the preferred approach and will give better precision. While in theory SIMS offers high sensitivity elemental and isotopic analysis, two factors limit its routine application to fluid inclusions. First, ion sputtering is a relatively slow process (0.2–1 μm/min depending upon the primary ion beam) and is only practical for inclusions within 20 μm of the surface. Secondly, the physical processes that lead to the formation of secondary ions are poorly understood, especially within deep +10 μm craters. No model accurately predicts either the observed variations in the degree of ionization for a single element between different matrices, or between different elements in the same matrix (Hinton, 1995). Hence, to obtain quantitative data, samples and standards must be closely matrix matched. It has not yet been demonstrated that natural variations in inclusion chemistry can be modeled for SIMS. For the moment, its strength lies in the analysis of silicate melt inclusions exposed at the surface of polished thin sections. These may be treated as silicate minerals, using NIST reference glasses or in-house standards as calibrants. The only special requirement is that the specimen is gold coated prior to analysis. Precision, accuracy, and detection limits generally conform with those established for mineral analysis (Table 14; Hinton, 1995 MacRae, 1995).

SEM-Electron Microprobe Analysis (SEM-EMPA)

On first inspection the electron microprobe may seem an unlikely instrument for single inclusion analysis because the depth of penetration of the electron beam is less than 2 to 4 μm. With ingenuity, however, EMPA can be used successfully to study daughter minerals and brine inclusions.

TABLE 14. Summary of main advantages and disadvantages of secondary ion mass spectrometry for fluid inclusion analysis

Good features	Poor features
Multi-element analysis	Destructive, time consuming analysis
Detection limits variable but capable of sub-ppm levels	Molecular interferences are a major problem. Theoretical models do not accurately predict ion yields for chemically complex inclusions
High spatial resolution (0.2 μm) with the facility for producing element images of the inclusion	Quantitative analysis difficult to achieve. Calibration standards must be very closely matrix matched
Good for acquiring relative element ratios especially for the light elements (Z <10)	Absolute abundances cannot be measured. Poor precision (> 50%).
Potentially useful for measuring isotope abundance ratios	Samples need to be conductively coated. Aqueous inclusions must be frozen for reproducible analysis
Suitable for silicate melt inclusions	Restricted to near-surface inclusions

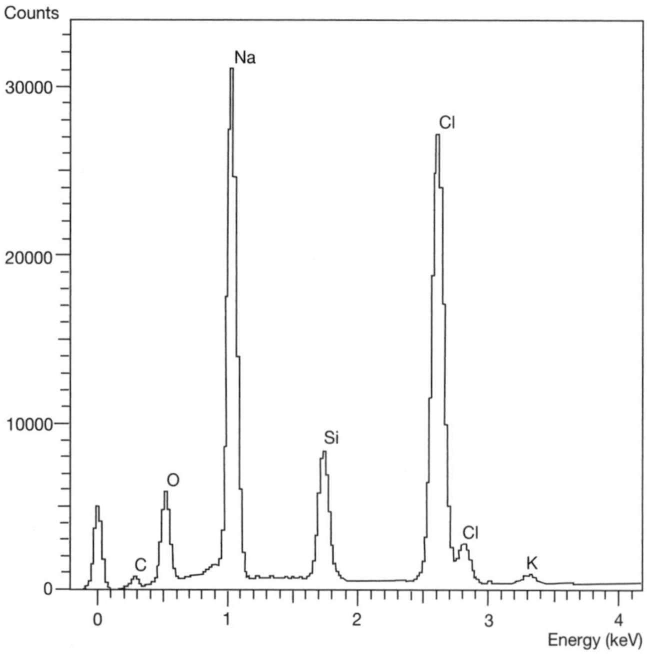

FIG. 9. Energy dispersive X-ray spectrum of a halite daughter mineral exposed on the broken surface of quartz. Elements detected include Na and Cl (in halite), a small amount of K (from associated daughters?), Si (from quartz), and C (from carbon coating).

Daughter minerals. One of the simplest applications is the identification of daughter minerals on fracture surfaces. When a sample is broken, some of the fractures will cross cut fluid inclusions without destroying or dislodging the daughter minerals. Those that remain can be characterized by energy dispersive analysis (Metzger et al., 1977; Anthony et al., 1984; Fig. 9) and crystal morphologies (SEM). As one might expect, there is no guarantee of success in finding a daughter mineral, and it is usually a matter of trial and error. Host minerals with a strong cleavage yield the best results. Various chloride, sulfate, sulfide, and silicate daughter minerals have been identified in this way, though not always uniquely, because the method cannot usually measure carbon or determine the water of hydration. Quantitative analysis of daughter minerals is therefore difficult to achieve, the main problems being: (1) their small size (<10 μm across), (2) their orientation with respect to the incident beam, and (3) interferences from adjacent daughter minerals and/or walls of the host material. After fracturing the sample, the newly exposed surfaces must be quickly coated with carbon or gold and stored in desiccators prior to analysis to minimize deliquescence and oxidation of the daughter minerals.

Brine inclusions. This application is very similar to that described above except that the sample is immersed in liquid nitrogen (–196°C) before being fractured. Fracturing is carried out directly within the SEM chamber using a special low temperature stage to keep the sample frozen. Once exposed, the frozen brine inclusions are gold coated in situ and analyzed by energy dispersive spectrometry. This technique is sometimes referred to as cryogenic X-ray microanalysis and was first described by Kelly and Burgio (1983). Since then the methodology has been refined by other workers, notably Ayora and Fontarnau (1989), and is now regarded as a primary, high precision, quantitative technique for the absolute determination of major solutes in brine inclusions in halite. Calibration is carried out using small droplets of frozen, matrix-matched, standard solutions. Analytical precision for 20-μm inclusions is routinely less than 10 percent with detection limits of about 800 ppm for Ca and K, 5,000 ppm for SO_4, and 10,000 ppm for Mg (Shepherd et al., 1997). The technique is not suited for minor or trace element analysis, however. Surprisingly, few results have been published for host minerals other than halite; presumably random fracturing has proven less effective in exposing frozen inclusions. A new development that could stimulate further EMPA research is the availability of environmental SEM instruments. These operate at 0.2 to 5 torr and do not require coated samples, thus permitting continuous observation of the frozen standards and inclusions, and considerably reducing the time of analysis (T. Lowenstein, pers. commun., 1997).

Inclusion salts. This application of EMPA utilizes the salts precipitated on the surface of a specimen caused by the rupture of near-surface or fracture-controlled inclusions. Depending upon the location and size of inclusions with respect to the surface, the analysis may represent one or more inclusions. The residues have been likened to miniature volcanoes and typically form small (5 to 20 μm diam) mounds. To enhance the rupture, the sample is momentarily heated above the inclusion decrepitation temperature and then quickly coated for energy dispersive analysis. The method has been used successfully on various types of inclusions but works best for high salinity fluids (e.g., Chryssoulis and Wilkinson, 1983). Cation and anion ratios for the major solutes (Na, K, Ca, Mg, Cl, and SO_4) are reported to have a variability of 10 percent (Haynes and Kesler, 1987). Difficulties are encountered, though, in producing micro-scale homogeneity for mixed salt calibration standards, and in interpreting multiple populations of fracture-controlled inclusions. The method lacks the precision and accuracy of cryogenic EMPA but has the advantage of being fast, simple, and applicable to most host minerals (Table 15).

Micro-laser Raman Spectroscopy (μLRS)

Raman spectroscopy holds a very special place in fluid inclusion analysis, as one of the few single-inclusion, non-destructive techniques to rank with microthermometric analysis for versatility and usefulness. For excellent reviews of its broader applications to Earth sciences the reader should consult McMillan et al. (1994) and Roberts and Beattie (1995). The technique is based on measuring frequency shifts in monochromatic light as it interacts with the sample. If a gas, liquid, or solid is illuminated with a monochromatic light source (i.e., single frequency) most of the light will pass through the sample and some will be scattered without undergoing any change. A small proportion (10^{-6}% of the incident intensity), however, will be scattered at a different frequency from the incident source. This is termed Raman scattering, and the shift in frequency is characteristic of the molecular species that give rise to the scattering. Measurement of the scattered light over a range of wavelengths in the visible spectrum yields a Raman spectrum, the individual peaks of which can be assigned to specific molecular species and quantified. Because the Raman effect is due to molecular vibrations it cannot be used to identify mono-atomic ions in solution. Most Raman spectrometers used for fluid inclusion analysis employ a continuous argon laser as a coherent light source in combination with a multichannel, charged coupled detector. This configuration produces a strong Raman signal that can be acquired within minutes. Sample preparation is simple and requires nothing more than a fluid inclusion wafer or cleavage fragment supported by a glass microscope slide. The laser beam is focused using a conventional optical microscope, and spot sizes of 2 μm can be routinely achieved using ×100 high-power objectives.

Table 15. Summary of main advantages and disadvantages of SEM-electron microprobe analysis for fluid inclusion analysis

Good features	**Poor features**
Instrumentation readily available	
Multi-element analysis suitable for a wide range of aqueous inclusions	Very shallow depth of beam penetration; restricted to opened inclusions
Quantitative, high precision analysis and accuracy for brine inclusions in halite. Precision 5–10%. Simple calibration standards	Only qualitative or semiquantitative for daughter minerals and inclusion decrepitates. Calibration standards must be matrix matched
Detection limits about 1,000–10,000 ppm for the light elements	Samples need to be given a conductive coating (Au or C)
Small beam diameter (2 μm)	
Relatively fast technique for rapid, qualitative analysis	Marked heterogeneity and compositional zonation in precipitates away from the point of "eruption" can occur

Micro-Raman has proven especially suitable for the measurement of inclusion gases (e.g., Pasteris et al., 1988; Dubessy et al., 1989) and is a prime analytical method for the identification of all the low molecular gases in the system C-O-H-N-S (CO_2, CO, CH_4, C_2H_6, C_3H_8, N_2, H_2S, COS, SO_2, H_2, H_2O). Papers describing the natural variation in inclusion volatiles are too numerous to mention, but without exception the greatest advances in scientific understanding have come from the close integration of microthermometic and micro-Raman data at levels of >1 to 10 mole percent. Application to the non-volatile constituents of aqueous inclusions is limited to the polyatomic anions, although in practice only SO_4^{2-}, HSO_4^-, HS^-, and HCO_3^- have been detected (Dubessy et al., 1992). The detection limit for these species is around 1,000 ppm. An important Raman phenomenon currently under investigation is the effect of chloride ions on the stretching vibrations of liquid water at room temperature (Mernagh and Wilde, 1989). Modifications in the shape and frequency of the Raman band as a function of chlorinity have also been used to measure the chloride concentration of single aqueous inclusions (Dubessy et al., 1997). This has important implications for facilitating the interpretation of ion data acquired by other methods (e.g., LA-ICP-MS). Another application of micro-Raman is the identification of daughter minerals (Fig. 10). Minerals having strong oxygen bonds (sulfates, carbonates, oxides, and phosphates) provide good Raman signals. Unfortunately, NaCl, KCl, and other minerals with predominantly ionic bonding are barely detectable. Progress is further constrained by the lack of a suitable Raman spectrum database for minerals.

How quantitative is micro-Raman? This is a much debated topic and there is still disagreement as to the influence of fluid density on Raman cross sections for the common gases (Pasteris, 1988; Dubessy et al., 1989). Experimentally derived values are gradually beginning to minimize these uncertainties, although in most cases unequivocal quantitative analyses can only be obtained using supporting microthermometric data. Finally, one should note that laser induced fluorescence is 10^6 times more intense than the Raman radiation and for some minerals (fluorite, calcite, plagioclase) the accompanying fluorescence can totally mask the weaker Raman spectra. Strong fluorescence is also generated by aromatic organic compounds and the user should consider alternative techniques (e.g., micro-infrared spectroscopy) for the study of individual hydrocarbon inclusions (Table 16).

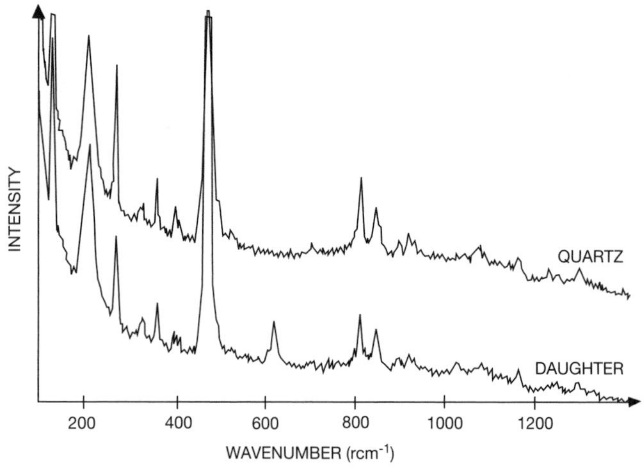

FIG. 10. Comparison of laser Raman spectra for inclusion-free quartz and for quartz containing a small inclusion plus daughter minerals. Note the peak at 618 cm-1, corresponding probably to titanite or rutile. Peaks for the major volatile components (e.g., CO_2) would occur at high wave numbers in a region relatively free from quartz interference (after Vanko et al., 1992).

TABLE 16. Summary of main advantages and disadvantages of micro-laser Raman spectroscopy for fluid inclusion analysis

Good features	Poor features
Instrumentation readily available	
Non-destructive, rapid technique for the analysis of molecular species (volatiles, polyatomic anions, and daughter minerals)	Unable to analyze mono-atomic ions in aqueous inclusions
Quantitative for simple gas mixtures (probably). Calibration using synthetic fluid inclusions.	Qualitative for aqueous liquids and daughter minerals
Detection limits dependent upon strength of Raman signal; typically greater than 1,000 ppm. Variable analytical precision; about 10% for near-surface inclusions	Weak Raman spectra masked by mineral fluorescence or fluorescence from liquid hydrocarbon inclusions
High spatial resolution (2 μm); applicable to inclusions >5 μm in diameter	Weak Raman spectra masked by strong Raman bands for some host minerals (e.g., carbonates)
No special sample preparation required	

However, future refinements and developments in μLRS may resolve this problem (e.g., Schrader et al., 1994). Valuable advice and tips on all practical aspects of laser Raman spectroscopy for the analysis of inclusions are given by Pasteris et al. (1988) and Burke (1994).

Fourier Transform Infrared (FTIR) Microspectroscopy

Infrared spectroscopy is based on the principle that bonds in molecular structures are constantly vibrating—stretching and bending in relation to each other. Changes in these vibrations are caused by absorption of light in the infrared part of the spectrum. These changes take place at different wavelengths, depending on the nature of the molecular bond. An infrared spectrum (absorbance vs. wavenumber in cm-1) of an organic molecule will contain characteristic absorption bands that can reveal much about the band types present (e.g., =C=O, $=CH_2$). Modern infrared spectrometers use Fourier transform techniques of spectral detection and analysis μFTIR spectroscopy). A Michelson detector picks up the frequencies in a composite signal which is then separated into its component parts using Fourier transformation. μFTIR spectroscopy is complementary to μLRS. The main advantages over μLRS are that water can be readily detected, and compositional data may be obtained on liquid hydrocarbons that fluoresce under conventional Raman excitation sources (Table 17). FT-near infrared Raman spectroscopy can be used, in theory, to overcome fluorescence problems (Schrader et al., 1994), but instrumentation is not yet widely available. The main disadvantages of μFTIR over micro-laser Raman are that many minerals (especially quartz) show strong absorption in the infrared, which can mask characteristic absorbance peaks for hydrocarbon bonds. In addition, specially-designed CaF_2 microscope optics are required because of the strong absorbance properties of silicate glasses in the near infrared. In μFTIR micro-spectroscopy, an aperture limits the amount of radiation passing through the optical path to the detector. In most instruments this minimum diameter is about 20 μm, which is effectively the minimum size of inclusion that can be studied. Spectra from the host and the inclusions are compared.

The μFTIR has proven to be a very powerful and effective method for determining the CO_2 and H_2O contents of silicate glass inclusions (e.g., Wallace and Gerlach, 1994; Barclay et al., 1996) including those thought to be representative of ore-forming magmas (Lowenstern, 1994). The glass inclusions are exposed on a polished surface of the specimen, and interference effects from the host are thus minimized. Through calibration against synthetic glass standards, it is possible to determine CO_2 and water contents below 1,000 ppm and 10,000 ppm respectively.

Quantitative analysis of CO_2 and H_2O of individual fluid inclusions in polished wafers has proven more problematical. Brown and Vry (1990) presented preliminary qualitative data on H_2O, CO_2 (aq), CO_2 (v), and CO_2 (l), and Pironon et al. (1997) record FTIR spectra related to different phases of H_2O and CO_2 over the temperature range –100° to +400°C. But, again, only qualitative data are presented. Quantitative data have been reported by Nambu et al. (1990) on the CO_2 concentrations in aqueous inclusions using FTIR spectroscopic methods. However, spectra were obtained from "powdered samples" (approximately 30–60 μm). Although CO_2 concentrations in the range from 16 to <2 mole percent were reported from mineralized quartz veins, they are not specific to a particular group or type of inclusions. This approach therefore falls within the realm of a "bulk" rather than microbeam method.

TABLE 17. Summary of main advantages of Fourier transform infrared microspectroscopy for fluid inclusion analysis

Good features	Poor features
Instrumentation readily available at moderate costs	Limited to inclusions >20 μm
Analysis of fluorescent HCs which cannot be studied by laser-Raman	Not quantitative for CO_2 and H_2O in aqueous inclusions; semi-quantitative for hydrocarbons
Very sensitive to CO_2 and H_2O. Quantitative measurements possible on glass inclusions	Special CaF_2 microscope optics required
Reference spectra for a range of organic compounds readily available	Absorption peaks for quartz overlap with those for hydrocarbons

In the period 1987 to 1990, a number of papers were published on the development and application of FTIR to the analysis of hydrocarbon phases in "oil" or "petroleum" inclusions in fluorite from MVT deposits (Barres et al., 1987; Guilhamou et al., 1990; Pironon and Barres, 1990, 1992; Rankin et al., 1990; Moser et al., 1992). Qualitative and semi-quantitative data on the types of organic components present (alkanes, alkenes, aromatic hydrocarbons, and those containing carbonyl bonds) were readily obtained from their characteristic absorption peaks (Fig. 11). Since this initial burst of activity, coincident with the commercial availability of μFTIR instruments, further advances have been minimal.

UV Fluorescence Microspectroscopy

Many natural oils are known to emit visible light when irradiated with ultraviolet light of lower wavelength (200–400 nm). This phenomenon is known as fluorescence. UV-fluorescence is a common phenomenon in petroleum-bearing fluid inclusions (e.g., Burruss et al., 1985; Bodnar, 1990; Jensensius and Burruss, 1990) and in oil-bearing fluid inclusions from some MVT deposits (e.g., Guilhaumou et al., 1990; Moser et al., 1992). Indeed, their bright blue, orange, green or yellow fluorescence is one of the main diagnostic features that aids their identification. A relationship has been proposed between the density of a crude oil (the API° Gravity) and the color of fluorescence under UV illumination (Bodnar, 1990). This parameter is useful in petroleum studies in determining the maturity of a particular oil. It is also relevant to the study of MVT deposits in helping to explain differences in fluorescent properties of oils trapped in different generations or different types of fluid inclusions from MVT deposits. Fluorescence emission spectra can be obtained by using a fixed UV excitation wavelength (e.g., 365 nm) and measuring fluorescence in 1 nm steps over the visible range (Moser et al., 1992). These spectra provide a crude fingerprint for the oils, but offer little in terms of compositional information (Fig. 12; Table 18). Recent advances in instrumentation have enhanced and extended this fingerprinting capability (Kihle, 1995; Stasiuk and Snowdon, 1997). To date there appear to be no other applications of UV-fluorescence microspectrometry to the study of fluid inclusions in ore deposits.

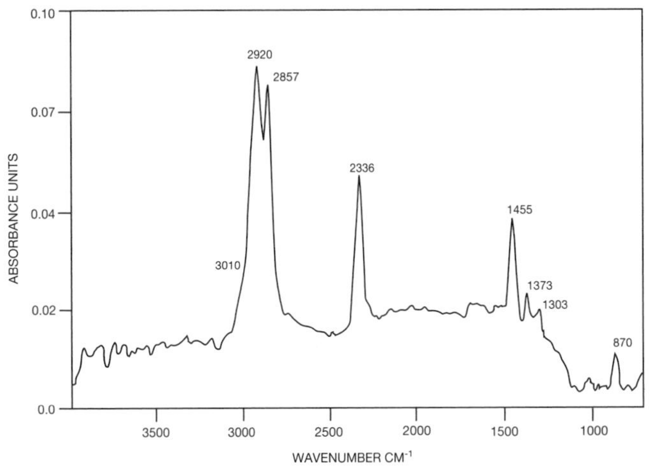

FIG. 11. FTIR spectrum of a "petroleum" inclusion in fluorite from an MVT deposit showing typical peaks due to aliphatic C-H stretching (2,920 and 2,857 cm^{-1}) and bending (1,455 and 1,373). CH_4 is indicated by the peak and shoulder at 1,303 cm^{-1} and 3,010 cm^{-1} respectively. CO_2 is inferred from the strong peak at 2,336 cm^{-1}. (from Moser et al., 1992).

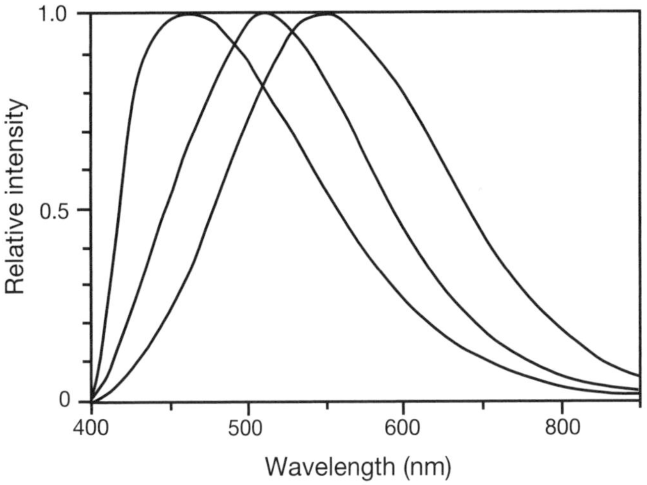

FIG. 12. UV fluorescence emission spectra for three different types of oil-bearing inclusions from an MVT deposit (from Moser et al., 1992).

TABLE 18. Summary of main advantages and disadvantages of UV fluorescence microspectroscopy for fluid inclusion analysis

Good features	Poor features
Relatively simple instrumentation	Restricted to liquid hydrocarbons in inclusions
Specific to hydrocarbon-bearing fluid inclusions	Not quantitative
Broad spectra obtained are simple to interpret. (L_{max} and Q are the only important features)	Resins and oils that fluoresce should be avoided during sample preparation
Insignificant host interference	Fluorescence intensity can decay with frequent use of UV-excitation

Concluding Remarks

It is inevitable that any review of such a dynamic and diverse subject will contain omissions and can only present the current state of knowledge. We have been selective in choosing techniques that we consider either to be most appropriate for widespread application or to hold the most potential for future development. We have attempted to offer practical advice and a critical evaluation of a range of methods, based on our own practical experience. Our best advice to the novice entering this world of bewildering choice is not to focus immediately on a particular technique, but to obtain a thorough understanding of the fluid inclusion population under investigation, and to ask the question, "What type and quality of data do I require for my particular purpose?" This will avoid the frustration and wasted effort in applying techniques to inappropriate samples and problems.

In writing this chapter, we have become increasingly aware of the need for suitable calibration standards and inter-laboratory comparisons to improve knowledge of both precision and accuracy of the various methods. Synthetic fluid inclusions offer some hope for simple chemical systems and microbeam methods. However, for natural inclusions possessing a much more complex chemistry, alternative approaches are needed. In the future, we see a pressing need for well-characterized, "homogeneous," inclusion-rich materials that can be used as international standards in much the same way as those used for conventional rock and mineral analysis. Only when we are able to satisfy this need will our data gain the respect they deserve from the wider geochemical community.

Acknowledgments

We thank Jeremy Richards for his help, encouragement, and patience throughout the production of this review. An earlier draft of the manuscript also benefited from the thoughtful and perceptive comments of the two referees, Ed Spooner (University of Toronto) and Dave Norman (New Mexico Tech). Finally we wish to express our sincere gratitude to Stella Bignold (Kingston University) for her efficiency and thoroughness in word-processing various drafts of the manuscript and chasing up references for us.

REFERENCES

Alderton, D.H.M., Thompson, M., Rankin, A.H., and Chryssoulis, S.L., 1982, Developments of the ICP-linked decrepitation technique for the analysis of fluid inclusions in quartz: Chemical Geology, v. 37, p. 203–213.

Alderton, D.H.M., Rankin, A.H., and Thompson, M., 1992, Fluid inclusion chemistry as a guide to tin mineralization in the Dartmoor granite, south-west England: Journal of Geochemical Exploration, v. 46, p. 163–185.

Anderson, A.J., Clark, A.H., Ma, X-P., Palmer, G.R., Macarthur, J.D., Bodnar, R.J., and Roedder, E., 1989, Proton-induced X-ray and gamma-ray emission analysis of unopened fluid inclusions: Economic Geology, v. 84, p. 924–939.

Anderson, M.R., Mayanovic, R.A., and Bajt, S., 1995, Determination of the local-structure and speciation of zinc in individual hypersaline fluid inclusions by micro-XAFS: Canadian Mineralogist, v. 33, p. 499–508.

Andrawes, F.F., and Gibson, E.K., 1979, Release and analysis of gases from geological samples: American Mineralogist, v. 64, p. 453–463.

Anthony, E.Y., Reynolds, T.J., and Beane R.E., 1984, Identification of daughter minerals in fluid inclusions using scanning electron microscopy and energy dispersive analysis: American Mineralogist, v. 69, p. 1053–1057.

Ayora, C., and Fontarnau, R., 1989, X-ray microanalysis of frozen fluid inclusions at –40°C: European Current Research on Fluid Inclusions, No. X, London, Imperial College, Abstracts, p. 7.

Banks, D.A., and Yardley, B.W.D., 1992, Crush-leach analysis of fluid incusions in small natural and synthetic samples: Geochimica et Cosmochimica Acta, v. 56, p. 245–248.

Banks, D.A., Yardley, B.W.D., Campbell, A.R., and Jarvis K.E., 1994, REE compositions of an aqueous magmatic fluid: A fluid inclusion study from Capitan Pluton, New Mexico, USA: Chemical Geology, v. 113, p. 259–272.

Barclay, J., Carroll, M.R., Houghton, B.F., and Wilson, C.J.N., 1996, Pre-eruptive volatile content and degassing history of an evolving peralkaline magma: Journal of Volcanological and Geothermal Research, v. 74, p. 75–87.

Barker, C., and Smith, M.P., 1986, Mass spectrometric determination of gases in individual fluid inclusions in natural minerals: Analytical Chemistry, v. 58, p. 1330–1333.

Barres, O., Burneau, A., Dubessy, J., and Pagel, M., 1987, Application of micro-FT-IR spectroscopy to individual hydrocarbon fluid inclusion analysis: Applied Spectroscopy, v. 41, p. 1000–1008.

Behr, H., and Gerler, J., 1987, Inclusions of sedimentary brines in post-Variscan mineralizations in the Federal Republic of Germany—A study by neutron activation analysis: Chemical Geology, v. 61, p. 65–77.

Bennett, B.A., Parry, S.J., and Christoula, M., 1992, Determination of chlorine, bromine and sodium in fluid inclusions by neutron-activation: Analyst, v. 117, p. 1627–1628.

Bodnar, R.J., 1990, Petroleum migration in the Miocene Monterey Formation, California, USA: Constraints from fluid inclusion studies: Mineralogical Magazine, v. 54, p. 289–304.

—— 1993, Revised equation and table for determining the freezing point depression of H_2O-NaCl solutions: Geochimica et Cosmochimica Acta, v. 57, p. 683–684.

Bohlke, J.K., and Irwin, J.J., 1992, Laser microprobe analyses of noble gas isotopes and halogens in fluid inclusions: Analyses of microstandards and synthetic fluid inclusions in quartz: Geochimica et Cosmochimica Acta, v. 56, p. 187–201.

Boiron, M-C., and Dubessy, J., 1994, Determination of fluid inclusion compositions: Microanalytical techniques, *in* de Vivo, B., and Frezzotti, M.L., eds., Fluid inclusions in minerals: Methods and applications: Short Course of the Working Group (IMA) Inclusions in Minerals: Sienna, p. 45–71.

Boiron, M-C., Essarraj, S., Sellier, E., Cathelineau, M., Lespinasse, M., and Poty, B., 1992, Identification of fluid inclusions in relation to their host microstructural domains in quartz by cathodoluminescence: Geochimica et Cosmochimica Acta, v. 56, p. 175–185.

Boiron, M-C., Dubessy, J., Moissette, A., Geertsen, C., Banks, D.A., Prieto, A.C. Lacour, J.L., and Mauchien, P., 1995, Elemental analysis of individual aqueous inclusions: Part I. New developments using micro-laser ablation optical emission spectroscopy: Boletín de la Sociedad Española de Mineralogía, v. 18–1, p. 28–29.

Bottrell, S.H., and Yardley, B.W.D., 1988, The composition of a primary granite-derived ore fluid from S.W. England, determined by fluid inclusion analysis: Geochimica et Cosmochimica Acta, v. 53, p. 585–588.

Bray, C.J., and Spooner, E.T.C., 1992, Fluid inclusion volatile analysis by gas chromatography with photoionization/microthermal conductivity detectors: Application to magmatic MoS_2 and other H_2O-CO_2 and H_2O-CH_4 fluids: Geochimica et Cosmochimica Acta, v. 56, p. 261–272.

Brown, P.E., and Vry, J.K., 1990, Applications of micro-FTIR spectroscopy to fluid inclusions [abs.]: Pan American Conference on Research on Fluid Inclusions, 3rd, Toronto Program and Abstracts, p. 23–24.

Burke, E.A.J., 1994, Raman microspectrometry of fluid inclusions *in* de Vivo, B., and Frezzotti, M.L., eds., Fluid inclusions in minerals: Methods and applications: Short Course of the Working Group (IMA) Inclusions in Minerals, Sienna, p. 25–44.

Burruss, R.C., Cercone, K.R., and Harris, P.M., 1985, Timing of hydrocarbon migration: Evidence from fluid inclusions in calcite cements, tectonics and burial history, *in* Schneidermann, N., and Harris, P.M., eds., Carbonate Cements Symposium. (SEPM) Society of Sedimentary Geologists, p. 277–289.

Campbell, A.R., and Panter, K.S., 1990, Comparison of fluid inclusions in coexisting (cogenetic) wolframite, cassiterite and quartz from St. Michael's Mount and Cligga Head, Cornwall, England: Geochimica et Cosmochimica Acta, v. 54, p. 673–681.

Campbell, J.L., Higuchi, D., Maxwell, J.A., and Teesdale, W.J., 1993, Quantitative PIXE microanalysis of thick specimens: Nuclear Instruments and Methods in Physics Research, v. B77, p. 95–109.

Channer, D.M.D. and Spooner, E.T.C., 1992, Analysis of fluid inclusion leachates from quartz by ion chromatography: Geochimica et Cosmochimica Acta, v. 56, p. 249–259.

—— 1994, Combined gas and ion-chromatographic analysis of fluid inclusions: Applications to Archaean granite pegmatite and gold-quartz veins: Geochimica et Cosmochimica Acta, v. 58, p. 1101–1118.

Chryssoulis, S.L., 1983, Study of the effects of feldspar and mica contamination upon the analysis of fluid inclusions by the decrepitation-ICP method: Chemical Geology, v. 40, p. 323–335.

Chryssoulis, S.L., and Rankin, A.H., 1988, Decrepitometry of fluid inclusions in quartz from the Guadalcazar granite of Mexico: Principles and application to mineral exploration: Mineralium Deposita, v. 23, p. 42–49.

Chryssoulis, S.L., and Wilkinson, N., 1983, High silver content of fluid inclusions in quartz from the Guadalcazar granite, San Luis Potosi, Mexico: A contribution to ore genesis theory: Economic Geology, v. 78, p. 302–318.

Coles, B.J., Gleeson, S.A., Wilkinson, J.J., and Ramsey, M.H., 1996, Improved detection limits for transient signal analysis of fluid inclusions by inductively coupled plasma atomic emission spectrometry using correlated background correction: Analyst, v. 120, p. 1421–1425.

Deloule, E., and Eloy, J.F., 1982, Improvements of laser probe mass-spectrometry for the chemical analysis of fluid inclusions in ores: Chemical Geology, v. 37, p. 191–202.

Diamond, L.W., Marshall, D.D., Jackman, J.A., and Skippen, G.B., 1990, Elemental analysis of individual fluid inclusions in minerals by secondary ion mass spectrometry (SIMS): Application to cation ratios of fluid inclusions in an Archaean mesothermal gold-quartz vein, Geochimica et Cosmochimica Acta, v. 54, p. 545–552.

Dubessy, J., Poty B., and Ramboz, C., 1989, Advances in C-O-H-N-S fluid geochemistry based on micro-Raman spectrometric analysis of fluid inclusions: European Journal of Mineralogy, v. 1, p. 517–534.

Dubessy, J., Boiron, M-C., Moissette, A., Monnin, C., and Sretenskaya. N., 1992, Determinations of water, hydrates and pH in fluid inclusions by micro-Raman spectroscopy: European Journal of Mineralogy, v. 4, p. 885–894.

Dubessy, J., Larghi, L., and Canals, M., 1997, Reconstitution of ionic composition of fluid inclusions [abs.]: European Current Research on Fluid Inclusions, No. XIV, Nancy, France, Abstracts volume, p. 90–91.

Etminan, H., and Hoffmann, C.F., 1989, Biomarkers in fluid inclusions: A new tool in constraining source regimes and its implications for the genesis of Mississippi Valley-type deposits: Geology, v. 17, p. 19–22.

Frantz, J.D., Mao, H.K., Zhang, Y.G., Wu, Y., Thompson, A.C., Underwood, J.H., Giauque, R.D., Jones, K.W., and Rivers, M.L., 1988, Analysis of fluid inclusions by X-ray fluorescence using synchrotron radiation: Chemical Geology, v. 69, p. 235–244.

Ghazi, A.M., McCandless, T.E., Vanko, D.A., and Ruiz, J., 1996, New quantitative approach in trace elemental analysis of single fluid inclusions: Applications of laser-ablation inductively coupled plasma-mass spectrometry (LA-ICP-MS): Journal of Analytical Atomic Spectrometry, v. 11, p. 667–674.

Graney, J.R., and Kesler, S.E., 1995, Factors affecting gas analysis of inclusion fluid by quadrupole mass-spectrometry: Geochimica et Cosmochimica Acta, v. 59, p. 3977–3986.

Guha, J., Lu, H-Z., and Gagnon, M., 1990, Gas composition of fluid inclusions using solid probe mass spectrometry and its application to study of mineralizing processes: Geochimica et Cosmochimica Acta, v. 54, p. 553–558.

Guilhamou, N. Szydlowski, N., and Pradier, B., 1990, Characterization of hydrocarbon fluid inclusions by infrared and fluorescence microspectroscopy: Mineralogical Magazine, v. 54, p. 311–324.

Gunther, D., Frischknecht, R., Heinrich, C.A., and Kahlert, H.J., 1997, Capabilities of an argon fluoride 193nm excimer laser for laser ablation inductively coupled plasma mass spectrometry microanalysis or geological materials: Journal of Analytical Atomic Spectrometry, v. 12, p. 939–944.

Haynes, F.M., and Kesler, S.E., 1987, Chemical evolution of brines during Mississippi-type mineralization: evidence from East Tennessee and Pine Point: Economic Geology, v. 82, p. 53–71.

Heinrich, C.A., Ryan, C.G., Mernagh, T.P., and Eadington, P.J., 1992, Segregation of ore metals between magmatic brine and vapor: A fluid inclusion study using PIXE microanalysis: Economic Geology, v. 87, p. 1566–1583.

Hinton, R.W., 1995, Ion microprobe analysis in geology, *in* Potts, P.J., Bowles, J.F.W., Reed S.J.B., and Cave, M.R., eds., Microprobe techniques in the Earth sciences: London, Chapman, p. 235–289.

Hoffmann, C.F., Henley, R.W., Higgins, H.C., Solomon, M., and Simmons, R.E., 1988, Biogenic hydrocarbons in fluid inclusions from the Aberfoyle tin-tungsten deposit, Tasmania, Australia: Chemical Geology, v. 70, p. 287–299.

Hollister, L.S., 1981, Techniques for analysing fluid inclusions, *in* Hollister, L.S., and Crawford, M.L., eds., Short Course in Fluid Inclusions: Applications to Petrology: Mineralogical Association of Canada, Short Course Handbook, No. 6, p. 272–277.

Horn, E.E., and Traxel, K., 1987, Investigations of individual fluid inclusions with the Heidelberg proton microprobe—a nondestructive analytical method: Chemical Geology, v. 61(1/4), p. 29–35.

Irwin, J.J., and Reynolds, J.H., 1995, Multiple stages of fluid trapping in the Stripa granite indicated by laser microprobe anlaysis of Cl, Br, I, K, U and nucleogenic plus radiogenic Ar, Kr and Xe in fluid inclusions: Geochimica et Cosmochimica Acta, v. 59, p. 355–369.

Irwin, J.J., and Roedder, E., 1995, Diverse origins of fluid in magmatic inclusions at Bingham (Utah, USA), Butte (Montana, USA), St. Austell (Cornwall, UK), and Ascension Island (mid-Atlantic, UK) indicated by laser microprobe analysis of Cl, K, Br, I, Ba + Te, U, Ar, Kr, and Xe: Geochimica et Cosmochimica Acta, v. 59, p. 295–312.

Jensensius, J., and Burruss, R.C., 1990, Hydrocarbon-water interactions during brine migration: Evidence from hydrocarbon inclusions in calcite cements from Danish North Sea oil fields: Geochimica et Cosmochimica Acta, v. 54, p. 705–713.

Jones, D.H., and Kesler, S.E., 1992, Fluid inclusion gas chemistry in east Tennessee Mississippi Valley-type districts: Evidence for immiscibility and implications for depositional mechanisms: Geochimica et Cosmochimica Acta, v. 56, p. 137–154.

Karlsen, D.A., Nedkvitne, T., Larter, S.R., and Bjorlykke, K.,1993, Hydrocarbon composition of authigenic inclusions: Applications to elucidation of petroleum reservoir filling history: Geochimica et Cosmochimica Acta, v. 57, p. 3641–3659.

Kelly, W.C., and Burgio, P.A., 1983, Cryogenic scanning electron microscopy of fluid inclusions in ore and gangue minerals: Economic Geology, v. 78, p. 1262–1267.

Kesler, S.E., Haynes, P.S., Creech, M.Z., and Gorman, J.A., 1986, Application of fluid inclusion and rock-gas analysis in mineral exploration: Journal of Geochemical Exploration, v. 25, p. 201–215.

Kesler, S.E., Martini, A.M., Appold, M.S., Walter, L.M., Huston, T.J., and Furman, F.C., 1996, Na-Cl-Br systematics of fluid inclusions from Mississippi Valley-type deposits, Appalachian Basin: Constraints on solute origin and migration paths: Geochimica et Cosmochimica Acta, v. 60, p. 225–233.

Kihle, J. 1995, Adaptation of fluorescence excitation-emission microspectroscopy for characterization of single hydrocarbon fluid inclusions: Organic Geochemistry, v. 23, p. 1029–1042.

Kozlowski, A., 1978, Pneumatolytic and hydrothermal activity in the Karkonosze-Izera block: Acta Geologica Polonica, v. 28, p. 171–222.

Kvenvolden, K.A., and Roedder, E., 1971, Fluid inclusions in quartz crystals from South-West Africa: Geochimica et Cosmochimica Acta, v. 35, p. 1209–1229.

Lazar, B., and Holland, H.D., 1988, The analysis of fluid inclusions in halite: Geochimica et Cosmochimica Acta, v. 52, p. 485–490.

Lowenstern, J.B., 1994, Dissolved volatile concentrations in an ore-forming magma: Geology, v. 22, p. 893–896.

Luckscheiter, P., and Parekh, P.P., 1979, A new method for the determination of dissolved elements in fluid inclusions: Neus Jahrbuch für Mineralogie, Monashefte, p. 135–144.

MacRae, N.D., 1995, Secondary-ion mass spectrometry and geology: Canadian Mineralogist, v. 33, p. 219–236.
Mancano D.P., and Campbell, A.R., 1995, Microthermometry of enargite-hosted fluid inclusions from the Lepanto, Philippines, high sulfidation Cu-Au deposit: Geochimica et Cosmochimica Acta, v. 59, p. 3909–3916.
Mavrogenes, J.A., and Bodnar, R.J., 1995, Hydrogen movement in and out of fluid inclusions in quartz: Experimental evidence and geologic implications: Geochimica et Cosmochimica Acta, v. 58, p. 141–148.
Mavrogenes, J.A., Bodnar, R.J., Anderson, A.J., Bajt, S., Sutton, S.R., and Rivers, M.L., 1995, Assessment of the uncertainties and limitations of quantitative elemental analysis of individual fluid inclusions using synchrotron X-ray-fluorescence: Geochimica and Cosmochimica Acta, v. 59, p. 3987–3995.
McMillan, P.F.M., Dubessy, J., and Hemley, R., 1994, Application to Earth, planetary and environmental sciences, *in* Corset, J., ed., Micro-Raman Spectroscopy. Elsevier, in press.
Mernagh, T.P., and Wilde, A.R., 1989, The use of the laser Raman microprobe for the determination of salinity in fluid inclusions. Geochimica et Cosmochimica Acta, v. 53, p. 765–771.
Metzger, F.W., Kelly, W.C., Nesbitt, B.E., and Essene E.J., 1977, Scanning electron microscopy of daughter minerals in fluid inclusions. Economic Geology, v. 72, p. 141–152.
Moissette, A., Shepherd, T.J., and Chenery, S.R., 1996, Calibration strategies for the elemental analysis of individual fluid inclusions by laser ablation ICP-MS. Journal of Analytical Atomic Spectroscopy, v. 11, p. 177–185.
Moissette, A., Dubessy, J., Boiron, M-C., Fabre, C., Mauchien, P., and Lacour, J-L., 1997, Laser ablation OES and its application to individual fluid inclusion analysis: State of the art: European Current Research on Fluid Inclusions, No. XIV, Nancy, France, Abstracts, p. 211–212.
Moser, M.R., Rankin, A.H., and Milledge, H.J., 1992, Hydrocarbon-bearing fluid inclusions in fluorite associated with the Windy Knoll bitumen deposit, UK: Geochimica et Cosmochimica Acta, v. 56, p. 155–168.
Nambu, M., Sato, T., Hayakawa, N., and Ohmori, Y., 1977, On the microanalysis of fluid inclusions with the ion microanalyzer [abs.]: Mining Geology (Japan), p. 10.
Nambu, M., Takeshi, M., and Nakatsuka, K., 1990, Quantitative analysis of CO_2/H_2O ratios in fluid inclusions using FT-IR. Pan-American Conference on Research on Fluid Inclusions, 3rd, Toronto, Canada: v. 3, p. 64.
Newman, B.D., Campbell, A., and Norman, D.I., 1997, A model for microbially induced precipitation of vadose zone calcite in fractures at Los Alamos National Laboratory: Geochimica and Cosmochimica Acta, v. 61, p. 1783–1792.
Norman, D.I., and Moore, J.N., 1997, Gaseous species in fluid inclusions: a fluid tracer and indicator of fluid processes [abs.]: European Current Research on Fluid Inclusions, No. XIV, Nancy, France, Abstracts, p. 243–244.
Norman, D.I., and Sawkins, F.J., 1987, Analysis of volatiles in fluid inclusions by mass spectrometry: Chemical Geology, v. 61, p. 1–10.
Norman, D.I., Kyle, P.R., and Baron, C., 1989, Analysis of trace elements including rare earth elements in fluid inclusion liquids: Economic Geology, v. 84, p. 162-166.
Norman, D.I., Benton, L.D., and Albinson, T.F., 1991, Calculation of $f(O_2)$ and $f(S_2)$ of ore fluids, and depth and pressure of mineralization from fluid inclusion gas analyses of the Fresnillo, Colorado Sombrerete Pb-Zn deposits, Mexico, *in* Pagel, M., and Leroy, J., eds., Source, transport and deposition of metals: Nancy (France), Balkema: p. 209–212.
Pasteris, J.D., Wopenka, B., and Seitz, J.C., 1988, Practical aspects of quantitative laser Raman microprobe spectroscopy for the study of fluid inclusions: Geochimica et Cosmochimica Acta, v. 52, p. 979–988.
Perin, K., 1973, Bitumens associated with lead, zinc and fluorite ore minerals in North Derbyshire, England: Geochimica et Cosmochimica Acta, v. 37, p. 401–417.
Piperov, N.B., and Penchev, N.P., 1973, A study of gas inclusions in minerals. Analysis of the gases from micro-inclusions in allanite. Geochimica et Cosmochimica Acta, v. 37, p. 2075–2097.
Pironon, J., and Barres, O., 1990, Semi-quantitative FT-IR microanalysis limits: Evidence from synthetic hydrocarbon fluid inclusions in sylvite: Geochimica et Cosmochimica Acta, v. 54, p. 509–518.
—— 1992, Influence of brine-hydrocarbon interactions on FT-IR microspectroscopic analyses of intracrystalline liquid inclusions: Geochimica et Cosmochimica Acta, v. 56, p. 169–174.
Pironon, J., Barres, O., and De Donato, P., 1997, Fluid inclusions FT-IR spectroscopy at varying temperature [abs.]: European Current Research on Fluid Inclusions, No. XIV, Nancy, France, Abstracts, p. 268–269.
Poty, B.P., Stalder, H.A., and Weisbrod, A.M., 1974, Fluid inclusion studies in quartz from fissures of western and central Alps. Schweizerische Mineralogisch Petrographische Mitteilungen, v. 54, p. 717–752.
Pouchou, J.L., and Pichoir, F., 1988, A simplified version of the 'PAP' model for matrix corrections in EPMA, *in* Newbury, D.E., ed., Microbeam Analysis: San Francisco Press, p. 315–318.
Ramsey, M.H., Coles, B.J., Rankin, A.H., and Wilkinson, J.J., 1992, Single fluid inclusion analysis by laser ablation-inductively coupled plasma-atomic emission spectrometry: quantification and validation: Journal of Analytical Atomic Spectrometry, v. 7, p. 587–593.
Rankin, A.H., and Graham, M.J., 1988, Na, K and Li contents of mineralizing fluids in the Northern Pennine Orefield, England and their genetic significance: Transactions of the Institution of Mining Metallurgy, v. 97, p. 99–107.
Rankin, A.H., Moser, M. and Hodge, B.L., 1990, Unusual oil-bearing inclusions in fluorite from Baluchistan, Pakistan: Mineralogical Magazine, v. 54, p. 335–342.
Rankin, A.H., Ramsey, M.H., Coles, B., van Langvelde, F., and Thomas, C.R., 1992, The composition of hypersaline, iron-rich granitic fluids based on laser-ICP and Synchrotron-SRF microprobe analysis of individual fluid inclusions in topaz, Mole granite, eastern Australia: Geochimica et Cosmochimica Acta, v. 56, p. 67–79.
Rankin, A.H., Herrington, R.J., Ramsey, M.R., Coles, B., Christoula, M., and Jones, E., 1993a, Current developments and applications of ICP-AES techniques for the geochemical analysis of fluid inclusions in minerals: Proceedings of the Quadriennial IAGOD Symposium, v. 8, p. 185–198.
Rankin, A.H., Wilkinson, J.J., Nolan, J. and Croudace, I., 1993b, Carbothermal fluids and gold mineralization; where are the gold-bearing carbonatites?: EUG VII, Terra Abstracts, Terra Nova, v. 5, p. 439–440.
Richards, J.P., and Kerrich, R., 1993, Observations of zoning and fluid inclusions in pyrite using a transmitted infrared-light microscope ($\lambda \leq 1.9$ μm): Economic Geology, v. 88, p. 716–723.
Roberts, S., and Beattie, I., 1995. Micro-Raman spectroscopy in the earth sciences, *in* Potts, P.J., Bowles, J.F.W., Reed S.J.B., and Cave, M.R., eds., Microprobe techniques in the earth sciences: London, Chapman, p. 387–408.
Roedder, E., 1958, Technique for the extraction and partial chemical analysis of fluid filled inclusions from minerals: Economic Geology, v. 53, p. 235–269.
—— 1972, Composition of fluid inclusions: U.S. Geological Survey Professional Paper 440-JJ.
—— 1984, Fluid Inclusions: Reviews in Mineralogy, Mineralogical Society America, no. 12.
—— 1990, Fluid inclusion analysis—prologue and epilogue: Geochimica et Cosmochimica Acta, v. 54, p. 495–507.
Roedder, E., Ingram, B., and Hall, W.E., 1963, Studies of fluid inclusions III: Extraction and quantitative analysis of inclusions in the milligram range: Economic Geology, v. 58, p. 353–374.
Ryan, C.G., Cousens, D.R., Heinrich, C.A., Griffin, W.L., Sie, S.H., and Mernagh, T.P., 1991, Quantitative PIXE microanalysis of fluid inclusions based on a layered yield model: Nuclear Instruments and Methods in Physics Research, v. B54, p. 292–297.
Ryan, C.G., Heinrich, C.A., and Mernagh, T.P., 1993, PIXE microanalysis of fluid inclusions and its application to study ore metal segregation between magmatic brine and vapour: Nuclear Instruments and Methods in Physics Research, v. B77, p. 463–471.
Salvi, S. and Williams-Jones, A.E., 1997a, Analyses of volatiles in fluid inclusions by gas chromatography: applications to the origin of reduced gases in alkaline rocks: European Current Research on Fluid Inclusions XIV, Nancy, France, Abstracts, p. 288–289.
—— 1997b, Fischer-Tropsch synthesis of hydrocarbons during subsolidus alteration of the Strange Lake peralkaline granite, Quebec/Labrador, Canada: Geochimica et Cosmoschimica Acta, v. 61, p. 83–99.

Schrader, B., Baranovic, G., Keller, S., and Sawatzki, J., 1994, Micro and 2-dimensional NIR FT Raman-spectroscopy: Fresenius Journal of Analytical Chemistry, v. 349, p. 4–10.

Shepherd, T.J., and Chenery, S.R., 1995, Laser ablation ICP-MS elemental analysis of individual fluid inclusions: An evaluation study: Geochimica et Cosmochimica Acta, v. 59, p. 3997–4007.

Shepherd, T.J., and Miller, M.F., 1985, Fluid inclusion volatiles as a guide to tungsten deposits, southwest England: Application to other Sn-W provinces of Western Europe, *in* Boissonnas, J., and Omenetto, P, eds., Mineral Deposits within the European Community: Berlin, Springer-Verlag, 558 p.

Shepherd, T.J., Rankin, A.H., and Alderton, D.H.M., 1985, A practical guide to fluid inclusion studies: London, Blackie, 239 p.

Shepherd, T.S., Ayora, C., Cendon, D., Chenery, S., Moissette, A., and Zimmermann, H., 1997, Interlaboratory evaluation of techniques for the chemical analysis of single fluid inclusions [abs.]: European Current Research on Fluid Inclusions, No. XIV, Nancy, France, Abstracts, p. 304–305.

Smith, M., Banks., D.A., Yardley, B.W.D., and Boyce, A., 1996, Fluid inclusion and stable isotope constraints on the genesis of the Cligga Head Sn-W deposit, S.W. England: European Journal of Mineralogy, v. 8, p. 961–974.

Stasiuk, L.D., and Snowdon, L.R., 1997, Fluorescence micro-spectrometry of synthetic and natural hydrocarbon fluid inclusions: Crude oil chemistry, density and application to petroleum migration: Applied Geochemistry, v. 12, p. 229.

Thompson, M., and Walsh, J.N., 1983, A handbook of inductively coupled plasma spectrometry: Glasgow, Blackie, 280 p.

Thompson, M., Rankin, A.H., Walton, S.J., Halls, C., and Foo, B.N., 1980, The analysis of fluid inclusion decrepitate by inductively-coupled plasma atomic emission spectroscopy: An exploratory study: Chemical Geology, v. 30, p. 121–133.

Turner, G., and Bannon, M.P., 1992, Argon isotope geochemistry of inclusion fluids from granite-associated mineral veins in southwest and northeast England: Geochimica et Cosmochimica Acta, v. 56, p. 227–243.

Vanko, D.A., Griffith, J.D., and Erickson, C.L., 1992, Calcium-rich brines and other hydrothemal fluids in fluid inclusions from plutionic rocks, Oceanographer Transform, Mid-Atlantic Ridge: Geochimica et Cosmochimica Acta, v. 56, p. 35–47.

Vanko, D.A., Sutton, S.R., Rivers, M.L., and Bodnar, R.J., 1993, Major-element ratios in synthetic fluid inclusions by synchrotron X-ray fluorescence microprobe: Chemical Geology, v. 109, p. 125–134.

Wallace, P.J., and Gerlach, T.M., 1994, Magmatic vapor source for sulfur dioxide released during volcanic eruptions: Evidence from Mount Pinatubo: Science, v. 265, p. 497–499.

Wilkinson, J.J., 1990, The role of metamorphic fluids in the development of the Cornubian orefield: Fluid inclusion evidence from south Cornwall: Mineralogical Magazine, v. 54, p. 219–230.

Wilkinson, J.J., Rankin, A.H., Mulshaw, S.C., Nolan, J., and Ramsey, M.H., 1994, Laser ablation-ICP-AES for the determination of metals in fluid inclusions: An application to the study of magmatic ore fluids, S.W. England and New Mexico: Geochimica et Cosmochimica Acta, v. 58, p. 1133–1146.

Williams-Jones, A.E., 1997, Mass spectrometric analysis of volatiles in fluid inclusions: Aliquot calibration valve to simulate inclusion rupture: Chemical Geology, v. 131, p. 155–166.

Yardley, B.W.D., Banks, D.A., Bottrell, S.H., and Diamond, L.W., 1993, Post-metamorphic gold quartz veins from NW Italy: The composition and origin of the ore fluid: Mineralogical Magazine, v. 57, p. 407–422.

Zimmermann, J.L., and Veeken, P.C.H., 1997, Permanent fluids in coals from the Fohnsdorf Basin, Austria: A preliminary quadrupolar mass spectrometric study [abs.]: European Current Research on Fluid Inclusions, No. XIV, Nancy, France, Abstracts, p. 358–359.

Chapter 7

Fluid Inclusion Modeling for Hydrothermal Systems

PHILIP E. BROWN

Department of Geology and Geophysics, University of Wisconsin, Madison, Wisconsin 53706

Introduction

Fluid inclusion analysis has the potential to provide some of the clearest data regarding the chemical and physical processes that result in mineral growth, deformation, and recrystallization. The purpose of this chapter is, first, to briefly introduce microthermometry, the most common analytical technique used to gain information from fluid inclusions and second, to discuss how to model and interpret the analytical data. The well-informed user must understand both how the data are gathered and how calculations are made. A detailed summary and critique of various analytical techniques and the thermodynamic data for the various chemical systems is beyond the scope of this chapter. The interested reader will need to follow up on the references throughout the text. However, what follows provides a solid basis to evaluate and interpret publications that use fluid inclusion data to constrain geochemical, geological and geophysical processes.

In the previous chapter, Shepherd and Rankin reviewed a variety of analytical techniques to determine the chemical and isotopic composition of either individual fluid inclusions or whole populations of inclusions in a sample. In this chapter, I will review microthermometry, the most widely used technique, and discuss how to interpret the data obtained with this method. The following Glossary defines several phase equilibria terms and abbreviations used in the sections that follow.

Phase Equilibria Terms

invariant point
: A fixed point in pressure-temperature space for a particular chemical system at which the maximum number of phases can stably coexist. For water, the invariant point at T = 0.01°C and P = 0.006 bars is the only set of conditions where liquid, vapor, and solid H_2O can coexist.

univariant line
: A line in P-T space with one thermodynamic degree of freedom—a small change in either P or T can be compensated for by a small change in the other, leaving the phase assemblage unchanged.

critical point
: The highest possible temperature at which liquid and vapor phases of a substance can exist in equilibrium.

critical curve
: The curve that connects the critical points of two substances in P-T space and below which the mixed fluid system can contain coexisting liquid and vapor phases.

isochore
: A line of constant density or molar volume on a pressure-temperature diagram.

isopleth
: A line of constant composition on a phase diagram.

bubble point curve
: The curve that defines the high P-T limit of a two-phase L + V field and separates it from a single, reasonably dense, liquid-like, one phase fluid. Crossing this boundary up-temperature, an inclusion will homogenize to a single fluid by disappearance of the vapor phase.

dew point curve
: The curve that defines the high T, low P limit of a two-phase L + V field and separates it from a single, low density, vapor-like, one-phase fluid. Crossing this boundary up-temperature, an inclusion will homogenize to a single fluid by disappearance of the liquid phase.

Terms and Abbreviations Used in Microthermometry

The following list of terms is slightly modified from the introductory pages of the annual Fluid Inclusion Research volumes (Roedder, 1996). If adopted by all fluid inclusion researchers, this common terminology would greatly simplify interpreting the published literature. Although Roedder suggests not subscripting the modifiers for simplicity, I have chosen to subscript this information in this paper to improve readability. This choice may be imposed by some journals.

Tt
: The temperature of trapping, i.e., the temperature of formation of the inclusion.

Tf
: The temperature of formation. Normally the same as Tt.

Th
: The temperature of homogenization. Unless otherwise indicated, this should refer to total homogenization. The phase into which homogenization occurs should be stated as well (e.g., Th_L or Th_V). Where only the homogenization of a given pair of phases is meant, these should be designated; thus: $Th_{L\text{-}V}$, $Th_{CO_2\ L\text{-}V}$, etc. The phase into which such homogenization occurs should also be stated; thus, in full: $Th_{L\text{-}V(L)}$, $Th_{CO_2\ L\text{-}V(V)}$, or $Th_{H_2O\text{-}CO_2(H_2O)}$.

Tm
The temperature of melting. For ordinary water-rich inclusions this may refer to the melting of ice, but ambiguity is all too common. The specific solid phase that melts (or dissolves) should always be designated; thus: Tm_{NaCl}, Tm_{ice}, Tm_{dms}, Tm_{CO_2}.

Te
The temperature of the eutectic. This is the first recognizable formation of liquid on warming a completely crystalline inclusion; it is only an approximate or "practical" value at best, because traces of other components will always result in undetectable traces of melting at lower temperatures.

Tn
The temperature of nucleation of a given phase. This generally refers to nucleation on cooling, normally from a supercooled, metastable fluid. Thus, Tn for an aqueous inclusion would be Tn_{ice}, and formation of a bubble in a previously homogenized L-V inclusion would be Tn_V.

Td
The temperature of decrepitation. This is used differently by various authors and cannot be defined exactly. Specific details on how such a temperature is determined, e.g., the start of decrepitation, the most rapid rise of decrepitation rate, the maximum number of impulses per unit increase in temperature, etc., will vary with the technique used and should be specified in each paper.

equiv. (or eq.) wt % NaCl
That quantity of NaCl dissolved in pure water that would yield the same Tm_{ice} value. Sometimes also used for a rough estimate, on NaCl dm-bearing inclusions, to signify total apparent NaCl content obtained by combining measurements of size (or Tm) of NaCl dm and an assumption as to the NaCl concentration of the solution at room temperature.

dm or dms
Daughter mineral(s) that have crystallized from the trapped fluid upon cooling or other chemical changes.

Microthermometry

Introduction

The most commonly used non-destructive analytical technique for fluid inclusions is microthermometry. A relatively inexpensive heating and freezing device (or stage) can be attached to a normal optical microscope and used, even by a relative novice, to measure fundamental physical and chemical properties of fluids trapped in a variety of minerals. Careful observation of phase changes (e.g., ice melting, solid dissolution) as a function of temperature in an individual fluid inclusion can be used, with experimental data, to constrain the compositional and physical properties of the fluid at the time of trapping. In general, the constraints are only semi-quantitative because we are comparing complex multi-component natural fluids to simplified experimental systems.

The simplest interpretation of thermometric observations generally requires the assumption that at the time of trapping, the inclusion sampled either a homogeneous fluid environment (a single-phase fluid) or, in a multiphase environment, that any individual inclusion trapped a sample of only one of the multiple phases present. For example, in a fluid undergoing "boiling," both liquid (high density) and vapor (low density) samples of the fluid may be present—simple fluid inclusion analysis assumes that an individual inclusion trapped either a sample of the liquid or a sample of the vapor, not a mixture of both. This assumption is probably more valid for the liquid-rich inclusions than it is for the vapor-rich ones (see Roedder, 1984, p. 26–35). After trapping, the inclusion and its host will experience differential contraction during cooling which commonly leads to the formation of a vapor bubble in the inclusion. Cooling of the inclusion may also result in the unmixing of a high-temperature, one-phase fluid, to form two or more fluid phases (e.g., the effervescence of CO_2 from H_2O). During cooling the fluid may also become saturated in one or more solutes which then precipitate forming daughter minerals. Microthermometry involves either heating the inclusion and observing when these unmixed systems undergo phase changes, or cooling the inclusion and inducing additional changes (i.e., freezing). These temperatures can be interpreted to constrain fluid density and chemistry.

Another fundamental assumption of traditional fluid inclusion workers is that once trapped, the inclusion is effectively sealed chemically from further interaction with the host mineral and the world outside it. This constant volume, constant composition assumption is under siege not only by possible necking down of the inclusions (Roedder, 1984) but also by hydrogen diffusion (Hall and Bodnar, 1990), water migration (Hollister, 1990), and a number of other changes potentially taking place in minerals undergoing post-trapping deformation events. The magnitude of such effects must be evaluated before drawing conclusions from inclusion microthermometry. Specific aspects of microthermometry will be touched on below in the context of our discussion of several simple chemical systems commonly used to interpret fluid inclusions.

Water

Many fluid inclusions have compositions approaching pure water and most brine inclusions are dominantly water. Therefore, the phase equilibria of the most important compound on Earth is the logical place to start this review.

In this one-component chemical system the solid-liquid-vapor triple point at +0.01°C and 0.006 bars is invariant—any change in pressure or temperature will reduce the number of phases stably coexisting (see Fig. 1 insert). The fact that the density of liquid water at the triple point temperature is greater than the density of ice, coupled with the existence of high-pressure polymorphs of the solid (ice), leads to several unique features in water's low temperature phase equilibria, and potential confusion in interpreting melting data for fluid inclusions. As discussed

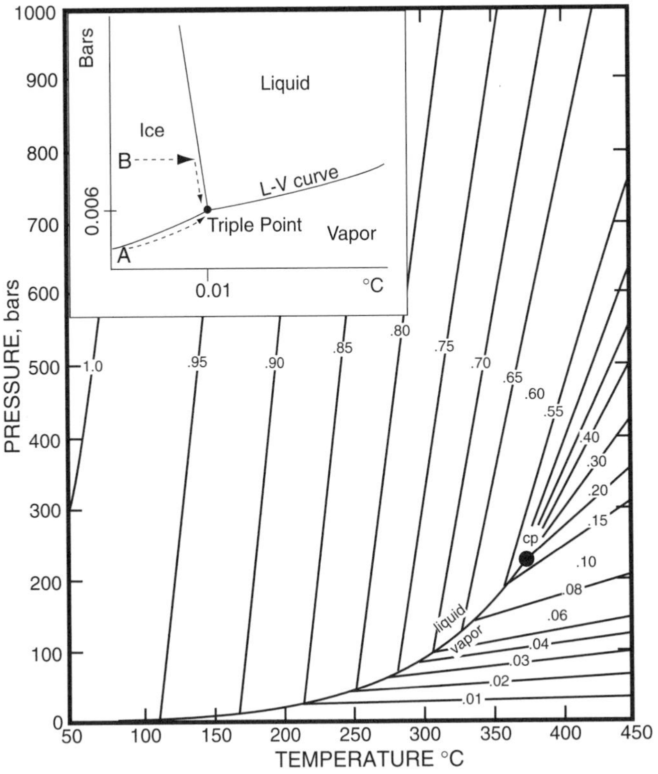

FIG. 1. P-T diagram for pure water showing the liquid-vapor curve and isochores for various densities of fluid inclusions. The inset shows an expanded view of the area in the vicinity of the triple point of water and the melting paths of two inclusions discussed in the text. CP = critical point at 374°C, 221 bars.

by Burruss (1981b, p. 44–45, fig. 3.3) three possible cases can occur:

1. Relatively low-density water inclusions containing a vapor bubble will freeze to ice plus vapor (inclusion A, Fig. 1). This inclusion will follow the Ice-Vapor curve during heating until it begins (and finishes) melting at +0.01°C.

2. Somewhat denser inclusions will have their vapor bubbles eliminated during freezing by the expansion of water (inclusion B, Fig. 1). Upon heating, this inclusion will begin to melt at temperatures below 0°C, and the final disappearance of ice should occur at 0.01°C where the bubble should renucleate.

3. Still denser inclusions (not shown in Fig. 1) without a vapor bubble at room temperature will freeze to a mixture of two polymorphs (Ice I and Ice III), begin melting at –21°C, and finish melting at temperatures below 0°C even though they are pure water.

The inevitable presence of other species dissolved in natural waters in any of these three cases will shift all of this behavior to temperatures below 0°C and complicate the interpretation (e.g., see the section below, Water-NaCl).

To a first order approximation, fluid inclusions are constant volume systems. The expansion and contraction of minerals during temperature and pressure changes can not be neglected by experimentalists doing precise P(pressure)-V(volume)-T(temperature) measurements using synthetic fluid inclusions. However, these small changes can be safely neglected in most studies of natural fluid inclusions because there are so many other larger uncertainties attending data acquisition and interpretation. Therefore, except as noted below, constant volume will be assumed in the following discussion. This allows the high temperature phase equilibria of water to be displayed on a P-T diagram and contoured with isochores—lines of constant density (Fig. 1). During microthermometry, the constant volume assumption means that we can use Figure 1 to track phase changes in the inclusion during heating.

After melting, a liquid (L) plus vapor (V) inclusion will, with continued heating above 0.01°C, begin to track along the univariant L + V curve joining the triple point and the critical point (CP) that lies at 374.1°C and 221 bars. The bulk density of the inclusion (ρ) can be calculated as:

$$\rho = [(\text{volume \% liquid}) \times (\text{its density})] + [(\text{volume \% vapor}) \times (\text{its density})]. \quad (7.1)$$

If this bulk density is greater than the density at the critical point (0.458 g/cc), the vapor phase will decrease in volume during heating until it disappears at the homogenization temperature (Th or $Th_{L\text{-}V(L)}$ in full). A fluid inclusion with a bulk density less than that of the critical point will homogenize by the expansion of the vapor and the eventual disappearance of the liquid phase $Th_{L\text{-}V(V)}$. The critical point is the highest possible homogenization temperature in the pure system and a pure water inclusion with a density of 0.458 g/cc will homogenize at 374°C by the fading of the meniscus separating the liquid and vapor phases.

It is usually easy to observe the disappearance of the vapor bubble in inclusions homogenizing to the liquid. The bubble tends to move rapidly around the inclusion (in response to slight temperature gradients and surface tension effects) as it decreases in size, and its disappearance is usually abrupt. However, it is nearly impossible to observe reliably the final homogenization temperature of an inclusion homogenizing to the vapor phase. The final thin rim of liquid is optically lost in the refractive index contrasts between the fluid and the walls of the host mineral. This liquid rim persists after it is last seen. Therefore, temperatures recorded for homogenization to the vapor will tend to be too low. In both types of homogenization, the re-appearance of the second phase during cooling usually occurs metastably several tens of degrees below the homogenization temperature. This fact can be used in a cycling technique, whereby the final Th is approached slowly from below, looking for the temperature below which the second phase does not immediately reappear upon slight cooling.

The homogenization temperature and mode (to L or to V) define the density or molar volume of the fluid in the inclusion and the isochore along which the inclusion was trapped. In most cases, either independent pressure or temperature data are needed to decide where along a particular isochore the individual inclusion was in fact trapped. In cases in which boiling or some other type of fluid phase separation was taking place during mineral growth, coexisting vapor-rich and liquid-rich inclusions may uniquely define both pressure and temperature at the time of trapping (see below, Boiling and Immiscibility). The equation of state for water is too complicated to reproduce it here–heating data should be interpreted either using diagrams such as Figure 1 or a variety of computer programs available from a number of sources (see below, Computer Programs).

Inclusions that have stretched or leaked since they formed will not yield valid density data because the inclusion now is either too large (stretching) or contains less material (leaking) than at the time of its trapping. However, some of these same inclusions may still preserve valuable compositional information and they should not be discounted out-of-hand. Although in theory the bulk composition and density of the inclusion could be derived from measurement of the relative percentages of liquid and vapor at any temperature, uncertainties in the 3-D geometry of the inclusion generally preclude this as a useful technique.

In summary, two distinct phase transitions should be observable in one-component pure water inclusions: the melting of ice (which fixes the composition), and the higher temperature L + V homogenization which fixes the bulk inclusion density or molar volume.

Water-NaCl

The addition of another component, here NaCl, increases the number of phases required to constrain the system to an invariant point (four phases) or a univariant line (three phases) on a P-T diagram. Although there is no a priori way of predicting it, two new solid phases can form in this system in addition to ice (H_2O): hydrohalite ($NaCl•2H_2O$) and halite (NaCl). Figures 2 and 3 provide T-X and P-T diagrams of some of the phase equilibria in this system; a good summary can be found in Bodnar et al. (1985).

For all compositions with less than 61.9 wt percent NaCl, at temperatures below –21.2°C, an inclusion at equilibrium will contain ice + hydrohalite + vapor (Fig. 2). Aqueous inclusions irrespective of their composition generally must be cooled to at least –30° to –40°C to nucleate ice. When this happens, they freeze instantaneously to a disequilibrium mixture of ice and halite, which may begin to melt upon heating at the metastable eutectic (–28°C). Coarsening and other subtle optical changes occur in inclusions as they are warmed, even below their true eutectic temperatures. Thus, to observe equilibrium phase changes, the inclusion should be warmed above its eutectic temperature (here –21.2°C), but not above its ice melting temperature, and then recooled to obtain a mixture of solids that approaches those expected at equilibrium.

Let's assume that inclusion A in Figure 2 has been frozen to an equilibrium mixture of ice + hydrohalite + vapor. Upon heating to the eutectic temperature of –21.2°C, liquid begins to form as the inclusion begins to melt. The temperature remains fixed until either all the ice or all the hydrohalite melts; here, because the bulk composition is to the left of the eutectic, the hydrohalite will disappear. Observation of the first melting at the eutectic is critical for determining the composition of the system under observation. Table 1 provides eutectic temperatures (Te) and compositions for a variety of simple and mixed salt-water systems. Shepherd et al. (1985, p. 74) provide a longer list that includes some much less common dissolved species. Stable eutectic temperatures cover at least the range from –10.6° to –57°C. However, first melting temperatures have been reported at temperatures approaching –100°C. First melting is difficult to observe,

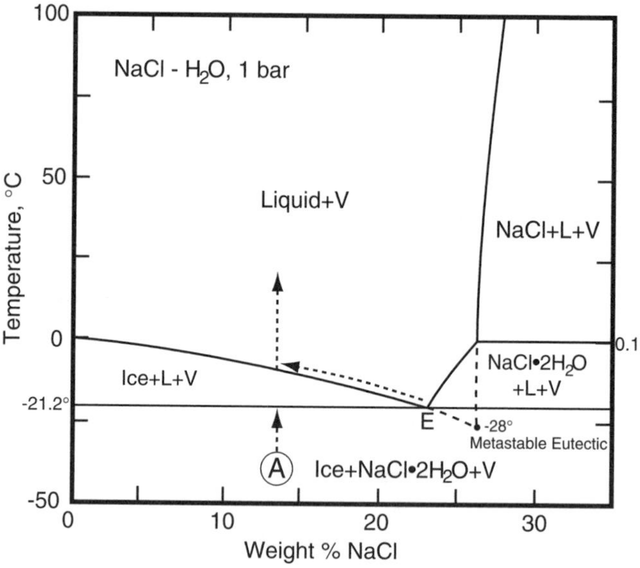

FIG. 2. NaCl-H_2O system. Data from Potter et al., 1978; Hall et al., 1988.

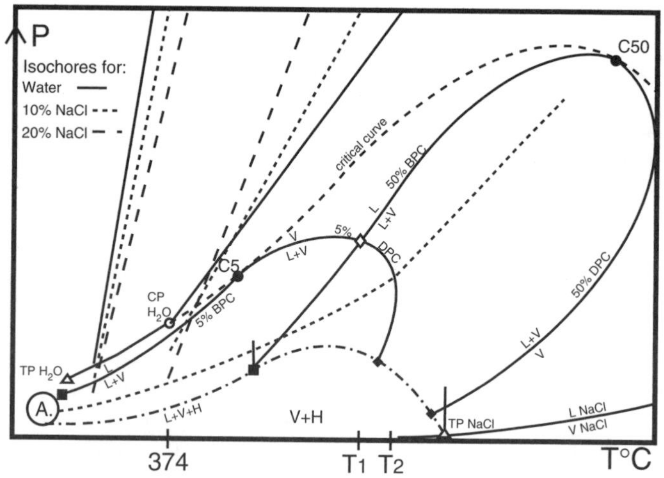

FIG. 3. Highly schematic and simplified P-T diagram for the system H_2O-NaCl after Pichavant et al. (1982) and Bodnar et al. (1985). The low P-T complexity comes from the presence of hydrohalite. The intersecting BPC and DPC will be discussed in the section on boiling.

especially in small inclusions. Haynes (1985) describes a sequential cooling and partial heating technique to make this important observation more accurately.

TABLE 1. Eutectic First Melting Temperatures for Selected Salts

System	Eutectic Temperature(°C)
H_2O-NaCl-$CaCl_2$-$MgCl_2$	–57
H_2O-NaCl-$CaCl_2$	–52
H_2O-$CaCl_2$	–49.5
H_2O-$FeCl_2$	–35
H_2O-$MgCl_2$	–33.6
H_2O-NaCl-KCl	–23
H_2O-NaCl	–21.2
H_2O-KCl	–10.6

Upon further warming of inclusion A, the liquid increases in abundance while the remaining ice decreases in abundance (remember the lever rule) until the ice disappears at a temperature that fixes its composition (Fig. 2). For salinities less than 23.2 wt percent NaCl, the final melting temperature (Tm) of the ice can be converted to salinity using the equation (Bodnar, 1993):

$$\text{wt \% NaCl} = (-1.78 \times \text{Tm}) - (0.0442 \times (\text{Tm})^2) - (0.000557 \times (\text{Tm})^3) \quad (7.2)$$

For example, the final melting temperature of inclusion A, –10°C, corresponds to a salinity of 13.9 wt percent. Note, however, that the same final melting of –10°C can also be observed for bulk compositions between 23.2 and 26.3 wt percent NaCl where the final phase to melt is hydrohalite rather than ice:

$$\text{wt \% NaCl} = 26.271 + (0.181 \times \text{Tm}) + (0.002 \times (\text{Tm})^2) \quad (7.3)$$

Distinguishing these two cases requires identifying the melting solid as either ice or hydrohalite. Ice has a lower refractive index (RI) than water while hydrohalite is strongly birefringent and has a significantly higher RI. Thus, especially in inclusions larger than 8 to10 μm, coupling the method described in Haynes (1985) with careful observation of the RI (using the Becke line test for instance) should allow the identification of the melting solid.

Inclusions containing more than 26.3 wt percent NaCl should have a halite daughter salt present at room temperature. The bulk salinity of such inclusions is determined by the dissolution temperature of the halite daughter salt using the equation (Sterner et al., 1988):

$$\text{wt \% NaCl} = 26.242 + (0.4928 \times \text{Td}) + (1.42 \times (\text{Td})^2) - (0.223 \times (\text{Td})^3) + (0.04129 \times (\text{Td})^4) + (0.006295 \times (\text{Td})^5) - (0.001967 \times (\text{Td})^6) + (0.00011112 \times (\text{Td})^7)$$

where Td = (dissolution temperature)/100. (7.4)

For example, dissolution of halite at 100°C fixes the salinity at 28.0 wt percent NaCl.

With continued heating after melting of the last solid (ice), inclusion A on Figure 3 containing 5 percent NaCl follows a liquid-vapor curve (dashed) across the divariant L+V field until it homogenizes on the dew point curve—that is, by expansion of the vapor bubble at T2. A higher density inclusion of the same composition could have homogenized on the bubble point curve (shrinkage of the vapor bubble) or possibly by critical behavior at C5, corresponding to a vapor pressure fixed by the composition and specific volume of the system (Fig. 3). The bubble-point and dew-point curve loop for a given composition is tangent to the binary critical curve at the critical point for that salt content. Isochores for a particular composition (derived from the freezing point) and density (derived from the liquid-vapor homogenization temperature) begin on either the bubble-point or dew-point curve depending on the mode of homogenization. Thus the 374°C critical isochore for pure water (solid line) begins at a higher pressure than the 374°C isochore for a 20 wt percent NaCl solution (long dashes) that begins on the 20 wt percent NaCl bubble-point curve (not shown). The slope of an isochore varies with composition as seen in Figure 3; it may be steeper or shallower than the isochore for pure water beginning at the same temperature. See Crawford (1981) or Bodnar and Vityk (1994) for a more complete discussion of these phase equilibria including those inclusions that homogenize by halite dissolution after L + V → L.

Most studies reporting freezing point depressions on aqueous fluids cast their results in terms of "equivalent wt percent NaCl" (equiv. wt % NaCl). One compelling reason to do this is that NaCl is commonly the dominant dissolved species reported from seawater, various brines, and even simple brackish fluids. An additional reason is provided by Figure 4: the wt percent salt versus freezing point depression curve for NaCl lies in the middle of the curves for the other less common salts. Thus NaCl serves, in the absence of other direct compositional determinations, as the proxy for the true dissolved salt content.

Carbon Dioxide

The phase equilibria of CO_2 can serve as a model for nearly every non-aqueous fluid. Figure 5 is a schematic T-V(molar volume) section for CO_2; Figure 6 is the corresponding quantitative P-T diagram. All three hypothetical inclusions in Figure 5, which contain L + V at room temperature (T1), should freeze when cooled below the invariant solid-liquid-vapor coexistence temperature T2. For actual inclusions, CO_2 normally freezes near –90° to –100°C, far below the equilibrium temperature. Warming these solid (S) + V inclusions results in the first appearance of liquid (and the complete melting of the solid) at T2; for pure CO_2 this occurs at –56.6°C. If S + L + V are observed to coexist over a temperature range, then additional gaseous components must be present in the inclusion.

After the disappearance of the solid, continued heating results in changing ratios (calculable by the lever rule) of liquid and vapor in inclusions 1 and 2. Inclusion 1 will homogenize by vapor disappearance at $\text{Th}_{CO_2\ \text{L-V(L)}}$ whereas inclusion 2 will homogenize by the elimination of

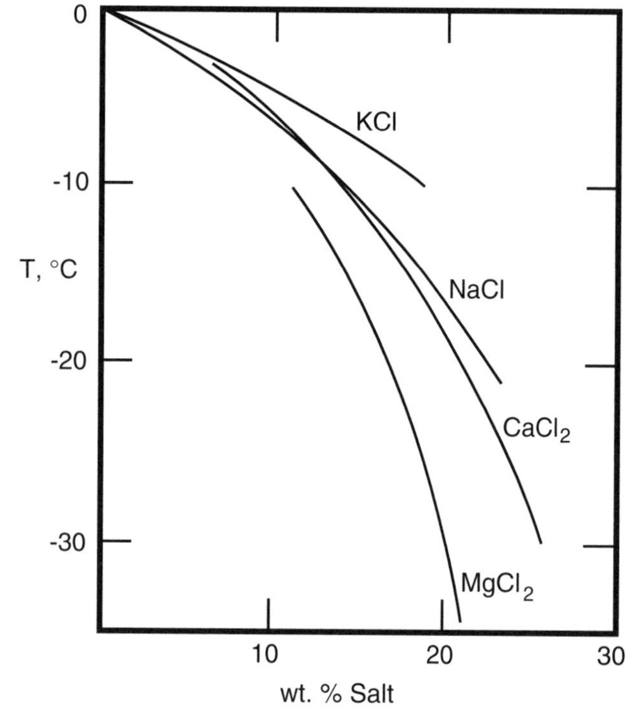

FIG. 4. Freezing point versus wt percent salt curves for four common chlorides. Note that data for NaCl provide good average values for unknown mixtures of these salts.

the liquid at Th $_{CO_2\ L\text{-}V(V)}$. Inclusion 3 will maintain a constant L/V ratio as temperature rises until it homogenizes by fading of the meniscus as the molar volumes of the

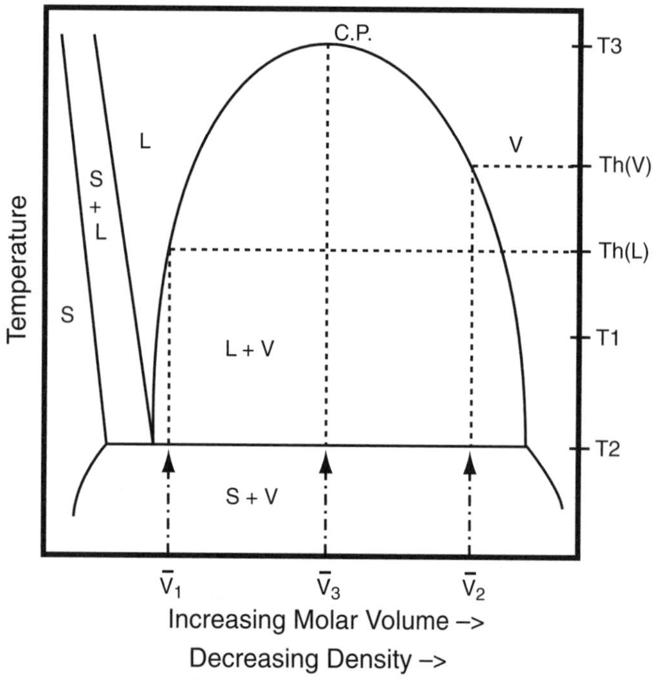

FIG. 5. Schematic temperature–molar volume diagram for CO_2. Dashed lines are visual aids only for discussing the behavior of three hypothetical inclusions; see the text for discussion.

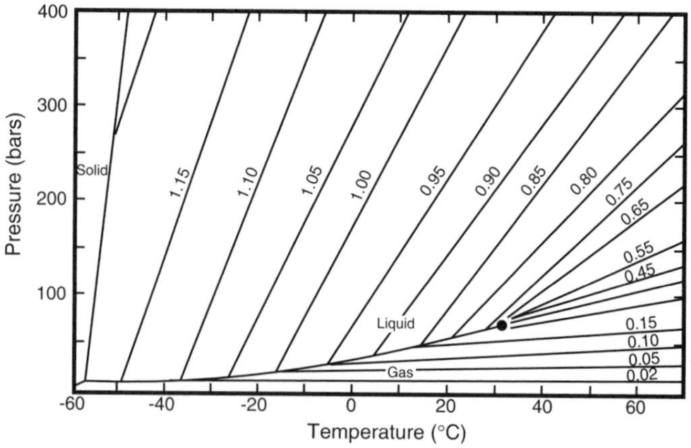

FIG. 6. P-T diagram for CO_2. Numbers on the isochores are the density of the fluid in g/cc.

liquid and vapor phases approach one another at T3, the critical temperature (31.1°C for pure CO_2).

There are many equations of state for CO available in the literature (Touret and Bottinga, 1979; Swanenberg, 1980; Bottinga and Richet, 1981; Holloway, 1981; Kerrick and Jacobs, 1981; Saxena and Fei, 1987; and Mader and Berman, 1991). There is good agreement among data sets as to the location of the L-V curve and the densities that correspond to homogenization temperatures. The various equations of state use different empirical fits to the experimental data to extrapolate the isochores to high P-T conditions; see Brown and Lamb (1989) for a comparison among several of the published studies. As discussed above, inclusion fluids more dense than the critical density will have relatively steep isochores whereas the low density fluids have isochores with shallow slopes (Fig. 6).

CO_2-CH_4

In addition to water and carbon dioxide, methane is a common fluid species found in fluid inclusions. Like CO_2, it is non-polar, and it exhibits topologically identical phase equilibria. Figure 7 presents a schematic P-T diagram (after Swanenberg, 1979) illustrating the important features of the CO_2-CH_4 system. See Donnelly and Katz (1954), Hollister and Burruss (1976), Swanenberg (1979), Burruss (1981a, b), and Thiéry et al. (1994) for more information.

Two L-V curves (a, b) link analogous points in the CO_2 and CH_4 systems (Fig. 7). The CO_2-CH_4 critical curve (c) links the critical point of CO_2 at 31.1°C with the critical point of CH_4 at –82.6°C. The invariant S + L + V triple points in the one component CO_2 (T_{CO_2}) or CH_4 (off figure) systems anchor the univariant S + L + V curves in the binary system. Lying between the critical and S + L + V curves are bubble-point and dew-point curves for every bulk composition between CO_2 and CH_4. The final melting temperature of CO_2 fixes the density and composition of both liquid and gas phases. For example, final melting at –60°C fixes the liquid composition at ~90 percent CO_2 (the bubble point curve corresponding to –60°C) and fixes the vapor composition at ~80 percent CH_4 (the dew point curve anchored at the same –60°C).

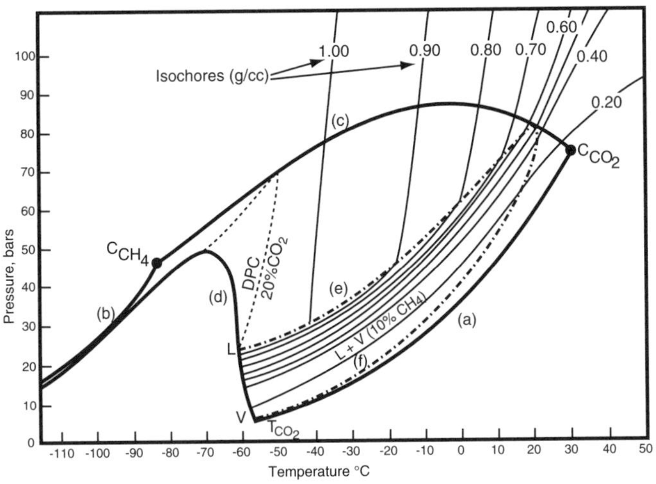

FIG. 7. Phase equilibria in the system CO_2-CH_4 (Swanenberg, 1979): (a, b) L-V curves for CO_2 and CH_4 respectively connecting their triple points to their critical points; (c) CO_2-CH_4 critical curve; (d) S-L-V triple point curve for CO_2-rich compositions extending from the CO_2 triple point to the quadruple point in the binary system (not shown); (e) bubble point curve for 90% CO_2-10% CH_4; (f) dew point curve for 90% CO_2-10% CH_4. The bubble- and dew-point curves bound the divariant L+V field for a particular composition, here 10% CH_4. Each curve through the L+V field corresponds to a single density and an isochore emanates from the intersection of each L-V curve for a particular composition and the bubble- or dew-point curve for that composition.

The bulk composition of the inclusion would be calculated by weighting these compositional data by the relative proportions of liquid and vapor at the final melting temperature. Therefore, any melting temperature between –56.6° and –184°C may correspond to many different bulk compositions and the temperature of melting needs to be coupled to an additional observation to fix the composition uniquely. One such additional piece of information can be the L/V ratio at the melting point (Swanenberg, 1979); however, as discussed by Roedder (1967) and others, phase ratio estimation is fraught with uncertainty in irregular shaped inclusions. Thiéry et al. (1994) provide diagrams that couple Th_{L-V} and Tm observations to fix composition and molar volume. Increasingly, laser Raman analyses are used to constrain the CO_2/CH_4 ratio in inclusions; such measurements can remove significant ambiguity from traditional microthermometry.

Assuming that the bulk composition can be ascertained, Figure 7 shows that the isochores for different molar volumes of the CO_2-CH_4 mixture sprout from the bubble-point and dew-point curves that join at the critical point, the origin for the critical isochore for the mixture. Note that all of the possible L-V homogenization temperatures lie between +31.1° and –184°C; the presence of more than one fluid phase at temperatures much above room temperature indicates that additional chemical species are present. The slopes of the CO_2-CH_4 isochores are reasonably well known (Swanenberg, 1979) and can be used to estimate trapping conditions in well constrained cases. As discussed in subsequent sections, care must be taken in drawing high temperature conclusions from low temperature equilibria, especially in this system. At elevated temperatures CO_2 and CH_4 will react to form water and graphite; these equilibria and the role of oxygen fugacity have been discussed at length in the literature (Holloway, 1981; Lamb and Valley, 1985).

CO_2-N_2 mixtures behave much like fluids in the CO_2-CH_4 system. While the triple point for nitrogen is at -210°C and the basic topology is similar, the critical curve loops to higher pressures, and the S-L-V curve intersects the critical curve and is therefore discontinuous. See Kerkhof and Thiéry (1994) for a complete discussion of the equilibria in this system. It is now well established that independent identification of the gas species causing a freezing point depression for the carbonic phase is required to constrain the roles of CH_4 and N_2 (and other possible species). These additional data generally come from nondestructive laser Raman analysis of individual inclusions.

H_2O-CO_2

The most important binary aqueous-volatile system contains CO_2, and provides an example of complicated low temperature phase behavior involving liquid-liquid immiscibility, compound solids (clathrates), discontinuous equilibria and metastability of fluid inclusions. See Burruss (1981a), Roedder (1984), Shepherd et al. (1985), Diamond (1994), and Goldstein and Reynolds (1994) for both introductory and detailed discussions of this system.

The fundamental complexity in the H_2O-CO_2 system arises from the volatility (and thus low temperature equilibria)of the large non-polar CO_2 molecule as it interacts with the less volatile (and thus higher temperature equilibria) of the small dipolar H_2O molecule. At high temperatures and pressures (T > 265°C, P > 2200 bars) these two dissimilar fluids are completely miscible. At lower temperatures a carbonic phase and an aqueous liquid coexist. Below room temperature three different solid phases are possible: ice, solid CO_2 and a clathrate hydrate of CO_2 with the nominal composition of $CO_2 \bullet 5\frac{3}{4}\ H_2O$. The clathrate is commonly observed during microthermometry and, in the absence of additional chemical species, melts at +10.0°C. As discussed in Diamond (1994), the extreme complexity of this binary system can be simplified by considering four compositional ranges of H_2O-CO_2 fluids that are reasonably diagnostic of different geological environments. Figure 8 after Diamond (1994, fig. 2) provides schematic P-T diagrams for each of the following four cases.

1. Minerals in *epithermal ore deposits* commonly contain very high $X(H_2O)$ fluids with $X(CO_2) < 0.015$ (Fig. 8a). For these compositions, any minor clathrate that may form during freezing melts first, followed by ice melting (point 3) at temperatures below 0°C (Diamond, 1994, p. 144). Homogenization takes place along either a bubble-point (point 2 on the dashed line for example) or a dew-point curve. Trapping could have occurred at point 1 or anywhere along the isochore above point 2. Only the rare observation of critical phase homogenization at temperatures

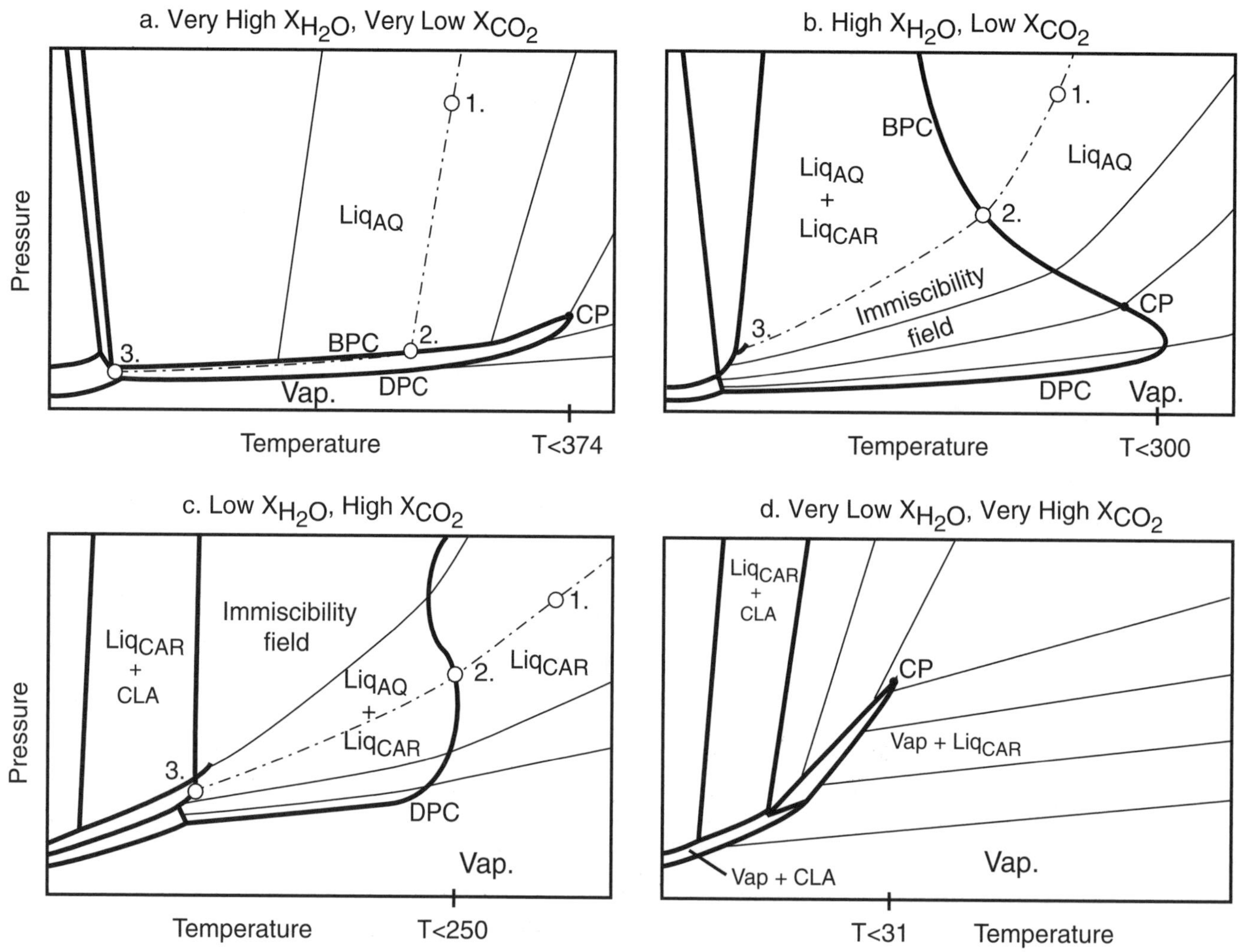

FIG. 8. Four schematic sections through the model of phase relations in the system H_2O-CO_2 (after Diamond, 1994). (a) $X(H_2O) \approx 0.99$, typical of epithermal ore deposits. (b) $X(H_2O) \approx 0.9$, typical of mesothermal gold deposits. (c) $(H_2O) \approx 0.4$, typical of pegmatites and boiling systems. (d) $(H_2O) \approx 0.001$, typical of high-grade metamorphism. BPC - boiling point curve, DPC - dew point curve, CP - critical point, LiqAQ - aqueous-rich liquid, LiqCAR - carbonic-rich liquid, CLA - clathrate. Selected isochores (finer lines) are shown for the fluid fields; dashed isochores are refered to in the text. The figures are not to scale.

below 374°C serves to identify CO_2 as the diluent instead of small amounts of NaCl, which would also slightly lower the Tm (ice) but would raise the critical point above 374°C. In the absence of critical behavior, either crushing tests (the presence of CO_2 raises the pressure above 1 bar at room temperature) or laser Raman analyses would be required to distinguish these two cases (Bodnar et al., 1985; Hedenquist and Henley, 1985).

2. *Mesothermal or hypothermal ore deposits* or medium-grade metamorphic rocks generally have high $X(H_2O)$ fluids with $X(CO_2)$ contents between 0.015 and 0.148 (Fig. 8b). There are a number of different paths that inclusions within this composition range can take after entrapment (and while undergoing microthermometry). However, one in particular is commonly observed.

Most inclusions in this range consist of three phases at room temperature: an aqueous liquid, a carbonic liquid, and a carbonic vapor. Cooling these inclusions should cause the formation of clathrate at +10°C but invariably the inclusion must be cooled to ~–30°C to nucleate the clathrate which then grows instantaneously to fill much of the inclusion. Ice commonly forms at ~–40°C and the four phases (two solids + CO_2(L) + CO_2(V)) coexist out of thermodynamic equilibrium until the CO_2 freezes at ~–100°C, forming yet another disequilibrium assemblage. This lack of equilibrium is usually ascribed to the clathrate forming a physical barrier in the inclusion which prevents the liquid water and liquid CO_2 from "seeing" each other, and thus reacting, until either the water or the CO_2 is used up. Upon heating from –100°C, the (metastable) melting of CO_2 is still a good measure of its purity and the ice should melt between –4.5° and –1.5°C. Clathrate melts progressively between –1.5° and +10°C at which point it should dissociate completely. Further heating causes the CO_2 phases to homogenize to either the liquid or the vapor (point 3 on the dashed line shown here) at temperatures below 31°C, and eventually complete homogenization (point 2) will occur to the aqueous phase unless the inclusion decrepitates first.

3. Medium to high grade metamorphic rocks, pegmatites, intrusive rocks, and *ore deposits in which boiling has occurred* commonly have moderate to low $X(H_2O)$ inclusions with $X(CO_2)$ contents between 0.148 and 0.998 (Fig. 8c). At the water-rich end of this range, inclusions may homogenize by either bubble or dew-point transitions. At the CO_2-rich end the upper critical curve has migrated to such high pressures that only the dew point curve has physical meaning for geology and the inclusions homogenize (point 2) by the expansion of the CO_2 phase. Three points are important here: this transition is very difficult to measure accurately; the high pressures of these inclusions commonly cause them to decrepitate before they homogenize; and, as befits their "dew point" origin, the isochores are relatively flat when compared to more water-rich compositions. Isochores for mixtures in the H_2O-CO_2 system fan out between the steep pure water isochore at relatively high pressure and low temperature and the pure CO_2 one which has a shallower slope at relatively high temperature and low pressure (Bowers and Helgeson, 1983; Brown and Lamb, 1989; Sterner and Bodnar, 1991).

Higher pressure inclusions may contain only two phases at room temperature and only form a CO_2 vapor bubble upon cooling. In such inclusions the clathrate may melt in the absence of CO_2(V) (after CO_2 L-V homogenization) and this may occur at temperatures above +10°C. Again, see Diamond (1994) for further discussion of this system.

4. *High grade metamorphic rocks* commonly contain essentially pure CO_2 inclusions: $X(CO_2) > 0.998$ (Fig. 8d). These inclusions are mentioned here only for completeness; no microthermometric measurement could identify the trace amount of water in these inclusions and thus they are considered "pure CO_2." The only phase transitions observable here would be the melting of solid CO_2 and CO_2 L-V homogenization at a temperature less than the lower critical end point, effectively 31.1°C.

More Complex Systems

The addition of even one more component to any of the binaries discussed above adds a fourth dimension to our phase diagrams and requires clever projections and simplifications to communicate effectively in our 3D world and on 2D paper. Three-dimensional computer modeling and visualization software promises to help interpret multi-dimensional data sets—even at the cost of removing geologists ever further from the actual rocks in the field.

NaCl-KCl-H_2O. Potassium chloride (KCl) is an important component in many aqueous systems and the ternary NaCl-KCl-H_2O system is commonly used to interpret inclusion fluids from porphyry copper, geothermal, and epithermal systems. Whereas the binary NaCl-H_2O system was complicated by the existence of hydrohalite (see Fig. 2), the KCl-H_2O binary has a simple eutectic at −10.6°C and 19.6 wt percent KCl. The ternary eutectic in this system lies at −22.9°C and water-rich compositions. Hall et al. (1988) used synthetic fluid inclusions to derive an equation that allows the total weight percent salt to be calculated from the measured freezing point depression and an assumed NaCl/KCl ratio in the fluid. Bodnar et al. (1988) published an algorithm for estimating fluid inclusion compositions from any two phase changes observed during microthermometry of a NaCl-KCl-H_2O inclusion.

Cloke and Kesler (1979) observed that halite and sylvite melting temperatures in fluid inclusions that contained both these daughter minerals from high-temperature hydrothermal deposits commonly defined linear trends when plotted in the NaCl-KCl-H_2O system. They dubbed these the "halite trends" and concluded that the trends formed by separation of KCl-bearing halite from the hydrothermal solutions before the liquid was trapped. Four distinct trends are associated with different P-T-vapor pressure scenarios, and Cloke and Kesler conclude that these trends document exsolution of the highly saline fluids directly from a granitic magma.

NaCl-$CaCl_2$-H_2O. Vanko et al.(1988) and Oakes et al., (1990) have published experimental data from synthetic fluid inclusions defining phase equilibria for the NaCl-$CaCl_2$-H_2O ternary. The Vanko et al. experiments were used to help explain fluid inclusion data from mid-ocean ridge spreading center hydrothemal systems. Very low eutectic temperatures (<−40°C) can be explained by the presence of either Mg or Ca chlorides (Table 1) and so these divalent cations should be considered routinely when low first melting temperatures are observed. Naden (1996) provides a computer program that will calculate weight percent equivalent NaCl + $CaCl_2$ from microthermometric data gathered on inclusions with a halite daughter salt. The required inputs (ice melting temperature, hydrohalite melting temperature and the halite melting temperature) are readily measured on many inclusions and the program provides a sensitive test for the presence of $CaCl_2$ in these inclusions.

H_2O-CO_2-NaCl. The addition of NaCl(±KCl) to the H_2O-CO_2 binary has several dramatic effects (Bowers and Helgeson, 1983, 1985; Brown and Lamb, 1989; Duan et al., 1995). First, salt substantially lowers the clathrate melting temperature; see Diamond (1992) for a quantitative treatment application to fluid inclusions. Secondly, as seen for the H_2O-NaCl system, salt also extends the critical curve, effectively increasing the two-fluid field in P-T space at the expense of the one-phase mixed fluid (see below). Thus salt increases the likelihood that a particular ore fluid will undergo "boiling" or "phase separation" as it rises through the crust.

The addition of NaCl also has the thermodynamic effect of adding another component to the system, and thus an additional observation is needed to constrain the interpretation of measured fluid inclusion data. Three variables must be observed and quantified in order to calculate isochores for this system; commonly these are $Th_{CO_2\,L\text{-}V}$, clathrate melting temperate (Tm_{clath}) and volume percent CO_2. As discussed by many workers, the volume percent estimation is fraught with uncertainly and ideally another actual measurement could be substituted for this estimate. Parry (1986) and Brown and Lamb (1989) present diagrams (e.g., Fig. 9) that replace the volume estimate with measured $Th_{H_2O\text{-}CO_2}$. Whereas fluid inclusions from many deeper metamorphic settings tend to decrepitate prior to H_2O-CO_2 homogenization, hydrothermal ore deposits that formed at pressures less than 2 to 2.5 kbars should contain fluid inclusions that will allow application of Figure 9 or analogous figures for other salt contents (Brown and Lamb, 1989).

Data Handling

Data Recording

Making good observations and keeping good records are key to both the immediate applicability and longer term usefulness of your hard-won fluid-inclusion data. One of the most critical steps in documenting fluid inclusions should take place prior to any heating or freezing work. Ideally, every fluid inclusion would be photographed both to preserve a record of its appearance and to place it spatially in the context of surrounding inclusions, grain boundaries, structural features in the sample such as microcracks, and the relationship to ore minerals. Because most chips for microthermometry contain many inclusions and the high magnification necessary to see individual inclusions is attended by low depth of field, this photo documentation may be both time consuming and expensive. However without recording the initial phase ratios, it is hard to know what the pressure changes attending microthermometry may have done to the inclusions.

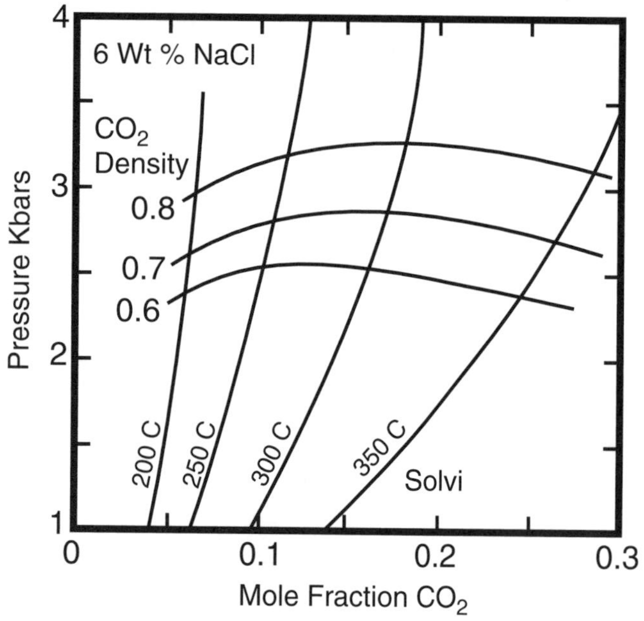

FIG. 9. P-X diagram from Brown and Lamb (1989) that allows rapid determination of $X(CO_2)$ and pressure in a ternary H_2O-CO_2-NaCl fluid inclusion from laboratory measurements of $Th_{CO_2\ L\text{-}V}$, Tm_{clath}, and $Th_{H_2O\text{-}CO_2}$. This figure, for the 6 wt % NaCl system, is contoured with CO_2 phase densities, as measured in the laboratory. The near vertical curves are the location of the H_2O-CO_2 solvus. Intersections between these two sets of curves yields both the mole fraction of CO_2 and the pressure at the time of H_2O-CO_2 homogenization.

The advent of video cameras and computer-based image capture technologies have provided a cost effective way to document the inclusions before, during, and after microthermometry. A complete, chip-wide survey prior to microthermometry is still time consuming, but the electronic pictures are immediately available and, given that each photo is effectively "free," there should be no hesitation in recording multiple views.

During microthermometry, a real-time video feed of the changing inclusion contents adjacent to the "before" picture on the computer monitor leaves very little to the imagination as to whether the contents have really changed and whether, upon return to room temperature, the inclusion has survived the experiment intact. Overlay software and appropriate hardware can capture temperature and size information on the same images for a permanent record of the microthermometry runs. Linkam Instruments provide an integrated, software-driven, Windows package designed to facilitate complete documentation and record keeping.

The Macintosh program MacFlinCor (Brown and Hagemann, 1994) provides a "note card" metaphor record keeping approach where sketches (or captured images) can be coupled with all the observational data on individual inclusions. Calculations made from the observed data are also stored on each card and can be exported to a database.

Initial microscopic observations allow the experienced inclusionist to identify the likely chemical systems to which individual inclusions or groups of inclusions belong. This, coupled with a knowledge of the phase equilibria in each system, serves as a guide to the temperature ranges for the subsequent microthermometry, the expected phase changes, and the order in which heating and freezing should be done. See Roedder (1984), Shepherd et al. (1985), and Goldstein and Reynolds (1994) for more in-depth discussion of the kinds of observations that should be made before beginning microthermometry.

Data Reduction

The goal of all fluid inclusion data reduction is to convert laboratory observations into derived quantities such as densities or molar volumes of observed or inferred fluid species, and concentrations of dissolved solutes. Theoretical, experimental, and empirical information may be used (commonly all three are needed) via a combination of mathematical and graphical approaches.

Theoretical models run the gamut from ideal gases through the van der Waals (1873) equation of state (EOS), the Redlich-Kwong EOS (Redlich and Kwong, 1949), and the Soave (1972) modification of the Redlich-Kwong EOS. Holloway (1977, 1981), Kerrick and Jacobs (1981), Jacobs and Kerrick (1981), and Bowers and Helgeson (1983, 1985) provide modified Redlich-Kwong formulations targeted at petrologists and fluid inclusionists. Recently

Duan et al. (1995) published a comprehensive EOS for H_2O-CO_2-NaCl and Bakker (in press) has re-examined the Bowers and Helgeson treatment and extended it to the system H_2O-CO_2-NaCl-CH_4-N_2. Many other equations of state are available in the literature for individual fluids or specific limited mixtures of species.

Experimental data on the behavior of combinations of gases and liquids are scattered throughout the chemical, physical, geological, and engineering literature. Most of these data were not collected with an eye to their utility for fluid inclusion research, and they must therefore be converted, recompiled, or re-interpreted before they are applicable to isochoric, isoplethic fluid inclusions. Individual experimental studies only cover a portion of P-T-V-X space for a given composition. Thus multiple data sets must be merged, and their inevitable discrepancies resolved, to begin to allow a single freezing/heating experiment to be interpreted. The biggest breakthrough in experimental geochemistry applicable to fluid inclusion research utilizes synthetic fluid inclusions. This technique was pioneered by R.J. Bodnar and his students and they have provided invaluable data on many chemical systems directly applicable to inclusions found in all kinds of ore deposits. In the last five years, many additional laboratories around the world have begun to produce data using synthetic fluid inclusions.

Empirical studies of carefully chosen fluid inclusion populations can provide important baseline data that may be applicable to other study areas around the world. For example, Hendel and Hollister (1981) empirically calibrated the H_2O-CO_2- 2.6 wt percent NaCl solvus based on some metamorphic fluid inclusions from British Columbia. This 2.6 wt percent NaCl solvus regularly shows up on graphical compilations of solvi used to interpret inclusion data.

These three types of information (theoretical, experimental, and empirical) may be combined graphically to provide the inclusionist with quantitative (or possibly semi-quantitative) data reduction. For example, Potter (1977) published diagrams for making pressure corrections to H_2O-NaCl fluids containing 1, 5, 10, 15, 20 and 25 wt percent NaCl. Figure 10 is his diagram for 5 wt percent NaCl, and most scientists find this easier to use than the same information presented on a P-T plot of isochores for the same composition.

As another example, Figure 11 (after Hagemann and Brown, 1996) is a P-T compilation of solvii in the H_2O-CO_2-NaCl system. Figure 12 is the common T-X presentation of some of this same information. Which of these is more useful for the inclusionist? None of these three diagrams can be directly used with numbers derived from the heating-freezing stage. In the H_2O-NaCl case, either independent pressure or temperature data are needed along with observed Th. Figure 11 assumes that both $X(CO_2)$ and weight percent NaCl have been calculated from observed data while Figure 12 assumes $X(CO_2)$ has been obtained and constraints on pressure are available. Obviously, data reduction must proceed in a particular order so that subsequent calculations can be based on previous analysis.

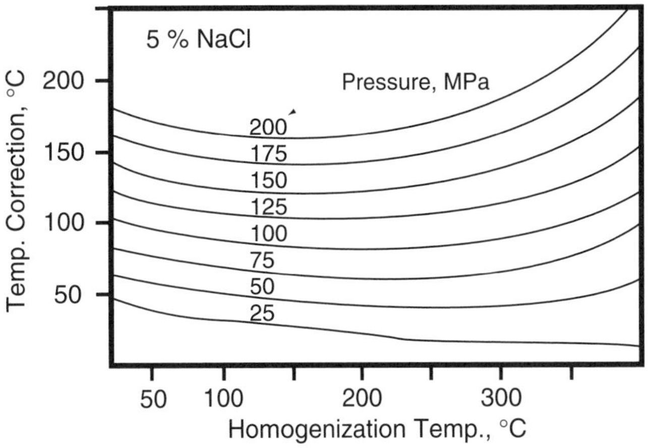

FIG. 10. Temperature correction to be applied to a measured homogenization temperature to compensate for confining pressure (after Potter, 1977).

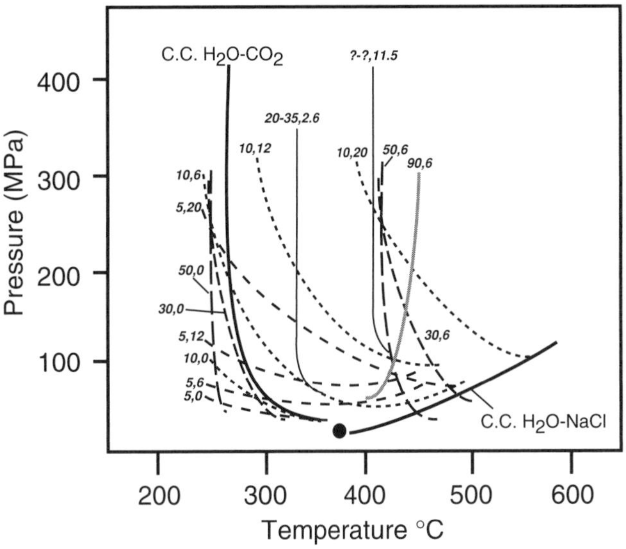

FIG. 11. P-T diagram displaying published solvi for different compositions in the H_2O-CO_2-NaCl system. Also shown are the critical curve for CO_2-H_2O (C.C. CO_2-H_2O) and H_2O-NaCl (C.C. H_2O-NaCl) as well as the critical point for H_2O (black dot). Numbers near the solvi (e.g., 5, 12) indicate mole % CO_2 and wt % NaCl (here 5 mole % CO_2 and 12 wt % NaCl). All solvi are from Bowers and Helgeson (1983) except for the two plotted as solid lines which are from Hendel and Hollister (1981; 2.6 wt % NaCl) and Frantz et al. (1992;11.5 wt % NaCl).

Computer Programs

As presented in the previous sections, the reduction and interpretation of fluid inclusion data requires both numerical and graphical techniques. Experimental fluid phase equilibrium data are scattered throughout the chemical, physical, engineering, and geological literature of the world in many languages and units of measurement. Drawing this material together and synthesizing it can be a daunting task. Sparse experimental data sets

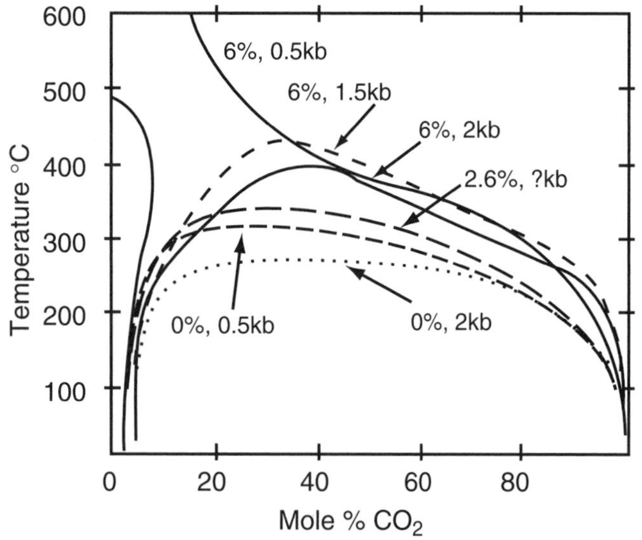

FIG. 12. Compilation of several published solvi for the system H_2O-CO_2-NaCl. The solvus moves to higher temperatures with decreasing pressure or increasing salinity. The asymmetry of the solvus becomes very pronounced at low pressures and moderate to high salt contents. 6 wt % NaCl data modified from Bowers and Helgeson (1983), 2.6 wt % NaCl from Hendel and Hollister (1981), 0 wt % NaCl lines from Tödheide and Franck (1963).

may only be presented diagramatically by their authors; in the absence of theoretical models, such data may not allow extrapolations to a wide enough range of conditions to be useful to fluid inclusionists. A variety of computer programs are available to interpret fluid inclusion data. Holloway (1981) presents a simple FORTRAN program that calculates isochores for mixtures of common gas species. Bowers and Helgeson (1983, 1985) and Nicholls and Crawford (1985) provide more involved Modified Redlich-Kwong (MRK) equations for H_2O, CO_2, H_2O-NaCl, and H_2O-CO_2-NaCl fluids. Haar et al. (1984) provide a fit for all the water data available in the mid-1980s—an equation that is still in common use today. Hall et al. (1988) provide a simple FORTRAN program to determine salinities for NaCl-KCl-H_2O inclusions from the freezing point depression. Bodnar et al. (1988) provide a more comprehensive program for this same chemical system that can handle many different combinations of microthermometric data. Naden (1996) provides a data reduction algorithm for NaCl-$CaCl_2$-H_2O fluids. Recently, Bakker (in press) has extended the formulation of Bowers and Helgeson (1983, 1985) by adding CH_4 and N_2 to the fluid mix.

Brown (1989) published a more complete fluid inclusion program (FLINCOR) designed to (1) calculate salinities, compositions, and densities from laboratory observations on fluid inclusions, (2) calculate isochores in P-T space from these fluid inclusion observations, (3) calculate isochores from hypothetical mixtures of fluids, and, importantly, (4) compare the results obtained by using well-known published equations of state commonly used to extrapolate fluid behavior and properties. This ability to reduce the same data using multiple equations of state is valuable because most published formulations only work well over restricted P-T-X ranges; there is not one comprehensive equation of state for all gas species and possible solutes. Brown and Hagemann (1994) increased the utility of FLINCOR by developing MacFlinCor, that, in addition to the four points outlined above, also (5) provides an electronic notebook designed to be used directly in the laboratory, and (6) generates interactive diagrams for those chemical systems that cannot be adequately described numerically. As mentioned in a previous section, Linkam Instruments provides a computer program with their heating-freezing stage that, in addition to providing the control environment for their stage, aspires to include the functionality of MacFlinCor and allow for complete data reduction and presentation.

Data Presentation

There are a limited variety of diagrams commonly used to report, summarize, and interpret fluid inclusion data. For hydrothermal ore fluids, plotting salinity of the ore fluid versus the homogenization temperature provides a powerful tool for identifying the roles of boiling, mixing, and cooling in the generation of a population of fluid inclusions. Figure 13, adapted from Roedder (1977, 1984), reports data from a single sample collected at the well-known and much studied Creede, Colorado, epithermal base-metal vein deposit. The interpretation here is that the primary ore fluid contained on average 8 to12 equivalent wt percent NaCl at a temperature of 240° to 270°C. Mixing with one or more cooler dilute surface waters (evidence from stable isotopes, Foley et al., 1982) is postulated to cause the spread of data to the lower left of this figure. The detailed stratigraphy in the banded sphalerite from this deposit that permitted the preparation of this figure is very unusual. Without the color banding, the remarkable consistency of data from individual time-correlative zones and the repeated mixing episodes interspersed with quiescent mineral growth would not be apparent. Boiling, that concentrates solutes in the residual liquid phase, would outline a trend upward and slightly to the left on this figure—assuming trapping of the boiled residua. As pointed out by many workers, there is in fact good evidence for boiling having occurred in the upper portions of the Creede system during some of the mineralization stages However, the vapor-rich inclusions resulting from this boiling occur in a stage different from that in which they appear in the crystal shown in Figure 13. Condensation of the evolved vapor phase could provide yet another reservoir to mix later with the ever-changing ore fluid.

Single types of observations such as ice or clathrate or daughter salt melting temperatures are usually summarized using one or more histograms. Assuming that they can be distinguished, multiple generations of fluids may be differentiated on a histogram using various symbols. For example, Figure 14a, from Thomas and Spooner (1988) shows a single peak of clathrate melting data for primary inclusions in tourmaline. Clathrate melting above +10°C is strongly supportive of the presence of CH_4. In other cases the interpretation of data histograms can be tricky.

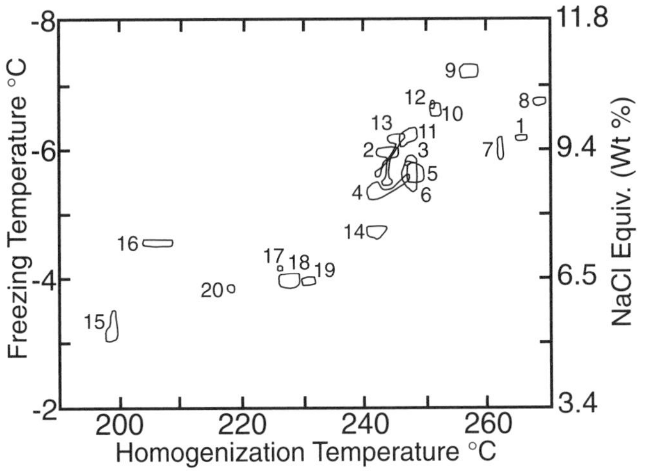

FIG. 13. Homogenization temperature plotted against freezing temperature for 221 primary inclusions in a 5-cm band of zoned sphalerite from Creede, Colorado. The numbered areas track the fluid evolution from the earliest fluid (zone 1) to the latest (zone 20). After Roedder (1977).

Figure 14b shows a skewed distribution of homogenization temperatures: how should this be interpreted? If the textural data support a single population of non-boiling inclusions, then the tail of data to the high temperature side of the peak may well document leakage or stretching of the inclusions: both of these processes result in lower density and hence higher Th. The same histogram for a population of inclusions that exhibit evidence of boiling or phase separation may be interpreted as showing evidence of heterogeneous trapping. Small but variable amounts of vapor trapped with the liquid will again lower the inclusion's bulk density causing the high temperature Th tail on the figure. The complementary vapor-rich inclusions will ideally be trapped in such samples as well, and may provide an analogous histogram if data can be gathered on these inclusions (although they are notoriously difficult to analyze). See Bodnar et al. (1985) for a more detailed discussion of fluid inclusion systematics in epithermal systems where these sorts of skewed histograms are the rule rather than the exception.

Compositions of gas-rich inclusions are commonly plotted on triangular diagrams. Figure 15 reports quadrupole mass spectrometer data for samples from the Broadlands geothermal area in New Zealand (Moore and Norman, 1996). Bulk inclusion fluids were liberated by crushing, water was separated by freezing, and the gas fraction was analyzed. Although not apparent in Figure 15, total gas contents were quite high, up to 23 percent. The locations of four fluid reservoirs are shown on the figure. The relatively wide range of N_2/Ar ratios and the variable N_2/CH_4 and CO_2/CH_4 ratios led Moore and Norman to conclude that the fluids were deeply circulating waters that scavenged upwards-fluxing magmatic volatiles. The very high gas contents are suggestive of phase separation and Figure 15b shows the calculated effects of boiling at 260°C on the gas ratios in the vapor and liquid phases.

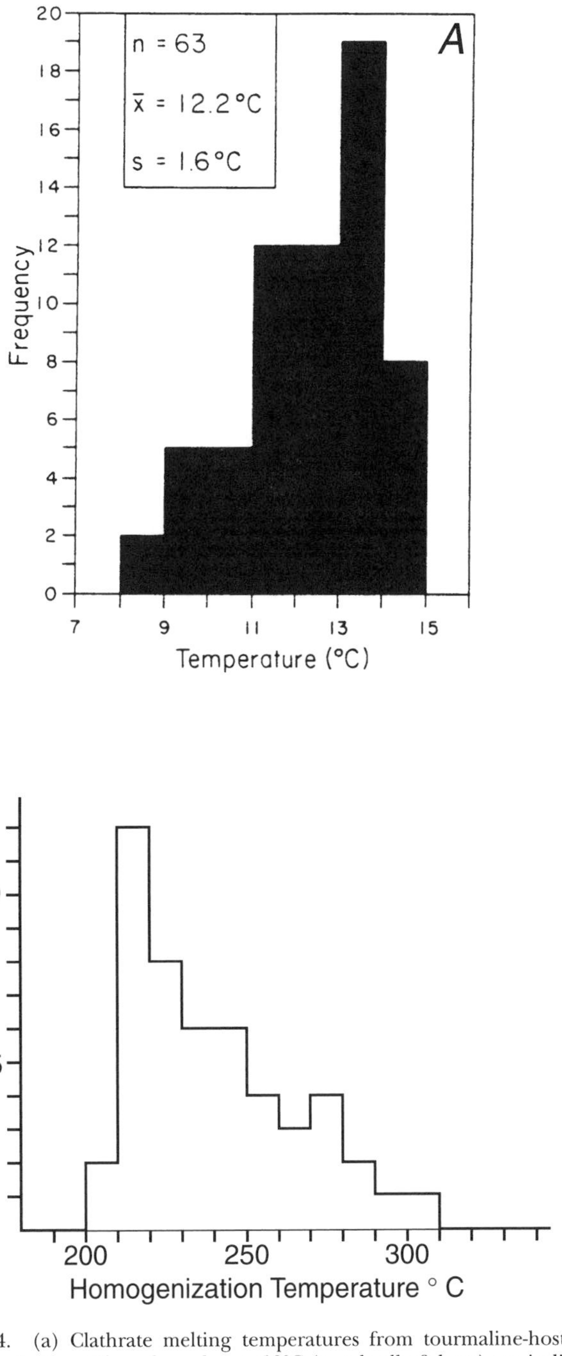

Fig. 14. (a) Clathrate melting temperatures from tourmaline-hosted fluid inclusions. The values above +10°C (nearly all of them) are indicative of the presence of methane—a conclusion supported by gas chromatography (Thomas and Spooner, 1992). (b) Skewed distribution of Th values from a hypothetical epithermal deposit.

A fluid inclusion data set is of most potential use to other scientists if it is reported in its entirety, inclusion by inclusion. This is impractical in traditional print media but some journals maintain optional data repositories. The internet provides another means to archive and access these primary data. Such archives can either be on personal worldwide web pages or better, on a site maintained by the journal or the Society that publishes a particular journal.

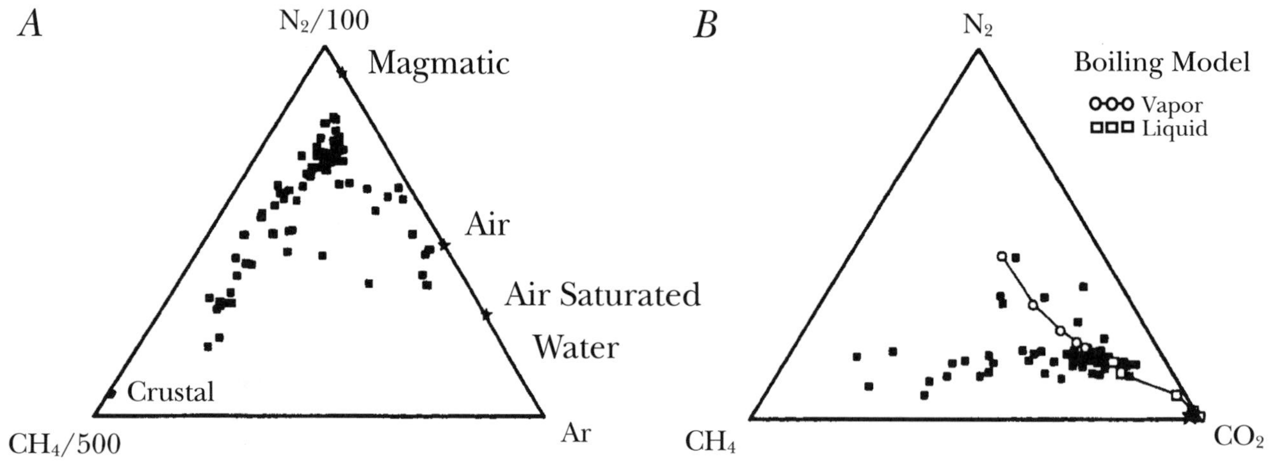

FIG. 15. Fluid inclusion gas compositions from a Broadlands, New Zealand, quartz crystal. (a) The gas ratios for air, air saturated water, and magmatic and crustal fluids are shown for comparison. (b) The calculated effects of boiling at 260°C on the evolved vapor (open circles) and coexisting liquid (open squares) are shown by the solid lines (from Moore and Norman, 1996).

Interpretation

Introduction

The fundamental cause of mineral deposition in most hydrothermal ore deposits can be traced to chemical or physical changes in the ore fluid near or at the site of deposition. These changes can be grouped under the headings of "mixing," "unmixing," "cooling," and "reaction." Each of these groups of processes may leave a relatively clear fluid inclusion record behind. In the following sections we will examine the predicted fluid inclusion characteristics of each of these mechanisms.

Metallic ore elements are invariably carried in solution as complexes—sometimes the complexing agent is fairly exotic, other times it may be very common (see Chap. 2). The stability of a gold-bisulfide complex depends on the total sulfur content, oxygen fugacity, pH and temperature of the fluid. Similarly the stability of a lead chloride complex requires a limited range of fluid salinities and temperatures. In both these cases, changes in pressure have second order effects on the longevity of a particular complex unless a reduction in pressure causes fluid unmixing. The tendency of species such as H_2S to partition into the unmixed volatile-rich phase causes the breakdown of bisulfide complexes and the deposition of the metal.

Identification of Daughter Salts

Although a very large number of solid phases have been reported from fluid inclusions, only a few are at all common. Table 2, adapted from table 3.3 in Shepherd et al. (1985), lists the five most common daughter salts and some of their distinguishing characteristics. The alkali halides NaCl and KCl are most common and their isotropic optics and cubic form serve to identify them. KCl is seldom observed as the only cubic daughter salt in an inclusion and its rounded edges distinguishes it from its usual companion and the much more common NaCl.

Anhydrite can be most readily distinguished from other prismatic, tabular, or rhombohedral crystals by its low birefringence. Although the daughter salts generally have nearly perfect crystal forms, distinguishing a rhombohedron from a monoclinic prism may be nearly impossible because of the general small size of the grains and the optical complexity caused by the presence of one or more solids, a vapor bubble, and the host cavity itself in a 50- to 150-μm-thick chip. The distinction between nahcolite and the rhombic carbonates is very difficult optically.

TABLE 2. Optical Characteristics for Common Daughter Salts

Mineral	Composition	Crystal System	Common Habit	Birefringence
Halite	NaCl	Cubic	Cube (Octahedra)	Isotropic
Sylvite	KCl	Cubic	Rounded Cube	Isotropic
Anhydrite	$CaSO_4$	Ortho-rhombic	Prismatic	Low
Nahcolite	$NaHCO_3$	Ortho-rhombic	Tabular	Very high
Rhombic Ca/Mg Carbonates	$(Ca,Mg)CO_3$	Trigonal	Rhombohedral	Very high

Upon heating, halite and sylvite commonly will dissolve quite readily while the other salts listed (as well as any oxides, sulfides, and silicates present in the inclusions) may persist in inclusions to temperatures well above those reasonable for the geologic setting of the sample. Four possible causes of this behavior must be considered and evaluated: accidental trapping of solids, kinetic metastability, and physical and chemical changes in the inclusion. Of these, chemical changes are the most interesting and problematic geologically.

Three clues may serve to distinguish accidentally trapped crystals from true daughter salts: inconsistent phase ratios in families of inclusions; unreasonably large crystals implying impossible solubilities (e.g., Plate 1; Roedder, 1972); and/or similar phases occurring as trapped solid-only inclusions in the host mineral. True daughter salts may well dissolve very slowly and *metastability* can be a serious problem. Holding a fluid inclusion chip at high temperatures in the stage or an oven for days or weeks is generally not practical but may be necessary to cause dissolution of carbonates. *Physical changes* such as necking down of an inclusion, or partial decrepitation or leakage of an inclusion subsequent to its trapping, likely invalidates any compositional or P-V-T data gathered in the laboratory (although identifying any trapped solid is still instructive). Cryptic *chemical changes*, such as oxidation or reduction, can cause the precipitation of daughter minerals or, by changing the chemistry of the inclusion fluid, prevent their dissolution during microthermometry. There is no doubt that hydrogen can quite readily pass through minerals over geologic time. Thus a grain boundary fluid either substantially more reduced or oxidized than previously trapped fluid inclusions can provide a chemical potential source or sink of hydrogen. Mavrogenes and Bodnar (1994) studied some natural chalcopyrite-bearing inclusions from Red Mountain, Arizona, in which the chalcopyrite does not dissolve during heating. Subjecting the samples to elevated hydrogen pressures at 600°C and 2.5 kbars for a week caused the chalcopyrite crystals to be dissolved easily upon subsequent heating. Repeated homogenization attempts on the hydrogen-enriched (as confirmed by Raman analyses) inclusions resulted in higher Tm_{Cpy} in each successive run as the hydrogen diffused back out of the inclusions during the microthermometric analysis. Hall et al. (1991) showed that some peak metamorphic inclusions from the Ducktown, Tennessee, massive sulfide deposit have chemical and isotopic compositions consistent with post-entrapment diffusion of hydrogen into the inclusion. In another experimental study, Morgan et al. (1993) document hydrogen diffusion through quartz and olivine leading to chemical speciation changes in the trapped fluids. There are additional natural examples of sulfides, hematite, and magnetite daughter salts that are best interpreted as resulting from non-reversible changes in the chemistry of individual inclusions due to hydrogen diffusion. Finally, work on inclusions in lode-gold deposits from the Southern Cross greenstone belt, Western Australia (Bloem and Brown, 1991; Hagemann and Brown, 1996; Ridley and Hagemann, in press), suggests that the current speciation of C-O-H fluids observed in amphibolite-facies gold deposits can be reconciled with peak metamorphic conditions by considering both changes during post-peak retrograde metamorphism and hydrogen diffusion at peak conditions.

Pressure Determinations

Roedder and Bodnar (1980) discuss the determination of pressures using fluid inclusion studies—this reference serves as a comprehensive resource to begin understanding this often misunderstood and abused aspect of fluid inclusion interpretation. They list six broadly different approaches to using fluid inclusions for geobarometry. Pressure may be constrained by considering (1) the vapor pressure of the solution, (2) a comparison of Th with an independent geothermometer, (3) the simultaneous trapping of two immiscible fluids, (4) the simultaneous trapping of two partly immiscible fluids, (5) the trapping of boiling fluids, and (6) inclusions containing daughter minerals. All of these approaches have been applied at one time or another to various hydrothermal ore deposits. Hagemann and Brown (1996) review these criteria in the context of Archean lode-gold deposits and conclude that constraint (4) is most likely applicable to hydrothermal fluids in the mid-crust. Clearly epithermal or geothermal settings are likely to be explicable using techniques/criteria (1), (4), and (5).

It should be recognized that many pressure determinations for hydrothermal ore deposits published in the literature are flawed or are over-optimistically precise. It takes both a rare set of geological parameters and a fortuitous collection of fluid inclusions to constrain pressures at the time of trapping closely and convincingly.

Fluid inclusion studies of shallow geothermal and epithermal systems commonly utilize arguments about both the vapor pressure of gases in solution (such as CO_2 and H_2S) and the P-T path of the boiling curve for the host fluid. Simmons and Browne (1997) report some measurements on fluid inclusions in rare sphalerite crystals from the Broadlands geothermal system, New Zealand. Unlike nearly all reported salinities for geothermal fluids from Broadlands (which are very low), these sphalerite-hosted inclusions have salinities from 6 to more than 20 wt percent NaCl equivalent. Simmons and Browne point out that the measured Th values are very close to the calculated boiling point for depth (BPD) temperature and thus boiling to near dryness is the best explanation for the origin of these high salinity inclusions. The alternative explanation of an input of saline magmatic fluids is not supported by any of the evidence surrounding the active geothermal system (they also caution that were the same inclusions observed in an epithermal ore deposit, the "exotic magmatic fluid" explanation might seem more reasonable and be adopted).

Moore et al. (1992) provide a detailed discussion of the formation and distribution of CO_2-enriched fluids in an epithermal setting with their study of the Zunil and Los Azufres geothermal systems. This paper compares the current chemical, mineralogical, and thermal structure of the geothermal systems with the record preserved in their fluid inclusions. Interpretation of the observed freezing point data for these inclusions (melting a few degrees above and below 0°C), requires a detailed understanding of CO_2 clathrate equilibria and the competing effects of NaCl and CO_2 on the freezing point of water (see Fig. 2 in Hedenquist and Henley, 1985). In the absence of analyses of the present day geothermal fluids and actual down-hole P-T measurements, interpretation of the fluid inclusions as they might be presented in an epithermal ore deposit would be equivocal. Their data document transient variations in gas contents of the reservoirs to depths of at least 2 km. Calculated pressures and temperatures of the inclusions are consistent with their depth of formation, and the operation of both boiling and mixing processes at work in the reservoirs. The CO_2 contents of the inclusions require greater than hydrostatic pressures and thus provide some insight into the tectonic regime attending fluid evolution.

Inclusions trapped from an ore fluid undergoing *boiling* (or effervescence or unmixing) will homogenize in the laboratory at the temperature of trapping assuming that individual inclusions trap either only liquid or only vapor. Data scattering to higher temperatures may be due to trapping of mixtures of vapor and liquid (see above). Thus, homogenization temperatures may be used directly as trapping temperatures without making a "pressure correction," even without knowing *anything* about the composition of the inclusions. To constrain the pressure of this boiling system,however, requires extensive knowledge of what is in the inclusions and appropriate experimental (or theoretical) PVTX studies. The L-V curves and solvii for most fluid compositions in hydrothermal ore deposits are reasonably well known for upper crustal conditions. Thus, pressure determinations in unmixing hydrothermal systems hinge on constraining the fluid inclusion compositions.

Inclusions trapped from an ore fluid precipitating ore and gangue minerals due to *fluid-wall rock reactions* do not directly fix either the temperature or pressure of trapping. As discussed above, the homogenization temperature of such inclusions at best provides the lower end of an isochore along which the inclusion was trapped. To determine where this isochore starts requires compositional information, usually gleaned from low temperature equilibria. Our knowledge of the P-T track of the isochore relies again on experimental PVTX data. Independent pressure (or more likely temperature) data are required to determine how far out along the isochore actual trapping occurred—this is the origin of the "pressure correction" so often referred to in the literature. Stratigraphic reconstruction or silicate phase geobarometry may provide independent pressure data; stable isotopes, mineral stability, or geothermometric analysis may provide much needed independent temperature data.

Boiling and Immiscibility

"If a system containing several homogeneous phases is in equilibrium, i.e., if internal equilibrium is realized for every phase and if all phases are in equilibrium with each other, then we shall say that these phases are immiscible. For instance, two coexisting phases of given compositions are said to be immiscible if their association defines a state of equilibrium at the specified T-P conditions." (Pichavant et al., 1982, p. 4). Starting with this definition, we see that "immiscibility" is equivalent to a stable mechanical mixture of fluids in contrast to a "chemical mixture" or "solution." Boiling is the special case of immiscibility in which both phases have the same chemical composition. So what are the conditions that lead to this situation and how might they be manifested in the fluid inclusion record preserved in a sample? To answer this question we must have a solid understanding of the phase equilibria of immiscibility.

Three constraints for immiscibility follow from the above definition (Pichavant et al., 1982):

1. The system must be at equilibrium with all the phases at the same pressure and temperature.

2. When the immiscible phases have different compositions (which is the usual case), these compositions are related to one another by the principles of chemical equilibrium.

3. The molar volumes of the immiscible phases are different but they are related to each other.

This can all be stated rigorously in terms of the phase rule which allows the number of independent observations required to characterize a system to be stipulated. If extra observations can be made, this will strengthen the conclusions reached. This is a luxury that seldom presents itself to the fluid inclusion researcher.

The chemical system C-O-H-N-S-electrolytes would cover essentially all geological environments. However, as we have seen above, we can approximate most settings using simpler systems such as C-O-H-NaCl or even simpler ones such as H_2O-NaCl, H_2O-CO_2, CO_2-CH_4, or H_2O-CO_2-NaCl. The first three of these simplest systems can be treated reasonably well as binary systems. These binary systems will have two divariant immiscibility surfaces ("boiling" surface and "dew" surface) that relate the compositions to temperature and pressure. These surfaces join each other along the phase transition (boiling) curves of the pure end members or along a critical curve in a binary system. Most of the figures presented in the first part of this paper are 2-D slices through the 3D P-T-X space occupied by one of these binary systems. These results can be directly extended to a ternary system that contains either a solid buffer and two fluids or three immiscible fluids (one additional constraint as required by the phase rule).

Because fluid inclusions are usually considered to have fixed bulk volume and bulk composition after trapping, rigorous application of the phase rule to these isochoric-isoplethic systems can take advantage of the following:

1. Because volume fractions can be estimated for each phase present, these can help characterize the system.

2. On a T-P section for a given composition, any isopleth-isochoric path is represented by one univariant line; for a homogeneous fluid such a line is called an isochore (Figs. 1, 6, and 8).

3. Isochores are unique and intersect phase boundaries at unique points. Conversely, two different points on a phase boundary must correspond to systems with different compositions (Fig. 3) and/or different densities (Fig. 7).

4. Any isochore cannot intercept a phase boundary more than once.

The limits on rigorous application of the phase rule to natural fluids trapped in inclusions are those (1) due to the fundamental nature of the inclusions themselves, (2) due to multiple generations of inclusions, and (3) due to the quantitative information available. *Individual inclusions* are subject to necking-down, leakage, natural decrepitation, and reactions with their host mineral leading to volume or compositional changes; in addition, they may have been heterogeneously trapped. *Multiple generations* of inclusions are especially problematic for deposits where immiscibility is suspected because in the absence of clear cross-cutting trails of inclusions, the confident assignment of cogenetic trapping or primary and secondary origins may be impossible. If these problems are not enough, gathering the quantitative information itself is problematic. Making good volume fraction estimates in an irregular 3-D inclusion is an art not easily learned. Phase transition temperatures need to be accurately measured and where possible, direct compositional analysis can be invaluable (Shepherd and Rankin, 1998) Finally, incomplete experimental data are available for even the simplistic binary systems, let alone natural fluids.

Let's review what happens during heating of an inclusion. With increasing temperature, the number of phases decreases and final, bulk homogenization occurs by either L-V homogenization or melting of a solid at a point on the corresponding phase boundary. From this point in P-T space, an isochore originates which never again intersects the same phase boundary; this point and isochore are characteristic of the composition and density of the fluid. Assuming homogeneous trapping, the fluid could have been trapped anywhere along the isochore, above the homogenization pressure and temperature. From observation of a single inclusion, there is theoretically no way to prove trapping at the point of origin of the isochore; we need other information. If immiscibility is suspected during trapping, then the true trapping temperature (Tt) (and pressure) are obtained during heating (although the pressure can't be directly measured). In the case of heterogeneous trapping, Tt ≤ Th. The coexistence of different types of inclusions can be used as evidence of unmixing if one can demonstrate close proximity of the two types and contemporaneity of trapping. In addition, as so well described by Ramboz et al. (1982), $Th_L \approx Th_V$ is a necessary but not sufficient condition for evidence of immiscibility. If the inclusions decrepitate prior to homogenizing, the decrepitation behaviors should be similar unless sizes and shapes of the liquid-rich and the vapor-rich inclusions are greatly different.

Intersecting isochores are commonly pointed to as evidence for immiscibility. In fact the intersection point commonly has no special significance or may in fact provide evidence for mixing of two different fluids (Roedder and Bodnar, 1980). If Th is less than the temperature of intersection, immiscible trapping is not possible. One can argue that homogenization to the vapor phase, being hard to see, could actually be in the correct temperature range. However, the maximum Th possible in the H_2O-CO_2 system (±NaCl) is in the 250° to 400°C range, much lower than the temperatures commonly proposed by using the intersecting isochore method. Also, the homogenization to the liquid of the brines is easily observed and is nearly always lower than temperature of intersection. Crosscutting isochores on a PT projection may therefore, have no special significance.

On the other hand, if the inclusions yielding the intersecting isochores are contemporaneous, they may be indicating the opposite of unmixing: i.e., mixing of fluids, with the intersection giving the P-T of the event. Mixing results in fluids with intermediate compositions and densities and should not be confused with heterogeneous trapping of stably immiscible fluids.

Whereas heterogeneous trapping is the bane of a tight, single-peak Th histogram, it can be very simple and good evidence of immiscibility. The population of interest should exhibit evidence of simultaneous trapping and histograms should show scattered densities, degrees of filling, and bulk compositions and therefore homogenization temperatures. The true trapping temperature is less than the measured Th and the Th histograms should be skewed toward high temperatures and should be similar for both the liquid- and vapor-rich populations.

A number of general conclusions can be drawn from the foregoing discussion.

1. The geometry of phase equilibria obeys rules.
2. If solids are present in an inclusion and the fluid is one phase of an unmixed fluid, then $Tm_{salt} \leq Th_{L\text{-}V}$ barring kinetic effects that keep the salt from dissolving.
3. Because an isochore can never again intersect the boundary on which it originated, a fluid inclusion can't unmix, upon further heating, once it has homogenized. An inclusion that does behave this way has probably leaked during heating and thus has lost internal pressure.
4. Th_L should equal Th_V for pairs of trapped immiscible fluids.
5. Unmixing leads to fluids with contrasting, but related, density and composition.
6. Mixing must be distinguished from unmixing.

An Exercise

The following photographs, sketches, and data have been taken from one of the classic fluid inclusion studies published in the literature. The reference for this study is given at the end of this section where the original authors' interpretation for the data is reprised. The data are given here as an exercise for the reader—using the discussion and some of the figures presented above, your mission, should you decide to accept it, is to interpret this data set and answer the leading questions interspersed below.

Questions

The paragenetically earliest mineralization is associated with open-space-filling quartz crystals that preserve beautiful large primary inclusions (Fig. 16). There are two ways to arrive at an estimate of the total salinity of this inclusion.

1. The measured melting temperature of the large halite cube is 400°C. Using equation (7.4), what is the salinity of this inclusion?
2. Knowing the salinity of a saturated NaCl solution (Fig. 2) and adding the estimated amount of NaCl in the large cube, you can determine a rough salinity without doing any microthermometry. Try this method.

3. What are the largest sources of uncertainty in each of these estimates?

4. Following halite dissolution, this inclusion underwent final homogenization at 430°C (the other daughter salts had also dissolved); would you predict that an inclusion that looked like this one would homogenize to the liquid or to the vapor? Why?

5. If you froze this inclusion, over what temperature range might you reasonably expect to see first melting (there is no evidence for CO_2 in this inclusion)? What observations should go into your answer?

Individual deposits in the district vary from one another but contain systematic trends in both Th and salinity. Figure 17 shows some primary fluid inclusions from early sphalerite in a different deposit from that shown in Figure 16. Freezing point depressions for inclusions of this generation cluster around −3.2°C with $Th_{L\text{-}V(L)}$ around 230°C.

6. Using equation (7.2), what is the salinity of this fluid?

A paragenetically early sample from a near-by deposit is shown in Figure 18. Both of the labeled inclusions in this isolated cluster homogenize at roughly 425°C. Samples such as this are relatively rare and are found only in a vertically restricted zone, close to the surface, and usually associated with high-grade ore.

7. In which inclusion would you predict the homogenization was more difficult to observe?

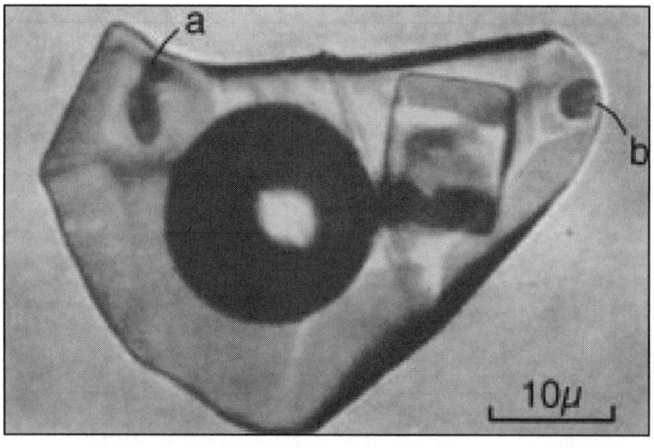

FIG. 16. Large primary inclusion containing a vapor bubble, large halite cube and two unidentified daughter minerals (a and b).

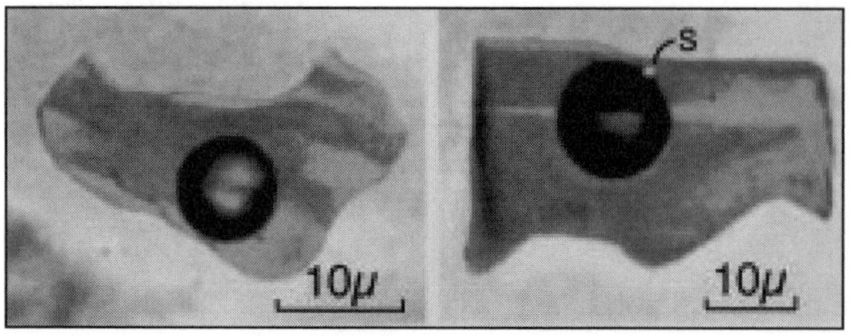

FIG. 17. Two inclusions in early fluorite. The photo on the right also shows a small unidentified daughter mineral.

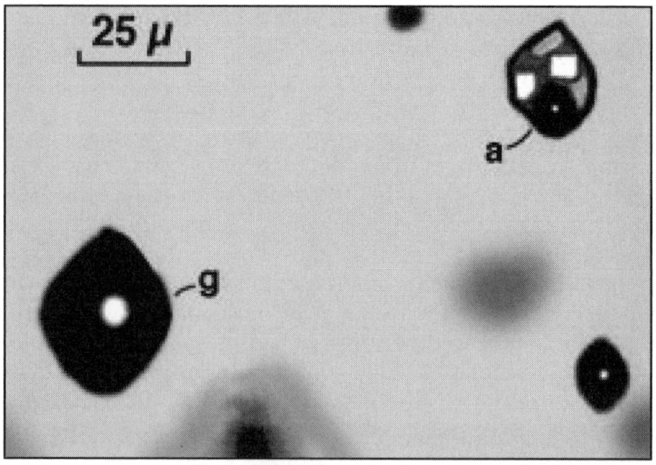

FIG. 18. Gas-rich and salt-bearing inclusions coexisting in early quartz crystal.

8. Which criteria for boiling are satisfied here? What techniques are available to further analyze and thus confirm the assignment of these inclusion fluids to a boiling system?

9. What does the high-grade ore association with these inclusion types tell us about (at least one of) the likely ore deposition mechanisms?

Figure 19 shows a small opaque daughter mineral that responds to a magnet at room temperature but loses its magnetic properties at 578°C and which does not dissolve (unlike all the other daughter salts) upon heating.

10. What mineral is this?

11. What are two possible interpretations of the inability to redissolve this phase? How can you test your hypotheses?

Finally, careful study of inclusions containing up to 8 daughter salts show that most of the daughters dissolve shortly before $Th_{L\text{-}V}$ and the rest (save the opaque one) dissolve very soon after $Th_{L\text{-}V}$.

12. Is this observation consistent with essentially saturated boiling fluids or the mixing of two fluids—one carrying the ore elements while the other delivers sulfur to the site of deposition? Explain your answer.

Answers

The preceding example is taken from Kelly and Turneaure's 1970 study of 53 tin-tungsten deposits in Bolivia. Their fluid inclusion study showed systematic trends of salinity and depositional temperatures across the district with the low-CO_2 fluid inclusions recording temperatures as high as 530°C in early and as low as 70°C in the latest stages.

1. Salinities ranged from 46 equivalent wt percent (Fig. 16) to essentially fresh water in the closing stages of mineralization.

2. Figure 2 shows that the saturated liquid should contain ~23 wt percent NaCl. The vapor phase will contain essentially no NaCl. The halite cube occupies roughly 10 percent of the non-vapor portion of this inclusion (see Degree of Fill estimation figure in Appendix II of

Shepherd et al., 1985). The density of halite is 2.16 g/cc so the bulk salinity of this inclusion is roughly:

$$\text{salinity (wt \%)} = (0.9\ (23\ \text{wt \%}) + (0.1\ (216\ \text{wt \%}) = 42.3\ \text{wt \%}$$

3. The only significant uncertainty in 1. is the assumption that we can ignore the other components in this inclusion; the analytical uncertainty is negligible. There are many uncertainties about method 2., most of which hinge on interpreting 3D volumes from imperfect 2D cross sections.

4. An inclusion containing this much dissolved matter and a relatively small vapor bubble will almost certainly homogenize to the liquid by vapor disappearance.

5. The presence of two additional daughter salts requires that the fluid be saturated in several other components, and therefore the eutectic temperature is almost certainly going to be depressed well below the –21.2°C that should be observed for pure NaCl-H_2O solutions (see Table 1).

6. The second fluid shown in Fig. 17 has an average salinity close to 5 equiv. wt percent NaCl.

7. Homogenization is always difficult to observe when the vapor phase is expanding at the expense of the liquid. Thus, the value for the left-hand inclusion in Figure 18 may only be a best guess based on careful observation and experience.

8. Most of the hypogene mineralization can be attributed to cooling of the ore fluids, but evidence for active boiling is preserved in some of the samples (Fig.18) recovered from a vertically restricted zone of high-grade cassiterite ore in a number of the mines. This pair of inclusions appears to satisfy the requirement that they are contemporaneously trapped, and furthermore, that they represent chemically distinct but related compositions—the liquid-rich one is solute-rich whereas the vapor inclusion is proportionately solute-poor. Finally, because they both apparently homogenize in the same temperature range, they may have coexisted in time and space. All these are necessary but not sufficient conditions for "proving" that boiling took place—taken in aggregate, the evidence is quite strong. To further prove this conclusion, direct destructive or non-destructive techniques of analysis should be brought to bear on these inclusions in order to define more completely their compositions and compare these data to experimental results for the appropriate chemical systems.

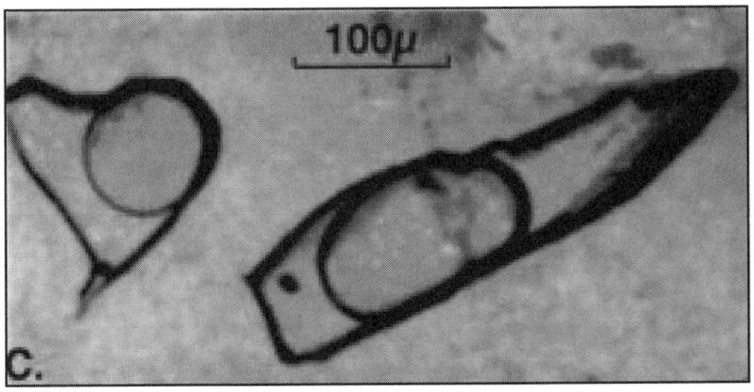

FIG. 19. Primary inclusions containing small opaque daughter minerals. The black crystals do not dissolve during heating runs.

9. As discussed in several sections above, boiling is a very good trigger for ore deposition due to the removal into the vapor phase of volatile species (such as the sulfur compounds) that are commonly involved in complexing transition metals in hydrothermal fluids.

10./11. The small crystals of magnetite (Fig. 19) that refuse to dissolve upon heating are thought to document hydrogen leakage and/or oxidation of the inclusion fluid—an explanation similar to that given by Mavrogenes and Bodnar (1994) for the Red Mountain chalcopyrite daughter crystals.

12. The dissolution of most daughter minerals at temperatures very close to Th were interpreted to be supportive of boiling of a single fluid and indicative of near saturation with respect to all the observed daughter phases. The inclusion data coupled with the field and mineralogical data support a single prolonged mineralizing event where the paragenesis can be explained in terms of decreasing temperature with time.

Acknowledgments

I would like to thank in particular Steffen Hagemann for his continued enthusiasm for fluid inclusions as a valuable geochemical tool—our discussions are always far reaching. I would like to thank Doug Crowe, Jon Naden, and Jeremy Richards for reviews of an earlier version of this manuscript. I only wish I had time to implement more of their fine ideas. The remaining errors and shortcomings are the responsibility of the author. Support for this study was provided by the National Science Foundation (EAR 94-06683 and EAR 95-08257) and the Graduate School at the University of Wisconsin-Madison.

REFERENCES

Bakker, R.J., 1998, Adaptation of the Bowers and Helgeson (1983) equation of state to the H_2O-CO_2-CH_4-N_2-NaCl system: Chemical Geology, in press.

Bloem, E.J.M., and Brown, P.E., 1991, Fluid inclusion evidence from amphibolite facies lode gold deposits: Variations on the greenschist theme: Geological Society of America Abstracts with Programs, v. 23, A173–174.

Bodnar, R.J., 1993, Revised equation and table for determining the freezing point depression of H_2O-NaCl solutions: Geochimica et Cosmochimica Acta, v. 57, p. 683–684.

Bodnar, R.J., and Vityk, M.O., 1994, Interpretation of microthermometric data for H_2O-NaCl fluid inclusions, *in* De Vivo, B. and Frezzotti, M.L., eds., Fluid Inclusions in Minerals: Methods and Applications: Virginia Polytechnic Institute and State University Press, p. 117–130.

Bodnar, R.J., Reynolds, T.J., and Kuehn, C.A., 1985, Fluid inclusion systematics in epithermal systems, *in* Berger, B.R., and Bethke, P.M., eds., Geology and geochemistry of epithermal systems: Reviews in Economic Geology, v. 2, p. 73–97.

Bodnar, R.J., Sterner, S.M., and Hall, D.L., 1988, Salty: A Fortran program to calculate compositions of fluid inclusions in the system NaCl-KCl-H_2O: Computers and Geosciences, v. 15, p. 19–41.

Bottinga, Y., and Richet, P., 1981, High pressure and temperature equation of state and calculation of the thermodynamic properties of gaseous carbon dioxide: American Journal of Science, v. 281, p. 615–660.

Bowers, T.S., and Helgeson, H.C., 1983, Calculation of the thermodynamic and geochemical consequences of nonideal mixing in the system H_2O-CO_2-NaCl on phase relations in geologic systems: Equation of state for H_2O-CO_2-NaCl fluids at high pressures and temperatures: Geochimica et Cosmochimica Acta, v. 47, p. 1247–1275.

—— 1985, FORTRAN programs for generating fluid inclusion isochores and fugacity coefficients for the system H_2O-CO_2-NaCl at high pressures and temperatures: Computers and Geosciences, v. 11, p. 203–213.

Brown, P.E., 1989, FLINCOR: A microcomputer program for the reduction and investigation of fluid inclusion data: American Mineralogist, v. 74, p. 1390–1393.

Brown, P.E., and Hagemann, S.G., 1994, MacFlinCor: A computer program for fluid inclusion data reduction and manipulation, *in* De Vivo, B., and Frezzotti, M.L., eds., Fluid Inclusions in Minerals: Methods and Applications: Virginia Polytechnic Institute and State University Press Press, p. 231–250.

Brown, P.E., and Lamb, W.M., 1989, P-V-T properties of fluids in the system H_2O-CO_2-NaCl: New graphical presentations and implications for fluid inclusion studies: Geochimica et Cosmochimica Acta, v. 53, p. 1209–1221.

Burruss, R.C., 1981a, Analysis of fluid inclusions: phase equilibria at constant volume: American Journal of Science, v. 281, p. 1104–1126.

—— 1981b, Analysis of phase equilibria in C-O-H-S fluid inclusions, *in* Hollister, L.S., and Crawford, M.L., eds., MAC Short Course in Fluid Inclusions: Mineralogical Association of Canada, v. 6, p. 39–74.

Cloke, P.L., and Kesler, S.E., 1979, The halite trend in hydrothermal solutions: Economic Geology, v. 74, p. 1823–1831.

Crawford, M.L., 1981, Phase equilibria in aqueous fluid inclusions, *in* Hollister, L.S., and Crawford, M.L., eds., MAC Short Course in Fluid Inclusions: Mineralogical Association of Canada, v. 6, p. 75–100.

Diamond, L.W., 1992, Stability of CO_2 clathrate hydrate + CO_2 liquid + CO_2 vapour + aqueous KCl-NaCl solutions: Experimental determination and application to salinity estimates of fluid inclusions: Geochimica et Cosmochimica Acta, v. 56, p. 273–280.

—— 1994, Introduction to pase relations of CO_2-H_2O fluid inclusions, *in* De Vivo, B., and Frezzotti, M.L., eds., Fluid Inclusions in Minerals: Methods and Applications: Virginia Polytechnic Institute and State University Press, p. 131–158.

Donnelly, H.G., and Katz, D.L., 1954, Phase equilibria in the carbon dioxide-methane system: Industrial and Engineering Chemistry, v. 46, p. 511–517.

Duan, Z., Moeller, N., and Weare, J.H., 1995, Equation of state for the NaCl-H_2O-CO_2 system: Prediction of phase equilibria and volumetric properties: Geochimica et Cosmochimica Acta, v. 59, p. 2869–2882.

Foley, N.K., Bethke, P.M., and Rye, R.O., 1982, A re-interpretation of δDH_2O values of inclusion fluids in quartz from shallow ore bodies [abs.]: Geological Society of America Abstracts with Programs, v. 15, p. 489–490.

Frantz, J.D., Popp, R.K., and Hoering, T.C., 1992, The compositional limits of fluid immiscibility in the system H_2O-NaCl-CO_2 as determined with the use of synthetic fluid inclusions in conjunction with mass spectrometry: Chemical Geology, v. 98, p. 237–255.

Goldstein, R.H., and Reynolds, T.J., 1994, Systematics of fluid inclusions in diagenetic minerals: SEPM Short Course, v. 31, 199 p.

Haar, L., Gallagher, J.S., and Kell, G.S., 1984, NBS/NRC Steam Tables. Thermodynamic and transport properties and computer programs for vapor and liquid states of water in SI units: Washington D.C., Hemisphere Publishing Corp., 320 p.

Hagemann, S.G., and Brown, P.E., 1996, Geobarometry in Archean lode-gold deposits: European Journal of Mineralogy, v. 8, p. 937–960.

Hall, D.L., and Bodnar, R.J., 1990, Methane in fluid inclusions from granulites: A product of hydrogen diffusion?: Geochimica et Cosmochimica Acta, v. 54, p. 641–651.

Hall, D.L., Sterner, S.M., and Bodnar, R.J., 1988, Freezing point depression of NaCl-KCl-H_2O solutions: Economic Geology, v. 83, p. 197–202.

Hall, D.L., Bodnar, R.J., and Craig, J.R., 1991, Evidence for postentrapment diffusion of hydrogen into peak metamorphic fluid inclusions from the massive sulfide deposits at Ducktown, Tennessee: American Mineralogist, v. 76, p. 1344–1355.

Haynes, F.M., 1985, Determination of fluid inclusion compositions by sequential freezing: Economic Geology, v. 80, p. 1436–1439.

Hedenquist, J.W., and Henley, R.W., 1985, The importance of CO_2 on freezing point measurements of fluid inclusions: Evidence from active geothermal systems and implications for epithermal ore deposition: Economic Geology, v. 80, p. 1379–1406.

Hendel, E.M., and Hollister, L.S., 1981, An empirical solvus for CO_2-H_2O-2.6 wt% salt: Geochimica et Cosmochimica Acta, v. 45, p. 225–228.

Hollister, L.S., 1990, Enrichment of CO_2 in fluid inclusions in quartz by removal of H_2O during crystal-plastic deformation: Journal of Structural Geology, v. 12, p. 895–901.

Hollister, L.S., and Burruss, R.C., 1976, Phase equilibria in fluid inclusions from the Khtada Lake metamorphic complex: Geochimica et Cosmochimica Acta, v. 40, p. 163–175.

Holloway, J.R., 1977, Fugacity and activity of molecular species in supercritical fluids, *in* Fraser, D.G., ed., Thermodynamics in geology: Boston, Reidel Publishing Co., p.161–181.

—— 1981, Compositions and volumes of supercritical fluids in the Earth's crust, *in* Hollister, L.S., and Crawford, M.L., eds., MAC Short Course in Fluid Inclusions: Mineralogical Association of Canada, v. 6, p. 13–38.

Jacobs, G.K., and Kerrick, D.M., 1981, Methane: an equation of state with application to the ternary system H_2O-CO_2-CH_4: Geochimica et Cosmochimica Acta, v. 45, p. 607–614.

Kelly, W.C., and Turneaure, F.S., 1970, Mineralogy, paragenesis and geothermometry of the tin and tungsten deposits of the Eastern Andes, Bolivia: Economic Geology, v. 65, p. 609–680.

Kerkhof, A.M. van den, and Thiéry, R., 1994, Phase transitions and density calculations in the CO_2-CH_4-N_2 system, *in* De Vivo, B., and Frezzotti, M.L., eds., Fluid Inclusions in Minerals: Methods and Applications: Virginia Polytechnic Institute and State University Press, p. 171–190.

Kerrick, D.M., and Jacobs, G.K., 1981, A modified Redlich-Kwong equation for H_2O, CO_2 and H_2O-CO_2 mixtures at elevated pressures and temperatures: American Journal of Science, v. 281, p. 735–767.

Lamb, W.M., and Valley, J.W., 1985, C-O-H fluid calculations and granulite genesis, *in* Tobi, A.C., and Touret, J.L.R., eds., The deep Proterozoic crust in the North Atlantic provinces: Boston, Reidel Publishing Co., p. 119–131.

Mader, U.K., and Burman, R.G., 1991, An equation of state for carbon dioxide to high pressure and temperature: American Mineralogist, v. 76, p. 1547–1559.

Mavrogenes, J.A., and Bodnar, R.J., 1994, Hydrogen movement into and out of fluid inclusions in quartz: Experimental evidence and geological implications: Geochimica et Cosmochimica Acta, v. 58, p. 141–148.

Moore, J.N., and Norman, D.I., 1996, Fluid inclusion gas analyses in active geothermal systems: Examples from liquid- and vapor-dominated fields [abs.]: Sixth Biennial Pan-American Conference on Research on Fluid Inclusions, Madison, Wisconsin, Program with Abstracts, p. 92–94.

Moore, J.N., Adams, M.C., and Lemieux, M.M., 1992, The formation and distribution of CO_2-enriched fluid inclusions in epithermal environments: Geochimica et Cosmochimica Acta, v. 56, p. 121–135.

Morgan, G.B., Chou, I.M., Pasteris, J.D., and Olsen, S.N., 1993, Re-equilibration of CO_2 fluid inclusions at controlled hydrogen fugacities: Journal of Metamorphic Geology, v. 11, p. 155–164.

Naden, J., 1996, CalcicBrine: a Microsoft Excel 5.0 add-in for calculating salinities from microthermometric data in the system NaCl-$CaCl_2$-H_2O [abs.]: Sixth Biennial Pan-American Conference on Research on Fluid Inclusions, Madison, Wisconsin, Program with Abstracts, p. 97–98.

Nicholls, J., and Crawford, M.L., 1985, FORTRAN programs for calculation of fluid properties from microthermometric data on fluid inclusions: Computers and Geosciences, v. 11, p. 619–645.

Oakes, C.S., Bodnar, R.J., and Simonson, J.M., 1990, The system NaCl-$CaCl_2$-H_2O: I. The ice liquidus at 1 atm total pressure: Geochimica et Cosmochimica Acta, v. 54, p. 603–610.

Parry, W.T., 1986, Estimation of XCO_2, P and fluid inclusion volume from fluid inclusion temperature measurements in the system NaCl-CO_2-H_2O: Economic Geology, v. 81, p. 1009–1013.

Pichavant, M., Ramboz, C., and Weisbrod, A., 1982, Fluid immiscibility in natural processes: Use and misuse: I. Phase equilibria analysis—A theoretical and geometrical approach: Chemical Geology, v. 37, p. 1–27.

Potter, R.W., 1977, Pressure corrections for fluid-inclusion homogenization temperatures based on the volumetric properties of the system $NaCl-H_2O$: Journal of Research of the U.S. Geological Survey, v. 5, p. 603–607.

Potter, R.W., Clynne, M.A., and Brown, D.L., 1978, Freezing point depression of aqueous sodium solutions: Economic Geology, v. 73, p. 284–285.

Ramboz, C., Pichavant, M., and Weisbrod, A., 1982, Fluid immiscibility in natural processes: Use and misuse of fluid inclusion data: II. Interpretation of fluid inclusion data in terms of immiscibility, *in* Kreulen, R., and Touret, J., eds., Current research of fluid inclusions: Chemical Geology, v. 37, p. 29–48.

Redlich, O., and Kwong, J.N.S., 1949, On the thermodynamics of solutions: V. An equation of state. Fugacities of gaseous solutions: Chemical Review, v. 44, p. 233–244.

Ridley, J.R., and Hagemann, S.G., in press, Interpretation of post-entrapment fluid inclusion re-equilibration at the Three-Mile Hill, Marvel Loch and Griffins Find high-temperature lode-gold deposits, Yilgarn Block, Western Australia: Chemical Geology.

Roedder, E., 1967, Fluid inclusions as samples of ore fluids, *in* Barnes, H.L., ed., Geochemistry of hydrothermal ore deposits—first edition: New York, Holt, Rinehart and Winston, p. 515–574.

—— 1972, Composition of fluid inclusions: U.S. Geological Survey Professional Paper, v. 440-JJ, 164 p.

—— 1977, Changes in ore fluid with time from fluid inclusion studies at Creede, Colorado: 4th IAGOD Symposium, Varna, v. 11, p. 179–185.

—— 1984, Fluid inclusions: Reviews in Mineralogy, v. 12, 644 p.

Roedder, E., ed., 1996, Fluid inclusion research for 1994, Virginia Polytechnic Institute and State University, Blacksberg, v. 27, 201 p.

Roedder, E., and Bodnar, R.J., 1980, Geologic pressure determinations from fluid inclusion studies. Annual Reviews in Earth and Planetary Science, v. 8, p. 263–301.

Saxena, S.K., and Fei, Y., 1987, Fluids at crustal pressures and temperatures: I. Pure species: Contributions to Mineralogy and Petrology, v. 95, p. 370–375.

Shepherd, T.J., and Rankin, A.H., 1998, Fluid inclusion techniques of analysis, Society of Economic Geologists Review; v. 10, p. 125–149.

Shepherd, T.J., Rankin, A.H., and Alderton, D.H.M., 1985, A practical guide to fluid inclusion studies: Glasgow, Blackie, 239 p.

Simmons, S.F., and Browne, P.R.L., 1997, Saline fluid inclusions in sphalerite from the Broadlands-Ohaaki geothermal system: A coincidental trapping of fluids being boiled toward dryness: Economic Geology, v. 92, p. 485–489.

Soave, G., 1972, Equilibrium constants from a modified Redlich-Kwong equation of state: Chemical Engineering Science, v. 27, p. 1197–1203.

Sterner, S.M., and Bodnar, R.J., 1991, Synthetic fluid inclusions: X: Experimental determination of P-V-T-X properties in the CO_2–H_2O system to 6kb and 700°C: American Journal of Science, v. 291, p. 1–54.

Sterner, S.M., Hall, D.L., and Bodnar, R.J., 1988, Synthetic fluid inclusions: V. Solubility relations in the system $NaCl-KCl-H_2O$ under vapor-saturated conditions: Geochimica et Cosmochimica Acta, v. 52, p. 989–1006.

Swanenberg, H.E.C., 1979, Phase equilibria in carbonic systems, and their application to freezing studies of fluid inclusions: Contributions to Mineralogy and Petrology, v. 68, p. 303–306.

—— 1980, Fluid inclusions in high-grade metamorphic rocks from southwestern Norway: University of Utrecht, Geologica Ultraiectina, v. 25, 147 p.

Thiéry, R., Kerkhof, A. M. van den, and Dubessy, J., 1994, vX properties modelling of CH_4-CO_2 and CO_2-N2 fluid inclusions (T<31°C, P<400 bar): European Journal Mineralogy, v. 6, p. 753–771.

Thomas, A.V., and Spooner, E.T.C., 1988, Fluid inclusions in the system H_2O-CH_4-NaCl-CO_2 from metasomatic tourmaline within the border unit of the Tanco zoned pegmatite, S.E. Manitoba: Geochimica et Cosmochimica Acta, v. 52, p. 1065–1075.

Thomas, A.V., and Spooner, E.T.C., 1992, The volatile geochemistry of magmatic H_2O-CO_2 fluid inclusions from the Tanco zoned granitic pegmatite, southeastern Manitoba, Canada: Geochimica et Cosmochimica Acta, v. 56, p. 49–65.

Tödheide, K., and Franck, E.U., 1963, Das Zweiphasengebiet und die kritische kurve im system Kohlendioxid-Wasser bis zu drucken von 3500 bar: Zeitschrieft Physikalische Chemie, v. 37, p. 387–401.

Touret, J., and Bottinga, Y., 1979, Equation of state of CO_2; application to carbonic inclusions: Bulletin de Minéralogie, v. 102, p. 577–583.

Vanko, D.A., Bodnar, R.J., and Sterner, S.M., 1988, Synthetic fluid inclusions: VIII. Vapor-saturated halite solubility in part of the system NaCl-$CaCl_2$-H_2O, with application to fluid inclusions from oceanic hydrothermal systems: Geochimica et Cosmochimica Acta, v. 52, p. 2451–2456.

Waals, J.D. van der, 1873, Over de continuiteit van den gas- en vloeistof toestand: Unpublished Ph.D. thesis, Sijtho, University Leiden, 184 p.

Chapter 8

Introduction to Stable Isotope Applications in Hydrothermal Systems

ANDREW R. CAMPBELL
Department of Earth & Environmental Sciences, New Mexico Institute of Mining and Technology, Socorro, New Mexico 87801

AND PETER B. LARSON
Department of Geology, Washington State University, Pullman, Washington 99164-2812

Introduction

Stable isotope and ore deposit studies have a long common history because many of the early developments in the application of stable isotopes to geological problems were from investigations of ore forming processes. Stable isotopes have now become an integral part of studying ore deposits. They provide information in four critical areas: (1) temperature of mineral deposition, (2) sources of the hydrothermal fluids, (3) sources of sulfur and carbon (and by extrapolation, metals), and (4) water-wall rock interactions. One of the most important roles that hydrogen and oxygen isotope studies have played is in the modern recognition that shallow, surface derived fluids are important components in many ore deposits. As stable isotope labs have become automated and the cost per analysis dropped, stable isotopes are also being used more commonly in mineral exploration. For example, isotopes can be used to define alteration halos and to aid in discriminating between mineralized and unmineralized quartz veins.

The purpose of this chapter is to provide a basis for understanding and utilizing light stable isotope data in the study of ore deposits. No previous knowledge of stable isotope geochemistry is assumed. However, one must recognize that stable isotopes can seldom provide unequivocal answers by themselves, and thus must be used in conjunction with other geological, mineralogical, petrological, and geochemical data. In other words, the knowledge in this chapter needs to be integrated with the types of studies described in the other chapters in this book in order to make sound interpretations of stable isotope data.

Isotope Terminology

The light stable isotopes commonly used in hydrothermal mineralization research include those of oxygen, hydrogen, sulfur, and carbon. Each of these elements has two or more stable isotopes (Table 1). In each case, the lightest isotope (e.g. ^{1}H, ^{12}C, ^{16}O, ^{32}S) is the most abundant. The stable isotopic composition of a mineral or other phase can be characterized by the ratio of the abundance of two isotopes (R; Table 2). Thus, R is defined as the ratio of the heavy to the light isotope such as $^{13}C/^{12}C$ or $^{2}H/^{1}H$. For oxygen and sulfur there are two heavy isotopes that could be used; ^{18}O, ^{17}O and ^{38}S, ^{36}S. For oxygen, ^{18}O is used because it has a higher abundance than ^{17}O and has a greater mass difference from ^{16}O. Isotopic fractionation is a function of the mass difference between the two isotopes, so ^{18}O will fractionate relative to ^{16}O to a greater extent (~2×) than ^{17}O, and the degree of fractionation is thus easier to measure. For sulfur, ^{34}S is chosen because it has great enough mass difference from ^{32}S to create sufficient fractionation and has a much greater abundance than ^{36}S (Table 1).

TABLE 1. Natural abundances and reference standards for light stable isotopes

Element	Isotope	Atomic Abundance+	Ratio	International Standards
Oxygen	^{16}O	99.763%	$^{18}O/^{16}O$	Vienna Standard Mean Ocean
	^{17}O	0.0375%		Water (VSMOW)
	^{18}O	0.1995%		Vienna Pee Dee Belemnite (VPDB) (for carbonates)
Hydrogen	^{1}H	99.9844%	D/H	VSMOW
	^{2}H (D)*	0.0156%		
Sulfur	^{32}S	95.02%	$^{34}S/^{32}S$	Cañon Diablo Troilite (CDT)
	^{33}S	0.75%		
	^{34}S	4.21%		
	^{36}S	0.02%		
Carbon	^{12}C	98.89%	$^{13}C/^{12}C$	VPDB
	^{13}C	1.11%		

*The mass 2 isotope of hydrogen is named deuterium (D)
+Compiled from Hoefs (1997)

TABLE 2. Terminology and definitions of stable isotope symbols

Stable Isotope Terminology		
Name	**Symbol**	**Definition**
Absolute Abundance Ratio	R	$R \equiv \frac{\text{Moles of heavy isotope}}{\text{Moles of light isotope}}$
Relative Isotopic Enrichment (delta)	δ	$\delta\ (‰\text{, or per mil}) \equiv \left[\frac{R_{Samp}}{R_{Std}} - 1\right]10^3$
Isotopic Fractionation Factor (alpha)	α_{xy}	$\alpha_{xy} \equiv \frac{R_x}{R_y}$ $\alpha_{xy} = \frac{\delta_x + 10^3}{\delta_y + 10^3}$ $10^3 \ln \alpha_{xy} \approx \Delta_{xy}$
Relative Isotopic Fractionation (big delta)	Δ_{xy}	$\Delta_{xy} \equiv \delta_x - \delta_y$

Although R is the basic expression of the isotopic composition, it is not the common way of referring to the compositions of minerals because stable isotopic measurements are made with respect to a standard and are reported as δ-values. Delta (δ) is based on the ratio of the isotopic ratio of a sample (R_{samp}) to the isotopic ratio of the standard (R_{std}) against which the measurement is made, and is reported in per mil (‰; Table 2). For example:

$$\delta^{18}O(‰) = \left[\frac{\left(\frac{^{18}O}{^{16}O}\right)_{Samp}}{\left(\frac{^{18}O}{^{16}O}\right)_{Std}} - 1\right] \times 10^3 = \left(\frac{R_{Samp}}{R_{Std}} - 1\right)10^3 \tag{8.1}$$

Stable isotopic measurements are made relative to a standard to increase the precision, accuracy, and ease of the measurements. Measurements of samples are typically made with respect to secondary standards and reported with respect to the accepted international standards, many of which have long been used up (Table 1). Positive δ-values (e.g., $\delta^{18}O$ = +3‰, or 3‰ hereafter) are enriched in the heavy isotope relative to the standard, whereas negative δ-values (e.g., $\delta^{18}O$ = –3‰) are depleted. Enriched samples are often referred to as "heavy" and depleted samples as "light"; however, these are relative terms and the basis of comparison needs to be defined. For example, quartz with a value of 2 per mil is referred to as "light" with respect to another sample that has a value of 5 per mil even though they are both enriched (or heavy) with respect to the standard. A summer rain at δD = –30 per mil is "heavy" when compared to winter snowfall in which the water has δD = –80 per mil.

The isotopic composition of a single mineral phase or other sample is reported as δ. However, in order to discuss the isotopic relationship between two minerals in isotopic equilibrium, one needs to use the isotopic fractionation factor (α), which is defined as the isotopic ratio (R) for one phase, divided by the isotopic ratio (R) for the other phase (Table 2). The correct notation for the fractionation between minerals x and y is:

$$\alpha_{xy} = \frac{R_x}{R_y} \tag{8.2}$$

It is essential to keep track of whether you are referring to α_{xy} or α_{yx} because

$$\alpha_{xy} = \frac{1}{\alpha_{yx}} \quad .$$

The isotopic ratios of two mineral phases in equilibrium are not very different, and thus α values are typically close to 1. For example, the α for oxygen isotope fractionation between quartz and water (α_{qw}) ranges from 1.0209 at 100°C to 1.0028 at 500°C.

The isotopic composition data that are obtained from a mass spectrometer are given as δ-values so it is useful to solve for α in terms of δ.

Given that

$$\alpha_{xy} = \frac{R_x}{R_y}$$

$$\delta_x(‰) = \left(\frac{R_x}{R_{Std}} - 1\right)10^3 \text{ and } \delta_y(‰) = \left(\frac{R_y}{R_{Std}} - 1\right)10^3$$

then $$R_x = \left(\frac{\delta_x}{10^3} + 1\right)R_{Std} \text{ and } R_y = \left(\frac{\delta_y}{10^3} + 1\right)R_{Std}$$

and $$\alpha_{xy} = \frac{\left(\frac{\delta_x}{10^3} + 1\right)R_{Std}}{\left(\frac{\delta_y}{10^3} + 1\right)R_{Std}} = \frac{\frac{\delta_x}{10^3} + 1}{\frac{\delta_y}{10^3} + 1} = \frac{\delta_x + 10^3}{\delta_y + 10^3} \tag{8.3}$$

This equation can be simplified by using the approximation $10^3 \ln (1.00X) \approx X$, which works well for small values of X (for example, $10^3 \ln 1.003 = 2.996 \approx 3$). Use your calculator to see how big X can get before the error of the approximation gets large compared to the analytical error (which should be about 0.1‰). In this case the term

$$\frac{\delta_x}{10^3} + 1$$

can be represented by $1.00\delta_x$ (for small values of δ_x), and equation (8.3) reduces to

$$10^3 \ln \alpha_{xy} = \delta_x - \delta_y \tag{8.4}$$

The difference between δ-values of two minerals, x and y, is defined as big delta (Δ_{xy}):

$$\Delta_{xy} = \delta_x - \delta_y \tag{8.5}$$

Thus, Δ_{xy} represents the measured fractionation of one phase relative to the other in per mil. If these minerals are in equilibrium then Δ can be substituted into equation (8.4):

$$\Delta_{xy} = \delta_x - \delta_y \approx 10^3 \ln\alpha_{xy} \tag{8.6}$$

This approximation works very well for Δ-values up to 10 per mil and works reasonably well for values up to 40 per mil, which covers nearly all oxygen Δ-values seen in geological systems. However, fractionations in the hydrogen system are often greater, and one needs to retreat to equation (8.3) for the exact formulation.

Isotopic Standardization

Stable isotope measurements of minerals are reported with respect to international standards. Typically, the actual measurements are made using a secondary standard and must be converted to the international standard by knowing the δ-value of the secondary standard on the international scale using the following equation:

$$\delta_{uy} = \frac{\delta_{xy}\,\delta_{ux}}{10^3} + \delta_{xy} + \delta_{ux} \tag{8.7}$$

where:

δ_{uy} = delta value of sample u on the international scale.

δ_{ux} = delta value of sample u with respect to the secondary standard.

δ_{xy} = delta value of secondary standard on the international scale.

The international standard for hydrogen is Vienna Standard Mean Ocean Water (VSMOW). Its value, as with all standards, is defined as 0 per mil. All values are reported relative to VSMOW on a normalized scale such that SLAP (Standard Light Antarctic Precipitate) has a δD value of –428 per mil. VSMOW is produced in Vienna by the International Atomic Energy Agency (IAEA) and is used as a replacement for the traditional SMOW. Isotopic values reported against SMOW should be identical to those using VSMOW.

VSMOW is also one of the international standards for oxygen, and the other is VPDB. The original standard, PDB, was a belemnite fossil from the Peedee Formation which has long since been exhausted. It is still used as a reporting standard (as VPDB) and is defined by measuring NBS-19, another carbonate standard distributed by the National Institute of Standards and Testing (NIST). Oxygen isotope ratios should be reported on a normalized scale such that SLAP has a $\delta^{18}O = -55.5‰$ relative to VSMOW. The new guidelines for reporting stable isotope values relative to VSMOW and VPDB are reported in Coplen (1996):

VSMOW is typically used for reporting the $\delta^{18}O$ of silicate minerals and rocks, and water samples, whereas VPDB is used for carbonate minerals and rocks. The $\delta^{18}O$ values can be converted from one scale to the other based on the following equation (Coplen et al., 1983):

$$\delta^{18}O_{SMOW} = 1.03091\ \delta^{18}O_{PDB} + 30.91‰ \qquad (8.8)$$

Carbon isotopes are reported relative to VPDB, and sulfur isotopes are reported relative to Cañon Diablo Troilite (CDT).

When samples are analyzed for stable isotopic composition, an internationally accepted standard should be run as well. The value of the international standard should be reported with the samples to allow the reader to assess the quality of the data, as well as to correct the data or convert it to another standard scale.

Sample Preparation and Analysis

Geologic samples include a variety of rock types, minerals, waters, or organic materials. From whatever its original state, the element of interest must be extracted and converted into a gas to be analyzed on the mass spectrometer. Preparation techniques vary almost as widely as the types of samples. One common feature of almost all of the extraction techniques is that they are done under vacuum in order to avoid contamination by ambient gases as well as to facilitate the mass spectroscopy.

Conventional Extraction Techniques

Carbonates are reacted with phosphoric acid to liberate CO_2 (McCrea, 1950). Mixtures of carbonates can be separated by their rates of reaction. Silicates are fluorinated with BrF_5, ClF_3, or F_2 at high temperatures and typically for 8 hours to produce O_2 (Clayton and Mayeda, 1963). The O_2 is reacted with hot carbon to produce CO_2 that can be introduced into the mass spectrometer. Alternatively, O_2 may be collected on a liquid N_2-cooled molecular sieve, and introduced directly into the mass spectrometer. Water can be fluorinated like silicates but is more commonly exchanged with CO_2 of a known isotopic composition. After the isotopic exchange is complete, the CO_2 is removed and analyzed on the mass spectrometer. By knowing the amounts of CO_2 and water, the temperature of equilibration, and the fractionation factor, the original $\delta^{18}O$ of the water can be calculated (Socki et al., 1992).

To measure the δD of water, it is reacted at high temperature with a metal such as zinc (Coleman et al., 1982) or uranium (Bigeleisen et al., 1952) to produce H_2 gas.

Sulfur isotope compositions are commonly measured on SO_2 gas. The masses measured for SO_2 are mass 64 ($S^{32}O^{16}O^{16}$) and mass 66 ($S^{34}O^{16}O^{16}$). One complication that arises is the contribution of O^{18} ($S^{32}O^{16}O^{18}$) to the abundance of mass 66. This problem is circumvented by fixing the $\delta^{18}O$ of the SO_2 with an external supply of oxygen. In sulfides the oxygen is supplied by roasting the mineral with an oxidizing agent (usually Cu_2O, CuO, or V_2O_5-SiO_2) to produce SO_2 (Robinson and Kusakabe, 1975). Sulfates are directly burned to SO_2 with silica glass or V_2O_5 to buffer the $\delta^{18}O$. If the standards are prepared in the same manner as the samples, then the ^{18}O contribution to mass 64 will be the same in both and thus will cancel out.

Most labs report overall reproducibility for conventional stable isotope techniques of about 0.1 per mil for $\delta^{13}C$, $\delta^{18}O$, and $\delta^{34}S$, and about 1 per mil for δD.

Emerging Extraction Techniques

Great advances have been made recently in the development of new extraction techniques for very small samples or for in situ analysis. These are discussed by several authors in McKibben et al. (1996). One of the most important advances has been utilizing the laser as a probe to analyze small spots within a mineral grain. The laser technique has been used with carbonates, silicates, oxides, and sulfides. With carbonates the laser is used to heat the sample to cause decarbonation, which results in the release of CO_2. Both $\delta^{18}O$ and $\delta^{13}C$ of the carbonate can be analyzed with this technique. For silicates and oxides the laser heats the sample to induce fluorination reactions to produce O_2 (Rumble and Sharp, 1996). For sulfides, either SO_2 or SF_6 can be produced by laser heating (Shanks et al., 1996). The laser extraction systems are typically hooked directly to a ratio mass spectrometer so the gas produced can be directly inlet for analysis. One drawback of this technique is that for in situ analysis fractionation occurs during sample reaction, but this can be corrected by careful standardization.

Another emerging technique has been the ion microprobe. As with other microbeam techniques, the advantage of the ion microprobe is the ability to analyze small points in a single grain. Although the precision of this technique is no better than ±1 per mil it has revealed much more small-scale isotopic variation than was known before. The $\delta^{18}O$ of silicates, $\delta^{34}S$ of sulfides, and δD of hydrous minerals can be determined with this technique (Eldridge et al., 1988; Graham and Valley, 1992; Riciputi and Paterson, 1994; Cole et al., 1997).

General Range of Isotope Values Found in Nature

It is useful to know the isotope values for common reservoirs involved in geologic processes. The isotopic compositions of many reservoirs, or large geochemically homogeneous masses of earth materials (for example, the oceans) are well-characterized, but the user should be wary when trying to "pigeon-hole" a particular substance into one of them because many exceptions are known. Ideally, the source reservoirs involved in a specific geologic study would always be directly measured, but in many cases this is simply not possible and the researcher must fall back on the generally accepted ranges.

Oxygen isotope δ values for common geologic substances range from +40 per mil to as low as about –55 per mil (Fig. 1). Sea water has a $\delta^{18}O$ value of 0 per mil by definition because it is the standard (VSMOW) against which other oxygen ratios are reported. In nature, the oceans exhibit slight local variations (±2‰) in $\delta^{18}O$ values due, in part, to either surface evaporation or the addition of polar melt waters. Nearly all fresh igneous rocks fall in the range of 5 to 10 per mil, although some values are as low as 0 per mil, and others exceed 15 per mil. Note that the only large reservoir with $\delta^{18}O$ values less than 0 per mil is meteoric water. Meteoric water is water that has been recently involved in atmospheric circulation. Most upper crustal groundwater in continents and islands is derived from precipitation and has values that reflect local precipitation values. The groundwater involved in many hydrothermal systems is often of meteoric origin, but may have undergone exchange or mixing with other fluids and its composition is no longer that of the original precipitation.

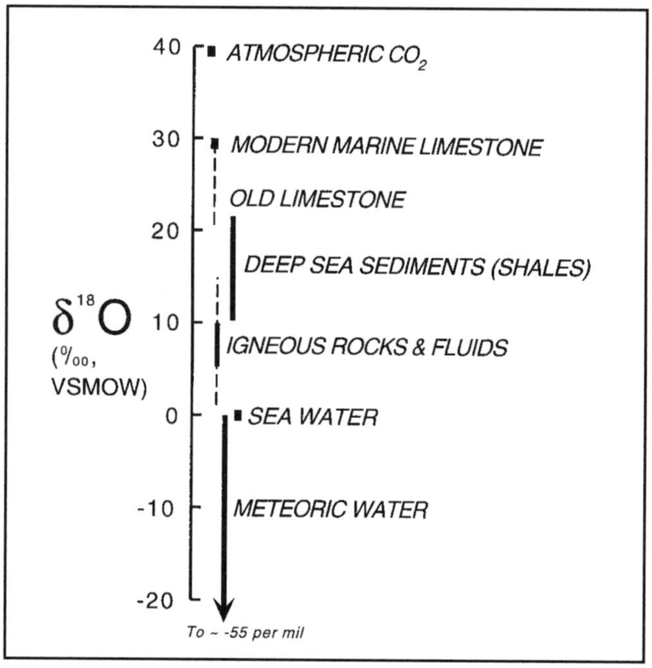

FIG. 1. The distribution of $\delta^{18}O$ values for common large earth reservoirs that are important in hydrothermal systems. Metamorphic rocks are typically close to protolith values, unless they have experienced extensive devolatilization or interaction with external fluids. These processes can significantly lower their values.

Many hydrogen isotope ratios in nature are intimately linked to oxygen ratios because water is a pervasive crustal geochemical agent. It is useful, therefore, to discuss the variation of hydrogen isotopes with respect to oxygen isotopes. Fluid and rock hydrogen and oxygen isotope reservoirs are shown on Figure 2. Again, sea water resides at 0 per mil for both elements. Meteoric and most continental and island groundwaters fall along the meteoric water line, where $\delta D = 8\,\delta^{18}O + 10$ (Craig, 1961). Meteoric water values greater than 0 per mil for both oxygen and hydrogen are found in east Africa where a complex climate system involves derivation of atmospheric water from large inland lakes and from the restricted Red Sea basin which are both reservoirs of heavier water due to evaporation. Waters at the light end of the range come from the polar regions. Evaporation trends can have slopes ranging from about 3 to 8 on the δD-$\delta^{18}O$ diagram. The slope of the evaporation trend is related to the relative humidity of the environment. Evaporation at high humidity, such as in a cave, can result in a slope near 8 and cause waters to move along the meteoric water line (Chapman et al., 1992). Under very dry conditions, such as evaporation from desert soils, evaporation slopes may be as low as 2 or 3 (Campbell et al., 1995).

Igneous rocks fall within restricted ranges of oxygen and hydrogen isotope ratios (Taylor, 1968). Magmatic

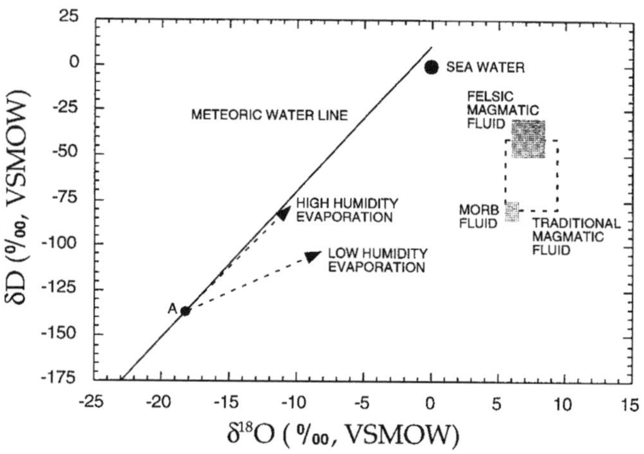

FIG. 2. The hydrogen and oxygen isotope ranges of some typical water reservoirs that are important in hydrothermal systems. Most precipitation, and groundwaters derived from it, lie along the meteoric water line where $\delta D = 8\delta^{18}O + 10$ (Craig, 1961). Sea water lies at or very near 0 per mil for both isotope systems because mean sea water is the standard against which both are measured. Aqueous fluids derived from felsic magmas and MORB fluids are also shown (Taylor, 1986). Evaporation and boiling produce trajectories with slopes from about 3 to 8, depending on the relative humidity of the environment (Chapman et al., 1992; Campbell et al., 1995). Shallow slopes are found in evaporation from desert soils.

fluids derived from these rocks usually inherit their oxygen isotope ratios directly from the magma without any significant fractionation. However, recent experiments (Dobson et al., 1989) show that the hydrogen isotope ratio of a magmatic fluid may vary from that of the magma as functions of temperature, magma composition, total water content of the magma, and, subsequently, the degree of degassing. Traditionally, the range in isotopic composition of magmatic water has been given a $\delta D = -40$ to -80 per mil and $\delta^{18}O = +6$ to $+10$ per mil. This was derived by calculating the water compositions in equilibrium with the measured values of igneous minerals at magmatic temperatures. However, more recent work looking at fumerolic waters suggests that felsic magmatic fluids are heavier. Giggenbach (1992) suggests that andesites related to subduction usually have H isotope ratios of about −20 per mil. Magmas derived from metamorphic crust have values near −45 per mil (Taylor, 1986). Shallow magma degassing can produce shifts in the volatiles' D/H ratio, and thus the δD value of a magmatic fluid can be a sensitive indicator of both magma source and the extent of magma degassing (Taylor, 1986, 1992). Basaltic magmas have primary D values near −60 per mil.

The δD value of a granitic (rhyolitic) magmatic fluid will change as degassing proceeds. Taylor (1992) showed that the initial magmatic fluid degassed from a typical obsidian would be about 10 per mil heavier than that in the magma. This fractionation would deplete the magma in heavy hydrogen, and continuous degassing would further this effect. Thus, as the degree of degassing proceeds, the "instantaneous" δD value of the magmatic fluid decreases. The magnitude of the depletion will be controlled in part by the open or closed nature of the magma-volatile system. Magmatic-hydrothermal ore deposits, such as porphyry or some skarn deposits, tend to lie near or within the source intrusions, where the magmatic nature of the hydrothermal fluids can be determined using stable isotope analyses of alteration and vein minerals. But large-scale circulation of meteoric or sea water geothermal fluids in large hydrothermal systems can serve as a sink for the magmatic fluids, whose presence may be difficult to detect in distal portions of these systems. Connate water, as defined originally, represents water trapped in sediment during its deposition. This term is often, incorrectly, applied to water filling pore spaces in rocks. Connate water in fact is not common in nature and isotope studies have shown that most continental and island groundwaters, even in deep sedimentary basins, have been derived dominantly, and in most cases entirely, from meteoric sources. Formation water is a non-genetic term that applies to any water filling spaces in rocks, regardless of the water's history. This term is preferred when the source of the water is unknown or speculative.

Carbon isotope ratios in most marine sedimentary carbonate rocks are near 0 percent ± 2 per mil because the standard for their measurement, VPDB, is a marine fossil. Most magmatic $\delta^{13}C$ values, usually measured on degassed CO_2, fall within the range of −4 to −8 per mil (Barnes et al., 1978), although there are a number of measurements outside that range. Volcanic CH_4 has lower $\delta^{13}C$ values, mostly in the range −25 to −30 per mil. Atmospheric CO_2 $\delta^{13}C$ values lie consistently near −7 per mil. The carbon isotope signature of organic matter is related to the type of photosynthetic pathway utilized by the plant. Organic carbon fixed in plants has values near −27 per mil for C_3 plants (Ehleringer, 1988) or −13 per mil for C_4 plants (Ehleringer et al., 1991). The values near −13 per mil are produced only by some younger Tertiary plants such as tropical grasses. Peat, coal, and petroleum usually have values corresponding to their source vegetation and lie near −27 per mil. The CH_4 associated with petroleum exhibits a wider range of $\delta^{13}C$ values from −30 to −50 per mil.

The three most important reservoirs for sulfur in hydrothermal ore deposits are magmatic sulfur, marine sulfate, and sedimentary sulfides. Sulfur in magmatic systems may be released into a fluid phase or sulfide melt via magmatic exsolution, or crystallized as magmatic sulfide or sulfates. In sulfide-dominated melts, little fractionation occurs between the melt, crystals, and fluid phases; all typically have $\delta^{34}S$ values in the range of −2 to +2 per mil. However, under oxidizing conditions, the exsolved magmatic fluid may range up to +5 per mil (Ohmoto, 1972). Magmatic sulfides leached by later fluids contribute magmatic sulfur to the hydrothermal fluid and may preserve a magmatic sulfur isotopic signature. This is because leaching is a non-equilibrium process.

Modern marine sulfate has a $\delta^{34}S$ of about 20 per mil. However, the isotopic composition of ancient marine sulfate has not been constant through time as evidenced by the secular variation of $\delta^{34}S$ values of evaporites. Heavier values (+30‰) occurred during the early Paleozoic, and lighter values (+10‰) in Permian time (Claypool et al., 1980). This range is attributed to the changing proportions of sulfur tied up in sedimentary sulfide and evaporite reservoirs. Sedimentary sulfides exhibit a wide range of $\delta^{34}S$ values from −70 to +70 per mil but are typically between 0 and −30 per mil (Ohmoto and Rye, 1979). This variability is ascribed to various mechanisms related to the bacterial reduction of sulfur, including the "openness" of the system to influx of sulfate, and the rate of sulfate reduction. In general, open systems will produce sedimentary sulfides with a light ^{34}S value, whereas closed systems can produce some late sulfides with heavier $\delta^{34}S$ values.

Isotope Fractionation

Equilibrium Isotope Fractionation

The light stable isotopes of an element are distributed unevenly, or partitioned, among phases during chemical reactions in which they are involved. For example, when quartz precipitates from a water-rich hydrothermal fluid, the isotopic ratio of oxygen ($^{18}O/^{16}O$) in the quartz will be different from that in the hydrothermal fluid. This partitioning is called fractionation. If fractionation did not occur, all substances would have the same isotope ratios for any given non-radiogenic element. Here, we will examine the equations by which fractionation is applied to natural systems, and give some examples of those applications.

First, however, you might be interested in knowing why equilibrium fractionation occurs. This is a brief explanation without mathematical formulations, but further details can be found in Urey (1947), Bigeleisen and Mayer (1947), Kieffer (1982), and O'Neil (1986). Isotopes are atoms of the same element that differ in atomic mass. Using C as an example, recall that an atom of ^{13}C and one of ^{12}C both have 6 protons and 6 electrons, but 7 and 6 neutrons, respectively. Thus, ^{13}C is about 8 percent heavier than ^{12}C. Atoms of each isotope have different vibrational frequencies in equivalent crystallographic sites because of their mass difference. The different frequencies produce slightly different bond energies, which lead to uneven distributions of the isotopes among competing atomic sites in different phases, each of which have different vibrational characteristics. Fractionation can occur even within one phase with distinct sites: for example, in muscovite, oxygen can go into a hydroxyl position or into a silica tetrahedron.

We will use oxygen isotopes as an example to present the fractionation equations. Identical discussions would hold for the stable hydrogen isotopes (H and D), carbon isotopes (^{12}C and ^{13}C), and sulfur isotopes (^{32}S and ^{34}S). All of these isotope systems use the same notation and fractionation formulations.

Consider quartz precipitating from a water-rich hydrothermal solution. Assume that this process occurs isothermally, that the precipitation proceeds under isotopic equilibrium between the phases, and that the mass of fluid is very large compared to the mass of quartz being precipitated. This latter assumption ensures that the $\delta^{18}O$ value of the fluid remains constant. This system is analogous to many cases where quartz precipitates in a vein. If we know the isotopic values of the two phases, $\delta^{18}O_{quartz}$ and $\delta^{18}O_{water}$, we can calculate their difference

$$\Delta^{18}O_{quartz-water} = \delta^{18}O_{quartz} - \delta^{18}O_{water} \tag{8.9}$$

where $\Delta^{18}O_{quartz\text{-}water}$ is called the measured "per mil" fractionation between the quartz and the water. The Δ is just the difference between two measured values, and does not imply that their difference represents an equilibrium fractionation. However, if the two phases are at equilibrium, is related to the fractionation factor, by equation (8.6), where, combined with equation (8.9) for this example,

$$\Delta^{18}O_{quartz-water} \approx 10^3 \ln\alpha_{quartz-water} \tag{8.10}$$

This result is important, because it relates the equilibrium fractionation factor, α, to measured δ values. For quartz precipitating in a vein in equilibrium with a fluid, let the $\delta^{18}O_{quartz}$ value be 6.7 per mil and the $\delta^{18}O_{water}$ value be −0.7 per mil. $\Delta^{18}O_{quartz\text{-}water}$ is then 7.4 per mil (6.7‰ minus −0.7‰). Using the approximation $10^3\ln 1.00X \approx X$, α is about equal to 1.0074.

Equilibrium isotope fractionation between two phases is a temperature dependent function. Equations that describe equilibrium fractionations between two phases, x and y, usually are presented in the form:

$$10^3 \ln\alpha_{xy} = A_{xy}(10^6/T^2) + B_{xy} \tag{8.11}$$

where A_{xy} and B_{xy} are constants that are unique to the pair of phases x and y. The temperature (T) scale used in fractionation equations is always Kelvin and never Celsius (recall that K = °C + 273.15). Other forms of fractionation equations are used occasionally, where additional exponential terms are included. Also, B is commonly (but not always) 0 for oxygen fractionations between two solid, anhydrous phases. Equation (8.11) can be applied to values through equations (8.9) and (8.10), where for our example (q is quartz and w is water)

$$\delta^{18}O_{quartz} - \delta^{18}O_{water} \approx A_{qw}\,(10^6/T^2) + B_{qw}. \tag{8.12}$$

Clayton et al. (1972) published a calibration for quartz-water equilibrium oxygen isotope fractionation where $A_{qw} = 3.38$ and $B_{qw} = -2.90$, valid in the temperature range 200 to 500°C. If we insert these values in equation (8.12), together with our "big delta" (Δ) quartz-water fractionation of 7.4 per mil, we calculate an equilibrium fractionation temperature of 573 K, corresponding to 300°C. Alternatively, given a quartz value of 8.6 per mil and a fluid inclusion trapping temperature of 450°C, we calculate that the water from which the quartz precipitated had a $\delta^{18}O$ value of 5.0 per mil (assuming equilibrium precipitation).

Fractionation equations, often called fractionation factors, have been published for a number of minerals in the format given in equation (8.11). Fractionation factors are determined in one of three ways: (1) experimental calibration studies in the laboratory, (2) theoretical calculations using spectroscopic data and statistical mechanics, or (3) studies of natural samples where their environment of formation is very well characterized.

Some useful fractionation factors are given in Appendix 1. Fractionation equations are reported as the fractionation of a mineral relative to a reference phase, which for oxygen and hydrogen is most commonly water, although for oxygen, quartz is also sometimes used. Recent experiments have measured oxygen fractionations relative to calcite to avoid certain experimental difficulties in the mineral-water experiments (Clayton et al., 1989). Fractionation factors are usually reported to be valid within specified temperature limits. It is important to remember that the factors are valid only within those limits, but it is not uncommon in practice to extrapolate the factors beyond this range in cases where appropriate data do not exist. Great care must be taken when interpretations are based on extrapolated fractionation factors.

Fractionation equations that define the fractionation factors of two phases of interest, each relative to the same reference phase, can be manipulated to produce a fractionation factor between the two phases of interest. For example, Appendix 1 lists oxygen isotope fractionation factors for quartz-water and muscovite-water. We can use these fractionation factors to determine a factor for quartz-muscovite. Each fractionation can be written in the form of equation (8.9), where musc is muscovite:

$$\Delta^{18}O_{quartz-water} = \delta^{18}O_{quartz} - \delta^{18}O_{water} \tag{8.13}$$

$$\Delta^{18}O_{musc-water} = \delta^{18}O_{musc} - \delta^{18}O_{water} \tag{8.14}$$

Then

$$\Delta^{18}O_{quartz-water} - \Delta^{18}O_{musc-water} = (\delta^{18}O_{quartz} - \delta^{18}O_{water}) - (\delta^{18}O_{musc} - \delta^{18}O_{water}) = \delta^{18}O_{quartz} - \delta^{18}O_{musc} \tag{8.15}$$

or

$$\Delta^{18}O_{quartz-musc} = \Delta^{18}O_{quartz-water} - \Delta^{18}O_{musc-water} \tag{8.16}$$

Using equations (8.10) and (8.11) with equation (8.16), we can write:

$$\Delta^{18}O_{quartz-musc} \approx 10^3 \ln\alpha_{quartz-water} - 10^3 \ln\alpha_{musc-water} = (A_{quartz-water} - A_{musc-water})(10^6/T^2) + (B_{quartz-water} - B_{musc-water}) \tag{8.17}$$

We can generalize this result for two phases, x and y, whose fractionation factors relative to a reference phase, r, are known:

$$\Delta^{18}O_{xy} = (A_{xr} - A_{yr})(10^6/T^2) + (B_{xr} - B_{yr}) \tag{8.18}$$

For our quartz-muscovite example, using the quartz-water fractionation of Matsuhisa et al. (1979; $A_{quartz\text{-}water} = 3.34$, $B_{quartz\text{-}water} = -3.31$, 250° to 500°C) and the muscovite-water fractionation of O'Neil and Taylor (1969; $A_{muscovite\text{-}water} = 2.38$, $B_{muscovite\text{-}water} = -3.89$, 400° to 650°C), the fractionation constants for equation 8.11 are $A_{quartz\text{-}muscovite} = 0.96$ and $B_{quartz\text{-}muscovite} = 0.58$. This quartz-muscovite fractionation factor would be valid over the temperature range 400° to 500°C.

Appendix 1 shows that some mineral fractionation factors have been determined more than once. The results are not always compatible (compare the different quartz-water fractionation factor constants). In practice, it is best to use sets of factors that have been produced by one laboratory, or that have been internally calibrated. Several such calibrations have been published (e.g., Bottinga and Javoy, 1973, for oxygen isotopes). However, it is not always possible to find an internally calibrated set of fractionation factors that contains all the phases that are of interest in a particular application. This problem is compounded by the fact that fractionation factors for many minerals of interest are simply not known. There is no simple path around these problems. The determination of isotope fractionation factors is an ongoing project in many laboratories.

Geothermometry

The temperature dependence of the fractionation factor between two minerals makes it possible to use mineral pairs as geothermometers. Isotope geothermometry has an advantage over most other types of geothermometry because it is pressure insensitive. Fluid inclusion microthermometry, for example, is pressure dependent and a pressure correction must be made to the homogenization temperature (see Chap. 7).

Mineral pairs that are to be used for geothermometry need to meet several criteria. First, they must have been co-deposited in equilibrium with each other. This necessitates that they formed at the same temperature from the same fluid. Second, they must have retained their isotopic composition and not have been changed by later re-equilibration or alteration. Of the four stable isotope systems discussed in this chapter, oxygen and sulfur provide the best geothermometers. Carbonate-graphite is the only frequently used mineral pair in the carbon system and the fractionation of hydrogen isotopes between two minerals is frequently independent of temperature.

In order to calculate the isotopic temperature of formation of an appropriate sulfide mineral pair one must first obtain the fractionation equation. For sulfur isotopes, fractionation factors for minerals are typically given with respect to H_2S. For the case of a galena-chalcopyrite pair we need to look up the galena-H_2S and chalcopyrite-H_2S fractionation factors:

$$\text{Galena-}H_2S\text{: } 10^3 \ln\alpha_{gal\text{-}H_2S} = -0.63\ (10^6/T^2) \approx \delta_{gal} - \delta_{H_2S} \tag{8.19}$$

$$\text{Chalcopyrite-}H_2S\text{: } 10^3 \ln\alpha_{cp\text{-}H_2S} = -0.05\ (10^6/T^2) \approx \delta_{cp} - \delta_{H_2S} \tag{8.20}$$

As shown earlier, (eq. 8.18) these two equations can be combined to yield the combined galena-chalcopyrite fractionation equation:

$$(10^3 \ln\alpha_{gal\text{-}H_2S}) - (10^3 \ln\alpha_{cp\text{-}H_2S}) = (-0.63\ (10^6/T^2)) - (-0.05(10^6/T^2))$$

Therefore:

$$10^3 \ln\alpha_{gal\text{-}cp} = -0.58(10^6/T^2) \approx \delta_{gal} - \delta_{cp} = \Delta_{gal\text{-}cp} \tag{8.21}$$

So: $$T(K) = \left(\frac{-0.58 \times 10^6}{\Delta_{gal\text{-}cp}}\right)^{1/2}$$

For a mineral pair with

$$\delta^{34}S_{gal} = 3.8‰ \text{ and } \delta^{34}S_{chalcopyrite} = 5.6‰ :$$

$$\delta^{34}S_{gal} - \delta^{34}S_{cp} = -1.8‰, \text{ and } T = 568K = 295°C.$$

Be sure to keep track of which way α has been defined: either $\alpha_{gal\text{-}cp} \approx \delta_{gal} - \delta_{cp}$ or $\alpha_{cp\text{-}gal} \approx \delta_{cp} - \delta_{gal}$.

The best mineral pairs for geothermometry are those that have the largest temperature dependence of fractionation. Figure 3 illustrates the fractionation of various sulfur minerals and compounds with respect to H_2S. Pyrite and galena have the greatest difference in slope of all the common sulfide mineral pairs. This means that $\alpha_{py\text{-}gn}$ will have the greatest temperature dependence and thus be the most sensitive sulfide pair geothermometer. On the other extreme is the chalcopyrite-sphalerite pair whose fractionations with respect to H_2S are almost identical. Note also that fractionation decreases as temperature increases. Typically, sulfur isotope measurements can be made to ±0.1 per mil; let us consider how that precision is translated into a temperature uncertainty in the py-gal and cp-sp temperature pairs. At 300°C, $\Delta_{py\text{-}gal}$ = 3.14‰ and $\Delta_{sp\text{-}cp}$ = 0.46‰. If each pair changed by 0.2 per mil due to analytical error, how much would the calculated temperature be affected? A $\Delta_{py\text{-}gal}$ = 3.34‰ will yield a temperature of 282°C and a $\Delta_{sp\text{-}cp}$ = 0.66‰ will yield 204°C, both compared with a "true" temperature of 300°C.

It is also true that the geothermometers are less precise at higher temperatures. With the py-gal pair, the same analytical uncertainty of 0.2 per mil at 500°C will result in a larger temperature discrepancy. At 500°C $\Delta_{py\text{-}gal}$ = 1.72 per mil; if we use the same 0.2 per mil shift due to analytical uncertainty, then $\Delta_{py\text{-}gal}$ = 1.92 per mil and yields T = 459°C. This is a bigger error in the calculated temperature than at 300°C for the same mineral pair.

It is evident from Figure 3 that in the sulfur system the mineral pairs with the greatest differences in slope would

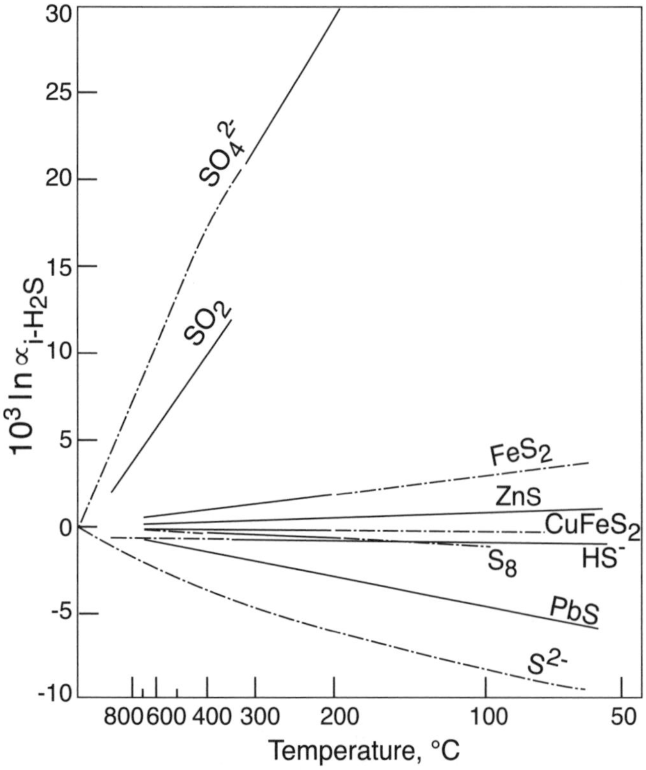

FIG. 3. Equilibrium fractionation of various sulfur compounds relative to H_2S. Dashed lines are extrapolated or theoretically calculated. Solid lines are experimentally determined. Note the decrease in fractionation as temperature is raised (redrafted from Ohmoto and Rye, 1979).

be sulfide-sulfate pairs. All sulfate minerals have approximately the same fractionation with respect to H_2S, so this fractionation factor may be used with barite, anhydrite, gypsum, etc. From this perspective, sulfide-sulfate pairs would seem to be a very sensitive geothermometer. However, Ohmoto and Lasaga (1982) have demonstrated that the aqueous sulfide and sulfate components are not likely to be in equilibrium below 300°C. It has been noted that sulfate-sulfide is commonly smaller than expected given other indications of low temperature. This results in geothermometry from sulfate-sulfide pairs yielding temperatures that are unrealistically high. Ohmoto and Lasaga (1982) describe this as $\alpha_{measured} < \alpha_{expected}$ and attribute it to the kinetics of isotopic exchange between oxidized and reduced sulfur through thio-sulfate as an intermediary reaction step. They document the temperature and pH control on the reaction rate and conclude that, for most hydrothermal systems below 300°C, sulfate minerals will not be in equilibrium with sulfide minerals.

It is important to note that the disequilibrium applies to sulfate-sulfide pairs and does not affect the equilibrium (and thus the geothermometry) between sulfide mineral pairs. This is because the kinetics of the $H_2S_{(aq)}$-sulfide (and the $SO^{2-}{}_{4(aq)}$-sulfate) exchange is much more rapid than the $H_2S_{(aq)}$-$SO^{2-}{}_{4(aq)}$ exchange.

$$\begin{array}{ccc} H_2S_{(aq)} & \underset{\text{Slow eq}}{\rightleftharpoons} & SO^{2-}{}_{4\,(aq)} \\ \text{(rapid eq.)} \downarrow\uparrow & & \downarrow\uparrow \text{(rapid eq.)} \\ \text{Sulfide} & & \text{Sulfate} \end{array}$$

Worked Example

Hydrothermal quartz and muscovite are intergrown on the edges of vein. The quartz has a $\delta^{18}O$ = 12.1 per mil and muscovite has a $\delta^{18}O$ = 9.0 per mil. At what temperature were they deposited?

$$10^3 \ln \alpha_{qtz\text{-}H_2O} = 3.34\ (10^6/T^2) - 3.31$$

$$10^3 \ln \alpha_{musc\text{-}H_2O} = 2.38\ (10^6/T^2) - 3.89$$

$$\text{So } 10^3 \ln \alpha_{qtz\text{-}musc} = 0.96\ (10^6/T^2) + 0.58 \approx \Delta_{qtz\text{-}musc}$$

$$\Delta_{qtz\text{-}musc} = 12.1 - 9.0 = 3.1$$

$$3.1‰ = 0.96\ (10^6/T^2) + 0.58$$

$$T = 617K = 344°C$$

The quartz-water and muscovite-water fractionation equations are from Matsuhisa et al. (1979) and Clayton et al. (1972), respectively. In some cases you will have more than one fractionation equation to pick from and your calculated temperature will depend on which equation you choose. For instance, if we chose the quartz-muscovite fractionation equation of Chacko et al. (1996) our calculated temperature would be 398°C. It is important to carefully evaluate the possible equations before selecting one.

A few words of caution about geothermometry. It is important to remember that the mineral pair must have been deposited in equilibrium. In some hydrothermal systems the $\delta^{34}S$, $\delta^{18}O$ or the temperature of the fluid may be changing with time. If so, two minerals from different parts of the paragenetic sequence will not be in equilibrium. Common minerals such as quartz or pyrite may be deposited over a wide time interval and thus while some of the pyrite may be cogenetic with another sulfide (such as chalcopyrite), other pyrite may not have been. Careful sample selection is necessary to maximize the chance of obtaining equilibrium pairs. It is also important to obtain pure mineral separates. If the two minerals in the pair are intergrown to the extent that they contaminate one another, each mineral's δ value will be pulled toward the other's resulting in a smaller Δ-value and thus a calculated temperature that is too high.

Calculated Fluid Values

In addition to calculating temperatures of mineral deposition, stable isotopes are used extensively to determine the source of the hydrothermal fluids. The first step in this process is to calculate the isotopic composition of the fluid component in equilibrium with the mineral. For oxygen and hydrogen, the fluid component is the water; for sulfides it is the aqueous H_2S; for sulfates it is $SO_4^=$ and for carbonates it is HCO_3^-.

For hydrogen and oxygen, calculating the equilibrium water is relatively simple. The mineral-water fractionation factor, the δ-value of the mineral, and the temperature are needed. In the worked example given earlier, plugging the temperature of 344°C (remember to convert °C to Kelvin in your calculation) into the fractionation equation yields a $10^3 \ln\alpha_{qtz\text{-}H_2O}$ value of 5.5 per mil. So:

$$\delta^{18}O_{qtz} - \delta^{18}O_{H_2O} = 5.5‰$$

$$\text{and } \delta^{18}O_{H_2O} = \delta^{18}O_{qtz} - 5.5‰.$$

In that example, $\delta^{18}O$ quartz = 12.1‰, which results in a calculated $\delta^{18}O_{H_2O}$ = 6.6‰. Similarly for the muscovite: $10^3 \ln\delta_{musc\text{-}H_2O}$ = 2.4‰, so:

$$\delta^{18}O_{musc} - \delta^{18}O_{H_2O} = 2.4‰$$

$$\delta^{18}O_{H_2O} = \delta^{18}O_{musc} - 2.4‰.$$

$$\delta^{18}O_{H_2O} = 9.0‰ - 2.4‰ = 6.6‰$$

Because the temperature was calculated using the mineral pair, the water compositions calculated from either mineral come out identical.

Even though δD values of mineral pairs are generally not good geothermometers, the mineral-water fractionation is temperature dependent and the equilibrium δD value of the water can be calculated given T, δD_{min}, and the appropriate α equation.

For sulfur and carbon it is much harder to calculate the isotopic composition of the sulfur or carbon source. This is due to the multiple oxidation states of sulfur and carbon that exist in the fluid. Sulfur, for example, will exist in many aqueous forms including: H_2S, HS^-, HSO_4^-, and $SO_4^=$. The different species will be related by oxidation/reduction and/or pH dependent equations. The various species will also have different isotopic compositions related by α-equations. Given a $\delta^{34}S_{mineral}$, temperature, and an α-equation for mineral-H_2S, the $\delta^{34}S_{H_2S}$ can be calculated. This, however, is only one of the sulfur components that might exist in solution. In order to use sulfur isotopes to determine the source of sulfur in the aqueous fluid one must know the bulk $\delta^{34}S$ of all sulfur in solution. To do this you must know the $\delta^{34}S$ of one species, the fractionation between species, temperature, and fraction of total sulfur in each species. In a solution containing H_2S, HSO_4^-, and $SO_4^=$:

$$\delta^{34}S_{Sol'n} = X_{H_2S}\,\delta^{34}S_{H_2S} + X_{SO_4^=}\,\delta^{34}S_{SO_4^=} + X_{HSO^-_4}\,\delta^{34}S_{HSO^-_4} \qquad (8.22)$$

where X_{H_2S} is the mole fraction of H_2S relative to all S-species. This equation should originally be written considering the atomic fractions of sulfur in each species. However, in this example, each phase has one sulfur atom per formula unit so the atomic fraction is the same as mole fraction.

The speciation of sulfur in solution is controlled by the fugacity of oxygen and the pH. Ohmoto (1972) presents the details of how to construct pH-f_{O_2} diagrams that depict the change in $\delta^{34}S$ of various sulfur species as the chemical speciation changes. Given the appropriate mineral assemblages, it may be possible to estimate the pH and f_{O_2} of the fluid.

For a fluid dominated by H_2S, the $\delta^{34}S_{H_2S}$ calculated from a sulfide mineral will be a good approximation of the $\delta^{34}S$ of the sum of the sulfur species (ΣS). For a fluid dominated by SO^{2-}_4 the $\delta^{34}S_{SO^{2-}_4}$ will be a good approximation of $\delta^{34}S_{\Sigma S}$. In other cases where the oxidation state is such that significant quantities of H_2S and SO^{2-}_4 are both present, it is vital to know the H_2S/SO^{2-}_4 ratio to calculate $\delta^{34}S_{\Sigma S}$.

The above discussion assumes isotopic equilibrium between the various aqueous species, but this situation is not always the case as discussed earlier in the section on geothermometry.

Processes and Reservoirs

Isotope Mass Balance

In a closed system, two phases (liquid, gas, mineral, or rock) will tend to evolve toward equilibrium through isotopic exchange reactions. Because it is a closed system, the total concentrations of the isotopes (^{16}O and ^{18}O for example) will not change but their distribution between phases will. This can be expressed in a mass balance equation:

$$X\,\delta^i_d + Y\,\delta^i_e = X\,\delta^f_d + Y\,\delta^f_e \qquad (8.23)$$

in which X,Y = atomic fraction of phase d and phase e respectively

δ^i_d, δ^i_e = initial isotopic values of phases d and e, respectively, before isotope exchange has occurred

δ^f_d , δ^f_e = final isotopic values of phases d and e, respectively, after isotopic exchange has occurred.

Because only isotope exchange reactions take place, the amounts of the two phases (X and Y) do not change.

Solving equation (8.23) yields:

$$X\,\delta^i_d - X\,\delta^f_d = Y\,\delta^f_e - Y\,\delta^i_e$$
$$X\left(\delta^i_d - \delta^f_d\right) = Y\left(\delta^f_e - \delta^i_e\right) \tag{8.24}$$

As mentioned above the atomic fractions equal the mole fraction only if both phases (d and e) have the same number of atoms of the element of interest in one formula unit. For the example given below for the equilibration of CO_2 and H_2O, water contributes one mole of oxygen per mole of water whereas carbon dioxide contributes two moles of oxygen per mole of carbon dioxide.

Depending on how one wants to use this equation it can be written in various ways. For instance, this equation is used to look at the isotopic equilibrium between liquid H_2O and gaseous CO_2, which is the process by which we analyze the $\delta^{18}O$ of water samples. CO_2 of a known initial composition is equilibrated with a water sample of unknown isotopic composition and from the change in the $\delta^{18}O_{CO_2}$, the $\delta^{18}O^i_{H_2O}$ of the water can be calculated. For this the equation is written as:

$$\delta^{18}O^i_{H_2O} = \frac{Y}{X}\left(\delta^{18}O^f_{CO_2} - \delta^{18}O^i_{CO_2}\right) + \delta^{18}O^f_{H_2O} \tag{8.25}$$

Y and X are controlled in the experiment. The $\delta^{18}O^i_{CO_2}$ is measured before equilibration, and $\delta^{18}O^f_{CO_2}$ is measured at the end of the experiment. If equilibrium has been reached, then $\delta^{18}O^f_{H_2O}$ can be calculated from $\delta^{18}O^f_{CO_2}$ and the temperature of equilibration.

$$\Delta_{CO_2-H_2O} = \delta^{18}O_{CO_2} - \delta^{18}O_{H_2O}$$

$$\text{So: } \delta^{18}O^f_{H_2O} = \delta^{18}O^f_{CO_2} + \Delta_{CO_2-H_2O}$$

Thus, equation (8.25) becomes

$$\delta^{18}O^i_{H_2O} = \frac{Y}{X}\left(\delta^{18}O^f_{CO_2} - \delta^{18}O^i_{CO_2}\right) + \delta^{18}O^f_{CO_2} + \Delta_{CO_2-H_2O} \tag{8.26}$$

The temperature dependence of the fractionation process is carried in the $\Delta_{CO_2-H_2O}$ term. This equation ignores the contribution of H_2O_{vapor} but that is usually negligible unless a very small amount of water is used in a relatively large equilibration vessel. This situation might occur when trying to analyze the $\delta^{18}O_{H_2O}$ of water extracted from fluid inclusions, in which case only a small amount of water is usually available. Later in this chapter, equation (8.24) will be used to calculate the water/rock ratio during water/rock interactions.

Rayleigh Fractionation

In contrast to closed system processes, in open system processes some product of the system is removed as it is made. Because the product is removed it has no possibility of re-equilibration with the original reservoir. Examples are the removal of crystals from a magma by crystal setting, or the removal of water vapor as steam during boiling. When fractionation occurs between the original system (i.e., the magma) and the removed product (i.e., the crystals), the isotopic composition of both phases is controlled by the process of Rayleigh fractionation. Steam at 100°C, for example, is isotopically lighter than the liquid water with which it is in equilibrium. So when steam separates from the water, the water must become isotopically heavier. The next portion of steam separated will be in equilibrium with the new, heavier, water composition and will thus be heavier than the original steam. When the fraction of steam separated nears unity, both the last bit of water and the corresponding incremental bit of steam will have very heavy isotopic values. Some of the most extreme isotopic compositions in nature are caused by this process.

The isotopic changes during open system processes can be modeled with the Rayleigh equation:

$$\frac{R}{R^\circ} = F^{\,\alpha-1} \tag{8.27}$$

where R° = isotope ratio of the initial phase
R = instantaneous ratio of separating phase
F = fraction of initial phase remaining

$$\alpha = \text{fractionation factor} = \frac{R_{\text{separating phase}}}{R_{\text{initial phase}}}$$

In the case of condensation of liquid (L) from vapor (V), the equation becomes:

$$\frac{R_V}{R^\circ_V} = F^{\alpha_{L-V}-1} \tag{8.28}$$

If one is interested in the changing composition of the liquid phase during condensation, it can be easily calculated using α:

$$\alpha_{L-V} = \frac{R_L}{R_V} \quad \text{so} \quad R_V = \frac{R_L}{\alpha_{L-V}}$$

substituting into equation (8.28):

$$\frac{R_L}{\alpha_{L-V}\,R^\circ_V} = F^{\alpha_{L-V}-1} \tag{8.29}$$

So

$$\frac{R_L}{R^\circ_V} = \alpha_{L-V}F^{\alpha_{L-V}-1} \tag{8.30}$$

For the case of evaporation:

$$\frac{R_L}{R^\circ_L} = F^{\left(\frac{1}{\alpha_{L-V}}-1\right)} \tag{8.31}$$

and

$$\frac{R_V}{R^\circ_L} = \frac{1}{\alpha_{L-V}} F^{\left(\frac{1}{\alpha_{L-V}}-1\right)} \tag{8.32}$$

During Rayleigh fractionation, if all of the removed product is collected, its average isotopic value will approach the isotopic composition of the original reservoir as the fraction remaining approaches zero. For the case of evaporation of water:

$$\frac{\overline{R_V}}{R^\circ_L} = \frac{1 - F^{\frac{1}{\alpha_{L-V}}}}{1 - F} \tag{8.33}$$

where $\overline{R}_v$ = the average composition of the accumulated product. These equations are relatively easy to manipulate when they are written in R. However, in most cases in order to apply the equation to data, the equations need to be written in terms of δ rather than R. By solving for R_V and R°_L in terms of δ_V and δ°_L, equation (8.32) becomes:

$$\frac{\delta_V + 1000}{\delta^\circ_L + 1000} = \frac{1}{\alpha_{L-V}} F^{\left(\frac{1}{\alpha_{L-V}}-1\right)} \tag{8.34}$$

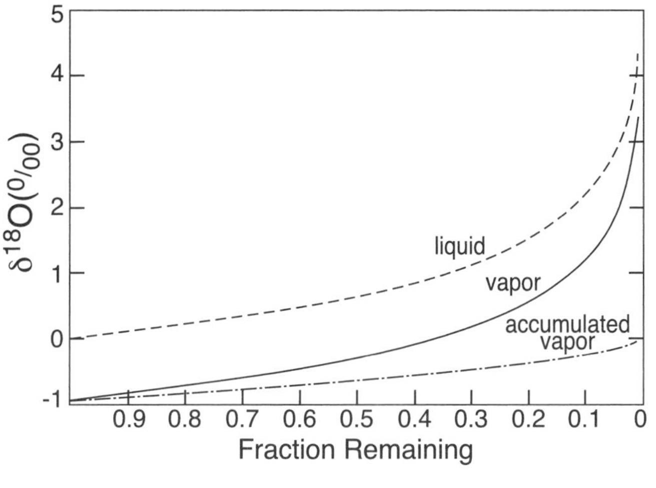

FIG. 4. The changing composition of liquid and vapor during Rayleigh fractionation during the boiling of water at 300°C (α = 1.00094). Initial water composition is 0 per mil. The initial vapor is isotopically lighter than the liquid, which makes the remaining liquid progressively heavier. Extreme changes in isotopic composition can arise at low fraction remaining (F). At lower temperatures the fractionation factor will be larger and the overall fractionation will be greater. The average composition of all separated vapor is given by the "accumulated vapor" curve.

Consider the case of water with an initial $\delta^{18}O$ of 0 per mil boiling at 300°C (α_{L-V} = 1.00094). The variation of δ_V, δ_L, and $\overline{\delta}_V$ can all be calculated as a function of F as it ranges from 1 at the beginning until it approaches 0 at the end (Fig. 4).

For $\delta^{18}O$, because α_{L-V} decreases with increased T, the changes in the water composition due to boiling decrease as the temperature of boiling is raised. The situation is different for the effects on δD of boiling of an aqueous fluid because of a change in the sense of fractionation (called the cross-over point) which occurs between 220° and 230°C (Horita and Wesolowski, 1994). At temperatures below the cross-over point, fractionation occurs in a normal way with the light isotope (^1H) being enriched in the vapor phase; but above the cross-over temperature, fractionation is reversed and the heavy isotope (^2H) is enriched in the vapor. Boiling near the cross-over temperature, where α is equal to 1, causes no isotopic change in the water composition.

Derivation of the Rayleigh Fractionation Equation

For those interested, here is a derivation of the basic Rayleigh equation. Feel free to skip this section or come back to it later. In order to derive the Rayleigh fractionation equation we will consider the evaporation of a liquid. The liquid has two components; i and j. These will represent the scarce and abundant isotopes respectively.

m = Total moles of initial liquid
X_i, X_j = Mole fractions of i and j in the liquid phase
Y_i, Y_j = Mole fractions of i and j in the vapor phase

As evaporation begins, some number of moles (dm) of the substance will transfer from the liquid to vapor phase. The concentration of i in the vapor phase is given by Y_i and the number of moles of i transferred will be Y_i dm. Because an equal amount of i has to have left the liquid phase:

$$Y_i dm = d(X_i m) = m dX_i + X_i dm$$

Rearranging: $(Y_i - X_i)\, dm = m\, d X_i$

$$\frac{dm}{m} = \frac{dX_i}{Y_i - X_i} \text{(general Rayleigh equation)} \tag{8.35}$$

We now need to modify the equation in order to apply it to stable isotopes. For that we need to know the relationship between Y_i and X_i. For stable isotopes this is given by the fractionation factor,

$$\alpha_{\text{liquid}-\text{vapor}} = \frac{R_{\text{liquid}}}{R_{\text{vapor}}}$$

which in this case is given by

$$\frac{R_x}{R_y} = \frac{n_{i,L}/n_{j,L}}{n_{i,V}/n_{j,V}} \quad (8.36)$$

where n_i and n_j are the number of moles of i and j, and where L and V refer to liquid and vapor phases, respectively. Using the total number of moles (n_T) this can be converted to mole fraction.

$$\alpha_{xy} = \frac{\dfrac{n_{i,L}}{n_{T,L}} \Big/ \dfrac{n_{j,L}}{n_{T,L}}}{\dfrac{n_{i,V}}{n_{T,V}} \Big/ \dfrac{n_{j,V}}{n_{T,V}}} = \frac{X_i/X_j}{Y_i/Y_j} = \frac{X_iY_j}{Y_iX_j} \quad (8.37)$$

Because there are only two components, the total mass relationship between i and j is:

$$Y_j = 1 - Y_i \quad \text{and} \quad X_j = 1 - X_i$$

or

$$\frac{1-Y_i}{Y_j} = \frac{1-X_i}{X_j} = 1$$

$$(1 - X_i)Y_j = X_j\,(1 - Y_i) \quad (8.38)$$

Because we are deriving this relationship for stable isotopes we can make a simplifying assumption: isotope i is very rare and isotope j very abundant, then:

$$X_j \approx 1$$

and

$$1 - X_i \approx 1$$

Therefore, substituting $1 - X_i \approx 1$ into equation (8.38) yields:

$$Y_i = 1 - \frac{Y_j}{X_j}$$

Substituting in an expression for $\frac{Y_j}{X_j}$ derived from equation (8.37):

$$Y_i \approx 1 - \frac{\alpha\, Y_i}{X_i}$$

Solve for Y_i:

$$Y_i \approx \frac{X_i}{X_i + \alpha}$$

but $\alpha \approx 1$ and $X_i << 1$, then $X_i + \alpha \approx \alpha$, and:

$$Y_i \approx \frac{X_i}{\alpha} \quad (8.39)$$

Substituting equation (8.39) back into the Rayleigh equation (8.35):

$$\frac{dm}{m} = \frac{dX_i}{\dfrac{X_i}{\alpha} - X_i} = \frac{dX_i}{\left(\frac{1}{\alpha} - 1\right) X_i}$$

and

$$\left(\frac{1}{\alpha} - 1\right)\frac{dm}{m} = \frac{dXi}{Xi} \quad (8.40)$$

To consider the case where evaporation proceeds from an original mass (m^o) to a new mass (m), we need to integrate this equation:

$$\left(\frac{1}{\alpha} - 1\right)\int_{m^\circ}^{m} \frac{dm}{m} = \int_{x_i^\circ}^{xi} \frac{dXi}{Xi} \quad (8.41)$$

$$\left(\frac{1}{\alpha} - 1\right)\ln\frac{m}{m^\circ} = \ln\frac{Xi}{X_i^\circ} \quad (8.42)$$

We designate m/m° as F, the fraction remaining.
The mole fraction term can be modified to the mole ratio, which because $n_i << n_j$, results in:

$$\frac{Xi}{R_i^\circ} = \frac{R_L}{R_L^\circ}$$

Combining these two changes into equation (8.42):

$$\left(\frac{1}{\alpha} - 1\right)\ln F = \ln\frac{R_L}{R_L^\circ}$$

and exponentiating both sides gives:

$$F^{\left(\frac{1}{\alpha} - 1\right)} = \frac{R_L}{R_L^\circ} \quad (8.43)$$

which is the form of equation given in (8.31) for the case of evaporation.

Applications to Hydrothermal Alteration

This section will explore some applications that use stable isotope ratios of altered rocks to estimate some parameters of wallrock exchange reactions. Oxygen, hydrogen, carbon, and sulfur can be exchanged between fluids and minerals as hydrothermal reactions proceed. The exchange reactions can include:

1. "Cryptic" exchange where an element exchanges between a fluid and a mineral with no visible alteration, for example, where O is exchanged between a fluid and potassium feldspar with no sericitization or other mineralogical change. Oxygen and hydrogen isotope exchange between minerals and fluids, without mineral alteration, is used in laboratory experiments to measure isotope diffusivities and fluid-mineral fractionations, and hydrothermal minerals that form at one time in the history of a hydrothermal system might exchange with later fluids with different isotope ratios and at a different temperature;
2. Dissolution-precipitation of minerals that alter the porosity of a rock, such as quartz precipitating in veinlets;
3. Mineral-mineral reactions when a reactant mineral is replaced by product minerals, for example, when chlorite and calcite replace primary hornblende in a granodiorite.

In each of these three cases, the reaction products form in presumed isotopic equilibrium with the fluid, and the reactions usually alter the $\delta^{18}O$ and δD values of both the rock and fluid while conserving mass balance of the isotopes in the system as a whole.

The final isotope ratios of altered rocks and fluids are functions of the initial values of these reservoirs, and of the parameters that control the mineral exchange reactions. These parameters include, among others, the temperature at which the water/rock exchange occurs, the permeability of the rock, and the prior exchange histories of the fluids and rocks. The progress of mineral/fluid reactions is rate dependent, so the duration of water/rock exchange is important. Oxygen and hydrogen are the most abundant elements in most hydrothermal systems, and both elements are common in rocks (most rocks contain about 50 mole percent oxygen, but have much lower concentrations of hydrogen). Thus, these two elements are ideally suited for stable isotopic studies of hydrothermal alteration.

Water/Rock Ratios

Water/rock ratios provide useful information about processes in hydrothermal systems, but their application has often been pushed beyond the limitations inherent in the development of the commonly used water/rock equations. Therefore, it is important to understand the rationale behind their formulation. An early study by Craig (1963) found a clear relationship between the oxygen and hydrogen isotope ratios of sodium chloride hot spring fluids and those of local meteoric waters from which they were derived (Fig. 5). It was noticed that the hot fluids had $\delta^{18}O$ values that were heavier than the local meteoric waters, but both fluids had the same δD values. This pattern for hot spring fluids is called the "^{18}O-shift." Local meteoric ground waters are drawn into convection systems driven by hot, cooling magmas in the shallow levels of the crust. These heated fluids react and exchange isotopes with the rocks before discharging on the surface as hot springs. It is this water/rock exchange that produces the ^{18}O-shift.

The other half of the story made its debut when Taylor (1971) published $\delta^{18}O$ values for altered rocks in the Bohemia Mining District, Oregon. Here, a broad area of propylitically altered andesite surrounds an area of productive veins and small intrusive stocks. $\delta^{18}O$ values for the altered rocks decrease systematically from unaltered values (~7‰) on the periphery towards low values (~−2‰) near the center of the altered area. The depleted values were interpreted to have been produced by oxygen exchange between the rocks and a low-^{18}O fluid. This concentric pattern of $\delta^{18}O$ depletion has since been found to be characteristic of broad propylitic zones centered on altered intrusions and veins where meteoric fluids have circulated (e.g., Criss and Taylor, 1983; Larson and Taylor, 1986a; Larson and Zimmerman, 1991).

The ^{18}O-depletion in the altered rocks is the complement to the ^{18}O-enrichment in the sodium chloride hot spring fluids. Isotopic mass balance has to be maintained between these two reacting reservoirs, and this requirement can be used to estimate the relative molar proportions of water and rock that exchanged isotopes in a hydrothermal system. The ratio of these exchanging proportions is called the "water/rock ratio" (W/R). Consider a volume of rock with its pore space filled with water, where the molar quantities of isotopically exchangeable oxygen in these two reservoirs are R and W, respectively. Assume that the rock and water are each isotopically homogeneous, and have oxygen isotope ratios δ_R and δ_W, respectively. We now, stipulate that oxygen exchange can only occur in the specified volume of rock, and let the water and rock react and exchange oxygen at some constant temperature. The mass balance equation (8.23) can

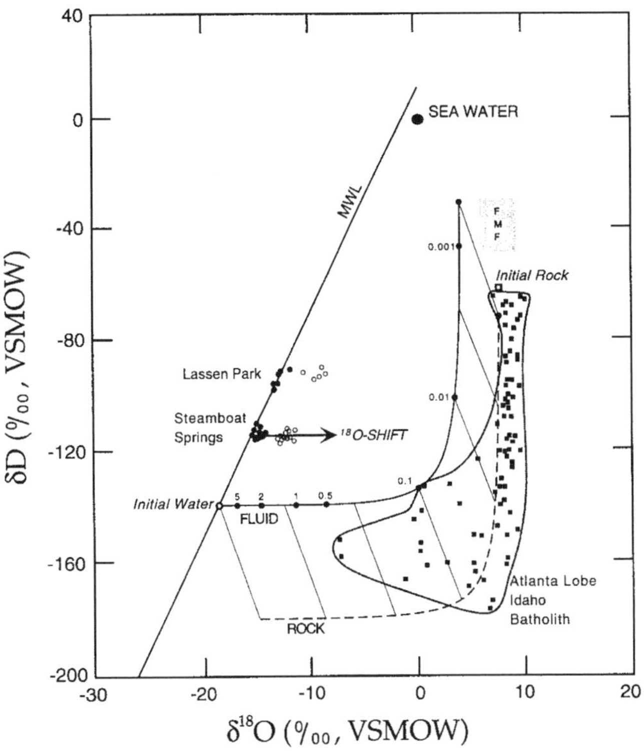

FIG. 5. Oxygen and hydrogen isotope ratios of sodium chloride hot spring fluids, and trajectories for a meteoric-hydrothermal fluid and a granite undergoing isotope exchange during hydrothermal alteration. The fields of sea water, the meteoric water line (MWL), and felsic magmatic fluids (FMF) are also shown. The open circles are NaCl-bearing hot spring waters for Steamboat Springs and Lassen Park, California. The filled circles on the MWL are local surface meteoric waters for both areas (Craig, 1963). The hydrothermal fluids bear a striking correlation to the local meteoric fluids, where their δD values correlate, but the thermal fluid $\delta^{18}O$ values are shifted to heavier ratios. This relationship, the "^{18}O-shift" labeled for the Steamboat Springs waters, is characteristic for NaCl-bearing hot spring fluids. The exchange curves for meteoric fluid (FLUID, initially δD = −140‰ and $\delta^{18}O$ = −18‰) with granite (ROCK, initially δD = −70‰ and $\delta^{18}O$ = 7‰ shown by the open square) at 400°C are shown as a function of water/rock (W/R) ratio (Campbell et al., 1984). W/R is given in weight units and W/R values are shown adjacent to dots along the FLUID trajectory. Thin lines connect equilibrium water and rock ratios. Note that at low W/R, both fluid and rock values lie near FMF, but at high W/R the trajectories become horizontal and can account for the "^{18}O-shift" shown by the hot spring fluids. Biotite/chlorite-feldspar mineral pairs from the Atlanta lobe of the Idaho batholith (Criss and Taylor, 1983) define a rock trajectory similar to the ideal curve.

be rewritten

$$\delta^i_R R + \delta^i_W W = \delta^f_R R + \delta^f_W W \quad (8.44)$$

for this isothermal, closed-exchange system, where the superscript i indicates initial and f indicates final δ values. Equation (8.44) can be rearranged so that

$$W/R = (\delta^f_R - \delta^i_R)/(\delta^i_W - \delta^f_W) \quad (8.45)$$

A final condition is imposed whereby the final water is assumed to be in isotopic equilibrium with the final rock, which can be represented by a fractionation equation where $\Delta_{R\text{-}W} = \delta^f_R - \delta^f_W$. The fractionation equation can be solved for δ^f_W and substituted into equation (8.45) to give

$$W/R_{CLOSED} = \left(\delta^f_R - \delta^i_R\right)/\left(\delta^i_W - \left(\delta^f_R - \Delta_{R\text{-}W}\right)\right), \quad (8.46)$$

which is the closed system, water/rock ratio equation of Taylor (1977, 1979). The temperature dependence of the exchange is taken into account in the Δ-term. In practice, the rock-water fractionation is usually assumed to be the fractionation for one of the rock's dominant minerals, for example, feldspar for oxygen. A single-pass open system W/R ratio can be derived from equation (8.46), in which each fluid packet equilibrates with the rock and then leaves the system (Taylor, 1977; Nabelek, 1987):

$$W/R_{OPEN} = \ln[W/R_{CLOSED} + 1]. \quad (8.47)$$

The open system equation is derived from the closed system equation by differentiating equation (8.46) and then integrating between the limits of initial and final rock values (see Nabelek, 1987, for a full derivation).

It is important to recall that equations (8.46) and (8.47) represent idealized end-member behaviors. Their limitations must be considered when they are applied to any natural system (Taylor, 1977, 1979; Ohmoto, 1986). Recall first that these are ratios of molar quantities of oxygen in waters and rocks. As a general rule of thumb, semi-quantitative volumetric water to rock ratios can be estimated from these molar oxygen W/R ratios by multiplying them by a factor of 2. Thus, a molar oxygen W/R of 0.7 corresponds to a volumetric ratio of about 1.4 cm^3 of water per about 1 cm^3 of rock. Secondly, the values calculated from these equations are ratios that are time-integrated over the entire volume of altered rocks. For example, it is not correct to apply them to a single sample, but should be calculated only for an estimated or calculated isotope ratio for the entire volume of altered rock. Note also that these are minimum ratios. Some fluid may pass through the system without exchanging any isotopes with the rocks. This could happen early in the history of a hydrothermal system, when temperatures are low and reactions are sluggish; late in its history when the rocks are already exchanged and equilibrated with the fluids; or when large volumes of fluid flow through fractures and interact minimally with the wall rocks. The equations also assume isothermal exchange, which is not realistic. Ohmoto (1986) provides a useful critique of these and other aspects and limitations of hydrothermal water/rock ratios.

With these limitations in mind, the W/R ratios provide useful information about hydrothermal systems. Curves showing oxygen isotope closed and open system water/rock exchange trajectories (from equations (8.46) and (8.47), respectively) are shown in Figure 6. These trajectories are calculated using typical values for hydrothermal systems in igneous rocks (e.g. Taylor, 1971; Criss and Taylor, 1983; Larson and Taylor, 1986a), where the initial rock $\delta^{18}O$ (δ^i_R) is 8 per mil, the initial $\delta^{18}O$ water (δ^i_W) is −15‰, and the plagioclase-water fractionation factor (O'Neil and Taylor, 1969) is used to represent the rock-water factor ($\Delta_{R\text{-}W}$ = 5.4‰ at 300°C, and 1.5‰ at 500°C). The range of the lowest igneous whole-rock oxygen isotope values (−2 to −4‰) in the proximal, upwelling plume portion of the Rico hydrothermal system, Colorado (where temperatures were about 300°C), are also shown on Figure 6 (Larson and Zimmerman, 1991; Larson et al., 1994). The intersection of the field of ^{18}O-depleted altered rocks with the W/R trajectories indicate that integrated molar oxygen W/R ratios were approximately 1 to 2. These ratios are typical for continental, meteoric-hydrothermal systems (Taylor, 1979).

Higher temperature oxygen isotope exchange at equivalent W/R produces more depleted altered rocks (Fig. 6) because $\Delta_{R\text{-}W}$ is smaller at higher temperatures. Thus, the

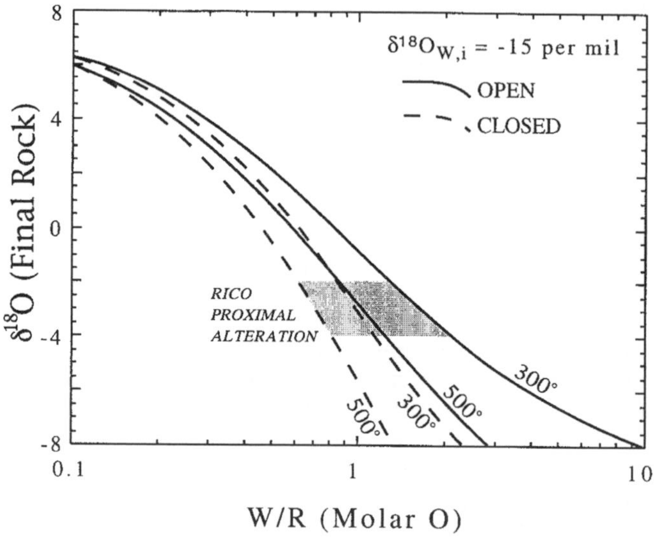

FIG. 6. A W/R plot for proximal hydrothermal alteration at Rico, Colorado (Larson and Zimmerman, 1991; Larson et al., 1994), where altered rock values of $\delta^{18}O$ between −2 and −4 per mil indicate an overall W/R ratio between 1 and 2 on a molar oxygen basis or 2 to 4 on a volume basis (see text). Theoretical curves for both open and closed systems constrain the W/R ratios, and were calculated from Taylor's (1977) W/R equations assuming water-rock fractionation is approximated by water-plagioclase fractionation. Temperatures are based on fluid inclusion trapping temperatures and on hydrothermal mineral geothermometers. Initial rock and initial water $\delta^{18}O$ values are 8 and −15, respectively; these were measured on unaltered rocks and by projecting $\delta^{18}O$-shifted vein fluids to the meteoric water line, respectively. The curves probably bracket natural conditions.

low $\delta^{18}O$ values of altered rocks that are typically found near and around centers of many ore-producing hydrothermal systems provide strong evidence for the dominance of meteoric components in these fluids. Magmatic fluids, which would have $\delta^{18}O$ values greater than at least 0 per mil, would produce exchange trajectories that would increase the altered rock $\delta^{18}O$ values on Figure 6 (meteoric hydrothermal fluids could also produce $\delta^{18}O$-enriched altered rock values at high W/R, but only for temperatures less than about 150°C).

Coupled Hydrogen and Oxygen Exchange: W/R Effects

Propylitic alteration in continental environments is characteristically produced by the interaction of rocks and meteoric-hydrothermal fluids, where W/R ratios are greater than about 1 on a molar oxygen basis. At these high W/R ratios, the fluids, if they have not boiled, exhibit characteristic ^{18}O-shifts (Fig. 5). But the fluids can also show a dramatic shift in δD values if the W/R ratio is very small. This is because rocks initially contain substantially less hydrogen than they do oxygen. Imagine a hypothetical spoonful of pristine meteoric water isothermally equilibrating isotopically with 20 tons of fresh granite. The initial exchange would produce a dramatic shift in the water hydrogen and oxygen isotope ratios (here the fluid is buffered by the rock), but very little overall change in the granite. Now, allow a second spoonful of pristine water to equilibrate with the granite. The rock has already been very slightly altered and the shifts in both rock and water values would be very slightly less than for the first spoonful. Then, pumping an infinite number of spoonfuls of water, one after the other, through the granite would ultimately produce an altered rock that was buffered by and in equilibrium with the initial pristine fluid.

Two equations in the form of either equations (8.46) or (8.47), one each for oxygen and hydrogen, can be solved simultaneously to show the effects of low W/R ratios on meteoric-hydrothermal fluids exchanging with a granite (Campbell et al., 1984). An example of the isotopic evolution of a fluid from low to high W/R ratios using these equations is shown in Figure 5. Rock-water equilibrium is first achieved among the hydrogen isotopes, at relatively low W/R ratios. Campbell et al. (1984) noted that D shifts are apparent in fluids that have experienced W/R ratios in the range 0.001 to 0.1, but at higher W/R ratios the hydrogen isotopes are dominated by the fluid and do not show any shift, whereas the oxygen isotope ratios continue to show a shift to W/R ratios greater than 5.

Meteoric-hydrothermal fluids that have experienced small W/R ratio exchange can look similar isotopically to some magmatic fluids (Fig. 5). These H-shifted low-W/R meteoric fluids are probably volumetrically minor and most likely are formed early in the history of a hydrothermal system. However, they can mix with unexchanged meteoric formation waters. Such a scenario has been proposed by Campbell et al. (1984) to account for the isotopic ratios of ore-forming fluids in the genesis of wolframite deposits. Note that these mixed fluids would fall on trajectories that lie above the ^{18}O-shifted trajectories, and they might be difficult to distinguish from a meteoric fluid mixed with a magmatic component. Rocks that exchanged isotopes with meteoric-hydrothermal fluids under low W/R conditions, and that fit the pattern shown in Figure 5, have been identified in altered areas of the Idaho batholith (Criss and Taylor, 1983).

Open System Hydrothermal Exchange Models

Hydrothermally altered rocks in most natural environments exhibit characteristics of open system infiltration of fluids (where closed system models define a limiting "end member" process). Several mathematical models that couple fluid flow, isotope exchange, and kinetic effects during hydrothermal alteration have been presented recently (e.g. Gregory and Criss, 1986; Criss et al., 1987; Lassey and Blattner, 1988; McKibben and Absar, 1989; Bowman et al., 1994). These models are useful because they use isotope ratios of mineral assemblages in altered rocks to evaluate mass balance and kinetic effects of isotope exchange in hydrothermal environments. Additionally, kinetic exchange models provide more realistic estimates of water/rock ratios than do the non-kinetic equations (8.46) and (8.47).

Mineral pair analyses illustrate a kinetic exchange effect in altered rocks. Figure 7 is a plot of mineral oxygen isotope ratios for quartz and feldspar mineral grains from samples of an altered granite in Colorado (data from Larson and Taylor, 1986b). The linear trajectory away from the equilibrium line of 45° slope is a characteristic pattern for hydrothermally altered granitic rocks (Gregory and Criss, 1986). Note on Figure 7 that the quartz shows little effect of oxygen exchange, yet the feldspar shows a dramatic change. The observed quartz-feldspar fractionations are large and cannot represent magmatic temperatures. These data show that the feldspar exchanged oxygen with the hydrothermal fluid much more readily than did the quartz. These data also suggest that quartz, once formed, nearly maintains its initial oxygen isotope ratio under typical hydrothermal conditions, regardless of interaction with later fluids. Vein quartz is often assumed to maintain its original $\delta^{18}O$ value, once formed, based on this argument.

Gregory and Criss (1986) showed that, for rapid fluid flow rates under isothermal conditions, the $\delta^{18}O$ values of two phases exchanging oxygen with a hydrothermal fluid can be modeled by

$$1-f_1 = (1-f_2)^{k1/k2} \tag{8.48}$$

where k1/k2 is the ratio of the isotope exchange rates of the two phases, and f_1 and f_2 are the degrees to which phases 1 and 2 have approached isotopic equilibrium with the fluid.

The term f is defined as

$$f = (\delta^i-\delta)/(\delta^i-\delta_{EQ}). \tag{8.49}$$

In equation (8.49), δ^i is the initial isotopic value of the phase, δ_{EQ} is the final isotopic value the phase would have when in complete equilibrium with the hydrothermal fluid (which is assumed to have constant isotope ratios in

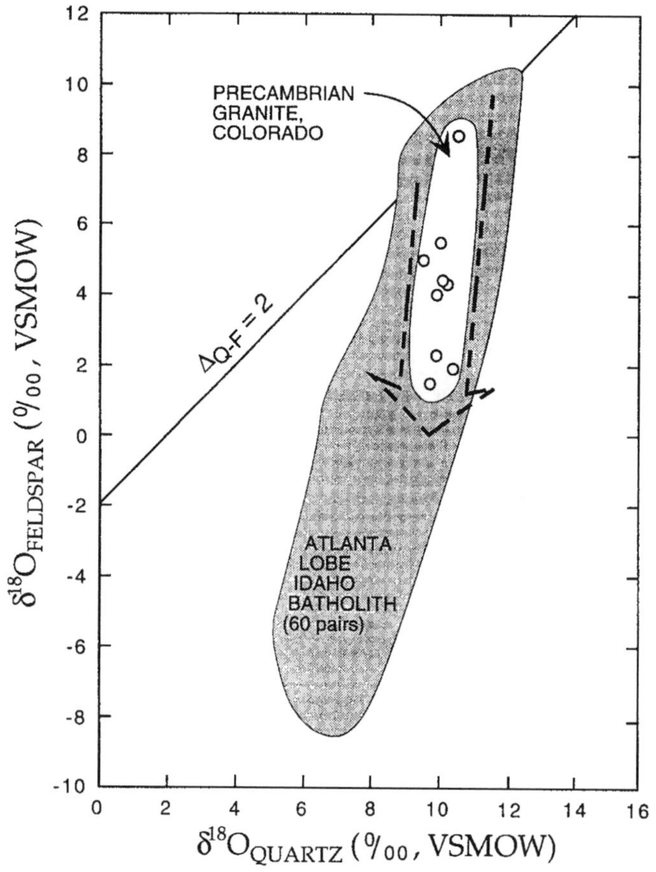

FIG. 7. Quartz-feldspar mineral-pair $\delta^{18}O$ values for samples from hydrothermally altered felsic intrusive igneous rocks define fields that are sub-parallel to the feldspar axis (Idaho batholith from Criss and Taylor, 1983; Precambrian Granite, Colorado, from Larson and Taylor, 1986b). Quartz-feldspar pairs from unaltered samples have fractionations near 2 per mil ($\Delta_{Q\text{-}F} = 2$ line). The dashed arrow shows the general exchange trajectory away from igneous values for the Precambrian granite (see text). Unaltered rocks lie near the 2 per mil fractionation line, but would move along the trajectory as W/R ratios increase and the amount of isotope exchange increases. Rocks farther from the 2 per mil fractionation line are more highly altered. The steep positive slope of the trajectory shows that feldspar exchanges oxygen with the hydrothermal fluid much faster than quartz during hydrothermal alteration.

this model), and δ is the value of the phase at some intermediate point in the exchange process. An f value of 0 indicates that no exchange has occurred ($\delta i = \delta$), and an f value of 1 indicates that the mineral has totally equilibrated with the infiltrating fluid ($\delta_{EQ} = \delta$). The only variables not accounted for in equation (8.48) are the actual isotopic exchange rates, but here only the relative rates need to be used. Relative exchange rates of 5 to 10 for feldspar relative to quartz oxygen exchange best fit the data, and seem to be characteristic of granite-hosted meteoric hydrothermal systems (Gregory and Criss, 1986).

Bowman et al. (1994) presented solutions to the one-dimensional fluid transport equations that account for various transport mechanisms, and which include variable isotopic exchange rates among phases. These solutions are not easily reproducible with a hand calculator or computer spreadsheet, and the equations are not, therefore, discussed here. It is enlightening, however, to examine their results. Bowman et al. (1994) conclude that infiltration usually produces an isotope exchange front within the fluid flow path. Behind the front (upstream), the rock is equilibrated with (buffered by) the fluid, which is analogous to a high water/rock ratio as defined earlier. Downstream from the front, the fluid is buffered by the rock, which is analogous to a low water/rock ratio. The exchange front migrates through the fluid flow path with time. If the front and a portion of the water-dominated part of the flow path are preserved in paleo-hydrothermal systems, their relative positions can be used as a guide to the direction of fluid flow. The model produced by Bowman et al. (1994) is the latest step along the path to understanding the story that stable isotope ratios tell us about hydrothermal water/rock exchange processes.

Reservoir-Limited Processes

In many processes the proportion of an element removed is substantial with respect to the amount remaining in the reservoir. In these cases the reservoir can not be considered infinite and thus will change isotopic composition as its mass decreases. The changing isotopic composition of the reservoir and the evolving phase can be modeled by using either a single stage separation process (batch fractionation) or a continuous process (Rayleigh fractionation). The difference between these two scenarios is in whether the removed phase remains intact and in isotopic equilibrium with the reservoir during the separation (batch process), or whether the product is instantaneously separated from the reservoir and does not re-equilibrate (Rayleigh process). For a constant temperature the Rayleigh process will result in greater fractionation than the batch process. However, if temperature is decreasing the batch process can result in greater fractionation due to the increasing fractionation factor (Truesdell, 1984). Two of the most common reservoir-limited processes applicable to the hydrothermal process are boiling and magmatic degassing.

Boiling. Boiling in hydrothermal ore deposits is most commonly treated as a Rayleigh process, but in geothermal systems both Rayleigh and batch processes are used. The details of calculating stable isotopic composition of geothermal fluids can be found in Truesdell (1984).

The basic equations for calculating the changing isotopic compositions of an ore fluid were given in the previous section on Rayleigh fractionation. Using those equations and the fractionation factor, we can calculate the changing fluid composition as a function of fraction of liquid remaining. For examples, let us pick a temperature of 350°C. The vapor phase will be enriched in ^{16}O and ^{2}H (because it is above the cross-over point) relative to the remaining liquid. So as boiling preceeds the aqueous fluid will become heavier in $\delta^{18}O$ (Fig. 4) and lighter in δD. The amount of isotopic change in the liquid reservoir that results from boiling away half of the aqueous fluid (F = 0.5) is not large. It is not until the end stages of the Rayleigh process (i.e., low F values) that extreme isotopic changes are seen. Below the cross-over point for hydrogen, the liquid will become heavier in both $\delta^{18}O$ and δD as boiling proceeds.

Metamorphic and magmatic degassing. The process of degassing in both metamorphic and magmatic environments are important in controlling the isotopic compositions of potential ore fluids. Metamorphic degassing consists primarily of dehydration and decarbonation during prograde metamorphism. In both cases the fraction of oxygen removed from the system is not great relative to the amount left behind as silicate minerals. For carbonate rocks this is referred to as the calc-silicate limit (Valley, 1986). Thus, the oxygen isotopic composition shifts in the residual rocks are expected to be minor. Major changes in the $\delta^{18}O$ value of metamorphosed carbonate rocks are typically attributed to influx of magmatic fluids. On the other hand, hydrogen and carbon can be essentially entirely removed from the rock during dehydration or decarbonation. Consequently, the δD and $\delta^{13}C$ values of the rock can show major changes.

The behavior of oxygen isotopes during magmatic degassing has certain similarities to metamorphic devolatilization. Because of the large reservoir of oxygen in the magma and the small fractionation factors at high temperatures, the $\delta^{18}O$ of a magma is unlikely to change during devolatilization. Hydrogen, however, can be almost completely degassed from a magma, and δD values of degassed magmas typically show evidence of large isotopic shifts. The volatile phase is enriched in D compared to the magma, thus depleting the magma. The changing δD of the magma is easily seen when plotting δD versus wt percent H_2O in the rock (Taylor, 1986).

Fluid Inclusions

In addition to being valuable recorders of temperature and the physical and chemical state of a mineralizing fluid, fluid inclusions can also preserve the stable isotopic composition of the fluid.

It can be highly advantageous to be able to measure directly the stable isotopic composition of the paleo fluid. By making a direct measurement of the fluid you sidestep the need to know the temperature precisely. When calculating the fluid composition from a mineral value one must consider how the error in temperature measurements propagates into uncertainty in the resulting water composition. However, there are some situations in which the negative aspects of direct measurement outweigh the advantages.

Fluid inclusions are most often used to determine the δD of the fluid and less frequently used to determine $\delta^{18}O$. The reason for this is the potential for isotopic exchange between the fluid in the inclusion and the host mineral. Most fluid inclusion studies are done with quartz. Because quartz contains oxygen, but no hydrogen, the δD of the fluid is not subject to change by equilibration with the host, whereas the $\delta^{18}O$ is.

Based on early studies by Rye (1966) at Providencia, the conventional wisdom is that the fluid oxygen in quartz-hosted inclusions has undergone isotopic exchange and no longer provides a record of the original $\delta^{18}O$ fluid. However, several investigators (Seal and Kelly, 1990; Deen et al., 1994) have shown in some cases that exchange may not be a problem. The post entrapment ^{18}O exchange between fluid and host quartz is dependent upon temperature, salinity, and time (Seal and Kelly, 1990). In young quartz samples that trapped fluids of low salinity at low to moderate temperature the $\delta^{18}O$ of the fluid may still closely reflect that of the original mineralizing fluid.

It is, however, possible to use fluid inclusions hosted in sulfide minerals to determine the $\delta^{18}O$ of the fluid because there should be no exchange. The problem with sulfide hosted inclusions is that most sulfides are opaque, and thus it is not possible optically to examine the inclusions that will be used. This brings up the biggest problem with using fluid inclusions for stable isotope measurements. No one has yet been able to determine the δD or $\delta^{18}O$ of individual inclusions due to the small amount of fluid they typically contain (e.g., a 10 μm aqueous fluid inclusion contains only about 3×10^{-8} micromoles of oxygen). A bulk sample must be used, which means that if primary and secondary inclusions are both present in the sample (a common situation), they will both contribute to the extracted fluid to be analyzed. In optically transparent minerals the proportions of primary and secondary inclusions can be determined and areas of the sample containing predominately primary inclusions can be selected for analysis. Foley et al. (1989) have shown that with painstaking sample preparation, areas of samples containing predominately primary inclusions can be identified in thick section and separated from the rest by careful sawing.

In most ore deposit studies the $\delta^{18}O$ of the mineralizing fluid is calculated from the $\delta^{18}O$ of a mineral, and the δD of the fluid is measured directly from fluid inclusion water. This can lead to a potential problem related to secondary fluid inclusions. The $\delta^{18}O$ of the quartz will be representative of the original water from which it was deposited but the δD measured from the extracted fluids will be a mixture of both primary and secondary inclusions. If one were to analyze a number of quartz samples that were deposited from the same primary fluid, but trapped differing amounts of a secondary fluid with a different δD, the result would be a vertical line on a δD-$\delta^{18}O$ diagram with a constant $\delta^{18}O$ and a variable $\delta^{18}D$.

This problem was noted by Campbell et al. (1984) in their study of the San Cristobal tungsten-base metal deposit in Peru. The water responsible for quartz and wolframite deposition had a tightly constrained $\delta^{18}O$ but a widely variable δD. In order to test the hypothesis that the range in δD might be related to secondary inclusions, they analyzed both δD and $\delta^{18}O$ of inclusion fluids from sulfide minerals. In this case if the low δD values were related to trapping of secondary fluids of a meteoric origin, the $\delta^{18}O$ values should show depletions as well. However, the waters from the sulfide-hosted inclusions showed the same $\delta^{18}O$ as those calculated from mineral values, thus supporting their interpretation that the variable δD values resulted from D-shifts produced by wall-rock exchange at very low water/rock ratios.

Closing Statement

Stable isotopes have played a powerful role in the study of ore deposits and hydrothermal processes. They are most useful when they can be combined with other geological studies including paragenetic sequence, fluid inclusion microthermometry, alteration, and mineral chemistry. With current and future advances in instrumentation and extraction techniques, stable isotopes should continue to provide valuable insights into hydrothermal processes. In particular, the recent advances in small sample analysis by laser extraction or ion probe analysis enable researchers to look at isotopic zoning within crystals. These studies often reveal much more heterogeneity than previously known and imply that hydrothermal processes can vary in a rapid time frame.

The introductory knowledge in this chapter should allow the reader to delve deeper into the subject of stable isotope geochemistry in specific areas of interest. Students of ore deposits are directed to the following references as classical summaries of isotope techniques and their application to ore genesis: Ohmoto (1972), Taylor (1979), Ohmoto and Rye (1979), Field and Fifarek (1985), Ohmoto (1986). There are also several excellent references for applications to other geological environments, such as Valley et al. (1986), Kyser (1987), and Hoefs (1997).

Acknowledgments

We would like to thank Bruce Taylor for his input on the initial organization of this chapter. We thank Fred Phillips for sharing his derivation of the Rayleigh equation with us. We appreciate the time taken by several students (Sarah Wilson and Beverly Chomiak) for initial reviews of this chapter as well as the detailed reviews by John Dilles and Ed Ripley.

REFERENCES

Barnes, I., Irwin, W.P., White, D.E., 1978, Global distribution of carbon dioxide discharges and major zones of seismicity: U.S. Geological Survey, Water-Resources Investigation, Open File Report 78–36. 12 p.

Bigeleisen, J., and Mayer, M.G., 1947, Calculation of equilibrium constants for isotopic exchange reactions: Journal of Chemical Physics, v. 15, p. 261–267.

Bigeleisen, J., Perlman, M.L., and Prosser, H.C., 1952, Conversion of hydrogenic materials for isotopic analysis: Analytical Chemistry, v. 24, p. 1356.

Bottinga, Y., 1969, Calculated fractionation factors for carbon and hydrogen isotope exchange in the system calcite-carbon dioxide-graphite-methane-hydrogen-water vapor: Geochimica et Cosmochimica Acta, v. 33, p. 49–64.

Bottinga, Y., and Javoy, M., 1973, Comments on oxygen isotope geothermometry: Earth and Planetary Science Letters, v. 20, p. 250–265.

Bowman, J.R., Willett, S.D., and Cook, S.J., 1994, Oxygen isotopic transport and exchange during fluid flow: One-dimensional models and applications: American Journal of Science, v. 294, pp. 1–55.

Campbell, A., Rye, D., and Petersen, U., 1984, A hydrogen and oxygen isotope study of the San Cristobal Mine, Peru: Implications of the role of water to rock ratio for the genesis of wolframite deposits: Economic Geology, v. 79, p. 1818–1832.

Campbell, A.R., Phillips, F.M., and Vanlandingham, R.J., 1995, Stable isotope study of soil water, WIPP Site New Mexico: Estimation of recharge to rustler aquifers: Radioactive Waste Management and Environmental Restoration, v. 19, p. 1–13.

Chacko, T., Xiangshen, H., Mayeda, T., Clayton, R., Goldsmith, J., 1996, Oxygen isotope fractionation in muscovite, phlogopite and rutile: Geochimica et Cosmochimica Acta, v. 60, p. 2595–2608.

Chapman, J.B., Ingraham, N.L., and Hess, J.W., 1992, Isotopic investigation of infiltration and unsaturated zone flow processes at Carlsbad Cavern, New Mexico: Journal of Hydrology, v. 133, p. 343–363.

Claypool, G.E., Holser, W.T., Kaplan, I.R., Sakai, H., and Zak, I., 1980, The age curves of sulfur and oxygen isotopes in marine sulfate and their mutual interpretation: Chemical Geology, v. 28, p. 199–260.

Clayton, R.N., and Mayeda, T.K., 1963, The use of bromine pentafluoride in the extraction of oxygen from oxides and silicates for isotopic analysis: Geochimica et Cosmochimica Acta, v. 27, p. 43–52.

Clayton, R.N, O'Neil, J.R., and Mayeda, T.K., 1972, Oxygen isotope exchange between quartz and water: Journal of Geophysical Research, v. 77, p. 3057–3067.

Clayton, R.N., Goldsmith, J.R., and Mayeda, T.K., 1989, Oxygen isotope fractionation in quartz, albite, anorthite and calcite: Geochimica et Cosmochimica Acta, v. 53, p. 725–733.

Cole, D.R., Chacko, T., Riciputi, L., and Horita, J., 1997, A new method for determining equilibrium hydrogen isotope fractionation factors using the ion microprobe: Application to the epidote-water system. [abs.]: Geological Society of America Abstracts with Programs, v. 29, p. A–25.

Coleman, M.L., Sheppard, T.J., Durham, J.J., Rouse, J.E., and Moore, G.R., 1982, Reduction of water with zinc for hydrogen isotope analysis: Analytical Chemistry, v. 54, p. 993–995.

Coplen, T.B., 1996, New guidelines for reporting stable hydrogen, carbon, and oxygen isotope-ratio data: Geochimica et Cosmochimica Acta, v. 60, p. 3359–3360.

Coplen, T.B., Kendall, C., and Hopple, J., 1983, Comparison of stable isotope reference samples: Nature, v. 302, p. 236–238.

Craig, H., 1961, Isotopic variations in meteoric waters: Science, v. 133, p. 1702–1703.

—— 1963, The isotopic geochemistry of water and carbon in geothermal areas, *in* Tongiorgi, E., ed., Nuclear Geology on Geothermal Areas, Spoleto: Pisa, Consiglio Nazionale della Richerche, Laboratorio de Geologia Nucleare, p. 17–53.

Criss, R. E., and Taylor, H. P., Jr., 1983, An $^{18}O/^{16}O$ and D/H study of Tertiary hydrothermal systems in the southern half of the Idaho batholith: Geological Society of America Bulletin, v. 94, p. 640–663.

Criss, R.E., Gregory, R.T., and Taylor, H.P., Jr., 1987, Kinetic theory of oxygen isotope exchange between minerals and water: Geochimica et Cosmochimica Acta, v. 51, p. 1099–1108.

Deen, J.A., Rye, R.O., Munoz, J.L., and Drexler, J.W., 1994, The magmatic hydrothermal system at Julcani, Peru: Evidence from fluid inclusions and hydrogen and oxygen isotopes: Economic Geology, v. 89, p. 1924–1938.

Deines, P., Langmuir, D., and Harmon, R.S., 1974, Stable carbon isotope ratios and the existence of a gas phase in the evolution of carbonate ground waters: Geochimica et Cosmochimica Acta, v. 38, p. 1147–1164.

Dobson, P.F., Epstein, S., and Stolper, E.M., 1989, Hydrogen isotope fractionation between coexisting vapor and silicate glasses and melts at low pressure: Geochimica et Cosmochimica Acta, v. 53, p. 2723–2730.

Ehleringer, J.R., 1988, Carbon isotope ratios and physiological processes in aridland plants, *in* Rundel, P.W., Ehleringer, J.R., and Nagy, K.A., eds., Applications of stable isotope ratios to ecological research: New York, Springer-Verlag, p. 41–54.

Ehleringer, J.R., Sage, R.F., Flanagan, L.B., and Pearcy, R.W., 1991, Climatic change and the evolution of C4 photosynthesis: Trends in Ecological Evolution, v. 6, p. 95–99.

Eldridge, C.S., Compston, W., Williams, I.S., Both, R.A., Walshe, J.L., and Ohmoto, H., 1988, Sulfur isotope variability in sediment-hosted massive sulfide deposits as determined using the ion microprobe SHRIMP, I. An example from the Rammelsberg orebody: Economic Geology, v. 83, p. 443–449.

Feng, X., and Savin, S.M., 1993, Oxygen isotope studies of zeolites-Stilbite, analcime, heulandite, and clinoptilolite: III. Oxygen isotope fractionation between stilbite and water or water vapor: Geochimica et Cosmochimica Acta, v. 57, p. 4239–4247.

Field, C.W., and Fifarek, R.H., 1985, Light stable-isotope systematics in the epithermal environment, *in* Berger, B.R. and Bethke, P.M., eds.,

Geology and geochemistry of epithermal systems: Reviews in Economic Geology, v. 2, p. 99–128.
Foley, N.K., Bethke, P.M., and Rye, R.O., 1989, A reinterpretation of the δD_{H_20} of inclusion fluids in contemporaneous quartz and sphalerite, Creede Mining District, Colorado: A generic problem for shallow orebodies?: Economic Geology, v. 84, p. 1966–1977.
Friedman, I., and O'Neil, J.R., 1977, Compilation of stable isotope fractionation factors of geochemical interest, *in* Fleischer, M., ed., Data of Geochemistry: U.S. Geological Survey, Professional Paper, 440kk.
Giggenbach, W.F., 1992, Isotopic shifts in waters from geothermal and volcanic systems along convergent plate boundaries and their origin: Earth and Planetary Science Letters, v. 113, p. 495–510.
Graham, C.M., and Valley, J.W., 1992, Sulphur isotope analysis of pyrites: Chemical Geology (Isotope Geoscience Section), v. 101, p. 169–172.
Graham, C.M., Viglino, J.A., and Harmon, R.S., 1987, Experimental study of hydrogen-isotope exchange between aluminous chlorite and water and of hydrogen diffusion in chlorite: American Mineralogist, v. 72, p. 566–579.
Gregory, R.T., and Criss, R.E., 1986, Isotopic exchange in open and closed systems, *in* Valley, J.W., Taylor, H.P., O'Neil, J.R., eds., Stable Isotopes in High Temperature Geological Processes: Reviews in Mineralogy, v. 16, p. 91–127.
Hoefs, J., 1997, Stable Isotope Geochemistry: Berlin, Springer-Verlag, 201 p.
Horita, J., and Wesolowski, D., 1994, Liquid-vapor fractionation of oxygen and hydrogen isotopes of water from the freezing to the critical temperature: Geochimica et Cosmochimica Acta., v. 58, p. 3425–3437.
Jibao, G., and Yaqian, Q., 1997, Hydrogen isotope fractionation and hydrogen diffusion in the tourmaline-water system: Geochimica et Cosmochimica Acta, v. 61, p. 4679–4688.
Kieffer, S.W., 1982, Thermodynamics and lattice vibrations of minerals: 5. Applications to phase equilibria, isotopic fractionation, and high-pressure thermodynamic properties: Reviews of Geophysics and Space Physics, v. 20, p. 827–849.
Kotzer, T.G., Kyser, T.K., King, R.W., and Kerrich, R., 1993, An empirical oxygen- and hydrogen-isotope geothermometer for quartz-tourmaline and tourmaline-water. Geochimica et Cosmochimica Acta, v. 57, p. 3421–3426.
Kulla, J.B., and Anderson, T.F., 1978, Experimental oxygen isotope fractionation between kaolinite and water: U.S. Geological Survey, Open File Report 78-701, p. 234–235.
Kyser, T.K., 1987, Short Course in Stable Isotope Geochemistry of Low Temperature Fluids. Mineralogical Association of Canada, Short Course Volume 13, 452 p.
Larson, P.B., and Taylor, H.P., Jr., 1986a, An oxygen isotope study of hydrothermal alteration in the Lake City caldera, San Juan Mountains, Colorado: Journal of Volcanology and Geothermal Research, v. 30, p. 47–82.
—— 1986b, An oxygen study of water/rock interaction in the granite of Cataract Gulch, western San Juan Mountains, Colorado: Geological Society of America Bulletin, v. 97, p. 505–515.
Larson, P.B., and Zimmerman, B.S., 1991, Variations in $\delta^{18}O$ values, water/rock ratios, and water flux in the Rico paleothermal anomaly, Colorado: The Geochemical Society Special Publication 3, p. 463–469.
Larson, P.B., Cunningham, C.G., and Naeser, C.W., 1994, Large-scale alteration effects in the Rico paleothermal anomaly, southwest Colorado: Economic Geology, v. 89, p. 1769–1779.
Lassey, K.R., and Blattner, P., 1988, Kinetically controlled oxygen isotope exchange between fluid and rock in one-dimensional advective flow: Geochimica et Cosmochimica Acta, v. 52, p. 2169–2175.
Leśniak, P.M., and Sakai, H., 1989, Carbon isotope fractionation between dissolved carbonate and CO_2(g) at 25° and 40°C: Earth and Planetary Science Letters, v. 95, p. 297–301.
Liu, K, and Epstein, S., 1984, The hydrogen isotope fractionation between kaolinite and water: Isotope Geoscience, v. 2, p. 335–350.
Matthews, A., and Beckinsale, R.D., 1979, Oxygen isotope equilibration systematics between quartz and water: American Mineralogist, v. 64, p. 232–240.
Matthews, A., Goldsmith, J.R., and Clayton, R.N., 1979, Oxygen isotopic fractionation in the system quartz-albite-anorthite-water: Geochimica et Cosmochimica Acta, v. 43, p. 1131–1140.
—— 1983a, Oxygen isotope fractionations involving pyroxenes: The calibration of mineral-pair geothermometers: Geochimica et Cosmochimica Acta, v. 47, p. 631–644.
—— 1983b, Oxygen isotope fractionation between zoisite and water: Geochimica et Cosmochimica Acta, v. 47, p. 645–654.
McCrea, J.M., 1950, The isotopic chemistry of carbonates and a paleotemperature scale: Journal of Chemical Physics, v. 18, p. 849–857.
McKibben, R., and Absar, A., 1989, A model for oxygen isotope transport in hydrothermal systems: Journal of Geophysical Research, v. 94, p. 7065–7070.
McKibben, M., Shanks, W., and Ridley, W., eds., 1998, Applications of microanalytical techniques to understanding mineralizing pProcesses: Reviews in Economic Geology, v. 7, in press.
Nabelek, P. I., 1987, General equations for modeling fluid/rock interaction using trace elements and isotopes: Geochimica et Cosmochimica Acta, v. 51, p. 1765–1769.
Ohmoto, H., 1972, Systematics of sulfur and carbon isotopes in hydrothermal ore deposits: Economic Geology, v. 67, p. 551–578.
—— 1986, Stable isotope geochemistry of ore deposits, *in* Valley, J.W., Taylor, H.P., O'Neil, J.R., eds., Stable isotopes in high temperature geological processes: Reviews in Mineralogy, v. 16, p. 491–559.
Ohmoto, H., and Lasaga, A.C., 1982, Kinetics of reactions between aqueous sulfates and sulfides in hydrothermal systems: Geochimica et Cosmochimica Acta, v. 46, p. 1727–1745.
Ohmoto, H., and Rye, R.O., 1979, Isotopes of sulfur and carbon, *in* Barnes, H., ed., Geochemistry of hydrothermal ore deposits, 2nd ed.: New York, Rinehart and Winston, p. 509–567.
O'Neil, J.R., 1986, Theoretical and experimental aspects of isotopic fractionation, *in* Valley, J.W., Taylor, H.P., O'Neil, J.R., eds., Stable isotopes in high temperature geological processes: Reviews in Mineralogy, v. 16, p. 1–40.
O'Neil, J.R., and Taylor, H.P., Jr., 1969, Oxygen isotope equilibrium between muscovite and water: Journal of Geophysical Research, v. 74, p. 6012–6022.
Riciputi, L.R., and Paterson, B.A., 1994, High spatial-resolution measurement of O isotope ratios in silicates and carbonates by ion microprobe: American Mineralogist, v. 79, p. 1227–1230.
Robinson, B.W., and Kusakabe, M., 1975, Quantitative preparation of sulphur dioxide for $^{34}S/^{32}S$ analyses from sulphides by combustion with cuprous oxide: Analytical Chemistry, v. 47, p. 1179.
Rumble, D., and Sharp, Z., 1998, Laser microanalysis of silicates for $^{18}O/^{17}O/^{16}O$ and of carbonates for $^{18}O/^{16}O$ and $^{13}C/^{12}C$: Reviews in Economic Geology, v. 7 in press.
Rye, R.O., 1966, The carbon, hydrogen, and oxygen isotopic composition of the hydrothermal fluids responsible for the lead-zinc deposits at Providencia, Zacatecas, Mexico: Economic Geology, v. 61, p. 1339–1427.
Sakai, H., and Tsutsumi, M., 1978, D/H fractionation factors between serpentine and water at 100°–500°C and 2000 bar water pressure, and the D/H ratios of natural serpentines: Earth and Planetary Science Letters, v. 40, p. 231–242.
Seal, R., II, and Kelly, W., 1990, Investigation of postentrapment retrograde ^{18}O exchange between inclusion fluids and quartz: [abs]: Geological Society of America Abstracts with Programs, v. 22, p. A–250.
Shanks, W.C., III, Crowe, D., and Johnson, C., 1998, Sulfur isotope analyses using the laser microprobe: Reviews in Economic Geology, v. 7, in press.
Socki, R., Karlsson, H., and Gibson, E., 1992, Extraction technique for the determination of oxygen-18 in water using preevacuated glass vials: Analytical Chemistry, v. 64, p. 829–831.
Stoffregen, R.E., Rye, R.O., and Wasserman, M.D., 1994, Experimental studies of alunite: I. ^{18}O-^{16}O and D-H fractionation factors between alunite and water at 250°–450°C: Geochimica et Cosmochimica Acta, v. 58, p. 903–916.
Suzuoki, T., and Epstein, S., 1976, Hydrogen isotope fractionation between OH-bearing minerals and water: Geochimica et Cosmochimica Acta, v. 40, p. 1129–1240.
Taylor, B.E., 1986, Magmatic volatiles: Isotopic variation of C, H, and S, *in* Valley, J.W., Taylor, H.P., O'Neil, J.R., eds., Stable isotopes in high temperature geological processes: Reviews in Mineralogy, v. 16, p. 185–225.

—— 1992, Degassing of H_2O from rhyolite magma during eruption and shallow intrusion, and the isotopic composition of magmatic water in hydrothermal systems, *in* Hedenquist, J., ed., Magmatic contributions to hydrothermal systems and the behavior of volatiles in magma: Geological Survey of Japan Report No. 279, p. 190–194.

Taylor, H.P., Jr., 1968, The oxygen isotope geochemistry of igneous rocks: Contributions to Mineralogy and Petrology, v. 19, p. 1–71.

—— 1971, Oxygen isotope evidence for large-scale interaction between meteoric ground waters and Tertiary granodiorite intrusions, western Cascade Range, Oregon: Journal of Geophysical Research, v. 76, p. 7855–7874.

—— 1977, Water/rock interactions and the origin of H_2O in granitic batholith: Journal of the Geological Society of London, v. 133, p. 509–558.

—— 1979, Oxygen and hydrogen isotope relationships in hydrothermal mineral deposits. *in* Barnes, H.L., ed., Geochemistry of hydrothermal ore deposits, 2nd ed.: New York, John Wiley, p. 236–277.

Truesdell, A.H., 1984, Stable isotopes in hydrothermal systems, *in* Henley, R.W., Truesdell, A.H., and Barton, P.B., eds., Fluid-mineral equilibria in hydrothermal systems: Reviews in Economic Geology, v. 1, p. 129–142.

Urey, H.C., 1947, The thermodynamic properties of isotopic substances: Journal of the Chemical Society (London), Part I, p. 562–581.

Valley, J.W., 1986, Stable isotope geochemistry of metamorphic rocks, *in* Valley, J.W., Taylor, H.P., O'Neil, J.R., eds., Stable isotopes in high temperature geological processes: Reviews in Mineralogy, v. 16, p. 445–489.

Valley, J.W., Taylor, H.P., and O'Neil, J.R., eds., 1986, Stable isotopes in high temperature geological processes: Reviews in Mineralogy, v. 16.

Yaqian, Q., and Jibao, G., 1993, Study of hydrogen isotope equilibrium and kinetic fractionation in the ilvaite-water system: Geochimica et Cosmochimica Acta, v. 57, p. 3073–3082.

Zhang, L.-G., Liu, J.-X., Chen, Z.-S., and Zhou, H.-B., 1994, Experimental investigations of oxygen isotope fractionation in cassiterite and wolframite: Economic Geology, v. 89, p. 150–157.

APPENDIX

Presented here are fractionation factors for some of the minerals and phases commonly used for ore deposit studies. More extensive lists of fractionation factors can be found in Friedman and O'Neil (1977), Ohmoto and Rye (1979), Field and Fifarek (1985), and O'Neil (1986).

TABLE A1. Oxygen Isotope Fractionation Factors

A-B	T RANGE °C	$1000\ln\alpha_{A-B}$	REFERENCE
Stilbite (framework O)-Water	220–300	$-2.4 + ((2.7 \times 10^6)/T^2)$	Feng and Savin (1993)
Quartz-toumaline	200–600	$1.0[\pm 0.17](10^6/T^2) + 0.39$ $[\pm 0.44]$	Kotzer et al. (1993)
Quartz-zoisite	400–700	$1.56(10^6/T^2)$	Matthews et al. (1983b)
Quartz-water	500–750 200–500	$2.51(10^6/T^2) - 1.96$ $3.38(10^6/T^2) - 3.40$	Clayton et al. (1972)
Quartz-water	265–465	$3.05(10^6/T^2) - 2.09$	Matthews and Beckinsale (1979)
Quartz-calcite	600–1000	$0.38(10^6/T^2)$	Clayton et al. (1989)
Quartz-mucovite	>400	$1.35(10^6/T^2) + 0.042$ $(10^6/T^2)^2 -$ $0.0086(10^6/T^2)^3$	Chacko et al. (1996)

TABLE A1. (*Cont.*)

A-B	T RANGE °C	$1000\ln\alpha_{A-B}$	REFERENCE
Quartz-plagioclase	500–800 400–500	$(0.46+0.55\beta)(10^6/T^2) -$ $(0.02+0.85\beta)$ $[\beta=X_{AN}]$ $(0.74+0.90\beta)(10^6/T^2) -$ $(0.43+0.30\beta)$ $[\beta=X_{AN}]$	Matsuhisa et al. (1979)
Quartz-wollastonite	400–800	$2.20(10^6/T^2)$	Matthews et al. (1983a)
Quartz-diopside	400–800	$2.08(10^6/T^2)$	Matthews et al. (1983a)
Quartz-jadeite	400–800	$1.09(10^6/T^2)$	Matthews et al. (1983a)
Alkali feldspar-water	350–800	$2.91(10^6/T^2) - 3.41$	O'Neil and Taylor (1969)
Albite-water	500–800 400–500	$1.59(10^6/T^2) - 1.16$ $2.39(10^6/T^2) - 2.51$	Matsuhisa et al. (1979)
Anorthite-water	350–800	$2.15(10^6/T^2) - 3.82$	O'Neil and Taylor (1969)
Anorthite-water	500–800 400–500	$1.04(10^6/T^2) - 2.01$ $1.49(10^6/T^2) - 2.81$	Matsuhisa et al. (1979)
Plagioclase-water	350–800	$(2.91-0.76\beta)(10^6/T^2) -$ $(3.41+0.41\beta)$ $[\beta=X_{AN}]$	O'Neil and Taylor (1969)
Albite-calcite	600–1000	$-0.57(10^6/T^2)$	Clayton et al. (1989)
Anorthite-calcite	600–1000	$-1.59(10^6/T^2)$	Clayton et al. (1989)
Muscovite-water	400–650	$2.38(10^6/T^2) - 3.89$	O'Neil and Taylor (1969)
Kaolinite-water	175–325	$2.05(10^6/T^2) - 3.85$	Kulla and Anderson (1978)
Alunite (SO_4)-water	250–450	$3.09(10^6/T^2) - 2.94$	Stoffregen et al. (1994)
Alunite (OH)-water	250–450	$2.28(10^6/T^2) - 3.90$	Stoffregen et al. (1994)
Cassiterite-water	250–500	$10.13(10^6/T^2) - 26.09$ $(10^3/T) + 12.58$	Zhang et al. (1994)
Wolframite-water	200–420	$3.13(10^6/T^2) - 6.42$ $(10^3/T) - 0.12$	Zhang et al. (1994)
$H_2O_{(l)}-H_2O_{(v)}$	25–350	$-7.685 + 6.7123(10^3/T)$ $- 1.6664$ $(10^6/T^2) + 0.35041$ $(10^9/T^3)$	Horita and Wesolowski (1994)
$CO_{2(v)}-H_2O_{(l)}$	0–100	$-0.021(10^6/T^2) +$ $17.994(10^3/T) - 19.97$	Friedman and O'Neil (1977)

Table A2. Hydrogen Isotope Fractionation Factors

A-B	T RANGE °C	$1000\ln\alpha_{A-B}$	REFERENCE
Tourmaline-water	200–600	$-27.2[\pm4.4](10^6/T^2)$ +28.1 [±9.8]	Kotzer et al. (1993)
Tourmaline-water	350–800	$-27.9\ (10^6/T^2) = 2.3$	Jibao and Yaqian (1997)
Ilvaite-water	350–550 550–750	−105.0±0.7 $29.95(10^6/T^2)-60.62$	Yaqian and Jibao (1993)
Alunite-water	250 & 450	−6 & −9, respectively	Stoffregen et al. (1994)
Chlorite-water	500–700 200–500	−28 (approximate) −30 to −40	Graham et al. (1987)
Muscovite-water	450–800	$-22.1(10^6/T^2)+19.1$	Suzuoki and Epstein (1976)
Biotite-water	450–800	$-21.3(10^6/T^2)-2.8$	Suzuoki and Epstein (1976)
Hornblende-water	450–800	$-23.9(10^6/T^2)+7.9$	Suzuoki and Epstein (1976)
Serpentine-water	150–550	$8.6(10^6/T^2)-33.92$	Sakai and Tsutsumi (1978)
Kaolinite-water	200, 250, 300, 352	7, −6, −15, −20, respectively	Liu and Epstein (1984)
$H_2O_{(1)}-H_2O_{(v)}$	25–350	$1158.8\ (T^3/10^9)-1620.1(T^2/10^6)+794.84\ (T/10^5)-161.04+2.9992\ (10^9/T^3)$	Horita and Wesolowski (1994)

Table A3. Sulfur Isotope Fractionation Factors

A-B	T RANGE °C	$1000\ln\alpha_{A-B}$
Sulfates – H_2S	200–350	$5.26\ (10^6/T^2) + 6.0$
SO_2 – H_2S	350–1050	$4.70\ (10^6/T^2) - 0.5$
FeS_2 – H_2S	200–700	$0.4\ (10^6/T^2)$
FeS – H_2S	200–600	$0.1\ (10^6/T^2)$
$CuFeS_2$ – H_2S	200-600	$-0.05\ (10^6/T^2)$
S – H_2S	200–400	$-0.16\ (10^6/T^2) \pm 0.5$
HS – H_2S	50–350	$-0.06\ (10^6/T^2) - 0.6$
PbS – H_2S	50–700	$-0.63\ (10^6/T^2)$
ZnS – H_2S	50–705	$0.1\ (10^6/T^2)$

Excerpted from Ohmoto and Rye, 1979. They arrived at these fractionation factors by critically examining the available raw data from various previous investigators.

Table A4. Carbon Isotope Fractionation Factors

A-B	T RANGE °C	$1000\ln\alpha_{A-B}$	REFERENCE
$CO_2 - CO_3^{=}\ _{(aq)}$	25	8.38	Lesniak and Sakai (1989)
	40	6.67	Lesniak and Sakai (1989)
$CO_2 - HCO_3^-$	0–100	$1.1(10^6/T^2)-4.5$	Deines et al. (1974)
CO_2 – Calcite	0–100	$1.19(10^6/T^2)-3.6$	Deines et al. (1974)
Calcite-graphite		$1.74(10^6/T^2)+5.22$	Field and Fifarek (1985) from data by Bottinga (1969)

Chapter 9

Application of Radiogenic Isotope Systems to the Timing and Origin of Hydrothermal Processes

JEREMY P. RICHARDS

Department of Earth and Atmospheric Sciences, University of Alberta, Edmonton, Alberta, Canada T6G 2E3

AND STEPHEN R. NOBLE

NERC Isotope Geosciences Laboratory, Keyworth, Nottingham, United Kingdom NG12 5GG

Introduction

The potential use of radiogenic isotopes in the study of geological problems was recognized at an early stage in the investigation of nuclear science. At the turn of the century, F. Soddy and E. Rutherford first proposed the law of radioactive decay, and in 1905, Rutherford obtained the first age estimates of uraniferous minerals by measuring their helium content. The first U-Pb chemical dates for uraninites were published two years later by B.B. Boltwood (1907). F.W. Aston's development of the mass spectrometer shortly after the end of World War I led to the confirmation that many elements consist of isotopes having different atomic mass (Aston, 1920). But it was A.O. Nier's refinements of mass spectrometer design during and after World War II that provided the technological breakthrough required for routine geochronological measurements (Nier, 1940). Subsequent instrumental developments have principally involved improvements in precision and sensitivity, with the current generation of thermal ionization multi-collector mass spectrometers (TIMS) offering rapid simultaneous measurement of several isotopes from nanogram-sized samples.

Despite the technological complexities of modern mass spectrometers, the underpinning theory of radioactive decay and its applications remains a relatively straightforward concept. It is the aim of this chapter to convince the non-specialist of this fact, and to show that radiogenic isotopes can be applied with good effect in field-based studies of ore-forming systems. Indeed, the success or failure of isotopic studies often lies in the hands of the field geologist who maps and collects the samples, and who is ultimately in the position of interpreting the results within a sound geological framework.

There are two primary types of information available from radiogenic isotope studies: age determination and isotopic source tracing. Both find applicability in the field of hydrothermal geology, and allow the investigator to establish age relationships between hydrothermal systems and associated lithologies, or internal histories of the systems themselves, and to delineate the sources of certain components within the systems in terms of likely reservoirs. In this chapter we discuss the systematics of the Rb-Sr, Sm-Nd, U-Pb, Pb-Pb, K-Ar, ^{40}Ar-^{39}Ar, and Re-Os geochronometers, the most common isotopic systems used in hydrothermal geological studies, before looking at the uses of Pb, Sr, Nd, and Os isotopes in source tracing.

The chapter is not intended to provide step-by-step instructions on how to conduct chemical separations or mass spectrometric measurements, but instead provides background information required for selecting appropriate methods and samples to solve real geological problems, for conducting some of the preparatory work, and for interpreting the isotopic data. Numerous references for further information are provided, but Faure's (1986) book on isotope geology is our touchstone throughout this chapter.

Please note that we use the following convention in terminology: the "age" of a sample is the actual time at which it was formed; we distinguish the word "date," which is a number that we calculate from geochronological analyses, and which may or may not be equal to the true age of the sample. Terms such as "model age," "isochron age," and "plateau age" have become entrenched in the literature, however.

Radiogenic Isotope Systematics

Radioactive Decay

The principles of radioactive decay are quite straightforward, and apply to any system in which an isotope of a given element (parent) decays spontaneously to an isotope of another element (daughter) at a characteristic rate. Most elements consist of more than one isotope in nature (gold being an annoying exception), and are denoted in the following way:

$$^{197}_{79}\mathrm{Au} \tag{9.1}$$

where 79 is the number of protons in the nucleus (the atomic number: defines the element, and is often left off as redundant), and 197 is the number of protons plus neutrons (the atomic mass). Because the number of neutrons in the nucleus can vary over a short range for some elements, these elements exist in different isotopic forms that display essentially identical chemical properties (controlled by the number of protons, and therefore electrons, in the atom) but different atomic mass (and therefore slightly different physical properties). Thus, for example, strontium has four naturally occurring isotopes, ^{84}Sr, ^{86}Sr, ^{87}Sr, and ^{88}Sr. The most abundant of these isotopes is ^{88}Sr

(~82.56% of naturally-occurring Sr), and hence the average atomic weight of Sr is ~87.62 (this value is variable over a short range because the proportion of ^{87}Sr in natural Sr is not constant, as explained below).

Some naturally occurring isotopes are radioactive because the mix of protons and neutrons in their nuclei is unstable. In the case of Rb, which exists as two isotopes, ^{85}Rb and ^{87}Rb, the latter isotope decays spontaneously to ^{87}Sr by the following reaction:

$$^{87}\mathrm{Rb} \rightarrow {}^{87}\mathrm{Sr} + \beta^- + \bar{\upsilon} + Q \tag{9.2}$$

where β^- is a beta particle, $\bar{\upsilon}$ is an antineutrino, and Q is a characteristic amount of energy. On an atomic scale, the decay process is random—any given atom of ^{87}Rb could spontaneously break down to ^{87}Sr at any time. Taken in bulk, however, ^{87}Rb displays a characteristic average decay rate (expressed as the half-life or decay constant), knowledge of which is the basis for the Rb-Sr geochronometer. Radioactive isotopes of use in geochronology are mostly long-lived, with half-lives (the time taken for half the original amount of parent isotope to decay) in the range 1 to 100 Ga (e.g., 48.8 Ga for ^{87}Rb; Table 1).

TABLE 1. Decay constants λ and half-lives for key radiogenic isotope systems (currently accepted values are shown in bold face)

Parent–daughter pair	Decay constant λ (a^{-1})	Half-life $t_{1/2}$ (Ga)	References
$^{40}K \rightarrow {}^{40}Ca$	**4.962×10^{-10}**	1.397	Steiger & Jäger (1977)
	4.72×10^{-10}		Wetherill (1966)
$^{40}K \rightarrow {}^{40}Ar$	**0.581×10^{-10}**	11.930	Steiger & Jäger (1977)
	0.585×10^{-10}		Wetherill (1966)
$^{87}Rb \rightarrow {}^{87}Sr$	**1.42×10^{-11}**	48.813	Davis et al. (1977) Neumann & Huster (1974)
	1.39×10^{-11}		Aldrich et al. (1956)
	1.47×10^{-11}		Flynn & Glendenin (1959)
$^{147}Sm \rightarrow {}^{144}Nd$	**6.54×10^{-12}**	105.986	Lugmair & Marti (1978)
$^{238}U \rightarrow {}^{206}Pb$	**1.55125×10^{-10}**	4.468	Jaffey et al. (1971)
	1.54×10^{-10}		Kovarik & Adams (1955)
$^{235}U \rightarrow {}^{207}Pb$	**9.8485×10^{-10}**	0.704	Jaffey et al. (1971)
	9.72×10^{-10}		Fleming et al. (1962)
$^{232}Th \rightarrow {}^{208}Pb$	**4.9475×10^{-11}**	14.010	Le Roux & Glendenin (1963)
	4.99×10^{-11}		Picciotto & Wilgain (1956)
$^{187}Re \rightarrow {}^{187}Os$	**1.666×10^{-11}**	41.606	Smoliar et al. (1996)
	1.64×10^{-11}		Lindner et al. (1989)

Dealing now with a general parent isotope N decaying to a daughter isotope D, the rate of decay of N in a rock or mineral will be proportional to the amount of N present. As N decays, however, there will be progressively less of it, so the rate of decay must decrease. This relationship is described by the following equation:

$$\frac{dN}{dt} = -\lambda N \tag{9.3}$$

where t is time, and λ is the decay constant, characteristic for each decay system (Table 1).

Integrating this equation from $t = 0$ to t, and with N_0 atoms of N present at $t = 0$,

$$\int_{N_0}^{N} \frac{dN}{N} = -\lambda \int_0^t dt \tag{9.4}$$

we obtain:

$$\ln\frac{N}{N_0} = -\lambda t \tag{9.5}$$

or

$$N = N_0.e^{-\lambda t} \tag{9.6}$$

Note that the half-life ($t_{1/2}$) is defined as the time after which $N = 0.5N_0$. Thus the half-life and decay constant are related as follows:

$$t_{1/2} = \frac{\ln 2}{\lambda} \tag{9.7}$$

In most geological situations we are unlikely to know N_0, which, for example, would be equivalent to the initial amount of ^{87}Rb in a mineral when it was formed perhaps billions of years ago. However, we may be able to measure the amount of radiogenic daughter isotope (D^*, or $^{87}Sr^*$) that has been produced by radioactive decay since formation. Because $D^* = N_0 - N$, or $N_0 = D^* + N$, we can eliminate N_0 from equation (9.6) to obtain:

$$D^* = N\left(e^{\lambda t} - 1\right) \tag{9.8}$$

We now have a chronometer for systems where all of the daughter isotope present has been generated by radioactive decay since the system formed. Unfortunately, examples of such systems in geology are rare, because most rocks and minerals incorporate significant amounts of both parent and daughter elements at the time of their formation. Two exceptions are uraninite (UO_2, containing essentially no "initial" Pb) and molybdenite (MoS_2, containing essentially no "initial" Os but sometimes percent-levels of Re). With most other analyses, we have to account for the fact that there may have been some of the daughter isotope present at $t = 0$, designated D_0, otherwise we will calculate an erroneously old age. Algebraically, this is represented as follows:

$$D = D_0 + N\left(e^{\lambda t} - 1\right) \quad (9.9)$$

where D is the total amount of daughter isotope present after time t.

In practice, quantitative measurements of individual isotope abundances are very difficult to make, but it is relatively easy to measure the ratio of two isotopes of an element using a mass spectrometer. Typically, we choose a reference isotope that is non-radiogenic, and similar in abundance and close in atomic mass to the radiogenic isotope (to minimize instrument-induced mass fractionation of the isotopic ratio). In the case of Sr, the choice is traditionally ^{86}Sr (9.86% of Sr). If we substitute ^{87}Rb and ^{87}Sr into equation (9.9), and divide through by ^{86}Sr, we obtain the isochron equation:

$$\left(\frac{^{87}Sr}{^{86}Sr}\right) = \left(\frac{^{87}Sr}{^{86}Sr}\right)_{initial} + \left(\frac{^{87}Rb}{^{86}Sr}\right)\left(e^{\lambda_{87} t} - 1\right) \quad (9.10)$$

where $\lambda_{87} = 1.42 \times 10^{-11}\ a^{-1}$.

We can measure the present-day $^{87}Sr/^{86}Sr$ ratio directly on a mass spectrometer, and $^{87}Rb/^{86}Sr$ by isotope dilution (see below), leaving only the initial $^{87}Sr/^{86}Sr$ ratio (sometimes called "common" Sr) and the age t as unknowns. In order to solve this equation for t, we can either (1) analyze a cogenetic daughter-rich mineral (see Table 6 for examples) that has preserved the initial Sr isotopic composition of the system, or (2) analyze several cogenetic minerals with different Rb/Sr ratios (but assumed identical initial Sr ratio), and plot them on a graph of $^{87}Rb/^{86}Sr$ versus $^{87}Sr/^{86}Sr$. If the criteria of cogeneticity, uniform initial Sr isotopic ratio, and closed system behavior have been met, the samples will define an isochron of slope

$$\left(e^{\lambda_{87} t} - 1\right)$$

from which the age t can be calculated, and the initial Sr isotopic ratio will be defined by the intercept with the y-axis. This subject is discussed in more detail in the following sections.

To summarize, we can use the known decay rates of certain naturally occurring radioactive isotopes such as ^{40}K, ^{87}Rb, ^{235}U, ^{238}U, ^{232}Th, ^{147}Sm, and ^{187}Re to construct geochronometers based upon the accumulation of daughter isotopes since the time of formation of the sample. We need to determine only the relative amounts of the parent and daughter isotopes to obtain the age of a closed system in which no daughter isotope was present initially. More commonly, however, a correction must be made for the presence of some amount of the daughter element at the time of mineral formation, and this is achieved either by use of an isochron method, or by obtaining an independent estimate for the initial isotopic ratio of the daughter element. In passing, we note that the initial isotopic ratio can in itself provide important information, inasmuch as it may be used to characterize the provenance or source of materials. This subject is discussed in more detail later in this chapter.

Treatment of Errors

There are a number of aspects of the treatment of errors associated with isotope measurements of which even the most casual reader of the literature should be aware. We present the barest of essentials here, and more detailed treatments with examples can be found in texts by Albarède (1995) and Taylor (1997). An air of apparent sophistication or mathematical rigor is sometimes encountered in isotope geology, partly arising from an association with complicated instrumentation. But there are instances in which error documentation of any kind is either totally lacking or is present only at the most rudimentary level. As a result, the usefulness of the data can be seriously eroded. When discussing errors in the context of isotope data, we do not imply mistakes, but rather the uncertainties in our knowledge of a measured quantity. Isotope data are the product of real measurements of physical quantities, and their associated uncertainties reflect contributions from a number of analytical sources; note that these uncertainties do not include natural (geological) errors, which cannot be quantified. The analytical errors must be adequately accounted for so that inter- and intra-laboratory comparisons of different data sets can be achieved.

It will be useful to keep in mind that the relative sizes of quoted errors do not provide an a priori yardstick for judging the usefulness of data. Depending on the analytical method and the problem to be solved, results with relatively large associated errors may be perfectly acceptable. There will always be a trade-off between obtaining the optimum precision for a measurement and pursuing the minimum size of the domain to be analyzed. For example, obtaining very accurate and precise $^{87}Sr/^{86}Sr$ isotope ratios to constrain seawater compositions typically requires the measurement of relatively large quantities of Sr in order to ensure that uncertainties arising from counting statistics and other analytical sources are minimized. The overall uncertainty assigned to the data would be controlled mainly by the performance of the mass spectrometer and uncertainties in the spike calibration. In other cases, precision can be sacrificed if very small amounts of material are to be analyzed, either because of limited sample availability, or because high spatial resolution is the primary goal. An example of the latter is U-Pb isotope analysis of fragments of individual zircon crystals, where uncertainty arising from corrections for common Pb "blank" is very important relative to other sources of error. Such errors are unavoidable, however, because of the need to obtain the best spatial resolution of domains of different age within a single grain.

An isotope ratio appearing in a data table is almost never the result of a single measurement, but is generally the mean of a number of measurements (typically 50–250), each obtained over a period of several seconds and accumulated over a total time of several tens of minutes to hours. This procedure permits occasional but necessary tuning of the mass spectrometer throughout the analysis period to ensure optimal data collection. The mean of these measurements $\overline{X}$ is calculated using:

$$\overline{X} = \frac{\sum_{i=1}^{n} x_i}{n} \tag{9.11}$$

where x_i are the individual measurements and n is the total number of measurements. The standard deviation of this population is typically defined as:

$$\sigma_x = \sqrt{\frac{1}{(n-1)} \sum_{i=1}^{n} (x_i - \overline{X})} \tag{9.12}$$

It turns out, however, that what we wish to know is not σ_x, which characterizes the uncertainty of the individual measurements x_i, but the uncertainty associated with the mean value, which is called the standard error, or standard error of the mean. The standard error is the quantity usually given in tables of raw data, and is calculated using:

$$\sigma_{\overline{X}} = \frac{\sigma_x}{\sqrt{n}} \tag{9.13}$$

It is usual to quote uncertainties at the 95 percent confidence level, which equates to ±2 standard errors. This means that there is a 95 percent probability that an analysis will be repeatable within the range

$$\overline{X} \pm 2\sigma_{\overline{X}}$$

With some types of isotope measurements the uncertainties are not simply the standard error. It is in fact often the case that the isotope ratios of interest are the products of two or more completely separate analyses, each with its own errors. In addition, it may have been necessary to correct the ratios for laboratory contamination or mass spectrum interferences from other elements, again with associated errors. There are basically three approaches taken in response to the challenge of analyzing the overall effect of the various sources of error. In the worst case, no assessment of error is made: in this case the result is of limited credibility, and cannot be fully compared with data obtained elsewhere. The second level of response is to use "blanket" errors, i.e., assigning errors to quantities based upon experience. This experience typically consists of an accumulation of values obtained over a significant period of time, for both carefully prepared standards and repeated analyses of geological materials. For example, the repeated analysis of rock powders in many laboratories indicates that the typical uncertainties for $^{87}Rb/^{86}Sr$, $^{147}Sm/^{144}Nd$, and ε_{Nd} values are around ±1 percent, ±0.1 to 0.3 percent, and ±0.4 units, respectively, and these are commonly quoted in the isotope literature. Blanket errors are useful if it is difficult to isolate the effects of a particular source of error, and provided that all quantities are measured to a sufficient precision then the worst effect is probably an overestimation of the total error. Nevertheless, caution must be exercised by the analyst, and instances of data with errors larger than the blanket uncertainties need to be recognized. Such situations commonly arise when data are generated by different users within the same laboratory, because analytical techniques may differ or vary in quality.

The third approach involves the application of full error propagation to all isotope data (cf. Mattinson, 1987). This approach involves the systematic identification and accurate accounting of all sources of error. An example is the calculation of errors for the $^{206}Pb/^{238}U$ and $^{207}Pb/^{235}U$ ratios used in U-Pb geochronology (Ludwig, 1980, 1989; Roddick, 1987). These final isotope ratios are calculated from data obtained in separate U and Pb isotope ratio measurements, along with a number of intermediate quantities used to correct the data for interferences and fractionation. These intermediate quantities and their attendant uncertainties are either experimentally determined or are estimated from mathematical models. The main sources of error beyond the mass spectrometric errors associated with measurement of isotope ratios include: uncertainties in the amount and isotopic compositions of Pb and U laboratory contamination (i.e., "blanks") and initial ("common") Pb in the mineral; U and Pb contributions from tracer solutions added to the sample (included in the blank); and fractionation of isotopes occurring during measurement within the mass spectrometer. The uncertainties associated with both the measured data and the laboratory environment are unique to each analysis and so overall uncertainties must be determined by propagating the effects of all sources of uncertainty through all calculations. A further complication is that some errors can be correlated to varying degrees and may even cancel each other out, and thus their effects must be carefully assessed.

One final point is that it is important that the isotope data are not affected to a significant degree by systematic errors that bias the entire data set. Normally, documentation of isotope data will include the results of repeated analysis of an international standard during the period of data collection. Such standard data are important because they provide a monitor for mass spectrometer performance, and thus give a good indication of systematic bias. Modern multi-collector mass spectrometers are capable, under ideal conditions, of achieving a between-sample variation of ≤0.003 percent, but it is possible that standard measurements can deviate from accepted values by much more than this. Such deviations may occur because of small biases in the mass spectrometer's ion detectors and electronics that are often difficult and expensive to identify and rectify. As long as the deviation of standard values is consistent and otherwise uncomplicated, then useful data for samples can be obtained. It is therefore important when comparing data from the literature to ensure that individual values are adjusted where necessary by normalizing to reported values for the standards. As a corollary, measured values for the standard should always be reported with the data to enable others to make this correction. Table 2A gives some typical standard data together with a range of values reported from the literature for Sr, Hf, and Nd isotopes, where optimal levels of precision are required. Lead isotope standards are a special case because until recently it has not been routinely possible to correct for instrumental mass fractionation effects except by normalizing results to the accepted standard values—something of a circular argument. The use of a double-spike in Pb isotopic analyses (see below) enables correction for fractionation effects, and revised values for some of the common Pb standards are shown in Table 2B.

TABLE 2A. Typical values for Sr, Nd, and Hf isotope standards (data from Thirlwall, 1991b, and Nowell et al., 1998)

Element and standard	Accepted value	Range reported in the literature (mean ± 2σ)
Nd: La Jolla	0.511860	0.511842 ± 19 to 0.511873 ± 21
Hf: JMC475	0.282160	0.282142 ± 21 to 0.282213 ± 12
Sr: NBS 987	~0.710240 to 0.710250	0.710197 ± 33 to 0.710280 ± 24

TABLE 2B. Accepted values for NBS Pb isotope standards

Standard	NBS value (Catanzaro et al., 1968)	Currently accepted value ± $2\sigma_m$ (Todt et al., 1993)
NBS 981		
$^{208}Pb/^{204}Pb$	36.7213	36.6856 ± 0.001
$^{207}Pb/^{204}Pb$	15.4913	15.4855 ± 0.001
$^{206}Pb/^{204}Pb$	16.9371	16.9322 ± 0.0008
NBS 982		
$^{208}Pb/^{204}Pb$	36.7449	36.7537 ± 0.001
$^{207}Pb/^{204}Pb$	17.1597	17.16136 ± 0.0004
$^{206}Pb/^{204}Pb$	36.7390	36.7479 ± 0.0008
NBS 983		
$^{208}Pb/^{204}Pb$	36.703	
$^{207}Pb/^{204}Pb$	191.43	
$^{206}Pb/^{204}Pb$	2695.0	

Rb-Sr Dating Techniques

Introduction

The Rb-Sr isotope dating method has been one of the stalwarts of geochronology, reaching the zenith of its influence between the late 1950s and 1970s. During this period, many classic studies were carried out, including Rb-Sr investigations of metamorphic rocks (Giletti et al., 1961), meteorites and lunar materials (Papanastassiou and Wasserburg, 1969, 1971), and ancient terrestrial rocks (Moorbath et al., 1977). The resulting data and their interpretations have served geology well, and Rb-Sr dating, often combined with K-Ar, has been used over the last fifty years to underpin the geochronological framework of many areas of the globe. Nevertheless, from the late 1970s onwards, enough data from other techniques were available to demonstrate that the method was not as robust in many terrestrial geological applications as perhaps some exponents of the technique would have liked. In particular, the problem of disturbance of the Rb-Sr system was especially apparent in areas that had experienced significant thermal and tectonic overprinting, such as many Archean granite-greenstone terrains. As a result, the Rb-Sr technique has been superseded in many instances by the more robust U-Pb zircon method, and in the Phanerozoic by the $^{40}Ar/^{39}Ar$ method. It would not be fair to say, however, that Rb-Sr work has been completely abandoned, and excellent high-precision data can be obtained with modern mass spectrometers, provided that analyses are obtained from materials that meet certain geological criteria (see below). In addition, if the protolith age is known from another more reliable chronometer, Rb-Sr data obtained from both minerals and rocks can place important constraints on post-crystallization processes or events such as alteration, fluid-rock interactions, and metamorphism (e.g., DePaolo and Getty, 1996, and references therein).

Systematics

Reviews of the Rb-Sr dating method as applied to a wide range of geological materials and processes are presented by Hamilton (1965), Faure and Powell (1972), Faure (1986), and Dickin (1995), and an excellent overview and summary is provided by Shirey (1991). The reader is directed to these sources for details beyond the basic information presented here.

The radioactive decay of ^{87}Rb to ^{87}Sr was discussed earlier in this chapter, and a relationship between the Rb/Sr ratio, Sr isotopic composition, and age t was given in equation (9.10) (reproduced below):

$$\left(\frac{^{87}Sr}{^{86}Sr}\right) = \left(\frac{^{87}Sr}{^{86}Sr}\right)_{initial} + \left(\frac{^{87}Rb}{^{86}Sr}\right)\left(e^{\lambda_{87}t} - 1\right) \quad (9.14)$$

To solve this equation, the present-day $^{87}Sr/^{86}Sr$ ratio is measured by mass spectrometry, and the $^{87}Rb/^{86}Sr$ ratio is obtained from the Rb and Sr abundances, typically determined by isotope dilution. The isotope dilution method involves dissolving an accurately weighed amount of the sample, and adding to this a measured aliquot of a tracer solution, or "spike," that has an accurately known isotopic composition, usually enriched in a low-abundance isotope of the element of interest. The spiked mixture is then analyzed on a mass spectrometer, and the observed isotopic composition can be mathematically "unmixed" to yield the spike/sample ratio for the element. Knowledge of the mass of each isotope added in the spike then enables calculation of the mass of the element in the sample. The $^{87}Rb/^{86}Sr$ ratio can then be calculated using the following equation:

$$\left(\frac{^{87}Rb}{^{86}Sr}\right) = \frac{[Rb]}{[Sr]} \bullet \left(\frac{\text{Abundance of } ^{87}Rb \times \text{Sr atomic wt.}}{\text{Abundance of } ^{86}Sr \times \text{Rb atomic wt.}}\right) \quad (9.15)$$

The present-day atomic weight of Rb is fixed for all terrestrial materials at 85.46776. However, the atomic weight of Sr is variable over a small range due to contributions of radiogenic ^{87}Sr, and must be calculated using the isotope ratios measured for the sample:

$$\text{Atomic wt. Sr} = \sum_{i=84}^{88} \left(\text{atomic wt. of isotope } {}^{i}\text{Sr}\right) \bullet \frac{\left({}^{i}\text{Sr}/{}^{88}\text{Sr}\right)}{k} \quad (9.16)$$

where

$$k = \sum_{i=84}^{88} {}^{i}\text{Sr}/{}^{88}\text{Sr} \quad (9.17)$$

Examples of these calculations can be found in many isotope textbooks (e.g., Faure, 1986, p. 119–120), and similar equations can be written for other systems such as U-Pb, Sm-Nd, and Re-Os.

Rb-Sr dates are obtained in one of two ways: as model ages for single mineral samples, or as dates calculated from a suite of samples. Model age determinations are made by measuring the Rb/Sr and $^{87}Sr/^{86}Sr$ ratios in a Rb-rich mineral such as muscovite or biotite, and using an independently determined value for the $^{87}Sr/^{86}Sr$ ratio at the time of formation to correct for "common" strontium. The age may then be calculated using:

$$t = \frac{1}{\lambda_{87}} \ln\left\{1 + \frac{^{86}\text{Sr}}{^{87}\text{Rb}} \bullet \left[\left(\frac{^{87}\text{Sr}}{^{86}\text{Sr}}\right) - \left(\frac{^{87}\text{Sr}}{^{86}\text{Sr}}\right)_{initial}\right]\right\} \quad (9.18)$$

In practice, model ages are seldom used because experience has shown that open system behavior is quite common, leading to erroneous age determinations. Instead, Rb-Sr isotope dates normally are calculated from $^{87}Rb/^{86}Sr$ versus $^{87}Sr/^{86}Sr$ isochron plots, which have the advantage of revealing isotopic disturbance between samples. These plots were first introduced by Allsopp (1961) and Nicolaysen (1961), and have since been adapted for use in other isotope systems. The details of the derivation of these diagrams are discussed elsewhere (e.g., Faure, 1986; Dickin, 1995), and only the major aspects are presented here.

A coeval suite of minerals or whole rocks, all starting with the same initial $^{87}Sr/^{86}Sr$ ratio and all remaining closed to migration (loss or gain) of Rb and Sr, will plot along a straight line on an isochron diagram. The slope of the line

$$\left(e^{\lambda_{87}t} - 1\right)$$

is obtained from the isochron equation (9.14), and the y-intercept represents the initial $^{87}Sr/^{86}Sr$ ratio of the sample suite.

Two types of isochrons are commonly encountered: internal isochrons, based on whole-rock and constituent mineral analyses; and whole-rock isochrons, based on suites of coeval and cogenetic rocks (Fig. 1). Experience has shown that internal isochrons are perhaps more susceptible to resetting during metamorphism than whole-rock isochrons, because Rb and Sr may be redistributed between adjacent mineral phases while remaining isochemical on the scale of whole-rock samples. In reality, combinations of a lack of closed system behavior, variable initial ratios within a sample suite, and/or failure to exclude samples that are not cogenetic, all conspire to introduce scatter in isochron plots.

The isochron age calculated for a sample suite is directly dependent upon the way a line is regressed through the data points. With real data, analytical errors and variations induced by geological processes always result in arrays that are dispersed to some degree from perfect linearity. Placing the "right" line through these data is a non-trivial exercise, and a tremendous amount of effort has been dedicated to developing sophisticated linear regression algorithms. In particular, these algorithms must take into consideration the effects of errors from two main sources: $^{87}Sr/^{86}Sr$ and $^{87}Rb/^{86}Sr$ measurement errors, and their correlation. The development of the theory of two-error linear regression models and their relative merits as they pertain to Rb-Sr systematics was presented by Brooks et al. (1972). By using suitable modifications, these techniques also form the basis for data regressions for other isotope systems.

A good isochron is one that can precisely and accurately constrain the age of a real geological event such as magma crystallization, mineral growth in a hydrothermal environment, or a particular stage of metamorphic mineral

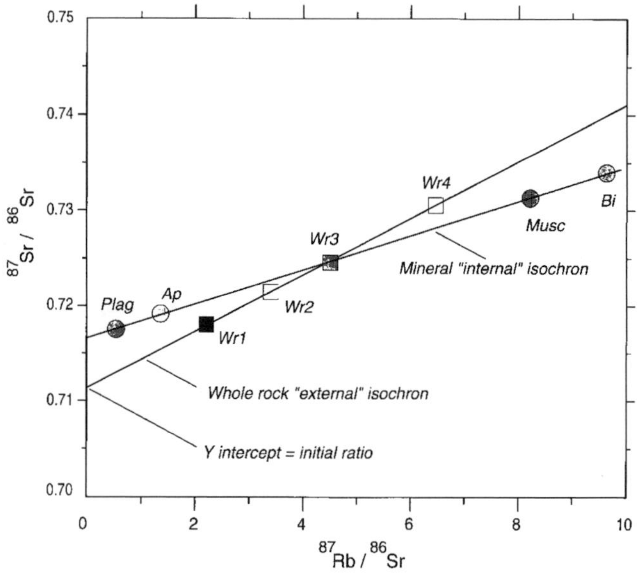

FIG. 1. Rb-Sr isochron diagram illustrating internal and external isochrons for whole-rock and mineral samples from a hypothetical suite of cogenetic igneous rocks that have experienced a metamorphic overprint. Whole-rock samples tend to preserve the original crystallization age of the suite better than individual minerals, because Rb and Sr may be redistributed amongst adjacent mineral grains during overprinting while remaining essentially isochemical on the scale of a whole-rock sample. Abbreviations: Ap = apatite, Bi = biotite, Plag = plagioclase, Musc = muscovite, Wr = whole-rock.

growth or thermal resetting. To achieve this, a significant range of Rb/Sr ratios is desirable in the data set in order to constrain the slope of the regression line. A high degree of collinearity of the data is also essential, and its absence is a good indication that some or all of the preconditions for defining an isochron have not been fulfilled. Brooks et al. (1972) introduced the mean square of weighted deviates (MSWD) as a means of testing for excess scatter beyond analytical uncertainty about a calculated isochron, and by extension testing for open system behavior or non-uniform initial ratios. The MSWD is defined as the sum of the squares of deviations of data from the isochron divided by the number of degrees of freedom of the population sampled (i.e., number of samples or data points minus two). MSWD values ≈ 1 indicate well-defined isochrons where analytical uncertainties can entirely account for the data scatter. MSWD values that are very much higher suggest that the isochron is suspect and that there are probably geological reasons for the scatter. The upper and lower limits of expected MSWD values indicating the validity of the isochron are dependent upon the number of degrees of freedom (f) of the data set. Wendt and Carl (1991) examined the probability distribution of the MSWD in detail, proposing that an isochron is suspect if the

$$\text{MSWD} > \left[1 + \sqrt{2/f}\right].$$

These authors also point out that for some data sets the MSWD may also have a lower limit, with values below that limit indicating an incorrect assessment of uncertainties for the data. It should be noted that useful indications of the age may still be provided by regressions with MSWDs in excess of the above limit, but that further testing would be prudent (see Kalsbeek, 1992). Regressions yielding geologically unreasonable dates and/or initial $^{87}Sr/^{86}Sr$ ratios may indicate that the line has no age significance at all, but has instead been generated by mixing between two or more different isotopic sources. Such situations should be further investigated either by employing an alternative geochronometer such as U-Pb or $^{40}Ar/^{39}Ar$, or by looking for other evidence of mixing relationships.

To illustrate the differences between simple and complex data arrays, examples of real data and regressions are shown in Figure 2A and B. The data in Figure 2A were obtained from cogenetic samples with a uniform initial ratio that have experienced closed system behavior; they define a well-constrained isochron and yield a geologically reasonable date. Figure 2B, on the other hand, contains a data set that probably does not have a unique initial ratio, and may include samples that have been variably disturbed after crystallization. A reliable Rb-Sr isochron age could not be obtained, and instead the age of the rocks had to be determined by the U-Pb zircon method (see below).

Distinguishing geologically meaningful from meaningless Rb-Sr dates is not the only problem that has affected Rb-Sr geochronology over the last few decades. Constraining the half-life for the beta decay of ^{87}Rb to ^{87}Sr has been challenging, and a number of different decay constants have been used (Table 1). It is essential that when comparing dates from different sources, all dates are re-calculated using the same decay constant. The International Union of Geological Sciences' preferred

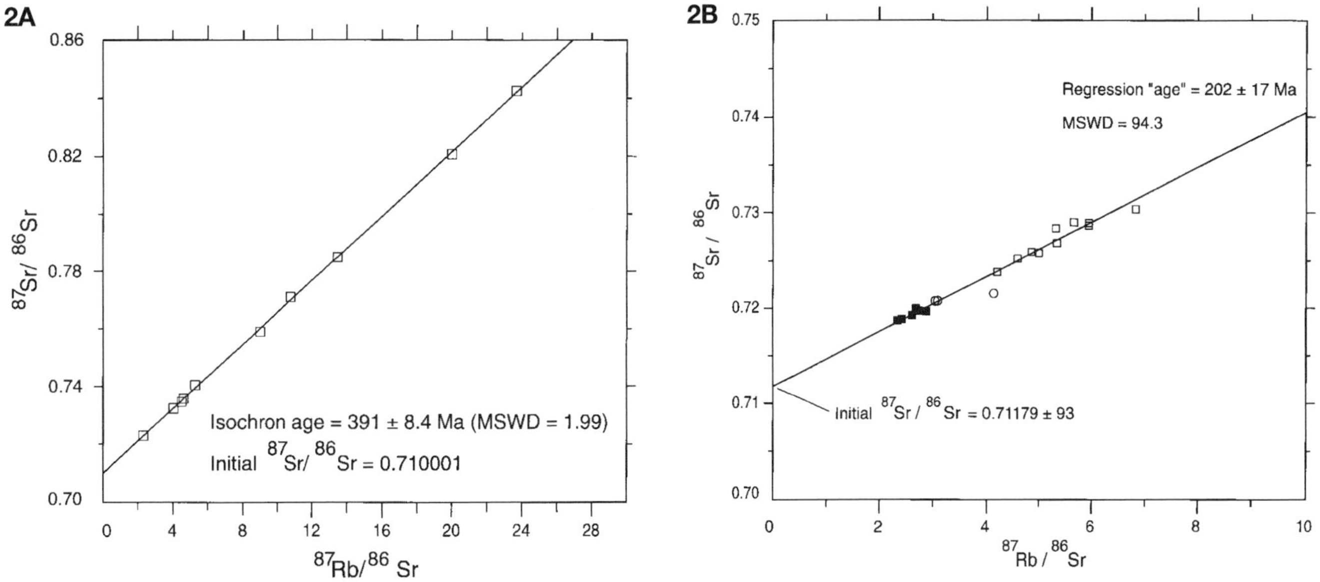

FIG. 2. Rb-Sr isochron diagrams illustrating (A) simple and (B) complex data. (A) Fluid inclusion data from the Carrock Fell wolframite-bearing hydrothermal veins. The data plot on a linear array giving an age of 391 ± 8.4 Ma and an MSWD of 1.99 (modified and recalculated from Shepherd and Darbyshire, 1981). (B) Whole-rock samples from the Tres Laguna S-type granite batholith, Ecuador, collected from three different sites as indicated by the different symbols. The data scatter around an "errorchron" with an apparent age of 202 ± 17 Ma (MSWD = 94.3). This scatter results from inhomogeneous initial $^{87}Sr/^{86}Sr$ ratios in the batholith, and post-crystallization disturbance. The age of the granite is currently constrained at 227.3 ± 2.0 Ma by U-Pb in zircon (Aspden et al., 1992; Noble et al., 1997).

value is 1.42×10^{-11} a^{-1}, determined by direct counting of β-decays from a thin Rb film (Neumann and Huster, 1974; Steiger and Jäger, 1977). This value is supported by careful mass spectrometric measurement of the quantity of ^{87}Sr produced from known amounts of Rb decaying over a known period of time (Davis et al., 1977). It might appear from this that the decay constant is now known with confidence, but this may not be the case: high-precision Rb-Sr and U-Pb studies of meteorites suggest that the constant should in fact be 1.402×10^{-11} a^{-1} (Minster et al., 1982).

Practical Considerations and Materials

Relative to other isotope systems, the Rb-Sr technique is intermediate in cost. The successful application of Rb-Sr isotopes to geochronology is very much dependent upon having the largest possible range in Rb/Sr ratios for a sample suite so that a well-constrained isochron may be obtained. Collecting suitable material is sometimes far from trivial. The weight of experience based on hundreds of studies in many geological environments shows that great care must be exercised during sampling because of the high probability of modification of Rb/Sr and $^{87}Sr/^{86}Sr$ ratios during weathering, hydrothermal alteration, metamorphism, and deformational events. Good geochronological information will only be obtained from minerals and rocks that formed cogenetically (i.e., have the same initial $^{87}Sr/^{86}Sr$ ratio) and that communally responded to geological events (i.e., closed or fully reset systems). Often an examination of thin sections from prospective samples will help filter out unsuitable samples, and if secondary minerals such as sericite, chlorite, carbonate, or epidote have replaced primary silicates, then Rb and Sr will almost certainly have been mobile. Suitable samples may in fact be impossible to collect from intrusions associated with hydrothermal ore deposits, where alkali- and alkali-earth-element mobility may be rampant; in these cases it is necessary to use other geochronological techniques, or to date associated unaltered rocks (e.g., a different but cogenetic pluton nearby).

Sampling for Rb-Sr isotope work is no different than for other isotope techniques, and requires collection of the freshest materials, and processing under conditions that ensure that cross-contamination is non-existent. Grain size must be considered for whole-rock samples, such that a representative split can be obtained. Sample sizes typically range from ~5 kg for coarse-grained (≥3 mm) equigranular rocks, down to 0.5 kg for fine-grained material (≤1 mm; see Wager and Brown, 1960). It is not uncommon to use 5 to 10 whole rock samples to generate an isochron. If internal isochrons are desired, then a range of Rb-Sr ratios can be obtained by judicious mineral selection, a typical suite consisting of feldspars (low Rb/Sr), apatite, biotite, and/or muscovite (high Rb/Sr), in addition to the whole rock which provides the bulk Rb/Sr ratio dependent on mineral proportions. In other cases it may be possible to use different size fractions of a single type of mineral, as has been done for illite-rich hydrothermal clays (Gilg and Frei, 1994). It also pays to be an opportunist, and unconventional approaches to sampling are fine so long as the isochron criteria are met. For example, in a study of shear-zone hosted pegmatites, Piasecki and van Breemen (1983) used a knife to pluck ~5 cm-wide muscovite books from the outcrop, and then cut out the unaltered cores with scissors!

Some isotope workers with considerable experience in the geochronology of plutonic rocks have found it useful to establish a number of sample stations, each covering a small area within a given pluton. In this way, samples with a range of Rb/Sr ratios can be obtained with potentially little variation in initial $^{87}Sr/^{86}Sr$ ratio. It must be noted, however, that it can be difficult to distinguish between variations in $^{87}Sr/^{86}Sr$ due to Rb decay, and mixing of different isotope reservoirs; this may occur, for example, during the generation of hybrid granodioritic melts from mantle and lower/middle crustal protoliths. Failure to discern mixing will result in meaningless isochrons, as has been noted for large batholiths where multiple magma batches with complex provenance are involved. Often the best results are obtained from late, unaltered, undeformed, and high-level granitic stocks, that may be characterized by an homogeneous initial isotopic ratio, but chemical inhomogeneity through differentiation (thus yielding a useful range of Rb/Sr ratios). Occasionally these stocks will include pegmatitic pods containing minerals with a wide range of Rb/Sr ratios, thereby yielding excellent isochrons.

Examples

The Rb-Sr geochronometer has proven particularly well suited to studies of hydrothermal systems because a number of vein and alteration minerals with either high or low parent/daughter ratios may be found. For example, K-(Rb)-rich wall-rock alteration minerals such as micas and amphiboles provide a good spread of data along an isochron, while Ca-(Sr)-rich vein minerals such as carbonates, sulfates, and fluorite establish the initial Sr isotope ratio (e.g., Ruiz et al., 1984; Böhlke and Kistler, 1986).

Fluid inclusions have also been used in several Rb-Sr isochron studies, taking advantage of either (1) variations in Rb/Sr ratios during the course of mineral deposition in a hydrothermal vein, leading to the possibility of sampling fluid inclusions with a spread of values on an isochron diagram (e.g., Shepherd and Darbyshire, 1981), or (2) differential, non-equilibrium fluid–mineral partitioning of Rb and Sr, yielding isochrons defined by fluid inclusions and their host mineral phases, such as quartz and sphalerite (e.g., Christensen et al., 1995; Pettke and Diamond, 1996).

Summary

The Rb-Sr method is useful in dating coeval minerals and whole rocks that started off with the same initial $^{87}Sr/^{86}Sr$ ratio and have remained closed to Rb and Sr through time, or have been fully reset isotopically during a secondary event. The method is of intermediate cost, somewhere between K-Ar and U-Pb (see below). The technique has been widely applied in the past and has provided large amounts of valuable data. Today, however, it has been replaced by the $^{40}Ar/^{39}Ar$, U-Pb, and Re-Os techniques in studies where high degrees of accuracy and precision are called for. The main limitation of the method is related to the mobility of Rb and Sr in many environments, including metamorphism, hydrothermal alteration, and deformation, resulting in a lack of closed system behavior. Nevertheless, with careful application, the Rb-Sr method can provide useful primary and secondary age information, as well as constraints on the sources of Sr and other chemically-related elements.

Sm-Nd Dating

Introduction

The primary use of Sm-Nd isotopes in many geological applications is as a tracer of processes. Sm-Nd isotopes can also, however, be used very effectively in geochronology. Sm-Nd dating was first used in the late 1970s and early 1980s, just before the explosive rise to prominence of the U-Pb and $^{40}Ar/^{39}Ar$ techniques. Early successes involved geochronological studies of extraterrestrial materials (e.g., Lugmair and Scheinin, 1975), Archean granite-greenstone terranes (e.g., Hamilton et al., 1977), and, in particular, mafic and ultramafic sequences that are often not readily dated by other methods (e.g., DePaolo and Wasserburg, 1979). Since this first flush of success, geochronological applications of the Sm-Nd system have been greatly overshadowed by its utility as an isotopic tracer, but Sm-Nd dating techniques have nevertheless found unique applications in the study of hydrothermal ore deposits.

Systematics and Methodology

Sm-Nd dating is an isochron-based technique, analogous to the Rb-Sr system with respect to the decay scheme equations, prerequisite conditions, manner of data presentation, and method of calculating ages.

Re-writing equation (9.10) for the Sm-Nd system yields:

$$\left(\frac{^{143}\text{Nd}}{^{144}\text{Nd}}\right) = \left(\frac{^{143}\text{Nd}}{^{144}\text{Nd}}\right)_{initial} + \left(\frac{^{147}\text{Sm}}{^{144}\text{Nd}}\right)\left(e^{\lambda_{147}t} - 1\right) \tag{9.19}$$

where $\lambda_{147} = 6.54 \times 10^{-12}\ a^{-1}$ (half-life = 105.986 Ga; Table 1). The long half-life of the system imparts some disadvantages, or at least analytical challenges, that are not so pronounced in other methods. The accumulation of radiogenic ^{143}Nd is much slower than that of ^{87}Sr, for example, with the result that measurement of the small differences in $^{143}Nd/^{144}Nd$ due to radioactive decay in terrestrial materials requires high degrees of accuracy and precision, thus pushing mass spectrometry to its limits.

Sm and Nd are adjacent REE in the periodic table and show very similar geochemical behavior. Consequently, parent/daughter element fractionation is limited in many geological environments, and it is commonly difficult to obtain a large spread of Sm/Nd ratios in coeval, cogenetic suites of rocks. This situation is only slightly improved by using mineral separates, such as plagioclase, hornblende, biotite, or apatite, which fractionate the REE to some extent. Hence, obtaining isochron ages with precisions approaching ±20 Ma is challenging for Archean materials, and extremely difficult for Phanerozoic materials.

There are circumstances, however, when high precision is not required or when particular minerals fractionate Sm and Nd to an unusual extent. In the realm of ore deposits research, the successful application of the Sm-Nd geochronometer depends upon recognition of environments or suites of minerals where Sm/Nd fractionation is particularly enhanced. Once again, the successful geochronologist needs to be an opportunist, and, furthermore, needs a good background knowledge of the system under study, particularly with regard to mineralogy.

It is useful here to point out that single Sm/Nd isotope analyses are sometimes used to provide a rough idea of the age of a rock or mineral by calculating a model age. This approach can be useful in reconnaissance studies, for example, where the question may be as basic as whether a rock is Archean, Proterozoic, or Phanerozoic, and where limited numbers of samples are available. The principle is similar to the calculation of Sr model ages (see equation 9.18). Nd isotope model ages are based on the premise that the sample is derived from an isotope reservoir whose Sm/Nd and Nd isotope ratios are known, and that the sample has remained a closed system with respect to the REE since formation. The equation describing the calculation of a model age is:

$$t = \frac{1}{\lambda_{147}} \ln\left\{1 + \left[\frac{\left(\frac{^{143}\text{Nd}}{^{144}\text{Nd}}\right)_{sample} - \left(\frac{^{143}\text{Nd}}{^{144}\text{Nd}}\right)_{reservoir}}{\left(\frac{^{147}\text{Sm}}{^{144}\text{Nd}}\right)_{sample} - \left(\frac{^{147}\text{Sm}}{^{144}\text{Nd}}\right)_{reservoir}}\right]\right\} \tag{9.20}$$

where the isotopic ratios are those measured in the sample and calculated for the model reservoir at the present day. This equation is for a single stage of Nd isotope evolution, but multistage model ages can be calculated using similar equations when there is a need to examine the role of evolving or discrete reservoirs. In many cases, the reservoir is taken to represent one of two possible model compositions for the mantle (see DePaolo, 1988, for examples and references). Using the mantle as a starting point for model age, calculations are not strictly valid for many crustal samples, but the diversity of terrestrial Nd isotopic compositions is relatively restricted compared to systems like Rb/Sr, and so a mantle reservoir can be a useful place to start.

The first reservoir proposed for terrestrial rocks was CHUR (chondritic uniform reservoir; DePaolo and Wasserburg, 1976). CHUR is an estimate of the bulk Earth Nd isotope evolution based on an average composition of chondritic meteorites. Despite the utility of CHUR for giving a general idea of bulk reservoir composition, the chemical evolution of the mantle is widely recognized to be complex. A number of alternative model compositions have therefore been proposed to accommodate the depletion processes affecting the mantle, commonly described as the Depleted Mantle reservoir. It is arguable which model for the depleted mantle is most applicable, but whatever composition is used, it is likely to be closer to what is actually going on in the upper mantle than CHUR.

Analytical techniques employed with Sm-Nd isotopes are similar to those used for Rb-Sr. A sample is typically spiked with enriched ^{149}Sm (or ^{147}Sm) and ^{150}Nd (or ^{145}Nd) tracer solutions, and then digested in acid. Chemical separation of Sm and Nd is generally a two-stage process: cation exchange is employed to separate Rb, Sr, and a bulk REE fraction; the REE fraction is then separated into individual elements typically by reverse phase chromatography (Richard et al., 1976), although other ion-exchange approaches are sometimes used (summarized by Dickin, 1995). Measurement of Nd isotope compositions, and Sm and Nd isotope dilution concentration measurements are obtained by TIMS, generally on multicollector instruments. Nd and Sm can be measured either as metal ions (e.g., Hooker et al., 1975; Noble et al., 1989), or as oxide ions (Thirlwall, 1991a).

Practical Considerations and Examples

Most laboratories that engage in Rb-Sr isotope research also have the facilities for Sm-Nd isotope determination, and studies may benefit from analysis of both isotope systems for only a modest increase in cost relative to Rb-Sr alone. Many of the sample selection and processing criteria discussed earlier also apply to the Sm-Nd system, although the cost of sample processing is often higher because mineral separates are generally required for Sm-Nd geochronology. It is prudent to inquire about the materials used in the construction of the crushing and mineral separation equipment to ensure that they will not contaminate the samples. Conversely, it is important for all parties concerned with excessively radioactive minerals to be informed about potential risks, and to implement special handling and equipment decontamination procedures when necessary.

Sm and Nd are often variably enriched in fluorides and tungstates, and are highly enriched in U-Th bearing oxides and silicates. Although the REE are relatively immobile in many geological environments, they may be transported to significant degrees by aqueous fluids under certain hydrothermal conditions. In addition, post-depositional mobility is an important consideration: for example, the great propensity of high-U minerals for self-destruction through time due to radiation damage limits their usefulness in many circumstances by enhancing open system behavior. An additional consideration is that fluids in many hydrothermal systems evolve through time both in terms of chemistry and possibly in terms of ambient radiogenic isotope ratios. No useful isochrons will be obtained if the initial ratio of the hydrothermal system varied excessively during mineral deposition. Bearing the above pitfalls in mind, an Sm-Nd date for an ore-forming system that withstands close scrutiny will ultimately be the product of carefully and unequivocally relating economic mineralization to minerals with a wide range of Sm/Nd ratios that crystallized from a common isotopic reservoir (Fig. 3).

Early studies of hydrothermal uranium deposits (Collins Bay, Saskatchewan; Fryer and Taylor, 1984) and massive sulphide ores and related altered volcanics (Kidd Creek, Ontario; Maas et al., 1986) first highlighted the potential application of Sm-Nd to direct dating of ore deposits. Subsequently, Sm-Nd has also been used to date scheelite in lode Au deposits, garnets in skarns, and fluorite in hydrothermal-vein and Mississippi Valley-type deposits (MVTs).

Uranium deposits frequently contain anomalously high concentrations of REEs, and in some but not all cases, uraninite and other coeval minerals are deposited in a hydrothermal environment where Nd is obtained from a single, or at least homogeneous, source. In a study of the Mary Kathleen U-REE mine, Maas et al. (1987) demonstrated that good mineral isochrons could be obtained by analysing a range of cogenetic U-bearing minerals. Uraninite, allanite, apatite, sphene, garnet, and diopside formed during a hydrothermal event that homogenized and remobilized U and REE from enriched igneous and contact metamorphic protoliths, with the Sm-Nd isotopes clearly showing that remobilization occurred approximately 250 Ma after intrusion.

In contrast to studies where several minerals are used to constrain isochrons, sufficient variation of Sm/Nd ratios combined with constant initial Nd isotope ratios have been found in hydrothermal fluorite (e.g., Chesley et al., 1991, 1994) and scheelite (Anglin et al., 1996; Darbyshire et al., 1996). In the case of MVT deposits, direct dating of mineralization has proven particularly

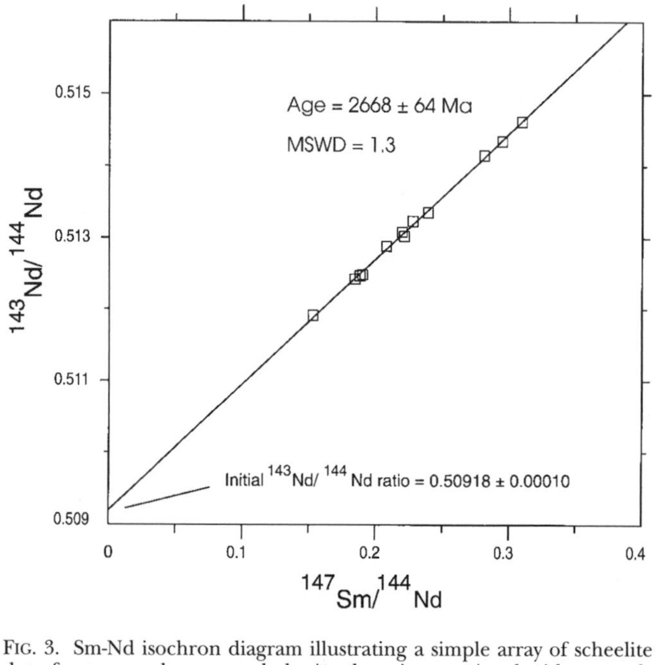

FIG. 3. Sm-Nd isochron diagram illustrating a simple array of scheelite data from several separate lode Au deposits associated with an early shear zone system in Zimbabwe. The low MSWD of the line (1.3) illustrates the undisturbed nature of the scheelites and the uniformity of initial Nd isotope ratios within the hydrothermal system (modified from Darbyshire et al., 1996).

elusive in the past, and Sm-Nd thus provides invaluable information, in some cases reducing the uncertainty of the age from ±200 Ma to ±20 Ma. Examination of the Illinois-Kentucky fluorite district by Chesley et al. (1994) showed that analysis of different components of banded fluorite crystals can yield good isochron ages that correlate well with regional geological and geochronological data. Excellent data have also been obtained from scheelite, which has been used to date individual mines (Anglin et al., 1996) or entire deposit associations (Darbyshire et al., 1996). The study of shear zone-hosted lode Au deposits in the Midlands craton of Zimbabwe (Darbyshire et al., 1996) is particularly remarkable in that scheelite Sm-Nd ages preserve records of two distinct mineralization events in the same area. Older shear zone systems that were active during a period of regional shearing in the Midlands craton, dated at 2.67 ± 0.06 Ga (MSWD = 1.3; Fig. 3) by scheelites from eight separate locations, correlate well with ca. 2.67 Ga intrusive activity in the craton. In contrast, later mineralized shear zones with fabrics distinct from the 2.67 Ga shears yield scheelite ages of 2.41 ± 0.07 Ga (MSWD < 1), broadly corresponding to reactivation of older high-strain zones and emplacement of the Great Dyke.

The key to the success of these studies is the fact that under certain conditions, large scale hydrothermal systems in the crust can carry significant concentrations of REE and isotopically homogeneous Nd obtained from sources external to the ore deposit. In contrast, Rb-Sr data from these same systems are often much more heterogeneous, reflecting local fluid/country rock interactions, and therefore do not provide good geochronologic data.

Summary

Sm-Nd isotope geochronology has often been overlooked in the study of ore deposits, perhaps because of the limited Sm/Nd fractionation in terrestrial materials. The examples given above show that Sm-Nd geochronology can be a valuable technique in dating particular types of hydrothermal mineralization that cannot be dated directly by U-Pb or $^{40}Ar/^{39}Ar$.

U-(Th)-Pb Dating

Introduction

The U-Pb dating method has found applicability in a wide range of geological environments, and is currently one of the most extensively used dating techniques. The method is versatile and reliable, and has the unique advantage of yielding data with an internal check on consistency, due to the existence of two parallel U-Pb decay systems (^{238}U-^{206}Pb, ^{235}U-^{207}Pb). In addition, the physical and chemical robustness of many of the minerals used (e.g., zircon) optimizes the likelihood of closed system isotopic behavior, while advances in chemical techniques and mass spectrometry have enabled routine delivery of precise and accurate data. These attributes have made the U-Pb technique one of the cornerstones of modern research in fields as diverse as time-scale calibration, provenance studies, regional tectonic syntheses, and continental reconstruction, as well as providing firm temporal foundations for many investigations of metamorphic, igneous, and hydrothermal processes.

There have been a number of major advances in U-Pb methodology in recent years, involving both improvements in instrumentation, and the widening of the range of geological applications, many of which have been revolutionary. Modern U-Pb geochronology typically involves the analysis of small groups of mineral grains, or even single grains, to obtain high precision dates. Alternatively, small regions within single grains (such as cores or growth zones) may be analyzed, albeit with lower precision, to establish detailed mineral histories in complex geological environments. Nevertheless, useful age determinations can also be made with very rudimentary data, and U-Pb and Pb-Pb isotopes were among the earliest systems to be explored in isotope geology (see reviews in Faure, 1986, and Armstrong, 1991). Some of the most important early works underpinning the development of U-Pb geochronology include the first mass spectrometric investigations of Pb isotope compositions by Aston (1927), Nier (1938, 1939), and Nier et al. (1941).

Systematics

There are four naturally occurring Pb isotopes, the abundance of only one of which (^{204}Pb) is not increased by the radioactive decay of U or Th. The other three isotopes, ^{206}Pb, ^{207}Pb, and ^{208}Pb, are the stable end-products of complex decay schemes for the parent isotopes ^{238}U, ^{235}U, and ^{232}Th, respectively. The three decay systems involve many short-lived intermediate daughter products, but for the purpose of investigating the age of most geological materials we need only concern ourselves with the Pb isotope end members of these systems.

The basic equations describing the relationship between time, and initial and present-day Pb isotopic composition for the U-Th-Pb systems are:

$$\left(\frac{^{206}Pb}{^{204}Pb}\right) = \left(\frac{^{206}Pb}{^{204}Pb}\right)_{initial} + \left(\frac{^{238}U}{^{204}Pb}\right)\left(e^{\lambda_{238}t} - 1\right) \tag{9.21}$$

where $\lambda_{238} = 1.55125 \times 10^{-10}\ a^{-1}$; half-life = 4.468 Ga;

$$\left(\frac{^{207}Pb}{^{204}Pb}\right) = \left(\frac{^{207}Pb}{^{204}Pb}\right)_{initial} + \left(\frac{^{235}U}{^{204}Pb}\right)\left(e^{\lambda_{235}t} - 1\right) \tag{9.22}$$

where $\lambda_{235} = 9.8485 \times 10^{-10}\ a^{-1}$; half-life = 0.704 Ga;

$$\left(\frac{^{208}Pb}{^{204}Pb}\right) = \left(\frac{^{208}Pb}{^{204}Pb}\right)_{initial} + \left(\frac{^{232}Th}{^{204}Pb}\right)\left(e^{\lambda_{232}t} - 1\right) \tag{9.23}$$

where $\lambda_{232} = 4.9475 \times 10^{-11}\ a^{-1}$; half-life = 14.01 Ga

The above equations use ^{204}Pb as a reference isotope because its abundance has not changed over geological time by radiogenic processes. In some special circumstances (e.g., Smith and Farquhar, 1989), where an entire suite of samples exhibits closed system behavior and uniform initial Pb isotope ratios, the above equations can be used to construct isochron diagrams. In other cases, when initial Pb ratios are either small enough to be ignored or can otherwise be adequately accounted for, then we can derive the following equations to describe the parent-daughter ratios, where radiogenic Pb is denoted Pb*:

$$\left(\frac{^{206}\text{Pb}*}{^{238}\text{U}}\right) = \left(e^{\lambda_{238}t} - 1\right) \quad (9.24)$$

$$\left(\frac{^{207}\text{Pb}*}{^{235}\text{U}}\right) = \left(e^{\lambda_{235}t} - 1\right) \quad (9.25)$$

$$\left(\frac{^{208}\text{Pb}*}{^{232}\text{Th}}\right) = \left(e^{\lambda_{232}t} - 1\right) \quad (9.26)$$

Division of equation (9.25) by equation (9.24) and rearrangement yields an expression involving only the present-day $^{207}Pb^*/^{206}Pb^*$ and $^{235}U/^{238}U$ ratios plus time as variables. The $^{207}Pb^*/^{206}Pb^*$ ratio is directly measurable, and the present-day $^{235}U/^{238}U$ ratio is a constant in nature (1/137.88):

$$\left(\frac{^{207}\text{Pb}*}{^{206}\text{Pb}*}\right) = \left(\frac{^{235}\text{U}}{^{238}\text{U}}\right)\left(\frac{e^{\lambda_{235}t} - 1}{e^{\lambda_{238}t} - 1}\right) = \left(\frac{1}{137.88}\right)\left(\frac{e^{\lambda_{235}t} - 1}{e^{\lambda_{238}t} - 1}\right) \quad (9.27)$$

This equation cannot be solved directly for t because it is transcendental, but tables of solutions exist (e.g., Faure, 1986, Table 18.3), or the equation may be solved iteratively. The resultant solutions are often referred to as "$^{207}Pb/^{206}Pb$ ages."

The half-lives of the two U isotopes are comparable to the age of the Earth, and so the U-Pb system can be applied over a broad range of geological time. It is possible to determine a date for the oldest terrestrial materials with a precision of 0.1 percent, but precision deteriorates for very young samples in which there has been insufficient time to build up detectable amounts of radiogenic Pb.

Equations (9.24), (9.25), and (9.26) describe three independent chronometers that can be used to check if the material being dated has remained isotopically closed with respect to U, Th, and Pb. Closed (i.e., concordant) systems will give the same date for all three chronometers. In order to provide a visual basis for assessing concordancy, U-Th-Pb data are usually presented on "concordia-type" diagrams. A number of such diagrams exist, but the most commonly used is the $^{207}Pb/^{235}U$-$^{206}Pb/^{238}U$ concordia plot (Fig. 4). This plot is particularly useful in the interpretation of samples that have not remained isotopically closed (i.e., discordant). An alternative concordia plot was developed by Tera and Wasserburg (1972) to assist in the interpretation of U-Th-Pb systematics in lunar

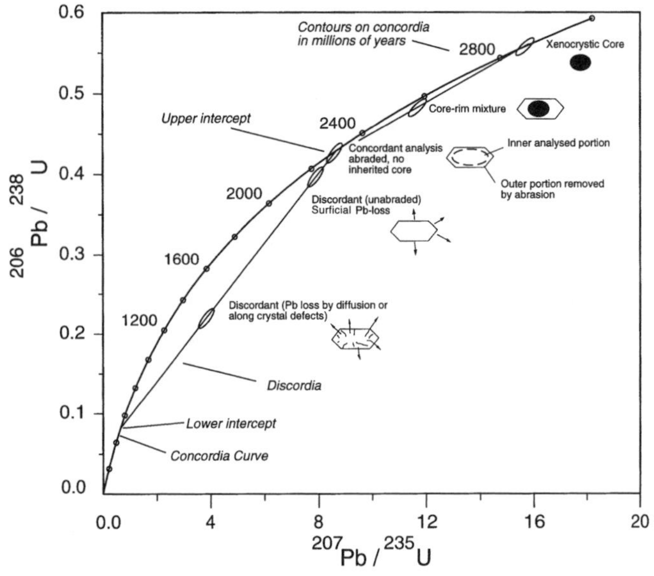

FIG. 4. $^{207}Pb/^{235}U$ vs. $^{206}Pb/^{238}U$ concordia diagram showing hypothetical analyses of concordant and discordant zircon samples, including samples with inherited older cores. See text for discussion.

materials, where $^{238}U/^{206}Pb$ is plotted against $^{207}Pb/^{206}Pb$ (Fig. 5). This type of diagram is sometimes used for the presentation of terrestrial Phanerozoic data, but its interpretation is essentially the same as for the $^{207}Pb/^{235}U$-$^{206}Pb/^{238}U$ plot.

During the 1950s it became clear that many geological materials yielded different $^{206}Pb/^{238}U$ and $^{207}Pb/^{235}U$ dates, indicating the operation of open system behavior. Non-graphical presentations of the data effectively limited further interpretation, but the introduction of concordia diagrams revealed systematic relationships. Initial

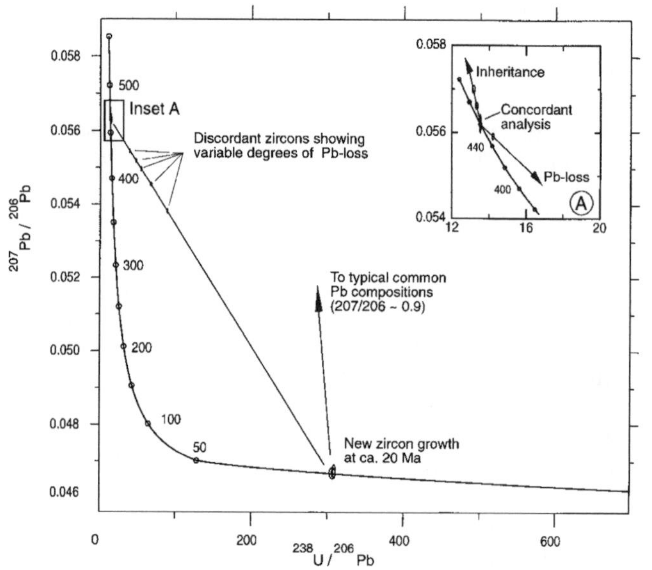

FIG. 5. Tera-Wasserburg concordia diagram showing a hypothetical set of analyses for a 450 Ma-old Himalayan granite that has experienced metamorphism with Pb-loss and new mineral growth at 20 Ma. See text for discussion.

discussions concerning the principles involved in the interpretation of discordant data are found in Ahrens (1955), Wetherill (1956), Tilton (1960), and Wasserburg (1963).

The concordia plot shown in Figure 4 illustrates some of the main concepts involved. The concordia curve, contoured in time units, is the locus of coeval solutions to equations (9.24) and (9.25). If a U-Pb analysis plots directly on top of the curve it is said to be concordant, and the interpretation is straightforward. The data record the time at which the sample became isotopically closed (e.g., the time at which a mineral formed, or a magma solidified). Because of the lack of ambiguity of such solutions, much effort is expended in obtaining concordant data. This may be achieved either by careful sample selection and processing, or by selective sampling at the micron-scale using an ion microprobe (see below).

However, despite these efforts, analyses commonly plot off the concordia curve. Discordant analyses can result from a number of causes, and although initially the data can be difficult to interpret, important insights can ultimately be obtained with careful assessment. In many cases, discordant data form linear, or sub-linear arrays. Collinear data are said to define a "discordia," whose upper and lower intercepts with the concordia curve may have age significance in terms of the times of original crystallization and subsequent disturbance (Fig. 4).

It is well known that some minerals, particularly zircon, can show discordance resulting from Pb-loss through time, and there are a variety of models involving aspects of both episodic and continuous diffusion, either during metamorphism or in response to radiation damage, that attempt to explain this behavior. For example, textural studies and accumulated empirical observations show that zircons with high U contents, small grain sizes, and physical damage (e.g., cracks, altered outer surfaces, etc.) may show significant Pb-loss (Silver, 1963; Silver and Deutsch, 1963; Krogh, 1982a, b). To eliminate these effects, mineral grains are usually carefully selected for crystallographic integrity, typically using a combination of screening using magnetic properties (damaged minerals are often more magnetic than perfect crystals), and inspection under a microscope and/or scanning electron microscope prior to analysis (Krogh, 1982a). High-quality data may also be obtained by selecting pristine regions within single crystals, such as cores or overgrowths. Clear overgrowths may sometimes be separated from damaged cores by careful handling with tweezers, while in other cases, pristine core regions may be isolated by abrading away the rims in a stainless steel cell (Krogh, 1982b).

In addition to Pb-loss, U-bearing minerals can yield discordant dates when a mixture of old and new domains within a single crystal are analyzed together. An important characteristic of some minerals used for U-Pb geochronology, particularly zircon, is that they can be formed in one geological environment and then recycled in another, and yet still retain age information from the first event. Crystals formed by a series of growth episodes may be composed of old core regions overgrown by younger zones. It is not uncommon to find zircons in granitoids, especially those crystallizing from magmas containing contributions from older continental crust, that show inherited cores surrounded by neocrystalline domains. Failure to completely separate cores from new growth zones prior to analysis results in isotope ratios that are mixtures, plotting on a mixing line between the $^{207}Pb/^{235}U$ and $^{206}Pb/^{238}U$ values for the old and new growths. A similar situation can arise when minerals grown initially during crystallization of a magma are overprinted by metamorphism, during which new overgrowths may nucleate on the original magmatic zircon cores.

Methodology

The two main analytical methods currently used in U-Pb geochronology are isotope dilution thermal ionization mass spectrometry (IDTIMS), and sensitive high mass-resolution ion microprobe (SHRIMP) analysis. In addition, the thermal evaporation (Kober) and laser-ablation microprobe inductively coupled plasma mass spectrometer (LAM-ICP-MS) techniques will be briefly discussed.

IDTIMS analysis. Isotope dilution thermal ionization mass spectrometry (IDTIMS) is the "conventional" method of analyzing single or multi-grain samples, although the term conventional should not be interpreted to mean simple. A typical experiment involves the separation of suitable minerals from a rock sample, careful grain-by-grain selection of the best crystals, and acid dissolution at high temperature in a Teflon-lined Monel or stainless steel "bomb," spiked with a mixed isotope tracer solution (usually containing ^{205}Pb, and ^{235}U or ^{233}U). The resulting solution is passed through ion-exchange columns to isolate the U and Pb from other ionic species, prior to analysis by mass spectrometry.

A number of different methods of thermal ionization mass spectrometric analysis are in use worldwide. In laboratories in which a ^{205}Pb spike is used, the U and Pb are loaded together onto a rhenium filament with silica gel and phosphoric acid. Pb thermally ionizes at lower temperatures (1,250°–1,550°C) than U, and so the Pb isotopes are measured first. Once these measurements are complete, the U is then ionized and analyzed as uranium oxide species at higher temperatures (1,500°–1,700°C). In an alternative method, U may be loaded separately from Pb and analyzed as metal ions, either by loading on a single rhenium filament in a graphite matrix, or by loading in nitrate form on a rhenium and/or tantalum multiple filament assembly. Laboratories that have access only to a ^{208}Pb spike must make two isotope measurements, one of a spiked aliquot (isotope dilution, to obtain the Pb and U concentrations), and the second of an unspiked aliquot (to determine the isotopic composition of the sample).

Under ideal circumstances, meaningful IDTIMS data can be obtained from single grains or even separate domains within single grains, provided they can be physically separated prior to dissolution. To achieve the best results, great care must be exercised throughout the entire procedure. It is particularly important to minimize contamination with common Pb during chemistry and analysis, and in a modern ultra-clean laboratory the total laboratory blank should be less than 10 picograms of Pb and 2 picograms of U per analysis. One of the most significant advances in reducing laboratory blanks was achieved by Krogh (1973), who introduced low-blank zircon decomposition techniques using Teflon dissolution capsules and anion exchange chromatography. Additional landmarks in technique development were (1) the manufacture of high purity (low U and Pb) reagents essential for dissolution and chromatography (Mattinson, 1972), and (2) the availability of an artificial ^{205}Pb spike that significantly improved the accuracy of Pb isotope and concentration determinations (Krogh and Davis, 1975; Parrish and Krogh, 1987).

SHRIMP in situ mineral analysis. The most refined and established in situ method of U-Pb analysis uses large ion-microprobe mass spectrometers. The technique has seen a rapid growth in popularity since the establishment of the SHRIMP at the Australian National University (e.g., Compston et al., 1984). This instrument was not the first ion microprobe to be used for U-Pb geochronology, but it represented the first routinely usable high-mass resolution machine. The success of the first instrument led to the production of the refined SHRIMP II machines that are now commercially available. SHRIMP technology uses a beam of oxygen ions, focused to a spot size of a few tens of microns, to ablate and ionize material directly from the surface of a mineral. The ionized material is then passed through a large mass spectrometer, with sufficient mass resolution to obviate the necessity of chemical separation of U and Pb from other species. Mineral standards with uniform physical properties and U-Pb-contents are used to calibrate the response of the machine, and data may be obtained under optimum conditions that are within an order of magnitude of the precision of good IDTIMS analyses (Fig. 6). This slightly lower precision is counterbalanced by the speed of analysis (no chemistry required), and the excellent spatial resolution of the instrument, permitting detailed internal analysis of zoned crystals. Enhanced spatial resolution is particularly useful when screening complex mineral populations that represent multiple sources (e.g., in sediments), examining detailed elemental zonation within mineral grains, and in deciphering inheritance patterns in single mineral grains that record several magmatic and metamorphic events.

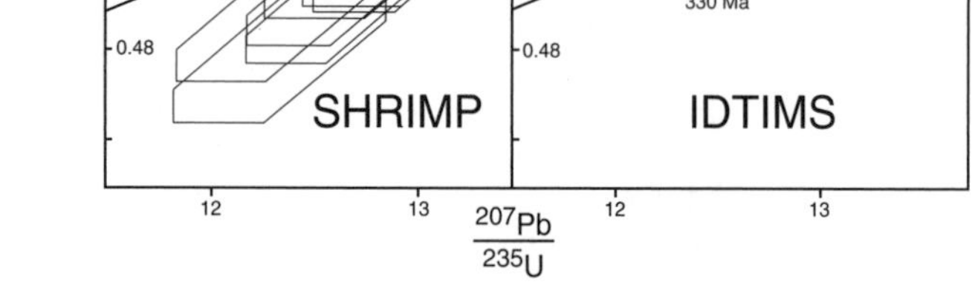

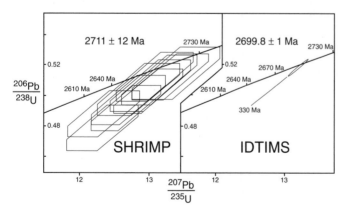

FIG. 6. A comparison of U-Pb zircon analyses from the Bourlamaque batholith, Quebec, using the SHRIMP ion microprobe (left) and IDTIMS (right). SHRIMP data from Claoué-Long et al., (1990); IDTIMS data from Corfu and Davis (1991). Modified from Corfu and Davis (1991). See text for discussion.

Based on a number of comparative studies, it can be said that IDTIMS analyses of carefully selected single- or multi-grain fractions give the most precise dates, whereas the ion microprobe is the most effective tool for investigating inheritance (see Roddick and Bevier, 1995).

Thermal evaporation (Kober) and LAM-ICP-MS analysis. The thermal evaporation technique, commonly described as the "Kober" method (Kober, 1986; 1987), involves the step-wise heating of a zircon crystal embedded within a rhenium filament in a conventional thermal ionization mass spectrometer. Pb is evaporated out of the crystal and is deposited on a second bare rhenium filament. The second filament is then heated, ionizing the Pb, and its isotopic composition is measured. A series of step-wise heating and measurement cycles are made, and step dates are calculated from the $^{207}Pb/^{206}Pb$ ratios using equation (9.27). The general principle is that portions of the crystal that release Pb at the highest temperatures (~1650 to 1750K) represent the most crystallographically coherent material, and thus have the highest probability of being isotopically closed systems. The $^{207}Pb/^{206}Pb$ dates calculated from these steps provide minimum estimates for the age of the sample, and approach the true age if closed-system behavior has been maintained. Lead evaporated at lower temperatures has probably been derived from near-surface or damaged parts of the crystal, and typically yields lower $^{207}Pb/^{206}Pb$ dates. It must be noted that the method does not enable the measurement of U/Pb ratios, and using only the $^{207}Pb/^{206}Pb$ ratio to calculate dates removes a crucial independent check on concordancy provided by the U-Pb concordia approach.

A second alternative and very promising U-Pb dating method now being developed involves in situ ablation of minerals using lasers. Ablation products are passed into an ICP source where U and Pb are ionized, and the resulting ions are then fed into a mass spectrometer. At present, the method provides a spatial resolution as small as 10 to 15 μm. Initial experiments by Feng et al. (1993) and Fryer et al. (1993) were successful in obtaining accurate $^{207}Pb/^{206}Pb$ dates from pitchblende and zircons. Further advances by Hirata and Nesbitt (1995) have produced the first acceptable $^{207}Pb/^{235}U$ and $^{206}Pb/^{238}U$ data, permitting the use of concordia diagrams. Using this relatively low-cost technology it is possible to determine the age profile of mineral populations rapidly, subsamples of which could then be investigated by high precision IDTIMS.

The laser ablation method cannot at present achieve the precision of SHRIMP analyses. Nevertheless, the field of ICP mass spectrometry is rapidly evolving, both in terms of technique and machine development. It is therefore possible, even likely, that results equivalent to those produced by the SHRIMP will be forthcoming in the near future.

Materials to Use

Materials suitable for U-Pb geochronology should have relatively high uranium contents (i.e., 10–500 ppm or greater) and minimal amounts of common lead at the time of formation. Whole rocks rarely satisfy these prerequisites and therefore minerals are usually employed. For a particular sample to be useful for U-Pb geochronology, a number of further conditions must also be met. First, it must be possible, with a reasonable degree of confidence, to link the minerals being analyzed to the geological processes to be dated. This factor is very important but sometimes non-trivial, especially in complex geological terrains and ore deposits. Secondly, the mineral must be relatively resistant to processes such as isotopic exchange occurring after formation if a primary mineral crystallization age is desired. And thirdly, the mineral should ideally be relatively common and recoverable without resorting to extreme measures, thus keeping it from becoming a geochronological novelty. The most useful and commonly analyzed minerals in U-Pb geochronology that fit the above criteria are listed in Table 3.

In many cases zircon is the ideal candidate because it crystallizes from a wide range of magma compositions, and can also grow during metamorphism. It has also been shown to grow from hydrothermal fluids under certain restricted conditions (e.g., Claoué-Long et al., 1990; Kerrich and Kyser, 1994). Monazite and titanite are also very useful, the former because it is perhaps less prone to inheritance in crustally-derived granitoids, and the latter because it often yields important constraints on igneous or metamorphic cooling histories. Other minerals listed in Table 3 are either of more restricted occurrence or typically have higher concentrations of common Pb, and are used when conditions permit.

Practical Considerations

There are no all-encompassing rules for collecting samples for U-Pb geochronology, but obtaining the largest sample possible of the freshest material available is the most common procedure. Where material is in unlimited supply, sampling may involve collection of up to 50 kg of fresh rock to ensure that sufficient U-bearing minerals are obtained (e.g., mafic rocks containing very small amounts of baddeleyite). At the other end of the spectrum, small sample sizes may be necessitated by physical or practical limitations (e.g., collection of samples from >6,000 m in the Himalayas; Noble and Searle, 1995), whereas coarse-grained crystal occurrences may simply require a dental pick for collection (e.g., >2 cm-long zircons and titanites removed from outcrops of Lewisian gneiss and Nain anorthosite, or 3 cm rutile euhedra from late quartz veins in a stratiform Cu deposit; Richards et al., 1988b). In general, however, it is probably wise to collect 2 to 10 kg of a typical granitoid or volcanic rock where possible.

TABLE 3. Minerals used in U-Pb geochronology

Mineral	Formula	U content (ppm)[1]	Common Pb (% of total Pb)[1]	Rock type[2]	Closure temperature (°C)[3]
Zircon	Zr [SiO_4]	1 to > 10,000	< 2	most	> 8
Titanite	CaTi[SiO_3] (O,OH,F)	4 to 500	5 to 40	k, c, a, m, ig	600
(sphene)				mp, gp, hv, gn, sk	
Monazite	(Ce,La,Th)PO_4	282 to > 50,000	< 2	mp, sg, hv, gp	700
Xenotime	YPO_4	5,000 to 29,000	< 5	gp, sg	> 650 (?)
Thorite	Th[SiO_4]	> 50,000	< 2	gp, sg	> 650 (?)
Allanite	$(Ca,Ce)_2(Fe^{+2}, Fe^{+3})$ $Al_2O{\bullet}OH[Si_2O_7][SiO_4]$	130 to 600	5 to 30	ig, gp, sk	650
Perovskite	(Ca, Na, Fe^{+2}, Ce) $(Ti, Nb)O_3$	21 to 348	< 2 to 90	k, c	
Baddeleyite	ZrO_2	58 to 3410	< 2	k,c,um, m, a	
Rutile	TiO_2	< 1 to 390	< 2 to 95	gp, gn, hv	400
Apatite	$Ca_5(PO_4)_3(OH,F,Cl)$	8 to 114	< 5 to 30	most	100 (?)

[1] Summarized from Heaman and Parrish (1991); data also from Parrish and Tirrul (1989), Noble and Searle (1995), and Noble (unpub. data).

[2] Summarized from Heaman and Parrish (1991): a = alkaline; c = carbonatite; k = kimberlite; m = mafic; ig = I-type granitoid; sg = S-type granitoid; mp = metapelite; hv = hydrothermal vein; gn = granite; gp = granitic pegmatite and leucogranite; sk = skarn; um = ultramafic.

[3] Summarized from Heaman and Parrish (1991); data from Parrish (1990), Copeland et al. (1988), Tucker et al. (1987), and Mezger et al. (1989). For the significance of closure temperatures, see below.

One critical factor whose importance cannot be overstated is the need to control how mineral separates are obtained. The high sensitivity of modern mass spectrometry permits analysis of very small samples, typically involving a few hand-picked mineral grains, or even fragments of single grains. It is therefore imperative that sample cross-contamination is reduced to zero to avoid dating someone else's sample. All separation equipment must be carefully cleaned, and to exercise sufficient control, most geochronology labs have dedicated crushing and mineral separation facilities.

Following crushing and coarse grinding, mineral grains are separated by a combination of magnetic and gravimetric techniques. A Wilfley or Rogers shaking table is commonly used to extract a heavy mineral concentrate from lighter minerals such as quartz and feldspar, which form the bulk of the rock. After drying and removal of magnetic phases with a hand magnet, selected minerals are separated from the concentrate using heavy liquids (e.g., tetra-bromo-ethane—specific gravity = 2.97; di-iodomethane—specific gravity = 3.33; sodium poly-tungstate—variable density) or a Magstream® magnetic-gravimetric separator, followed by use of a Frantz isodynamic or magnetic barrier separator. For zircons, several magnetic fractions are usually collected, the least magnetic fraction usually proving to be the most concordant. The best grains from each fraction are then selected by hand-picking under a microscope; clear, uncracked crystals with no inclusions or cores are sought. These grains (often less than a dozen) are abraded to remove leached rims, and then re-examined under the microscope to select the best grain or grains for analysis.

The U-Pb method is in general not cheap, but the data are of the highest accuracy and precision. Getting the right sample is fundamental to the ultimate success of the project, and it is worth discussing collection strategy with one's geochronological co-workers prior to setting out for the field. Not every rock is a suitable candidate for dating, but with determination an appropriate sample can usually be found. There are thus many examples in the literature where U-Pb dates are the key evidence underpinning geological interpretations and models on all scales from local to intercontinental.

The U-Pb literature presents a record of interpretations and data obtained at different stages of the dynamic evolution of the U-Pb technique. As a result, a number of things are worth stating by way of a literature survival guide for the non-specialist. Firstly, it is important to note that data are presented with uncertainties stated in different ways. When comparing data from different sources it is important to determine if errors are quoted at the 1σ or 2σ level so that like is compared with like. Secondly, the value of concordant data cannot be overstated. Before the advent of modern mineral separation and sample abrasion techniques, discordant data were the norm, and conceptual and mathematical models were generated to derive better estimates of the "true" age. However, these models inevitably introduce uncertainty, which is often, but not always, reflected in an increase in quoted error. A model may yield a very precise, but wholly inaccurate, result. Thirdly, U-Pb dates are often quoted in different ways and the reasons for doing so should be understood. The curvature of concordia is such that the error ellipses for concordant (or nearly concordant) data older than ~400 Ma will have high-angle, well-defined intersections with the curve, and the $^{207}Pb/^{206}Pb$ date will provide the best estimate of the true age (Fig. 7A). For younger samples, the error ellipses have increasingly acute intersections with concordia, leading to less precise definitions of the intercept (Fig. 7B). If the data are only

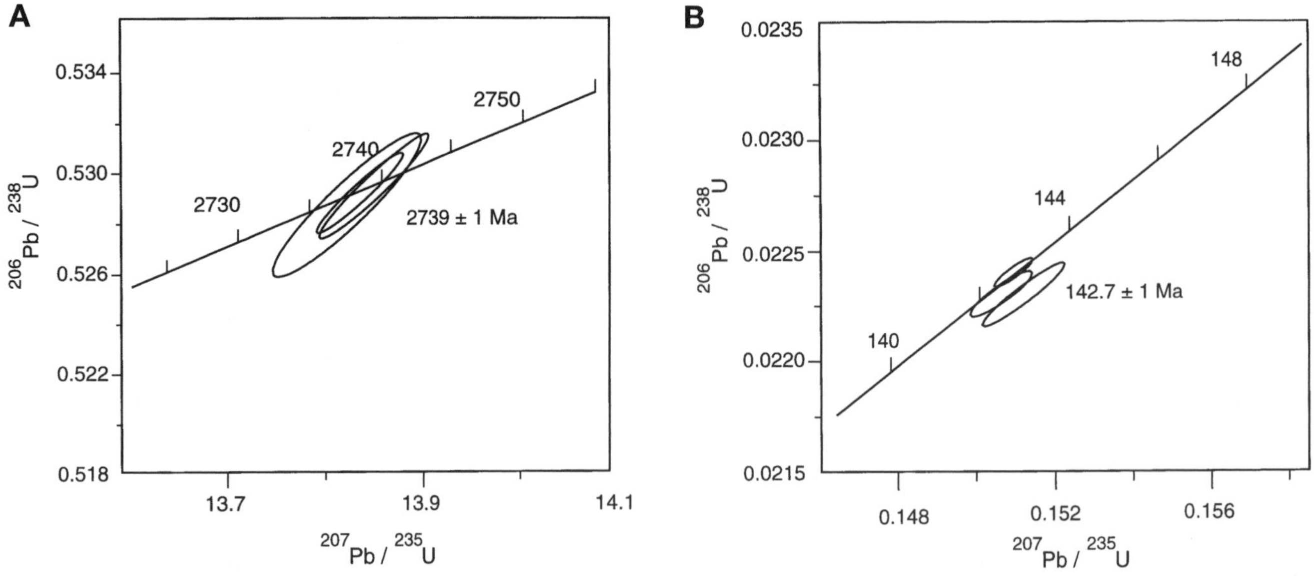

FIG. 7. $^{207}Pb/^{235}U$ vs. $^{206}Pb/^{238}U$ concordia diagrams showing how the angle of intersection of the error ellipses with the concordia curve is dependent upon age, and how this affects the precision with which the age can be calculated. Old samples with steep intersections (A) provide precise ages, whereas young samples with shallow intersections (B) yield less precise results (as a percentage of the sample age). All of the analyses have similar U-Pb error correlations. Data are taken from Noble et al. (in press) and S. Noble (unpub. data).

slightly discordant then the $^{207}Pb/^{206}Pb$ date is no longer the optimum quantifier of the true age, and instead $^{207}Pb/^{235}U$ or $^{206}Pb/^{238}U$ dates are quoted, the choice depending on which ratio has the least uncertainty stemming from the particular technique and mineral used. It may not be possible to avoid comparing dates calculated from different Pb-Pb or U-Pb ratios, but the conditions for doing so should be clearly defined.

Summary

U-Pb isotope data obtained from minerals such as zircon, monazite, and titanite provide some of the most accurate and precise dates available. The method is perhaps the most expensive of the available geochronological techniques, but often a few key U-Pb dates provide more useful information than a large number of K-Ar or Rb-Sr isochron ages. The U-Pb technique requires careful sample selection and mineral separate preparation because single mineral grains are often analyzed, and sample cross-contamination must be avoided. The U-Pb technique is applicable to many geological situations, but particularly for dating igneous events, because the minerals used are not uncommon and are chosen specifically for their ability to resist modification during alteration and tectonothermal events. In hydrothermal ore deposits, the U-Pb system may be used to date associated magmatism, or in certain circumstances the age of alteration or mineralization itself (e.g., hydrothermal zircon, rutile, or titanite). The dates obtained are based on two independent chronometers providing a test for closed system behavior which is not possible with other isotope methods.

Pb-Pb Dating

Introduction

In the preceding section, we concerned ourselves with minerals such as zircon that have high parent/daughter ratios (i.e., high U/Pb or Th/Pb). Decay equations (9.21–9.23) were derived using the non-radiogenic isotope ^{204}Pb for reference, but in practice this isotope is only monitored on the mass spectrometer as a measure of common lead contamination in the sample; small corrections to the radiogenic Pb isotope compositions are then made on the basis of that measurement. Nevertheless, age information can also be obtained from Pb isotopes in samples that do not have unusually high U/Pb or Th/Pb ratios. In these cases, isotopic variations simply reflect the decay of background levels of U or Th, which contributes to the bulk composition of Pb in the system. Compared to the situation with U- or Th-rich minerals, the observed variations in Pb isotopic ratios are small, but this method has the advantage that we can study the bulk evolution of Pb in the system, rather than just within a single mineral. Indeed, one of the first applications of this method was in establishing the age of the Earth (Gerling, 1942; Holmes, 1946; Houtermans, 1946, Patterson, 1956).

Holmes and Houtermans, and subsequently Cumming and Richards (1975) and Stacey and Kramers (1975), proposed models for the isotopic evolution of Pb in the Earth based on the assumption that at the time of formation, or shortly thereafter, the Earth was isotopically and chemically homogeneous. The build-up of the three radiogenic Pb isotopes relative to ^{204}Pb over the course of time was then modeled using various parameters, and was tested against the compositions of Pb from stratiform orebodies of known age. The Holmes-Houtermans model involved only a single stage of Pb isotope evolution throughout Earth history, whereas the more refined models of Stacey and Kramers (1975) and Cumming and Richards (1975) invoked a second stage or continuous process of chemical fractionation of U and Th from Pb, reflecting segregation of the continental crust. These models can be illustrated as isotopic "growth curves" on $^{206}Pb/^{204}Pb$ vs. $^{207}Pb/^{204}Pb$, or $^{206}Pb/^{204}Pb$ vs. $^{208}Pb/^{204}Pb$ diagrams (Fig. 8).

Model Pb-Pb ages can be obtained for samples of galena from ore deposits provided that they have had a simple two-stage history. Unfortunately, such well-behaved materials are largely restricted to stratiform deposits in oceanic or arc environments; continental leads are much more diverse because U/Pb and Th/Pb ratios in crustal source rocks are highly variable. Papers by Gale and Mussett (1973), Doe and Zartman (1979), and Zartman and Haines (1988) have presented useful models for rationalizing such complex systems, but it is not possible (or perhaps necessary) to plumb these complex waters in the space available here. Instead, we have two useful tools readily at hand: we can either take the isotopic data from Pb-rich minerals at face value and use them as tracers for sources of Pb (and other metals by association—see section on source tracing, below), or use the local variability of U/Pb ratios in rocks and minerals to generate secondary Pb-Pb isochrons, as described below.

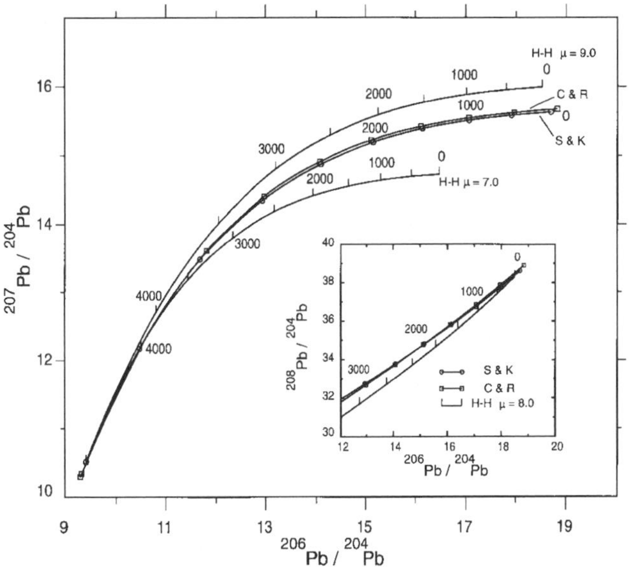

FIG. 8. Model Pb-isotope growth curves for the whole Earth, showing the build-up of ^{206}Pb, ^{207}Pb, and ^{208}Pb from decay of natural concentrations of ^{238}U, ^{235}U, and ^{232}Th, respectively. The models shown are Holmes-Houtermans (H-H), Cumming and Richards (C & R), and Stacey and Kramers (S & K). The Holmes-Houtermans model permits choice of different parent/daughter ratios (μ-values), and curves are plotted for $\mu = {}^{238}U/^{204}Pb = 7.0$, 8.0, and 9.0. See text for discussion.

Systematics and Methodology

The Holmes-Houtermans model of Pb isotope evolution is based on the basic decay equations introduced earlier, e.g.:

$$\left(\frac{^{207}\mathrm{Pb}}{^{204}\mathrm{Pb}}\right) = \left(\frac{^{207}\mathrm{Pb}}{^{204}\mathrm{Pb}}\right)_{t_0} + \left(\frac{^{235}\mathrm{U}}{^{204}\mathrm{Pb}}\right)\left(e^{\lambda_{235}t_0} - 1\right) \qquad (9.28)$$

If t_0 is taken to be the initial age of the system, we can calculate the composition of Pb at any later time t_1:

$$\left(\frac{^{207}\mathrm{Pb}}{^{204}\mathrm{Pb}}\right)_{t_1} = \left(\frac{^{207}\mathrm{Pb}}{^{204}\mathrm{Pb}}\right)_{t_0} + \left(\frac{^{235}\mathrm{U}}{^{204}\mathrm{Pb}}\right)\left(e^{\lambda_{235}t_0} - 1\right) - \left(\frac{^{235}\mathrm{U}}{^{204}\mathrm{Pb}}\right)\left(e^{\lambda_{235}t_1} - 1\right) \qquad (9.29)$$

and on re-arranging:

$$\left(\frac{^{207}\mathrm{Pb}}{^{204}\mathrm{Pb}}\right)_{t_1} - \left(\frac{^{207}\mathrm{Pb}}{^{204}\mathrm{Pb}}\right)_{t_0} = \left(\frac{^{235}\mathrm{U}}{^{204}\mathrm{Pb}}\right)\left(e^{\lambda_{235}t_0} - e^{\lambda_{235}t_1}\right) \qquad (9.30)$$

If we divide equation (9.30) by the similar equation for $^{206}Pb/^{204}Pb$, we obtain:

$$\frac{\left(\frac{^{207}\mathrm{Pb}}{^{204}\mathrm{Pb}}\right)_{t_1} - \left(\frac{^{207}\mathrm{Pb}}{^{204}\mathrm{Pb}}\right)_{t_0}}{\left(\frac{^{206}\mathrm{Pb}}{^{204}\mathrm{Pb}}\right)_{t_1} - \left(\frac{^{206}\mathrm{Pb}}{^{204}\mathrm{Pb}}\right)_{t_0}} = \frac{\left(\frac{^{235}\mathrm{U}}{^{204}\mathrm{Pb}}\right)\left(e^{\lambda_{235}t_0} - e^{\lambda_{235}t_1}\right)}{\left(\frac{^{238}\mathrm{U}}{^{204}\mathrm{Pb}}\right)\left(e^{\lambda_{238}t_0} - e^{\lambda_{238}t_1}\right)} \qquad (9.31)$$

or:

$$\frac{\left(\frac{^{207}\mathrm{Pb}}{^{204}\mathrm{Pb}}\right)_{t_1} - \left(\frac{^{207}\mathrm{Pb}}{^{204}\mathrm{Pb}}\right)_{t_0}}{\left(\frac{^{206}\mathrm{Pb}}{^{204}\mathrm{Pb}}\right)_{t_1} - \left(\frac{^{206}\mathrm{Pb}}{^{204}\mathrm{Pb}}\right)_{t_0}} = \left(\frac{^{235}\mathrm{U}}{^{238}\mathrm{U}}\right)\left(\frac{e^{\lambda_{235}t_0} - e^{\lambda_{235}t_1}}{e^{\lambda_{238}t_0} - e^{\lambda_{238}t_1}}\right) \qquad (9.32)$$

and on re-arranging:

$$\left(\frac{^{207}\mathrm{Pb}}{^{204}\mathrm{Pb}}\right)_{t_1} - \left(\frac{^{207}\mathrm{Pb}}{^{204}\mathrm{Pb}}\right)_{t_0} = \left[\left(\frac{^{206}\mathrm{Pb}}{^{204}\mathrm{Pb}}\right)_{t_1} - \left(\frac{^{206}\mathrm{Pb}}{^{204}\mathrm{Pb}}\right)_{t_0}\right] \bullet \left[\left(\frac{^{235}\mathrm{U}}{^{238}\mathrm{U}}\right)\left(\frac{e^{\lambda_{235}t_0} - e^{\lambda_{235}t_1}}{e^{\lambda_{238}t_0} - e^{\lambda_{238}t_1}}\right)\right] \qquad (9.33)$$

This is the equation of a straight line, or isochron, in $^{206}Pb/^{204}Pb$ versus $^{207}Pb/^{204}Pb$ space, which passes through the point $[(^{206}Pb/^{204}Pb)t_0, (^{207}Pb/^{204}Pb)t_0]$, and has slope m, where:

$$m = \left(\frac{^{235}\mathrm{U}}{^{238}\mathrm{U}}\right)\left(\frac{e^{\lambda_{235}t_0} - e^{\lambda_{235}t_1}}{e^{\lambda_{238}t_0} - e^{\lambda_{238}t_1}}\right), \text{ and } \left(\frac{^{235}\mathrm{U}}{^{238}\mathrm{U}}\right) = \left(\frac{1}{137.88}\right) \qquad (9.34)$$

Samples from a system that was isotopically homogeneous at t_0 but contained small variations in U/Pb (μ value), will evolve in such a way that they will lie along an isochron with slope m at any time t_1 (Fig. 9). The greater the range of U/Pb in the samples and/or the longer the time between t_0 and t_1, the greater the spread of the data along this line. This in turn will allow the fit of the line to be determined more precisely, and hence a more precise date to be calculated from m.

In the case of mineral deposits studied today, t_0 is the age of ore-formation, and t_1 is zero. Equation (9.34) therefore reduces to:

$$m = \left(\frac{1}{137.88}\right)\left(\frac{e^{\lambda_{235}t} - 1}{e^{\lambda_{238}t} - 1}\right) \qquad (9.35)$$

which must be solved by iteration (cf. equation 9.27).

Let us review where we have got to. From the basic decay equations for the U-Pb system, we have derived a simple expression in terms of age for the slope of an isochron formed by any initially isotopically homogeneous system. We have bypassed complex issues relating to how that system might have evolved to its starting isotopic composition at t_0, and we have assumed that the system subsequently remained closed and undisturbed to the present day. Theoretically, therefore, we can obtain an estimate for the age of an undisturbed (or isotopically re-homogenized) ore deposit by measuring the Pb isotopic compositions of various co-genetic ore and gangue

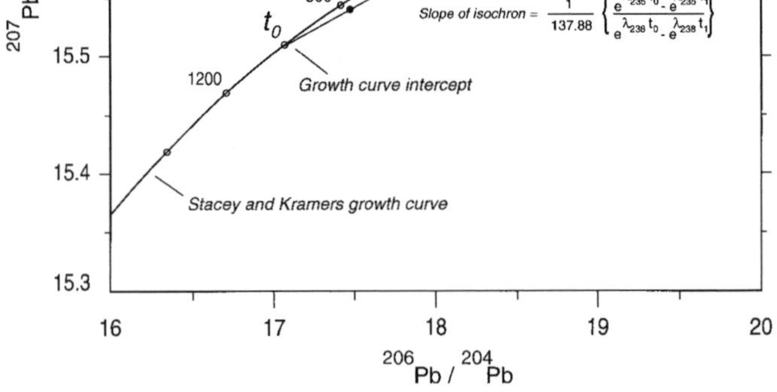

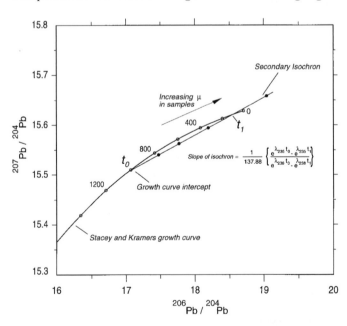

FIG. 9. $^{206}Pb/^{204}Pb$ versus $^{207}Pb/^{204}Pb$ diagram showing a hypothetical secondary isochron formed by a set of coeval, cogenetic samples having slightly different U/Pb ratios (μ values). The lower intercept of the isochron with the Pb isotope growth curve yields a model age for the formation of the system, while the upper intercept is the model age at which isotopic evolution ceased. The slope of the line yields the isochron age. Note that a meaningful model age will only be obtained if the system was derived from a source which lay on the growth curve at t_0—this is often not the case.

minerals. Galena (U/Pb ≈ 0) will define the initial isotopic composition of the system, and other minerals with higher U/Pb ratios will scatter to more radiogenic compositions along an isochron with time-dependent slope m, that passes through the galena point. Note that we do not need to determine U concentrations, although this information can sometimes provide a useful cross-check for our interpretations.

An important technique that has been employed to obtain isochrons from single minerals is sequential leaching (e.g., Cumming et al., 1982, 1984; Richards et al., 1988a; Frei and Kamber, 1995). This method assumes that U and Pb may be distributed inhomogeneously within individual mineral grains—particularly likely in view of the fact that U does not substitute conveniently into the lattice of many minerals, and may therefore be concentrated (in trace amounts) at the edges of grains, or along defects. By sequentially leaching the sample with various acids of increasing strength, samples of Pb from domains with different U/Pb ratio can be obtained. If the sample was originally isotopically homogeneous and has since behaved both internally and externally as a closed system—i.e., no U or Pb have been lost or gained since closure—then the various leachate analyses should define an isochron (Fig. 10). It is common to find that the early leachates yield relatively radiogenic data because they represent analyses of surface layers of the minerals, or readily leachable material along cracks or defects where U was concentrated. Later leachates, representing the most coherent and probably U-poor material, may approach the initial Pb isotopic composition of the system.

Practical Considerations

In practice, a number of natural and analytical difficulties arise with the Pb-Pb isochron method. First, Pb is a relatively mobile element, and problems with its loss (or addition) have been noted above. In dealing with materials other than Pb-rich or highly robust minerals,

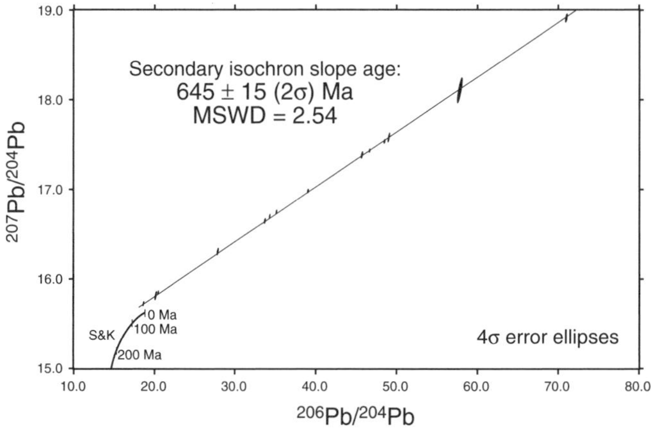

FIG. 10. $^{206}Pb/^{204}Pb$ versus $^{207}Pb/^{204}Pb$ diagram, showing a well-defined secondary isochron formed by leach-residue analyses of sulfide separates from three ore samples from the Musoshi stratiform Cu deposit, Zaire. The slope date = 645 ± 15 Ma (2σ), and MSWD = 2.54; error ellipses are shown at 4σ for clarity (modified from Richards et al.,1988a).

therefore, we should be aware of the likelihood of post-formation isotopic disturbance. Knowledge of the local geologic history will warn us of the possibility of metamorphic or hydrothermal resetting, and we should bear these scenarios in mind when interpreting the data. Indeed, complete re-homogenization of Pb isotopes is not uncommon, particularly in sulfides, and in these cases isochrons may be obtained relating to the resetting event, rather than the original formation age (e.g., Cumming and Gudjurgis, 1973; Richards et al., 1988a).

In the case of samples containing relatively small amounts of Pb (e.g., sulfides other than galena, silicates, whole rocks, etc.) a further problem is contamination from external sources of Pb. Samples collected should, therefore, be in pristine condition, and material obtained from underground workings should be free of diesel soot and dust; drill metal smeared on cores should also be removed.

Both of these problems, isotopic disturbance and contamination, will show themselves in the final analysis as scatter from the hoped-for isochron, either resulting in degradation of its precision, or its rejection as a meaningful age determination. We have discussed above how reported errors can be assessed to give an indication of the reliability of a quoted date, and it is ultimately up to the user to decide whether or not the date is meaningful, or what geological reliability to place on it.

A further natural pitfall is incomplete isotopic mixing. Linear data arrays can be generated in Pb-Pb diagrams not only by closed-system isotopic evolution, but also by mixing Pb of two different compositions (i.e., from two different sources). In fact, linear arrays are very common in Pb-Pb studies, and perhaps the majority of them originate from such mixing processes. Mixing lines of course have no age significance, despite the fact that apparent ages can be calculated from their slopes. Fortunately, however, it is rare that statistically collinear arrays of data are generated by isotopic mixing because (1) the original end-member leads were typically not entirely homogeneous, and (2) there may have been more than two sources of Pb involved. Mixing arrays are commonly diffuse, therefore, and are likely to give spurious apparent ages with poor precision. For example, Mukasa et al. (1990) obtained an apparent Pb-Pb isochron age of ~3.2 Ga for skarn mineralization associated with the Mesozoic-Cenozoic coastal batholith of Peru, and interpreted this to be the result of isotopic mixing. Similarly, Gulson et al. (1983) obtained an apparent age of ~1900 Ma for sulfides associated with Cu mineralization at the Mount Isa deposit in Queensland, although the age of the host rocks was constrained to 1710 ± 25 Ma.

Analytical problems stem mainly from the fact that natural Pb consists of only one non-radiogenic isotope, ^{204}Pb, and three heavier radiogenic isotopes (^{206}Pb, ^{207}Pb, and ^{208}Pb). In contrast, Sr and Nd have at least two non-radiogenic isotopes, whose ratios are constant in nature (^{84}Sr, ^{86}Sr, ^{88}Sr; ^{144}Nd, ^{145}Nd, ^{146}Nd, ^{148}Nd, ^{150}Nd). These constant ratios can be used as internal standards to measure and correct for isotopic fractionation during mass spectrometric analysis of Sr and Nd, but this possibility is not available for Pb. Furthermore, because isotopic fractionation is a function of the mass difference between the isotopes in question, particularly large effects can be expected when the lightest of the Pb isotopes, ^{204}Pb, is used for reference (e.g., four atomic mass units difference in the case of $^{208}Pb/^{204}Pb$). Note that this problem is less serious in U-Pb dating where it is the $^{207}Pb/^{206}Pb$ ratio that is most commonly used (only one atomic mass unit difference), and ^{204}Pb is only measured to make small corrections for the presence of common Pb.

In most laboratories, corrections for mass-dependent fractionation are made by analyzing standards alternately with the unknowns, and applying a correction on the basis of observed fractionation in the former. For this correction to be accurate, however, analyses must be made under strictly controlled conditions, because any difference in, for example, the temperature of the filament or the duration of the analysis will cause different degrees of fractionation in the samples and standards. Uncontrolled or poorly corrected fractionation will introduce correlated errors in Pb-Pb analyses, which in certain circumstances can yield linear arrays in Pb-Pb diagrams that could be misinterpreted as isochrons.

One solution to the problem of mass fractionation of Pb isotopes is to use a "double-spike" enriched in two isotopes such as ^{204}Pb and ^{207}Pb, or better still an artificial isotope such as ^{202}Pb or ^{205}Pb (e.g., Compston and Oversby, 1969; Hoffman, 1971; Hamelin et al., 1985; Richards et al., 1991; McCulloch and Woodhead, 1993). Both methods have their drawbacks: the scarcity and expense of artificial isotopes renders the latter technique inappropriate except for high-precision U-Pb work, whereas the double-spike technique is time-consuming, involving separate spiked and unspiked isotopic analyses. Nevertheless, these methods do provide data free of instrument-induced mass fractionation errors, and are essential if high-precision analyses are required (e.g., to better than 0.1%).

Remaining errors are mostly caused by difficulties in measuring the small ^{204}Pb peak on the mass spectrometer (^{204}Pb is the least abundant of the natural Pb isotopes, at 1.4%). The magnitude of this error will depend on the mass of sample analyzed (i.e., the amount of Pb on the filament), and the sensitivity of the mass spectrometer. Correlated errors will again be generated, but these errors are easier to spot than fractionation errors, because the precision of the analysis will typically be poor (revealed as a large error ellipse with long axis parallel to the ^{204}Pb-error line; Fig. 11).

Materials to Use

Because Pb is geochemically relatively mobile and can substitute in small amounts for common elements such as K in mineral lattices, many silicate minerals as well as sulfides and whole rocks are suitable for Pb-Pb studies. The mobility of Pb is also one of the main drawbacks to the method, however, because this renders systems vulnerable to isotopic disturbance and resetting, as noted above.

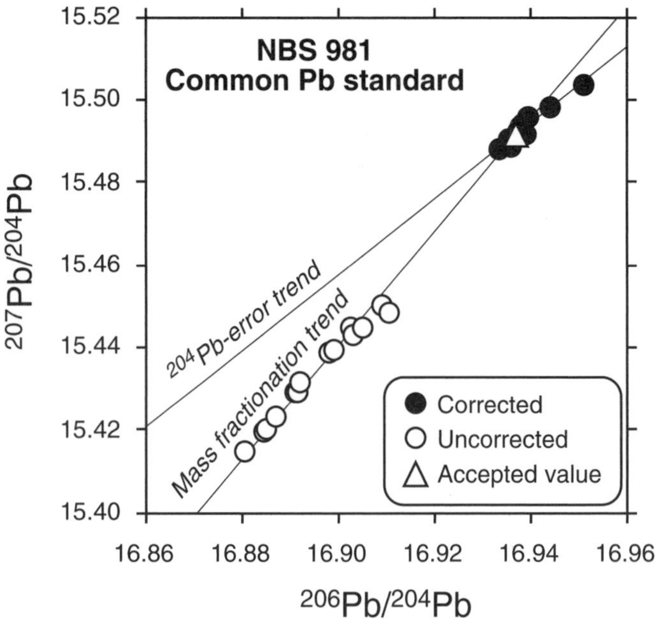

FIG. 11. $^{206}Pb/^{204}Pb$ versus $^{207}Pb/^{204}Pb$ diagram, showing repeat analyses of the NBS 981 common Pb standard. Measured ratios are shown in as open circles, and double-spike-corrected ratios are shown as filled circles. Unspiked results scatter along a mass-fractionation error line, whereas spike-corrected results plot close to the accepted value for the standard; remaining errors are due to imprecision in measurement of the small ^{204}Pb signal, and the data spread along a line with this trend (J.P. Richards, unpub. data).

When selecting samples for analysis, therefore, contaminated or altered material should be avoided. The samples should also be clearly co-genetic, because an isochron will not be obtained from materials of different age or initial isotopic composition. Ideally, pristine mineral samples should be extracted from single veins or mineralization zones, whereas wall-rock alteration zones should be avoided because of the likelihood that they will contain Pb inherited from the protolith. Such samples may be of interest in source-tracing studies, however, or as a means of tracking the movement of ore fluids in a system (Stein and Hannah, 1985; see below).

Examples

Numerous examples of the use of Pb isotopes in geochronology exist in the economic geology literature, including the establishment of the Stacey and Kramers (1975), and Cumming and Richards (1975) model isotopic growth curves. Subsequently, these curves have been used to obtain model ages for deposits containing simple one- or two-stage leads, such as certain Mississippi Valley-type (e.g., Cumming et al., 1990; Kesler et al., 1994) and stratiform deposits (e.g., Doe and Zartman, 1979; Franklin et al., 1983; Carr et al., 1995).

Successful applications of the Pb-Pb isochron method are perhaps less common, because of the prerequisites that the system was initially isotopically homogeneous, and has remained undisturbed. Indeed, because of the susceptibility of Pb isotopes to resetting, there are several instances in the literature in which the isochron ages obtained relate not to initial formation of a deposit, but to its subsequent overprinting (e.g., Cumming and Gudjurgis, 1973; Richards et al., 1988a). Difficulties in providing unequivocal interpretations for the origin of linear trends in Pb-Pb diagrams have fueled long-standing controversies, particularly where geological constraints are also equivocal (e.g., Archean gold deposits: Browning et al., 1987; Carignan and Gariépy, 1993; Kerrich and Cassidy, 1994; Frei and Pettke, 1996; Richards and Wagner, 1997).

Summary

A considerable amount of information can be obtained from the Pb isotopic compositions of commonly occurring rocks and minerals, without resorting to high precision U-Pb analyses. In Pb-rich deposits of simple one- or two-stage origin (e.g., stratiform massive sulfides), it may be possible to obtain a model age for ore formation by fitting the initial Pb isotopic composition of the system to an appropriate crustal growth curve. Alternatively, deposits containing "normal" abundances of U as well as Pb may be dated by the isochron method, and in particular by the sequential leach method. Such systems are susceptible to isotopic resetting and contamination, however, and particular care must be taken to select appropriate samples of known history.

The use of Pb isotopes in source tracing is considered separately later in this chapter.

K-Ar Dating

Introduction

The $^{40}K/^{40}Ar$ isotope system has served the economic geology community well for many years, principally because K is a major component of many alteration minerals, as well as of a variety of minerals in igneous, metamorphic, and sedimentary rocks. Thus, in principle, it is possible to date both hydrothermal alteration and host rocks in an ore deposit. Although the K-Ar technique has largely been superseded by the $^{40}Ar/^{39}Ar$ method, the fundamentals of the K-Ar system apply to both methods.

The history of the method dates back to Nier's (1935) discovery of the ^{40}K isotope, and Thompson and Rowlands' (1943) subsequent demonstration that ^{40}Ar is formed from ^{40}K by electron capture. Development of this system as a geochronometer followed rapidly, and by the mid-1950s a routine methodology had been established (e.g., Wasserburg and Hayden, 1955; Folinsbee et al., 1956). Much of the early work focused on dating authigenic minerals in sedimentary rocks, for which an effective geochronometer had not previously been available (e.g., Lipson, 1956; Wasserburg et al., 1956; Evernden et al., 1961). Application of the method to dating mineral deposits followed more slowly (e.g., Bassett et al., 1963; Ohmoto et al., 1966) but flowered in the seventies with the surge of interest in porphyry copper deposits and the need to relate the host intrusions to regional tectonic and magmatic frameworks (e.g., Quirt et al., 1971; Page and McDougall, 1972).

In 1977, the Subcommission on Geochronology of the International Union of Geological Sciences published new preferred values of radioisotope decay constants (Steiger and Jäger, 1977; Table 9.1). It is important to remember that K-Ar dates published before (and for some time after) this date will have used other λ values such as those recommended by Wetherill (1966), and these dates will have to be recalculated to obtain dates compatible with current usage (see Dalrymple, 1979, for a table of conversion factors).

Systematics and Methodology

The K-Ar dating method has been described in detail by Schaeffer and Zähringer (1966), Dalrymple and Lanphere (1969), Hunziker (1979), Faure (1986), Geyh and Schleicher (1990), and Hanes (1991). ^{40}K undergoes branched decay by beta emission to form ^{40}Ca ($\lambda_\beta = 4.962 \times 10^{-10}\ a^{-1}$), and electron capture or positron emission to form ^{40}Ar ($\lambda_\epsilon = 0.581 \times 10^{-10}\ a^{-1}$). In K-Ar dating we are principally interested in the ^{40}Ar-forming branch, which $\lambda_\epsilon/(\lambda_\epsilon + \lambda_\beta)$ or λ_ϵ/λ of the ^{40}K atoms will follow (where $\lambda = \lambda_\epsilon + \lambda_\beta = 5.543 \times 10^{-10}\ a^{-1}$). Thus the decay equation becomes:

$$^{40}Ar^* = \frac{\lambda_\varepsilon}{\lambda}\, ^{40}K\left(e^{\lambda t} - 1\right) \qquad (9.36)$$

(where $^{40}Ar^*$ represents radiogenic ^{40}Ar derived from the in situ decay of ^{40}K), and:

$$t = \frac{1}{\lambda}\ln\left[\frac{^{40}Ar^*}{^{40}K}\left(\frac{\lambda}{\lambda_\varepsilon}\right) + 1\right] \qquad (9.37)$$

This equation assumes that the system has remained closed to both ^{40}K and $^{40}Ar^*$ (i.e., neither of these components have been lost or gained other than by radioactive decay), and that no ^{40}Ar was present in the sample at its time of formation t years ago. If these conditions are met, then the age of a rock or mineral can be obtained by measurement of its ^{40}K and ^{40}Ar concentrations.

The ^{40}K isotope constitutes 0.01167 mole percent of natural potassium, and so measurement of the total K content in an aliquot of the sample by atomic absorption, flame photometry, or isotope dilution will enable calculation of the ^{40}K concentration. The $^{40}Ar^*$ content is measured by isotope dilution after fusion of the sample in vacuo, addition of a ^{38}Ar spike, and purification of the gas. The argon mass spectrum is deconvoluted according to a standard isotope dilution formula (Dalrymple and Lanphere, 1969; Faure, 1986) to separate the contributions of $^{40}Ar^*$, the spike, and atmospheric argon (which has a present-day $^{40}Ar/^{36}Ar$ ratio of 295.5, and will be present as blank). The $^{40}Ar^*$ content is reported as a concentration in moles per gram of sample, and when combined with the ^{40}K concentration, enables solution of equation (9.37) for t.

Unfortunately, the conditions set out above may not be met in practice. Three common failings are:

1. Potassium has been lost from (or added to) the sample after formation, most commonly during alteration or metamorphism;

2. $^{40}Ar^*$ has likewise been lost from (or rarely added to) the sample after formation;

3. Argon may have been present during crystallization of the rock or mineral. For young samples, if this Ar was of atmospheric origin, then it will simply be corrected for as though it were system blank. If it did not have a $^{40}Ar/^{36}Ar$ ratio of 295.5, however, then there will be a contribution to the total ^{40}Ar concentration of the sample that we cannot correct for (except by use of an isochron method; Hunziker, 1979; Faure, 1986). In general, the $^{40}Ar/^{36}Ar$ ratio of this extraneous argon is higher than the atmospheric value ("excess ^{40}Ar"), and thus the calculated concentration of $^{40}Ar^*$ will be too high, yielding dates that are too old.

Both K and Ar are mobile elements, the latter particularly so, and therefore the K-Ar system is highly susceptible to disturbance by post-formation processes that either affect the mineral chemistry or allow loss of Ar by diffusion. Thus, alteration or metamorphism can readily invalidate protolith K-Ar age determinations, normally resulting in dates that are too young through loss of $^{40}Ar^*$ (cf. the opposite problem with excess ^{40}Ar). If isotopic resetting is complete, however, then we have a powerful tool for dating these resetting processes—a tool that is of ideal application to the dating of hydrothermal alteration in ore deposits, for example.

Diffusive loss of Ar from minerals has been the subject of detailed study since the early days of K-Ar dating because of its commonly deleterious effects on calculated results. Argon, being a noble gas, has no place in the chemical structure of minerals, and only remains trapped due to the physical constraints of the enclosing crystal lattice. Diffusion of Ar through the lattice occurs readily therefore, and is a function of temperature according to the Arrhenius relationship:

$$D = D_o e^{-E/RT} \quad (9.38)$$

where D is the diffusion coefficient, D_o is a characteristic constant, E is the activation energy for diffusion, R is the gas constant, and T is absolute temperature (Dalrymple and Lanphere, 1969). Hence, any process that increases the temperature of a mineral after formation will promote diffusion and loss of Ar. In practice, because of the exponential dependence of D on temperature, diffusion at low temperatures is negligible, but increases rapidly above a certain range characteristic of the mineral. Most minerals therefore display a "closure temperature" (Dodson, 1973), below which the mineral is effectively closed to diffusion, but above which diffusion will progressively increase (see Table 4). Obviously, closure temperatures are not unique values because diffusion varies smoothly with temperature and is also a function of time and distance (i.e., grain size), but theory and experience allow us to place some approximate limits on these values, and to rank different minerals in terms of their argon retentivity with temperature. Amphiboles, for example, retain argon to higher temperatures than do feldspars or clays.

It should be noted that the concept of closure applies to materials during cooling as well as during heating. K-Ar dates of igneous or metamorphic rocks and minerals will represent the time at which the rock or mineral passed through its closure temperature, which will be some time after emplacement and solidification of the magma, or peak metamorphism. In orogens and large, slowly cooled plutons, the difference between formation and closure ages can be substantial, sometimes measured in millions of years, but for hypabyssal intrusions and volcanic rocks where cooling rates are rapid the difference is usually negligible.

Finally, Ar loss by diffusion is also a function of grain-size. Diffusion is a random process at the atomic scale, and we can think of it in terms of an argon atom moving a certain average distance d over a given period of time, at any given temperature; at a higher temperature or over a longer time interval, d will be greater, and vice versa. If the grain-size of the mineral is comparable to or less than d, then most of the Ar will be able to diffuse out of the grain under these conditions; but if the grain-size is much larger, then only a rim of width $\approx d$ will have lost significant Ar, and the core may retain much of its original concentration—a classic core-to-rim diffusion profile will have been developed. We can use this knowledge to our advantage in the $^{40}Ar/^{39}Ar$ method (see below), but when using K-Ar we must minimize Ar loss at all costs. Thus, we should aim to collect coarse-grained materials that are not altered and have not undergone metamorphism (unless we're actually trying to date that metamorphic event, of course).

Materials to Use

A wide variety of geological materials has been used for K-Ar dating, including whole-rocks, glasses, and minerals (Table 4). In fact, most materials that contain potassium can be dated by the K-Ar method, albeit with varying degrees of success. In most cases, the limitations of the material for this purpose stem from its ability to retain Ar. Thus, fine-grained materials such as clays (e.g., illite, glauconite), volcanic rocks, and glasses are highly susceptible to argon loss under conditions of only mild metamorphism, hydrothermal alteration, weathering, or diagenesis. Where such conditions have not occurred, however, these materials may provide otherwise unobtainable geochronological information, particularly in the fields of sedimentology and volcanology. In addition, dating of fine-grained K-bearing minerals formed in the surficial and supergene environments, such as alunite and certain Mn-oxides, has provided valuable insights into weathering histories of regolith and ore deposits (e.g., Gustafson and Hunt, 1975; Ashley and Silberman, 1976; Alpers and Brimhall, 1988; Bird et al., 1990; Vasconcelos et al., 1994; Dammer et al., 1996).

TABLE 4. Minerals suitable for K-Ar dating, and estimates of closure temperatures

Mineral	Lithological environment[1]	Closure temperature (°C)[2]
K-feldspar	V, H	200 to 250
Microcline	V, H	100 to 150
Adularia	H	
Plagioclase	V	125 to 225
Feldspathoids	V	
Hornblende	V, P, M, (H)	480 to 550
Biotite	V, P, M, H	250 to 400
Muscovite	P, M, H	250 to 350
Roscoelite	H	
Illite	S, H	< 200
Glauconite	S	
Alunite	S, H	
Mn-oxides	S, H	

[1] H = hydrothermal; M = metamorphic; P = plutonic; S = sedimentary/surficial/supergene; V = volcanic.
[2] Typical closure temperature ranges calculated for grain-sizes of 100–1,000 μm and at typical geological cooling rates; summarized from Faure (1986), McDougall and Harrison (1988), Gilg and Frei (1994), and Dahl (1996).

More commonly, however, the K-Ar (or $^{40}Ar/^{39}Ar$) technique is used to provide age constraints on primary processes such as igneous or hydrothermal events, and in these cases, fresh, coarse-grained material is optimal. The most common minerals used for dating in the igneous environment are amphiboles, micas (both biotite and muscovite), and feldspars, listed in approximate order of their Ar retentivity (Table 4). The general availability of at least one or another of these minerals in most medium- to coarse-grained or porphyritic igneous rocks explains the importance of the K-Ar and $^{40}Ar/^{39}Ar$ methods in igneous petrology.

In hydrothermal systems, the common occurrence of potassium metasomatism renders many types of ore deposits amenable to K-Ar dating. For example, K-feldspars (including adularia), micas, alunite, and K-bearing clays are commonly used to establish the ages of hydrothermal alteration, often relative to an associated magmatic event that may have been dated using primary igneous minerals as above.

Practical Considerations

The K-Ar method is applicable to rocks and minerals of almost any age. However, Ar loss is to be expected from older materials, whereas mass spectrometer sensitivity ultimately limits our ability to measure the small amounts of radiogenic Ar in very young samples (Table 5). Nevertheless, there are many examples of K-Ar dates younger than 1.0 Ma in the literature (e.g., Fitch, 1972; Moyle et al., 1990; Aoki et al., 1993), and younger rocks (i.e., Phanerozoic) tend to yield more reliable dates than older rocks (i.e., Precambrian). Realistically, the method is ideal only in young, unmetamorphosed terrains, and in other circumstances a more robust geochronometer, such as zircon U-Pb, or $^{40}Ar/^{39}Ar$ step-heating should be considered (see above and below). The relative cheapness and simplicity of the K-Ar method is its strength where geological conditions permit, however.

TABLE 5. Typical potassium contents and minimum age limits for minerals commonly dated by the K-Ar method (data summarized from McDougall and Harrison, 1988; Deer et al., 1992).

Mineral	Typical K_2O (wt%)	Typical minimum age (Ma)	Ideal conditions minimum age (Ma)
Leucite	~20	0.02	< 0.005
Sanidine–anorthoclase	5 – 15	0.05	< 0.005
Whole-rock	0.1 – 8	0.05	0.01
Mica	8 – 11	0.5	0.1
Plagioclase	0.0 – 0.4	0.5	0.1
Amphibole	0.0 – 2.7	1.0	0.3

When selecting samples in the field for K-Ar dating, samples displaying obvious causes of Ar loss should be avoided. Metamorphic overprinting has been discussed, but local contact metamorphic and hydrothermal effects must also be considered, particularly when dealing with ore-forming systems. Propylitic alteration halos can extend for several kilometers around large porphyry systems, for example, and will cause chloritization and saussuritization of mafic minerals and feldspars. It is therefore best to collect from fresh exposures where possible (road-cuts or drill core are ideal), and avoid altered and/or weathered material.

The size of sample to be collected will depend on the abundance and identity of the mineral to be used for dating, and the expected age. The younger the sample, the lower the abundance of the target mineral in the rock, and the lower the K-content of that mineral, then the larger the sample size needed to yield a measurable quantity of $^{40}Ar^{*}$. If in doubt, over collect. A typical geochronological sample should weigh several kilograms to allow for inefficiencies in mineral separation. If sample size is an insuperable problem, for example when dealing with small intersections in drill core, then an alternative (but likely more expensive) method such as laser-probe $^{40}Ar/^{39}Ar$ dating should be considered (see below).

Probably the most time-consuming step in mineral age-determination is separation of the target mineral from its host. Thus, it is well worth cutting a thin section of the sample to check for alteration before consigning it to the crushing and separating rooms. Petrographic examination will also allow estimation of the average grain size of the target mineral, and hence the ideal size fraction that will ensure complete liberation of the mineral grains while not over-reducing them (mineral separation becomes increasingly tedious as grain size decreases).

Standard sample preparation procedures involve jaw-crushing and grinding, followed by sieving to collect specific size fractions (commonly in the range 500–250 μm, 250–100 μm). Wet sieving, or use of an ultra-sonic bath prior to sieving, helps to disaggregate multi-mineral grains and wash fines from the size fraction. Mineral separation is then usually achieved by a combination of density and magnetic procedures as for zircon separation (see above). Final purification to >99 percent is usually achieved by hand picking under alcohol—this is where the value of choosing the coarsest possible grain-size will be most appreciated! The amount of handpicked material required will vary according to the expected age of the sample, the K-content of the mineral, and the sensitivity of the mass spectrometric equipment to be used; up to one gram of hand-picked material may be required for low-K Neogene amphiboles, for example. Unfortunately, much of this material is required for replicate K analyses to check for sample homogeneity (a major source of error in this method: Engels and Ingamells, 1970).

Summary

The K-Ar method is probably the cheapest and easiest method of dating minerals (and sometimes whole rocks) that have experienced a simple history since crystallization. It is particularly useful in the hydrothermal environment where primary and secondary K-bearing minerals are commonplace. Limitations of the method are mainly due to diffusive Ar loss caused by metamorphism (resulting in erroneously young dates), or the inclusion of extraneous Ar of non-atmospheric composition in the mineral at the time of crystallization (resulting in erroneously old dates). Many of these problems can be resolved by using a modification of the simple K-Ar method, $^{40}Ar/^{39}Ar$ dating, which is the subject of the next section.

$^{40}Ar/^{39}Ar$ Dating

Introduction

The $^{40}Ar/^{39}Ar$ dating method is an elegant modification of the standard $^{40}K/^{40}Ar$ technique discussed above. First described in detail by Merrihue and Turner (1966), the method's initial aim was to enable more precise determination of the K-content of the sample aliquot by first converting a calculable proportion of ^{39}K into $^{39}Ar_K$ by neutron activation. The original $^{39}K/^{40}Ar$ ratio, and thus the $^{40}K/^{40}Ar$ ratio from which age is calculated ($^{40}K/^{39}K = 0.000125$ in nature), could then be determined from the $^{39}Ar_K/^{40}Ar$ ratio as measured with a mass spectrometer (conventionally reported as $^{40}Ar^*/^{39}Ar_K$, where $^{40}Ar^*$ represents ^{40}Ar derived in situ by decay of ^{40}K). This approach has several advantages over the conventional K-Ar method: (1) problems of sample splitting and inhomogeneity inherent in measuring the K and Ar contents on separate aliquots of the sample are avoided; (2) smaller sample sizes can be analyzed, because there is no need for separate chemical analyses of K content; and (3) isotope ratios can be measured with much greater precision compared with most quantitative chemical techniques, thus yielding a more precise and accurate determination of the $^{40}K/^{40}Ar$ ratio through the proxy $^{39}Ar_K/^{40}Ar$ ratio.

In their landmark 1966 paper, Merrihue and Turner also documented the first step-heating experiments, in which they progressively degassed samples up to the melting point, and analyzed the composition of the Ar released at each step. They showed that this technique could be used to reveal different sources of Ar within a sample, and also to elucidate conditions of partial Ar loss through thermal overprinting. Turner (1966, 1970) and Davis et al. (1971) presented early examples of the now familiar step-heating age spectrum, in which apparent age as represented by the $^{40}Ar^*/^{39}Ar_K$ ratio is plotted on the y-axis, versus the incremental fraction of $^{39}Ar_K$ released during each heating step on the x-axis. Sequential steps with similar apparent ages form a plateau on these diagrams, leading to the definition of $^{40}Ar/^{39}Ar$ plateau ages (Fleck et al., 1977).

Much of this early work focused on the study of meteorites, and subsequently lunar rocks, where sample size was a major limiting factor. Later studies applied the method to the investigation of disturbed samples that had lost Ar through metamorphism (e.g., Fleck et al., 1977), while application of Dodson's (1973) theories of diffusion led to the concept of thermochronology, in which the ages of different minerals with different blocking temperatures in a rock enabled the assessment of thermal histories and cooling rates in metamorphic terrains (e.g., Berger and York, 1981).

The ability of the $^{40}Ar/^{39}Ar$ method to "see through" partial thermal overprinting and to resolve problems of excess ^{40}Ar contamination has made it a particularly powerful tool in studies of mineralizing systems, where such conditions are commonplace. For example, Richards and McDougall (1990) were able to obtain a plateau age of 6.0 ± 0.3 Ma for hornblende from mafic intrusions at the Porgera gold deposit, Papua New Guinea, whereas conventional K-Ar dates for the same samples scattered from 7 to 14 Ma due to the presence of excess ^{40}Ar. Excess ^{40}Ar was also detected in hydrothermal minerals from the deposit, reflecting a high partial pressure of non-atmospheric Ar in the magmatic-hydrothermal system. The step-heating method can also be used to date older materials where partial resetting often invalidates conventional K-Ar dates: Arehart et al. (1993) successfully applied the method to the notoriously intractable problem of dating Carlin-type gold deposits, while Hanes et al. (1992) were able to resolve small age differences between metamorphic/plutonic and mineralization events in Archean gold deposits of the Abitibi greenstone belt, Canada. A further notable result was that of York et al. (1982), who showed that ore minerals such as pyrite could be dated by the $^{40}Ar/^{39}Ar$ method.

The most recent advancement of the method has been the use of lasers to fuse irradiated samples on a microscopic scale, thereby providing an "age-microprobe" (e.g., York et al., 1981; Maluski and Schaeffer, 1982; Sutter and Hartung, 1984; Hu et al., 1994; Kelley et al., 1994; Clark et al., 1998). This technique enables micro-scale investigation of Ar diffusion profiles in minerals, and permits analysis of much smaller samples than previously possible.

Excellent reviews of the $^{40}Ar/^{39}Ar$ method have been given by Dallmeyer (1979), Faure (1986), McDougall and Harrison (1988), Geyh and Schleicher (1990), and Hanes (1991), to which the reader is referred for more detailed information.

Systematics and Methodology

The basis of the $^{40}Ar/^{39}Ar$ method centers on the fact that ^{39}K can be converted to ^{39}Ar by irradiation with fast neutrons in a nuclear reactor. The reaction is described by the formula below, in which neutron (n) bombardment results in emission of a proton (p) from the ^{39}K nucleus, thereby converting it to an isotope of Ar:

$$^{39}_{19}\mathrm{K}\,(n,p)\,^{39}_{18}\mathrm{Ar} \tag{9.39}$$

The concentration of the parent element in the K-Ar geochronometric system can be measured in terms of its neutron activation product, $^{39}Ar_K$, and the $^{40}K/^{40}Ar^*$ ratio can therefore be calculated directly from the $^{40}Ar^*/^{39}Ar_K$ ratio as measured on a mass spectrometer.

There are, of course, many details that need to be taken into account before this simple theory can be used to obtain reliable age information. Some of these considerations are listed below:

1. Neutron activation reactions are extremely complex, and the proportion of ^{39}K atoms that will be converted to ^{39}Ar is a function of the duration of irradiation, the neutron capture cross-section of ^{39}K, and the intensity and energy spectrum of the radiation experienced by the sample in the reactor. The neutron flux density and energy spectrum vary for and within each reactor, so these variables are hard to quantify. Instead, the problem is solved by including a standard sample of known age with the samples to be irradiated (the flux monitor; Roddick, 1983). Recall from equation (9.36) that:

$$^{40}\mathrm{Ar}^* = \frac{\lambda_\varepsilon}{\lambda}\,^{40}\mathrm{K}\left(e^{\lambda t}-1\right) \tag{9.40}$$

Thus:

$$\frac{^{40}\mathrm{Ar}^*}{^{40}\mathrm{K}} = \frac{\lambda_\varepsilon}{\lambda}\left(e^{\lambda t}-1\right) \tag{9.41}$$

Because ^{39}K occurs in fixed proportion to ^{40}K in nature, the $^{39}Ar_K$ generated in the reactor will also be in proportion to ^{40}K, albeit by a factor that we do not know. Thus, we define a parameter J, which includes all the constants and unknowns:

$$\frac{^{40}\mathrm{Ar}^*}{^{39}\mathrm{Ar_K}} = \frac{e^{\lambda t}-1}{J} \tag{9.42}$$

We can now calculate J for our specific sample batch by measuring the $^{40}Ar^*/^{39}Ar_K$ ratio of the flux monitor (age = t_m):

$$J = \frac{e^{\lambda t_m}-1}{^{40}\mathrm{Ar}^*/^{39}\mathrm{Ar_K}} \tag{9.43}$$

Equation (9.42) is now soluble in terms of t for all of the unknown samples in the batch:

$$t = \frac{1}{\lambda}\ln\left[\left(\frac{^{40}\mathrm{Ar}^*}{^{39}\mathrm{Ar_K}}\right)\bullet J+1\right] \tag{9.44}$$

2. The $^{39}K(n,p)^{39}Ar$ reaction is unfortunately not the only neutron activation reaction that can take place during irradiation, and some of these others also generate isotopes of Ar. McDougall and Harrison (1988) list twenty such reactions involving various isotopes of Ca, K, Ar, and Cl that produce Ar isotopes in the range ^{36}Ar to ^{40}Ar. Calcium is the biggest problem, generating Ar isotopes right across this range. Fortunately, the Ca contribution can be assessed by monitoring the generation of ^{37}Ar, an unstable isotope formed principally by the reaction $^{40}Ca(n,\alpha)^{37}Ar$. The contribution to ^{36}Ar (used to assess atmospheric Ar "blank") and to ^{39}Ar from other calcium reactions can then be subtracted. Nevertheless, uncertainties in these corrections may lead to significant errors for young or Ca-rich samples. Chlorine contributes ^{38}Ar by the reaction $^{37}Cl(n,\gamma,\beta^-)^{38}Ar$, and the release of ^{38}Ar can therefore provide a useful monitor of Cl distribution in the sample, and provide a check on sample homogeneity. The correct choice of irradiation time and the use of cadmium shielding (to reduce sample exposure to slow neutrons) can help minimize unwanted neutron activation effects.

3. Both ^{37}Ar and ^{39}Ar are unstable nuclei with half-lives of 35.1 days and 269 years respectively. Corrections for their decay since the time of irradiation must therefore be made. Normally, isotopic measurements are not made until a few months after irradiation to allow the decay of other unwanted, highly radioactive, short-lived isotopes.

Total fusion analyses. Release of all of the argon in one step by heating the sample to fusion in vacuo will provide a result that is directly equivalent to the K-Ar date, the only real advantage of which is the fact that no separate K analysis needs to be done. Total fusion analyses are therefore sometimes carried out where sample size is limited, or where the $^{40}Ar^*$ content is very low (e.g., York et al., 1982); they are also most easily obtained from laser extraction lines, although step heating is also possible by this method. The analysis of the flux monitor used to determine the J value for an irradiated sample batch is obtained by total fusion, and similar analyses may be carried out on aliquots of the samples as a check against the conventional K-Ar date.

Step-heating analyses. The real power of the $^{40}Ar/^{39}Ar$ method is realized in step-heating analyses, whereby the sample is heated in incremental steps to fusion, with analysis of the Ar released at each step. Ideally, this procedure results in progressive degassing from rim to core of the mineral grains by thermal diffusion, thus revealing inhomogeneities in $^{40}Ar^*$ distribution resulting from geological Ar-loss, or the presence of extraneous Ar. The $^{40}Ar^*/^{39}Ar_K$ ratio or apparent age of each step is plotted against the incremental fraction of $^{39}Ar_K$ released, to form an age-spectrum diagram (Fig. 12).

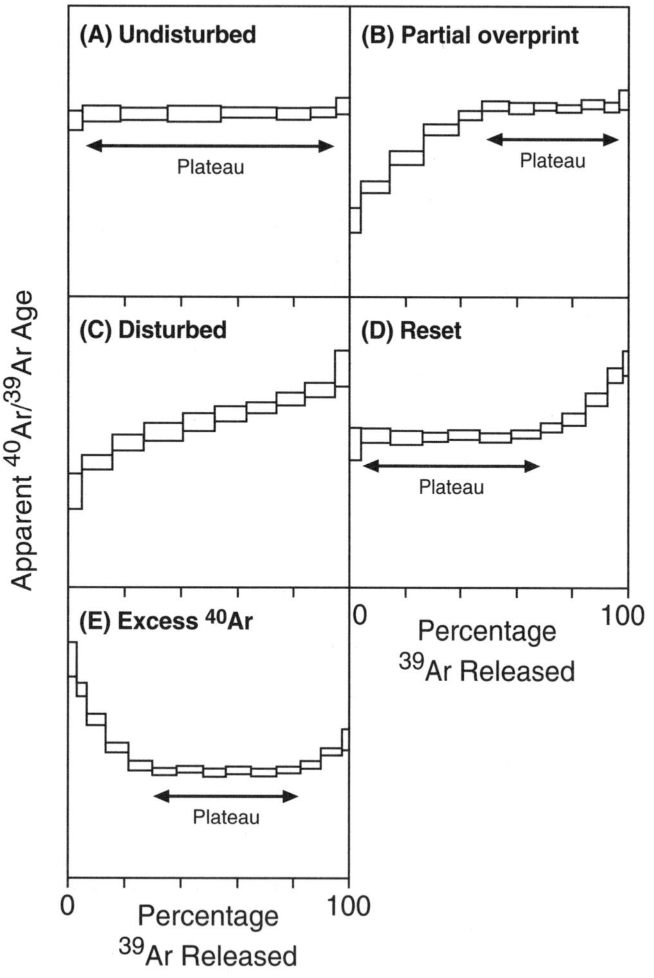

FIG. 12. Schematic $^{40}Ar/^{39}Ar$ age spectra: (A) an undisturbed sample yielding a plateau across almost the entire gas release; (B) a sample showing slight disturbance leading to younger apparent ages in early gas releases, but forming a plateau in later (higher temperature) releases; (C) a disturbed sample yielding no plateau; (D) a reset sample yielding a plateau corresponding to the age of overprinting; later gas releases rise to older apparent ages, reflecting preservation of some precursor Ar in the core of the sample; (E) a saddle-shaped spectrum reflecting the presence of excess ^{40}Ar in the sample; a plateau section defined during mid-stage gas releases may approximate the true age of the sample, but high apparent ages of early and late gas releases are fictitious.

A perfectly undisturbed sample will yield identical dates for each step of the degassing experiment, but this situation is rare (Fig. 12A). More commonly, the lowest temperature steps yield low apparent ages, reflecting diffusive loss of $^{40}Ar^*$ from the rims of the mineral grains, for example in response to metamorphic overprinting. As stepwise degassing progresses to sample deeper parts of the grains where geological Ar loss may have been less, the apparent age of each step increases, ideally rising to a plateau where sequential steps yield statistically identical dates (Fig. 12B). This plateau may be taken to represent the true age of the sample if certain criteria are met (Fleck et al., 1977):

> A 'plateau' is that part of an age-spectrum diagram composed of contiguous gas fractions that together represent more than 50% of the total ^{39}Ar released from the sample and for which no difference in age can be detected between any two fractions at the 95% level of confidence.

The Critical Value test (McIntyre, 1963; Dalrymple and Lanphere, 1969) is used to assess this second criterion, and for any two steps in a plateau with apparent ages t_1 and t_2, each with associated errors σ_1 and σ_2, the difference in these two dates must be less than the Critical Value (CV):

$$|t_1 - t_2| < CV = 1.960\sqrt{\left(\sigma_1^2 + \sigma_2^2\right)} \tag{9.45}$$

Ideally, at least 5 steps should be included in the plateau, excluding small gas fractions of <3 percent of the total $^{39}Ar_K$ released (Fleck et al., 1977; Berger and York, 1981). The plateau age is then calculated by averaging the step ages, with weighting for the step size and associated error.

In many cases a plateau is not reached, and a monotonically rising spectrum indicates extensive degassing of the sample (Fig. 12C). The highest apparent age reached can be taken as a minimum estimate of the original age of the sample. In other cases resetting may be almost complete, and the plateau will occur at the start of the spectrum marking the age of overprinting. A tail to higher apparent ages in the later, higher temperature steps may hint at the original formation age of the sample (Fig. 12D).

The presence of excess ^{40}Ar often yields characteristic saddle-shaped spectra, in which anomalously high apparent ages are found in the earliest, and sometimes also the latest, steps (Fig. 12E). The lowest point of the saddle may provide a maximum estimate of the sample age, and in some circumstances may yield a valid plateau age (e.g., Richards and McDougall, 1990). The behavior of excess ^{40}Ar during stepwise degassing is poorly understood, but it is thought that the early gas releases may be of weakly-held argon, perhaps trapped in crystal defects, or fluid or melt inclusions. Late-degassing excess ^{40}Ar may represent Ar trapped in anion vacancies in the lattice (Harrison and McDougall, 1981).

Argon isotope data may also be represented on correlation diagrams, of which two types are commonly used. The first is the isochron diagram (Merrihue and Turner, 1966), in which $^{39}Ar/^{36}Ar$ is plotted against $^{40}Ar/^{36}Ar$ (Fig. 13A). The slope of a line in this diagram is the $^{40}Ar^*/^{39}Ar_K$ ratio, thus yielding the age, whereas the intercept on the $^{40}Ar/^{36}Ar$ axis is the composition of trapped atmospheric or extraneous Ar. The second type is called the "inverse" diagram (Dalrymple et al., 1988), in which $^{39}Ar/^{40}Ar$ is plotted against $^{36}Ar/^{40}Ar$ (Fig. 13B). In this case the two intercepts yield the inverse of the trapped Ar composition and the $^{40}Ar^*/^{39}Ar_K$ ratio respectively, with the data ideally defining a mixing line between these compositions. Although not as visually informative as the age-spectrum diagram, these constructions provide a powerful test for the presence of extraneous Ar components in the sample.

Materials to Use

In principle, the same minerals that were used for K-Ar dating can be analyzed by the $^{40}Ar/^{39}Ar$ method, with the

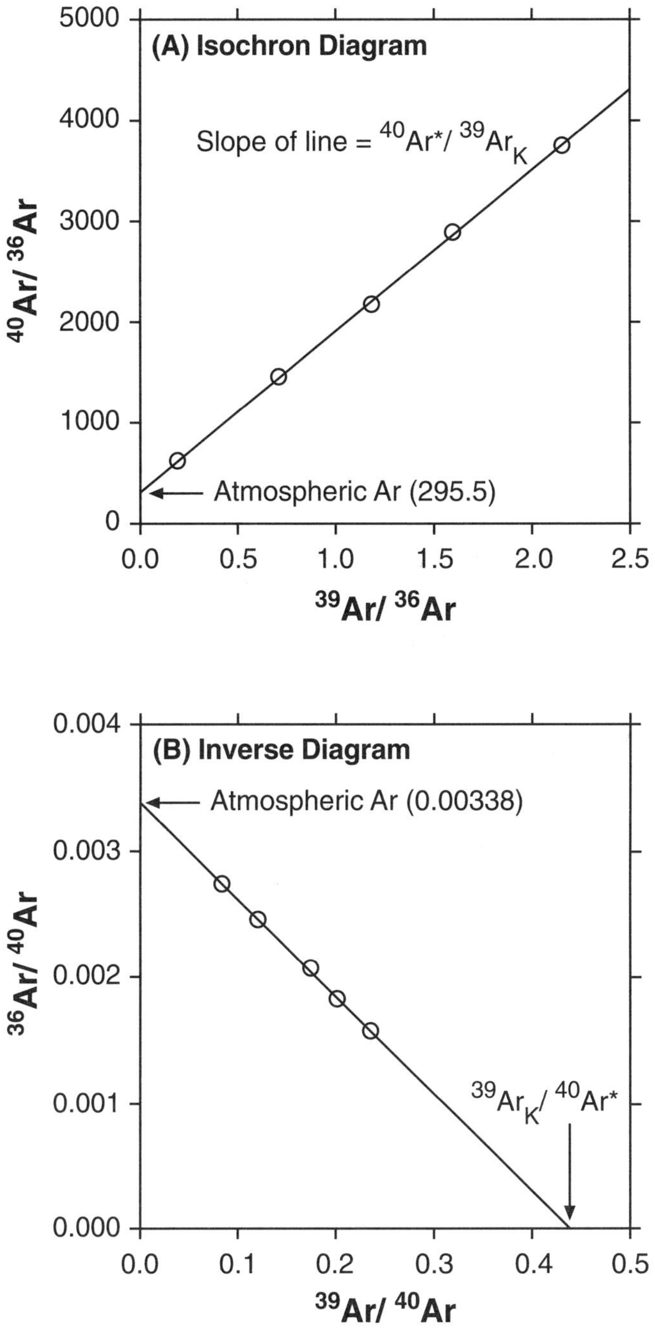

FIG. 13. Schematic Ar isotope correlation diagrams: (A) $^{39}Ar/^{36}Ar$ vs. $^{40}Ar/^{36}Ar$ isochron diagram of Merrihue and Turner (1966); (B) $^{39}Ar/^{40}Ar$ vs. $^{36}Ar/^{40}Ar$ "inverse" diagram of Dalrymple et al. (1988). See text for discussion.

proviso that the grain size is greater than about 5 to 10 μm. This limitation is due to the potential loss of $^{39}Ar_K$ by recoil during the neutron activation reaction. The recoil distance will vary with the energy of the incoming neutrons, and has been calculated to extend up to 0.5 μm (average ~0.08 μm; Turner and Cadogan, 1974). Thus, fine-grained materials such as clays may yield anomalously old dates if this effect is not taken into account. A solution to this problem has been to encapsulate the sample in a sealed silica-glass vial prior to irradiation, thereby trapping the recoiling $^{39}Ar_K$; this gas is then recombined with the rest of the Ar during total fusion to yield a K-Ar-equivalent date (Foland et al., 1992; see also Dong et al., 1995).

Good plateau ages are usually obtained only from very fresh material, but this restriction also applies to K-Ar dating if an accurate date is to be expected. The advantage of the $^{40}Ar/^{39}Ar$ method is that useful information can also be obtained from slightly altered or overprinted material, providing an indication of the minimum formation age, or maximum resetting age. The development of laser-extraction techniques also enables the investigation of inter- or intra-grain distribution of Ar isotopes, and thus direct testing of diffusive $^{40}Ar^*$-loss profiles.

Practical Considerations

Sample collection and preparation techniques are similar to those used for K-Ar dating, the objective being to end up with a >99 percent-pure separate of the mineral to be analyzed. Less of the purified material is normally required, however, because separate K-analyses are not necessary.

Consideration of grain size is again important in $^{40}Ar/^{39}Ar$ dating, but this time not only from the point of view of ease of mineral separation. The entire theory of step-heating analysis assumes that mineral grains will be degassed from rim to core as the experiment progresses. Thus, it is assumed that each mineral grain in the extraction furnace actually represents a complete grain as it existed in the rock. If, instead, the concentrate consists of small fragments of these original grains, then we will be degassing fragments of core material alongside fragments of rim material at each step. A good plateau will likely be produced, but it will represent a mechanical homogenization of the K-Ar distribution in the sample (and will simply be equivalent to the K-Ar or total fusion date). Petrographic examination of average mineral grain size and collection of an appropriate size fraction is therefore of crucial importance for step-heating analysis. Note, however, that this does not necessarily mean trying to separate out whole centimeter-sized phenocrysts, because in detail these crystals are often naturally fractured into domains. These fractures or cleavages represent surfaces of potential Ar loss, so it is the size of the intervening coherent domains that is critical.

Packaging of the samples for irradiation, inclusion of flux monitors, and selection of irradiation times will normally be carried out by the facility where the Ar-Ar analyses are to be conducted. They will also have appropriate equipment for storing the irradiated material and preparing it for analysis. The complexities and infrastructure requirements of this method place it beyond the routine capabilities of many institutions, and explain why such facilities are relatively uncommon, and why $^{40}Ar/^{39}Ar$ analyses are considerably more expensive than conventional K-Ar dates. It is therefore well worth considering carrying out a few cheaper K-Ar analyses first, to see whether the problem really requires application of the

$^{40}Ar/^{39}Ar$ method. For example, concordance of K-Ar dates for two or three samples from an intrusive complex or ore deposit probably means that the K-Ar system is undisturbed, and that no further work is required. Geologically unreasonable discordance of dates, however, may require use of the $^{40}Ar/^{39}Ar$ method for resolution.

Summary

The $^{40}Ar/^{39}Ar$ method is a modification of the conventional K-Ar dating technique, in which a proportion of ^{39}K in the sample is converted to ^{39}Ar by neutron activation. The $^{40}K/^{40}Ar^*$ ratio is then measured directly in terms of the $^{39}Ar_K/^{40}Ar^*$ ratio using a mass spectrometer. The method has the advantages over conventional K-Ar of: (1) not requiring separate K analyses; (2) using smaller sample sizes; and (3) providing more precise measurement of the K/Ar ratio through isotopic ratio measurement. Analysis of Ar released during stepwise heating furthermore enables recognition of $^{40}Ar^*$ loss from disturbed samples, and the presence of excess ^{40}Ar. Recent advances in laser extraction techniques have enabled dating of single mineral grains and the study of Ar diffusion profiles. Thus, although the method is more involved and expensive than conventional K-Ar analysis, the $^{40}Ar/^{39}Ar$ method offers the potential to obtain useful age information from disturbed and complex samples that would otherwise be intractable.

Re-Os Dating

Introduction

The Re-Os radiogenic isotope system is becoming one of the most important geochronological and isotopic tracing techniques in the field of mineral deposits research (see Stein et al., 1998a, for a recent overview). This is because both the parent and daughter elements are both chalcophile and siderophile in character, and are therefore readily incorporated into the lattices of sulfide and oxide minerals. Consequently, not only do we have an isotopic system that is specifically tuned to the metallic components of ore-forming systems, but the system should be relatively insensitive to post-crystallization processes such as deformation and metamorphism, because there will be little tendency for either the parent or daughter isotopes to migrate from the host sulfide phase (cf. the behavior of argon, earlier in this chapter). In comparison, in the U-Pb system (the only other system that involves a base or precious metal), the parent element U is not a sulfide-forming element, and its application in the geochronology of sulfide ore deposits is generally restricted to the dating of host rocks and alteration phases.

Although the Re-Os method was first applied in the 1950s, it has only recently become a serious competitor in terrestrial geochronology. The main breakthroughs have involved improved analytical methodology and mass spectrometric techniques, and most importantly a more accurate determination of the ^{187}Re decay constant. It is now possible to obtain Re-Os dates on natural minerals that are comparable in terms of accuracy and precision to those obtained from the U-Pb and $^{40}Ar/^{39}Ar$ techniques.

Systematics and Methodology

Re-Os is entirely analogous to the Rb-Sr system discussed previously, and an isochron equation similar to (9.10) can be written:
where λ_{187} = 1.666 × 10^{-11} a^{-1} (half-life = 41.606 Ga; Smoliar et al., 1996).

$$\left(\frac{^{187}Os}{^{188}Os}\right) = \left(\frac{^{187}Os}{^{188}Os}\right)_{initial} + \left(\frac{^{187}Re}{^{188}Os}\right)\left(e^{\lambda_{187}t} - 1\right) \quad (9.46)$$

Re and Os are strongly fractionated in some geological materials, such that a good spread of Re/Os ratios can be obtained for isochron definition. The common sulfide mineral molybdenite is particularly useful in this regard, because it often contains high concentrations of Re, but virtually excludes Os during crystallization. Thus, no correction is required for the presence of initial Os. Other common sulfide and oxide minerals also contain measurable quantities of Re and Os, and may be used to obtain isochron dates.

Analytical techniques are conceptually similar to those used for other non-gaseous isotopic systems, and involve equilibration of the sample with a spike (normally enriched in ^{185}Re and ^{190}Os) prior to chemical separation of Re and Os, and isotopic analysis by mass spectrometer. However, many details of the technique are unique to this system (see Stein et al., 1998b, and references therein, for a full description of procedures). For example, early problems with sample-spike equilibration have necessitated the development of specialized sample fusion procedures to ensure isotopic homogeneity. Re can be purified by ion exchange, as for other metals such as U and Pb, but Os is separated by distillation, taking advantage of the volatility of the oxide species OsO_4. Another difference between Re-Os analysis and the other condensed systems discussed above, is that both Re and Os emit negative ions more efficiently than cations during heating in a vacuum. Thus, Creaser et al. (1991) and Volkening et al. (1991) first realized that a standard thermal ionization mass spectrometer could be used to focus negative ions instead of the usual positive ion beam. Negative thermal ionization mass spectrometry (NTIMS) is now routinely used in Re-Os isotope analysis.

Practical Considerations and Materials

As with all of the other radiogenic systems discussed above, Re-Os is susceptible to isotopic resetting under certain circumstances. The hydrothermal mobility of these elements is poorly known, but McCandless et al. (1993) showed that Re-loss can occur in molybdenites during hydrothermal overprinting at temperatures as low as ~150°C, and can also occur in the supergene environment. These authors showed that careful examination of prospective molybdenite samples by a combination of infrared microscopy and electron microprobe, backscattered electron, and X-ray diffraction analysis can reveal the effects of these processes, and enable suitable samples to be selected. In practice, of course, samples should be collected at the outset to minimize the extent of these effects, and great care should be taken in areas where overprinting is known to have occurred (as with all other isotopic methods).

There is also considerable evidence that redistribution of Re and Os can occur within single crystals of molybdenite, leading to internal isotopic heterogeneity. This effect may not be a problem if the molybdenite crystal is analyzed as a whole, assuming that the elements have simply been redistributed and there has been no net loss from the crystal. Stein et al. (1998a) suggest that mineral separates should be analyzed in their entirety, therefore, rather than extracting fragments of crystals.

Examples

Because of its strong affinity for Re, molybdenite has historically been the mineral of choice for Re-Os dating studies. The widespread occurrence of this mineral has resulted in its use to date mineral deposit types as diverse as chromitites, skarns, greisens, pegmatites, and hydrothermal veins, as well as porphyry Cu-Mo deposits (Marcantonio et al., 1993; McCandless and Ruiz, 1993; Suzuki et al., 1993, 1996; Stein et al., 1997, 1998a). However, the Re-Os method is not restricted to molybdenite dating, and whole rocks and other minerals have been used in favorable circumstances to date ore deposits. For example, Walker et al. (1994) used whole-rock igneous and ore samples to obtain isochron dates for Noril'sk-type Cu-Ni-sulfide deposits in Siberia that are within error of $^{40}Ar/^{39}Ar$ and U-Pb dates for similar rocks. Similarly, Stein et al. (1993, 1998a) and Freydier et al. (1997) used magnetite, sphalerite, galena, and pyrite mineral separates, as well as molybdenite, to obtain isochron dates for Climax-type and porphyry-type mineral deposits in Colorado and Chile.

It is clear that this method has great potential for the direct dating of ore deposits, and, as discussed later, the isotopic tracing of metallic ore components. Perhaps the main obstacle to its more widespread use at this time is the scarcity of laboratories set up to undertake the necessary specialized chemical and mass spectrometric analyses.

Isotopic Source Tracing

Introduction

The use of light stable isotopes in isotopic source tracing of volatile components in hydrothermal systems has been discussed in Chapter 8. In that case, the bulk isotopic composition of water, carbon, or sulfur was compared with the compositions of possible source reservoirs for these components. A match with one or another of these reservoirs was sought, or mixing models were applied in cases where there was evidence for multiple sources of components. Such investigations can provide important constraints for modeling of hydrothermal fluid sources and evolution.

In exactly the same way, radiogenic isotopes can be used as tracers to reveal the sources of non-volatile solutes, such as Sr, Pb, Nd, and Os. By inference, the sources of other chemically similar elements, including base and precious metals, can also be deduced.

In contrast to light stable isotopes, isotopic fractionation of heavy elements during natural processes is not a concern. However, corrections may need to be made for accumulation of radiogenic daughter isotopes since the time of formation of the rock or mineral, because it is the initial isotopic composition of the element at the time of rock or mineral (or mineral deposit) formation that we are interested in. To minimize the effect of radiogenic isotope build-up, we therefore choose samples that have the lowest possible parent/daughter ratios (Table 6; compare the high parent/daughter ratios preferred in materials suitable for dating purposes—Tables 3 and 4). Thus, for example, galena is the perfect mineral to use for Pb isotope tracing, because its isotopic composition will not have changed since the time of its crystallization. Corrections for radiogenic growth in samples with small but non-zero parent/daughter ratios become increasingly important as their age increases, but are often negligible in young (i.e., Late Cenozoic) materials.

A typical radiogenic isotope source tracing problem might involve trying to distinguish between magmatic and crustal sources of metals in an ore deposit. The outcome might have relevance, for example, when attempting to establish the exploration significance of a particular suite of intrusions emplaced in a supra-crustal sequence: is mineralization genetically associated with this specific magma type, or will any type of intrusion suffice so long as it generates a hydrothermal convection cell in the country rocks? A solution to this question might involve analyzing

TABLE 6. Minerals suitable for isotopic tracing studies (summarized from Staatz et al., 1977; Wedepohl, 1978; Bell et al., 1989; King and Kerrich, 1989; Richards et al., 1991; Whitford et al., 1992; Griffin et al., 1996, and pers. commun., 1997).

Isotope system	Mineral	Parent element (ppm)	Daughter element (ppm except where stated)	Parent/ daughter ratio
Rb-Sr	Strontianite	0	60 wt %	0
	Barite	0	0.1 to 1.3 wt %	0
	Anhydrite	0	variable to high	0
	Calcite	0	up to 2000	0
	Sphene	0	up to 2000	0
	Apatite	0	400 to 6000	0
	Epidote	low	1000 to 5000	low
	Scheelite	< 2	100 to 11000	low
	Tourmaline	< 20	50 to 4000	$\leq 10^{-2}$
	Plagioclase	1 to 35	20 to 1000	10^{-3} to 1.75
	K-feldspar	100 to 1000	20 to 1000	10^{-1} to 50
U-Pb	Galena	0	87 wt %	0
	Other sulfides	low	variable to high	low
	Native metals	low	variable to high	low
	Tourmaline	1 to 6	< 3 to 4000	10^{-3} to 1
	K-feldspar	0.1 to 10	10 to 100	10^{-3} to 1
Sm-Nd	Monazite	~15000	~90000	$\sim 10^{-1}$
	Apatite	~350	~900	~10–1
	Sphene	~1000	2000 to 10000	$\sim 10^{-1}$
Re-Os	PGM alloys	≤ 1	up to 100 wt %	0 to low
	Laurite	low	0 to 21 wt %	low

the isotopic compositions of minerals or whole-rock samples from the ore deposit, the associated (unaltered) intrusions, other intrusive rocks in the district, and the country rocks, perhaps in combination with a geochronological study. As in the case of light stable isotopes, a match between the isotopic composition of the ore and one or a mixture of the potential source rocks is sought. Where possible it is always best to apply several different isotopic techniques, including stable isotopes, because it is rare that any single technique will provide an unequivocal result. It should be remembered, however, that different chemical components in the system may have been derived from different sources: for example, the Sr isotopic composition of a skarn deposit may be dominated by that of the host limestone, but Pb, and by inference other metals, may reflect input from a magmatic fluid source. Ore-forming systems are rarely simple!

Systematics and Methodology

The systematics of radiogenic isotopes and some of the practical techniques for collecting and preparing samples for analysis have been presented above. Exactly the same considerations apply to the determination of isotopic ratios for source tracing, except that if one is using a mineral with very low parent/daughter ratio (or a young mineral with a low ratio), then there is no need to measure the parent isotope concentration. In other materials, the parent/daughter ratio may have to be measured in order to make an age correction to determine the initial isotope ratio.

In cases where the age of the sample is known (to within a few million years), the age correction is quite straightforward, simply involving a rearrangement of the standard decay equation. Using Sr as an example, rearranging equation (9.10) gives:

$$\left(\frac{^{87}\mathrm{Sr}}{^{86}\mathrm{Sr}}\right)_{initial} = \left(\frac{^{87}\mathrm{Sr}}{^{86}\mathrm{Sr}}\right) - \left(\frac{^{87}\mathrm{Rb}}{^{86}\mathrm{Sr}}\right)\left(e^{\lambda_{87}t} - 1\right) \quad (9.47)$$

Three similar equations can be derived from equations (9.21), (9.22), and (9.23) for the $^{238}U/^{206}Pb$, $^{235}U/207Pb$, and $^{232}Th/^{208}Pb$ systems. In each of these examples, the isotopic ratios on the right hand side of the equations are those measured in the lab, and t is the age of the sample. Note that the method of calculation of the $^{87}Rb/^{86}Sr$ ratio from the measured $^{87}Sr/^{86}Sr$ ratio and Rb and Sr concentrations was discussed above, and a similar method is used for U/Pb and Th/Pb.

If the age of the system is not known and there are no low parent/daughter ratio minerals available, then it will be necessary to construct an isochron diagram using several different samples and to obtain the initial ratio from the intercept of the isochron with the y-axis.

In contrast to the widely variable isotope ratios obtained from the parent-element-rich minerals used in geochronology, values from minerals used for isotopic source tracing are relatively uniform, and fall within a narrow range of initial or "common" isotopic compositions that broadly characterize certain crustal or mantle reservoirs. It is thus often necessary to obtain highly precise and accurate isotope ratio measurements in order to compare the compositions of potential sources with the materials of interest. This situation is particularly acute in common Pb studies because of the lack of an internal standard to monitor isotopic fractionation during mass spectrometric analysis. Where precision to better than 0.1 percent is required, it may be necessary to use the double-spike technique, as described above.

Practical Considerations

As with all analytical studies, knowledge of the provenance of the sample is crucial for a correct interpretation of the results. In hydrothermal systems, for example, there are usually at least two possible sources of components: the hydrothermal fluid(s), and the wall rocks. Sampling should therefore aim to isolate the end-member components, and care should be taken to ensure that contamination from unexpected sources is avoided; in the above example, this might involve either taking samples from near the centre of a large vein, or from unaltered wallrock well away from the hydrothermal system.

Similar strictures regarding alteration and secondary contamination apply as in the case of geochronological isotopic studies, although it is harder to alter the isotopic composition of a mineral containing a large amount of the element in question, compared with a mineral in which it is only a trace.

Examples

Numerous examples of isotopic source tracing studies exist in the economic geology literature, and this is not the place for a comprehensive review of such work. However, a few examples may prove instructive:

Pb isotopes. Lead is an ideal element for tracing the source of metals in ore-forming systems. Because of its chemical similarity to other base metals such as Cu and Zn, source information derived from Pb is often extended to them without debate. The case of precious metals, such as gold, is perhaps more tenuous, although the assumption of a relationship is often made. The lack of a direct tracer for most precious metals means that construction of an alternative hypothesis is often impossible, and the information provided by Pb isotopes may have to be accepted as the best available solution. Recent advances in Re-Os measurement techniques indicate the potential of this method for tracing Os in platinum group element-rich and other deposits (see below).

The Pb isotope systematics of Pb-rich systems such as Mississippi Valley-type, SEDEX, and volcanic-hosted massive sulfide deposits have been studied extensively, both with respect to age determination, and tracing of source components. For example, Heyl et al. (1974) analyzed galenas from the Mississippi Valley district, and concluded that their relatively radiogenic isotopic compositions indicated a shallow-crustal source for Pb (as opposed to a magmatic source, for example; cf. Heyl et al., 1966). More recently, Kesler et al. (1994) and Goldhaber et al. (1995)

have confirmed this interpretation, and have isotopically identified at least two different aquifers along which the ore-forming fluids flowed. In another development, ion microprobes have facilitated detailed studies of isotopic zonation within single crystals of galena, revealing complex histories of local fluid mixing (e.g., Hart et al., 1981; Deloule et al., 1986).

The sources of other base metals have also been investigated using Pb isotopes, Cu in porphyry-type deposits being a classic example. For example, McNutt et al. (1979) showed that the Pb isotope compositions of porphyry-associated intrusions in the Central Andes were too radiogenic to have been derived from melting of depleted mantle or basaltic oceanic crust, but instead overlapped with the compositions of pelagic sediments and old continental crust. Similar conclusions were reached by Tilton et al. (1981), Kontak et al. (1990), and Mukasa et al. (1990) in studies of rock and ore leads from Chile and Peru, except that mixing between mantle and crustal sources of Pb was more clearly demonstrated. In contrast, Sillitoe and Hart (1984) concluded that the Pb isotope compositions of porphyry Cu deposits in Columbia were dominated by a subducted pelagic sediment source, with little upper crustal involvement. See also Puig (1988) and Zentilli et al. (1988).

Lead isotopes have been used to help trace the source of Au in several instances, with varying degrees of success. The technique is perhaps best suited to the young epithermal environment, where the possibilities for post-mineralization overprinting and disturbance are limited. Two examples of such studies are the gold deposits of the Creede district, Colorado, and Porgera, Papua New Guinea. At Creede, Doe et al. (1979) showed that the relatively radiogenic compositions of Pb in some vein minerals were inconsistent with derivation from the host volcanic rocks, but instead pointed towards a basement origin, with implications for the depth of fluid circulation. Foley and Ayuso (1994) subsequently showed that the Pb isotope compositions of ore minerals from the North Amethyst vein system could be further subdivided on the basis of paragenesis. They found that Pb from an early stage of Au-rich mineralization (β-stage) was distinctly less radiogenic than that from later Ag- and base-metal-rich stages (Fig. 14), and suggested a change in hydrology between the two stages, from early shallow interaction with the volcanic sequences, to later deeper basement penetration. They furthermore suggested that the Pb isotope compositions of untested veins in the region could be used as an exploration indicator for Au.

Richards et al. (1991) similarly used Pb isotopes to help elucidate the contributions of igneous and sedimentary sources to the metal budget in the Porgera gold deposit. They observed that the Pb isotope compositions of various ore minerals were remarkably uniform throughout the paragenesis, and fell midway between the compositions of uncontaminated alkalic intrusions with which the deposit is associated, and Jurassic sediments of the Om Formation which underlies the deposit. Only minor contributions to the Pb isotope composition of the ore were observed from the Cretaceous Chim Formation, which hosts the deposit (Fig. 15). Taking into account other evidence for the involvement of magmatic fluids in ore formation, the authors concluded that the main zone of hydrothermal activity was located within and around an unexposed parental pluton located within the Om Formation, 2 to 3 km beneath the current surface. Metals were precipitated from these hydrothermal fluids on ascent to shallower levels within the overlying Chim Formation.

Pb isotopes have also been used as a reconnaissance tool in mineral exploration programs. For example, Gulson (1986) described a method whereby the isotopic compositions of Pb in gossans could be related to the type of underlying mineralization, and used this to distinguish between prospective and barren targets.

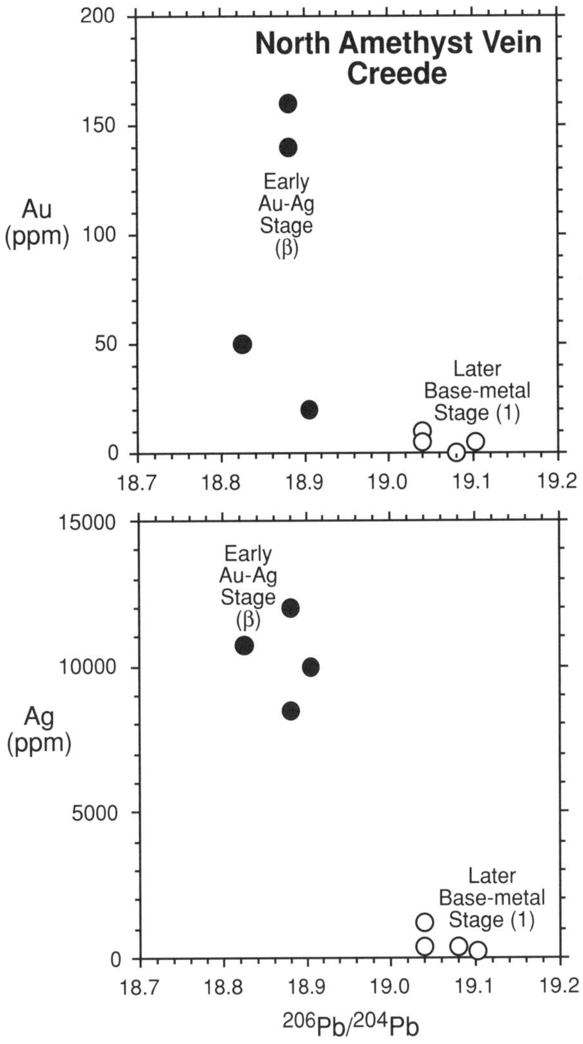

FIG. 14. $^{206}Pb/^{204}Pb$ compositions of galenas from early Au-Ag-rich and later base metal-rich stages of veining in the North Amethyst vein system, Creede, Colorado. Early precious metal-rich veins are characterized by distinctly less radiogenic Pb isotope compositions compared with later veins, suggesting a change in hydrology during evolution of the hydrothermal system (modified from Foley and Ayuso, 1994).

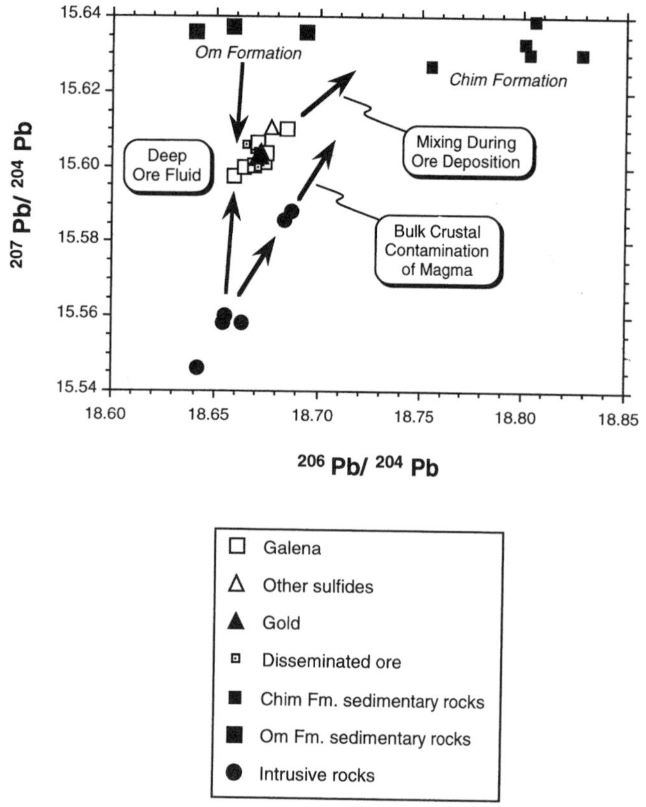

FIG. 15. $^{206}Pb/^{204}Pb$ versus $^{207}Pb/^{204}Pb$ diagram, showing isotopic compositions of ore minerals and intrusive and sedimentary rocks from the Porgera gold deposit, Papua New Guinea. The data suggest that ore-Pb was derived from a mixture of igneous and sedimentary sources (specifically the underlying Om Formation). Contamination by local sedimentary Pb at the site of intrusion and ore deposition is shown by trends in isotopic compositions of both the intrusive rocks and ore towards the host Chim Formation (modified from Richards et al., 1991).

Sr isotopes. In contrast to Pb, Sr isotopes can tell us little about the source of metallic components in an ore-forming system. However, they may provide useful information about the sources of chemically similar elements such as Ca, Ba, and even Na and K, which frequently constitute important if not essential components of ore fluids. In addition, Sr isotopes may reveal histories of fluid rock interaction and paleohydrology. Used in combination with Pb and S isotopes in ore minerals, and C, O, and H isotopes in gangue minerals and fluid inclusions, we have a powerful array of tracers for most of the major components of a hydrothermal system (e.g., Stein, 1988; Frei, 1995).

Because of the relative abundance of Sr in crustal rocks (average ~250 ppm) and its ready substitution for Ca in many minerals, including common gangue minerals (Table 6), there are few mineral deposit types for which Sr isotopic data are not available. Some selected examples of their use are given below.

Carbonate and sulfate gangue minerals in Mississippi Valley-type deposits typically show increasingly radiogenic Sr isotope compositions with degree of mineralization, rising from background values consistent with seawater composition at the time of deposition of the host sediments. These more radiogenic compositions have been interpreted to indicate a terrigenous source of Sr derived from silicate components in the aquifers through which the mineralizing fluids flowed (Fig. 16; Kessen et al., 1981; Medford et al., 1983). However, the more recent data of Kesler et al. (1988) and Brannon et al. (1991) show that the situation may be more complex in detail.

Similar studies have been applied to stratiform sulfide deposits to establish the provenance of ore-forming fluids. For example, Sr isotope compositions of interbedded barite, anhydrite, and gypsum from volcanic-hosted massive sulfide deposits are typically more radiogenic than those of the enclosing rocks, suggesting that the circulating hydrothermal fluids either interacted with the basement as well as the volcanics beneath the deposits, or involved Sr of seawater origin, or both (Farrell and Holland, 1983; Whitford et al., 1992).

Strontium isotopes have been employed in the perennial debate over the origin of mesothermal gold deposits, but an unequivocal interpretation has yet to be provided (Kerrich, 1991). For example, Bell et al. (1989), King and Kerrich (1989), and Mueller et al. (1991) observed highly variable Sr isotope ratios in hydrothermal minerals from Archean gold deposits in Ontario-Quebec and Western Australia, and concluded that they reflected mixing of Sr from various different crustal and perhaps mantle reservoirs.

Strontium isotopes have also been used widely in studies of fluid provenance in intrusion-related mineral deposits. Almost without exception, Sr is found to have been derived from a mixture of igneous and country-rock sources, with intrusion-hosted mineralization mirroring the magmatic composition, but more distal mineralization displaying increasing involvement of externally-derived Sr (Fig. 17; Norman and Landis, 1983; Dickin et al., 1986; Richards et al., 1991; Frei, 1995). McNutt et al. (1975), Farmer and DePaolo (1984), Anthony and Titley (1988),

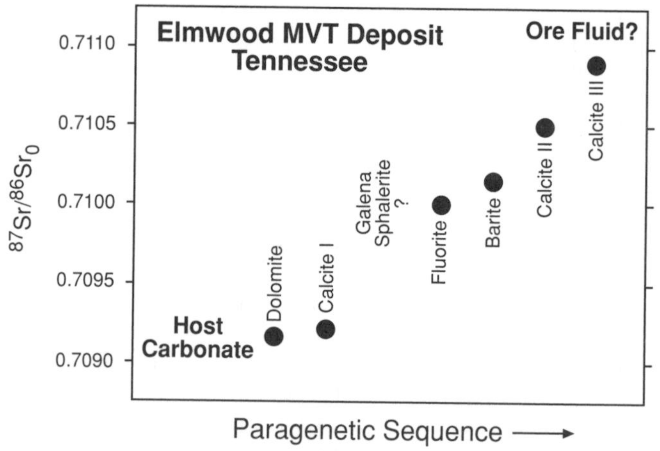

FIG. 16. Initial $^{87}Sr/^{86}Sr$ ratios of gangue minerals from the Elmwood Mississippi Valley-type deposit, Tennessee, showing a progression to more radiogenic values through the paragenetic sequence. Ore-forming fluids are thought to have carried radiogenic Sr into the depositional environment, which was characterized by relatively non-radiogenic Sr-bearing carbonate sequences (modified from Kessen et al., 1981).

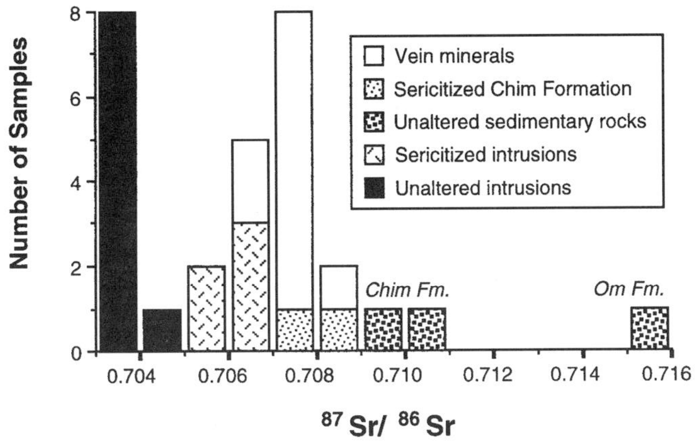

FIG. 17. Initial $^{87}Sr/^{86}Sr$ ratios of vein minerals, and fresh and altered igneous and sedimentary rocks from the Porgera gold deposit, Papua New Guinea. The isotopic compositions of vein and altered samples fall between the compositions of the associated intrusive rocks (less radiogenic) and host sediments (more radiogenic), suggesting that Sr was derived from both of these sources and homogenized by the hydrothermal fluids (modified from Richards et al., 1991).

and Stein and Crock (1990) also used Sr and Nd isotopes to investigate the petrogenesis of granitoids associated with porphyry Cu and Mo mineralization in North and South America, and concluded that the magmas were derived from mixtures of mantle and crustal sources, with the more evolved intrusions showing the greatest crustal input (Fig. 18).

Nd isotopes. Initial Nd, Sr, and Pb isotope compositions are routinely obtained in studies of magmatic provenance, and several investigations have also focused on the sources of ore forming magmas, as noted above. In contrast, however, the restricted aqueous solubility of rare-earth elements (REEs) places limits on the applicability of Nd isotopes in source tracing studies of hydrothermal ore deposits. In addition, the strong chemical similarity of Sm and Nd means that fractionation of these elements to generate high or low Sm/Nd mineral phases is rarely achieved in natural systems; thus, no minerals exist that are significantly enriched in Nd over Sm, and which could therefore be used to determine directly the initial Nd isotope composition (cf. galena). Nevertheless, significant REE mobility has been documented in a number of ore deposit types, and this has enabled calculation both of isochron ages and initial ratios in favorable circumstances.

McLennan and Taylor (1979) and Fryer and Taylor (1984) showed that REE mobility is high in fluids forming unconformity-type uranium deposits. Capitalizing on this fact, Maas et al. (1987) and Maas (1989) investigated the Sm-Nd systematics of uranium ores at the Mary Kathleen mine, Queensland, and the Alligator Rivers uranium field, Northern Territory (Australia), and showed that the initial Nd isotope composition of the ore could be compared with that of potential source rocks. They interpreted these data to reflect a basement source for U and REEs at Mary Kathleen, but a post-unconformity sedimentary source in the case of most of the Northern Territory deposits.

In contrast, Maas et al. (1986) showed that intense hydrothermal alteration in the footwall of the Kidd Creek massive sulfide deposit (Ontario) resulted only in localized redistribution of REEs. A wide range of Sm/Nd ratios was observed, from which an isochron age for mineralization was obtained, but the initial Nd isotopic composition was found to be identical to that of the protolith. The authors interpreted this observation to indicate local derivation of both REE and ore metals from within the footwall volcanic sequence, consistent with volcanic-leaching models for seafloor massive sulfide formation.

Fluorite commonly contains high concentrations of REEs, and although Sm/Nd ratios are typically high and uniform within a given deposit (such that isochrons often cannot be constructed), initial Nd isotope compositions can be calculated using model ages or other information to constrain t_0. Halliday et al. (1990) adopted this approach in their study of Mississippi Valley-type Pb-Zn-barite-fluorite deposits in the North Pennine orefield, England, and showed that the Nd and Sr isotopic compositions of the ore were consistent with derivation from the Lower Carboniferous sedimentary rocks that host the deposit, but did not match the composition of the underlying Devonian Weardale granite, previously suggested to have been a source of fluids and/or metals.

Os isotopes. As noted earlier in this chapter, the Re-Os system is a relatively recent addition to the geochemist's toolbox, but its potential contribution to the study of ore deposits is clear. The limited number of studies completed

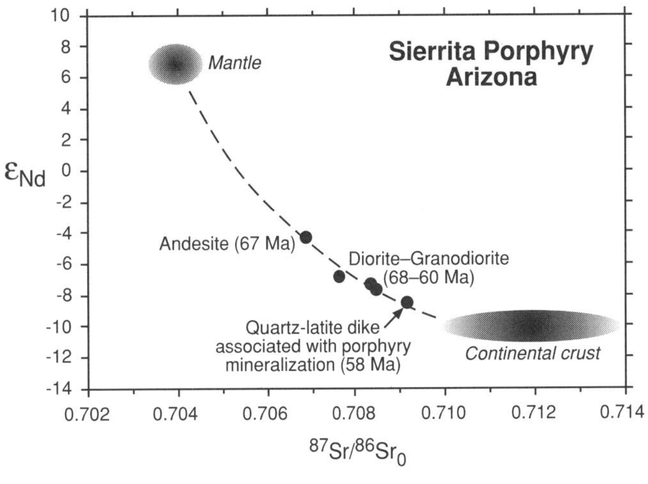

FIG. 18. Initial ε_{Nd} vs. $^{87}Sr/^{86}Sr$ plot showing an increase in crustal influence with time in magmatic suites from around the Sierrita porphyry Cu deposit. Late quartz-latite dikes directly associated with alteration and mineralization show the strongest crustal signature (modified from Anthony and Titley, 1988).

Note that the parameter ε_{Nd} is used to represent the measured Nd isotopic ratio of a sample normalized to the present-day isotopic composition of the CHUR "bulk Earth" reservoir (see text). It is defined as:

$$\varepsilon_{CHUR} = \left[\frac{\left({}^{143}Nd/{}^{144}Nd \right)_{sample}}{\left({}^{143}Nd/{}^{144}Nd \right)_{CHUR}} - 1 \right] \times 10^4$$

to date have shown that Os isotopes can be used as a powerful tracer for platinum group elements (PGEs), and can provide an additional perspective on the source of base metals in hydrothermal systems.

Osmiridium and other Os-rich platinoid alloys are ideal materials for the study of initial Os isotopic compositions, and some of the first ore-deposit studies focused on orthomagmatic and placer-type deposits enriched in these minerals. Thus, Martin (1989) and Hart and Kinloch (1989) concluded that Os in the Stillwater (Montana) and Bushveld (RSA) complexes was derived at least in part from crustal sources through country-rock assimilation. Hart and Kinloch (1989) warned, however, that mantle-derived magmas would be sensitive to crustal contamination of Os isotopes, because, although the abundance of Os in the continental crust is low, it typically has highly radiogenic compositions compared with the mantle. Marcantonio et al. (1993) subsequently argued that variations in Os isotope compositions within the Stillwater complex were caused by hydrothermal overprinting, and that 95 percent of the PGEs were in fact mantle-derived.

Hart and Kinloch (1989) also studied the Os isotope compositions of platinoid alloys from the Witwatersrand (RSA) gold deposits, and concluded from model ages that only a few individual grains were consistent with a paleoplacer source, the remainder being indicative of a younger, epigenetic origin.

More recently, Ruiz et al. (1997) and Freydier et al. (1997) published the results of Re-Os dating and isotopic tracing studies of sulfide minerals from porphyry- and manto-type deposits in Chile. Although these papers were based on the same data, different conclusions were reached concerning the source of Os in the porphyry deposits (El Teniente and Andacollo). Ruiz et al. (1997) argued for a crustal source of Os, and by inference other ore-forming metals, on the basis of a few relatively radiogenic analyses in a dataset of otherwise mantle-like values (average $^{187}Os/^{188}Os \approx 0.2$, compared with 0.13 for the sub-continental mantle and >1 for the continental crust). In contrast, Freydier et al. (1997) proposed that these radiogenic data reflect later overprinting, and that the bulk of the data are consistent with a magmatic, and ultimately mantle origin for Os and other metals.

Summary

The isotopic compositions of the daughter elements in radiogenic isotope systems can be used as tracers where radioactive decay has been minimal (i.e., where concentrations of the parent element are low, or the system is young), or where radiogenic contributions can be quantified and corrected for. In these cases, we are looking for the initial isotopic composition of the daughter element at the time of ore formation (for example), with a view to comparing this value with the compositions of various potential source rocks, magmas, or fluids, again corrected if necessary to the value at that time. An overlap in initial isotopic compositions, or linear trends between end-member reservoirs, can provide supporting evidence for the involvement of these reservoirs as sources of the element in question, and by inference, related elements. Thus, Pb is commonly used as an isotopic tracer for base and sometimes precious metals; Sr is used as a tracer for alkali and alkali-earth elements; Nd is used as a tracer for rare earth elements; and Os as a tracer for platinum group elements and precious metals, and sometimes also base metals.

Acknowledgments

We thank Holly Stein, Larry Heaman, Greg Anderson, and Peter Larson for perceptive and constructive reviews of this chapter, and apologize to all those whose work we have not cited because of space constraints.

REFERENCES

Ahrens, L.H., 1955, Implications of the Rhodesia age pattern: Geochimica et Cosmochimica Acta, v. 8, p. 1–15.

Albarède, F., 1995, Introduction to geochemical modeling: Cambridge, Cambridge University Press, 543 p.

Aldrich, L.T., Wetherill, G.W., Tilton, G.R., and Davis, G.L., 1956, The half-life of ^{87}Rb: Physics Reviews, v. 104, p. 1045–1047.

Allsopp, H.L., 1961, Rb-Sr age measurements on total rock and separated mineral fractions from the old granite of the central Transvaal: Geophysical Research Letters, v. 66, p. 1499–1508.

Alpers, C.N., and Brimhall, G.H., 1988, Middle Miocene climatic change in the Atacama Desert, northern Chile: Evidence from supergene mineralization at La Escondida: Geological Society of America Bulletin, v. 100, p. 1640–1656.

Anglin, C.D., Jonasson, I.R., and Franklin, J.M., 1996, Sm-Nd dating of scheelite and tourmaline: Implications for the genesis of Archean gold deposits, Val d'Or, Canada: Economic Geology, v. 91, p. 1372–1382.

Anthony, E.Y., and Titley, S.R., 1988, Progressive mixing of isotopic reservoirs during magma genesis at the Sierrita porphyry copper deposit, Arizona: Inverse solutions: Geochimica et Cosmochimica Acta, v. 52, p. 2235–2249.

Aoki, M., Comsti, E.C., Lazo, F.B., and Matsuhisa, Y., 1993, Advanced argillic alteration and geochemistry of alunite in an evolving hydrothermal system at Baguio, northern Luzon, Philippines: Resource Geology, v. 43, p. 155–164.

Arehart, G.B., Foland, K.A., Naeser, C.W., and Kesler, S.E., 1993, $^{40}Ar/^{39}Ar$, K/Ar, and fission track geochronology of sediment-hosted disseminated gold deposits at Post-Betze, Carlin trend, northeastern Nevada: Economic Geology, v. 88, p. 622–646.

Armstrong, R.L., 1991, A brief history of geochronometry and radiogenic isotopic studies: *in* Heaman, L., and Ludden, J.N., eds., Applications of radiogenic isotope systems to problems in geology: Mineralogical Association of Canada Short Course Handbook, v. 19, p. 1–26.

Ashley, R.P., and Silberman, M.L., 1976, Direct dating of mineralization at Goldfield, Nevada, by potassium-argon and fission-track methods: Economic Geology, v. 71, p. 904–924.

Aspden, J.A., Harrison, S.H., and Rundle, C.C., 1992, New geochronological control for the tectono-magmatic evolution of the metamorphic basement, Cordillera Real and El Oro Province of Ecuador: Journal of South American Earth Sciences, v. 6, p. 77–96.

Aston, R.W., 1920, The constitution of atmospheric neon: Philosophical Magazine, s. 6, v. 39, p. 449–455.

—— 1927, The constitution of ordinary lead: Nature, v. 120, p. 224.

Bassett, W.A., Kerr, P.F., Schaeffer, O.A., and Stoenner, R.W., 1963, Potassium-argon dating of the late Tertiary volcanic rocks and mineralization of Marysvale, Utah: Geological Society of America Bulletin, v. 74, p. 213–220.

Bell, K., Anglin, C.D., and Franklin, J.M., 1989, Sm-Nd and Rb-Sr isotope systematics of scheelites: Possible implications for the age and genesis of vein-hosted gold deposits: Geology, v. 17, p. 500–504.

Berger, G.W., and York, D., 1981, Geothermometry from $^{40}Ar/^{39}Ar$ dating experiments: Geochimica et Cosmochimica Acta, v. 45, p. 795–811.

Bird, M.I., Chivas, A.R., and McDougall, I., 1990, An isotopic study of surficial alunite in Australia: 2. Potassium-argon geochronology: Chemical Geology, v. 80, p. 133–145.

Böhlke, J.K., and Kistler, R.W., 1986, Rb-Sr, K-Ar, and stable isotope evidence for the ages and sources of fluid components of gold-bearing quartz veins in the northern Sierra Nevada foothills metamorphic belt, California: Economic Geology, v. 81, p. 296–322.

Boltwood, B.B., 1907, On the ultimate disintegration products of the radioactive elements: American Journal of Science, v. 23, p. 77–88.

Brannon, J.C., Podosek, F.A., Viets, J.G., Leach, D.L., Goldhaber, M., and Rowan, E.L., 1991, Strontium isotopic constraints on the origin of ore-forming fluids of the Viburnum Trend, southeast Missouri: Geochimica et Cosmochimica Acta, v. 55, p. 1407–1419.

Brooks, C., Hart, S.R., and Wendt, I., 1972, Realistic use of two-error regression treatments as applied to rubidium-strontium data: Reviews of Geophysics and Space Physics, v. 10, p. 551–577.

Browning, P., Groves, D.I., Blockley, J.G., and Rosman, K.J.R., 1987, Lead isotope constraints on the age and source of gold mineralization in the Archean Yilgarn block, Western Australia: Economic Geology, v. 82, p. 971–986.

Carignan, J., and Gariépy, C., 1993, Pb isotope geochemistry of the Silidor and Launay gold deposits: Implications for the source of Archean Au in the Abitibi subprovince: Economic Geology, v. 88, P. 1722–1730.

Carr, G.R., Dean, J.A., Suppel, D.W., and Heithersay, P.S., 1995, Precise lead isotope fingerprinting of hydrothermal activity associated with Ordovician to Carboniferous metallogenic events in the Lachlan fold belt of New South Wales: Economic Geology, v. 90, p. 1467–1505.

Catanzaro, E.J., Murphy, T.J., Shields, W.R., and Garner, E.L., 1968, Absolute isotopic abundance ratios of common, equal atom and radiogenic lead standards: Journal of Research of the National Bureau of Standards A, v. 72-A, p. 261–267.

Chesley, J.T., Halliday, A.N., and Scrivener, R.C., 1991, Samarium-neodymium direct dating of fluorite mineralization: Science, v. 252, p. 949–951.

Chesley, J.T., Halliday, A.N., Kyser, T.K., and Spry, P.G., 1994, Direct dating of Mississippi Valley-type mineralization: Use of Sm-Nd in fluorite: Economic Geology, v. 89, p. 1192–1199.

Christensen, J.N., Halliday, A.N., Leigh, K.E., Randell, R.N., and Kesler, S.E., 1995, Direct dating of sulfides by Rb-Sr: A critical test using the Polaris Mississippi Valley type Zn-Pb deposit: Geochimica et Cosmochimica Acta, v. 59, p. 5191–5197.

Claoué-Long, J.C., King, R.W., and Kerrich, R., 1990, Archaean hydrothermal zircons in the Abitibi greenstone belt: Constraints on the timing of gold mineralisation: Earth and Planetary Science Letters, v. 98, p. 109–128.

Clark, A.H., Archibald, D.A., Lee, A.W., Farrar, E., and Hodgson, C.J., 1998, Laser-probe ^{40}Ar-^{39}Ar ages of early- and late-stage alteration assemblages, Rosario porphyry copper-molybdenum deposit, Collahuasi district, I Region, Chile: Economic Geology, v. 93, in press.

Compston, W, and Oversby, V.M., 1969, Lead isotope analyses using a double spike: Journal of Geophysical Research, v. 74, p. 4338–4348.

Compston, W., Williams, I.S., and Meyer, C., 1984, U-Pb geochronology of zircons from Lunar breccia 73217 using a sensitive high mass-resolution ion microprobe: Journal of Geophysical Research, v. 89, Supplement, p. B525–B534.

Copeland, P., Parrish, R.R., and Harrison, T.M., 1988, Identification of inherited radiogenic Pb in monazite and its implications for U-Pb systematics: Nature, v. 333, p. 760–763.

Corfu, F., and Davis, D.W., 1991, Comment on "Archean hydrothermal zircon in the Abitibi greenstone belt: constraints on the timing of gold mineralization," by Claoué-Long, J.C., King, R.W., and Kerrich, R.: Earth and Planetary Science Letters, v. 104, p. 545–552.

Creaser, R.A., Papanastassiou, D.A., and Wasserburg, G.J., 1991, Negative thermal ion mass spectrometry of osmium, rhenium, and iridium: Geochimica et Cosmochimica Acta, v. 55, p. 397–401.

Cumming, G.L., and Gudjurgis, P.J., 1973, Alteration of trace lead isotopic ratios by post-ore metamorphic and hydrothermal activity: Canadian Journal of Earth Sciences, v. 10, p. 1782–1789.

Cumming, G.L., and Richards, J.R., 1975, Ore lead in a continuously changing Earth: Earth and Planetary Science Letters, v. 28, p. 155–171.

Cumming, G.L., Eckstrand, O.R., and Peredery, W.V., 1982, Geochronologic interpretations of Pb isotope ratios in nickel sulfides of the Thompson belt, Manitoba: Canadian Journal of Earth Sciences, v. 19, p. 2306–2324.

Cumming, G.L., Krstic, D., Worden, J.M., and Baadsgaard, H., 1984, Isotopic composition of lead in galena and Ni-arsenides of the Midwest deposit, northern Saskatchewan: Canadian Journal of Earth Sciences, v. 21, p. 649-656.

Cumming, G.L., Kyle, J.R., and Sangster, D.F., 1990, Pine Point: A case history of lead isotope homogeneity in a Mississippi Valley-type district: Economic Geology, v. 85, p. 133–144.

Dahl, P.S., 1996, The effects of composition on retentivity of argon and oxygen in hornblende and related amphiboles: A field-tested empirical model: Geochimica et Cosmochimica Acta, v. 60, p. 3687–3700.

Dallmeyer, R.D., 1979, $^{40}Ar/^{39}Ar$ dating: Principles, techniques, and applications in orogenic terranes, *in* Jäger, E., and Hunziker, J.C., eds., Lectures in isotope geology: Berlin, Springer-Verlag, p. 77–104.

Dalrymple, G.B., 1979, Critical tables for conversion of K-Ar ages from old to new constants: Geology, v. 7, p. 558–560.

Dalrymple, G.B., and Lanphere, M.A., 1969, Potassium-argon dating: San Francisco, W.H. Freeman, 258 p.

Dalrymple, G.B., Lanphere, M.A., and Pringle, M.S., 1988, Correlation diagrams in $^{40}Ar/^{39}Ar$ dating: Is there a correct choice?: Geophysical Research Letters, v. 15, p. 589–591.

Dammer, D., Chivas, A.R., and McDougall, I., 1996, Isotopic dating of supergene manganese oxides from the Groote Eylandt deposit, Northern Territory, Australia: Economic Geology, v. 91, p. 386–401.

Darbyshire, P.D.F., Pitfield, P.E.J., and Campbell, S.D.G., 1996, Late Archean and Early Proterozoic gold-tungsten mineralization in the Zimbabwe Archean craton: Rb-Sr and Sm-Nd isotope constraints: Geology, v. 24, p. 19–22.

Davis, D.W., Gray, J., and Cumming, G.L., 1977, Determination of the ^{87}Rb decay constant: Geochimica et Cosmochimica Acta, v. 41, p. 1745–1749.

Davis, P.K., Lewis, R.S., and Reynolds, J.H., 1971, Stepwise heating analyses of rare gases from pile-irradiated rocks 10044 and 10057: Proceedings of the Second Lunar Science Conference, v. 2, p. 1693–1703.

Deer, W.A., Howie, R.A., and Zussman, J., 1992, An introduction to the rock-forming minerals, 2nd Edition: Harlow, Longman Scientific and Technical, 696 p.

Deloule, E., Allègre, C., and Doe, B., 1986, Lead and sulfur isotope microstratigraphy in galena crystals from Mississippi Valley-type deposits: Economic Geology, v. 81, p. 1307–1321.

DePaolo, D.J., 1988, Neodymium Isotope Geochemistry: New York, Springer-Verlag, 187 p.

DePaolo, D.J., and Getty, S.R., 1996, Models of isotopic exchange in reactive fluid-rocks systems: Implications for geochronology in metamorphic rocks: Geochimica et Cosmochimica Acta, v. 60, p. 3933–3947.

DePaolo, D.J., and Wasserburg, G. J., 1976, Nd isotopic variations and petrogenetic models: Geophysical Research Letters, v. 3, p. 249–252.

—— 1979, Sm-Nd age of the Stillwater complex and the mantle evolution curve for neodymium: Geochimica et Cosmochimica Acta, v. 43, p. 999–1008.

Dickin, A.P., 1995, Radiogenic isotope geology: Cambridge, Cambridge University Press, 452 p.

Dickin, A.P., Rice, C.M., and Harmon, R.S., 1986, A strontium and oxygen isotope study of Laramide magmatic and hydrothermal activity near Central City, Colorado: Economic Geology, v. 81, p. 904–914.

Dodson, M.H., 1973, Closure temperature in cooling geochronological and petrological systems: Contributions to Mineralogy and Petrology, v. 40, p. 259–274.

Doe, B.R., and Zartman, R.E., 1979, Plumbotectonics, the Phanerozoic, *in* Barnes, H.L., ed., Geochemistry of hydrothermal ore deposits, 2nd edition: New York, Wiley, p. 22–70.

Doe, B.R., Steven, T.A., Delevaux, M.H., Stacey, J.S., Lipman, P.W., and Fisher, F.S., 1979, Genesis of ore deposits in the San Juan volcanic field, southwestern Colorado—Lead isotope evidence: Economic Geology, v. 74, p. 1–26.

Dong, H., Hall, C.M., Peacor, D.R., and Halliday, A.N., 1995, Mechanisms of argon retention in clays revealed by laser ^{40}Ar-^{39}Ar dating: Science, v. 267, p. 355–359.

Engels, J.C., and Ingamells, C.O., 1970, Effect of sample inhomogeneity in K-Ar dating: Geochimica et Cosmochimica Acta, v. 34, p. 1007–1017.

Evernden, J.F., Curtis, G.H., Obradovich, J., and Kistler, R., 1961, On the evaluation of glauconite and illite for dating sedimentary rocks by the potassium-argon method: Geochimica et Cosmochimica Acta, v. 23, p. 78–99.
Farmer, G.L., and DePaolo, D.J., 1984, Origin of Mesozoic and Tertiary granite in the western United States and implications for pre-Mesozoic crustal structure: 2. Nd and Sr isotopic studies of unmineralized and Cu- and Mo-mineralized granite in the Precambrian craton: Journal of Geophysical Research, v. 89, p. 10141–10160.
Farrell, C.W., and Holland, H.D., 1983, Strontium isotope geochemistry of the Kuroko deposits: Economic Geology Monograph 5, p. 302–319.
Faure, G., 1986, Principles of isotope geology, 2nd ed.: New York, John Wiley, 589 p.
Faure, G., and Powell, J.L., 1972, Strontium isotope geology. New York, Springer-Verlag, 188 p.
Feng, R., Machado, N., and Ludden, J., 1993, Lead geochronology of zircon by laserprobe–inductively coupled plasma mass spectrometry (LP–ICPMS): Geochimica et Cosmochimica Acta, v. 57, p. 3479–3486.
Fitch, F.J., 1972, Selection of suitable material for dating and the assessment of geological error in potassium-argon age determination, *in* Bishop, W.W., and Miller, J.A., eds., Calibration of hominoid evolution: Scottish Academic Press, University of Toronto Press, p. 77–91.
Fleck, R.J., Sutter, J.F., and Elliot, D.H., 1977, Interpretation of discordant $^{40}Ar/^{39}Ar$ age-spectra of Mesozoic tholeiites from Antarctica: Geochimica et Cosmochimica Acta, v. 41, p. 15–32.
Fleming, G.H. Jr., Ghiorso, A., and Cunningham, B.B., 1962, Specific alpha activities and half lives of U^{234}, U^{235} and U^{236}: Physics Reviews, v. 88, p. 642.
Flynn, K.F., and Glendenin, L.E., 1959, Half-life and beta spectrum of Rb^{87}: Physics Reviews, v. 116, p. 744–748.
Foland, K.A., Hubacher, F.A., and Arehart, G.B., 1992, $^{40}Ar/^{39}Ar$ dating of very fine-grained samples: An encapsulated-vial procedure to overcome the problem of ^{39}Ar recoil loss: Chemical Geology, v. 102, p. 269–276.
Foley, N.K., and Ayuso, R.A., 1994, Lead isotope compositions as guides to early gold mineralization: The North Amethyst vein system, Creede district, Colorado: Economic Geology, v. 89, p. 1842–1859.
Folinsbee, R.E., Lipson, J., and Reynolds, J.H., 1956, Potassium-argon dating: Geochimica et Cosmochimica Acta, v. 10, p. 60–68.
Franklin, J.M., Roscoe, S.M., Loveridge, W.D., and Sangster, D.F., 1983, Lead isotope studies in Superior and Southern Provinces: Geological Survey of Canada Bulletin 351, 60 p.
Frei, R., 1995, Evolution of mineralizing fluid in the porphyry copper system of the Skouries deposit, northeast Chalkidiki (Greece): Evidence from combined Pb-Sr and stable isotope data: Economic Geology, v. 90, p. 746–762.
Frei, R., and Kamber, B.S., 1995, Single mineral Pb-Pb dating: Earth and Planetary Science Letters, v. 129, p. 261–268.
Frei, R., and Pettke, T., 1996, Mono-sample Pb-Pb dating of pyrrhotite and tourmaline: Proterozoic vs. Archean intracratonic gold mineralization in Zimbabwe: Geology, v. 24, p. 823–826.
Freydier, C., Ruiz, J., Chesley, J., McCandless, T., and Munizaga, F., 1997, Re-Os isotope systematics of sulfides from felsic igneous rocks: Application to base metal porphyry mineralization in Chile: Geology, v. 25, p. 775–778.
Fryer, B.J., and Taylor, R.P., 1984, Sm-Nd direct dating of the Collins Bay hydrothermal uranium deposit, Saskatchewan: Geology, v. 12, p. 479-482.
Fryer, B.J., Jackson, S.E., and Longerich, H.P., 1993, The application of laser ablation microprobe-inductively coupled plasma-mass spectrometry (LAM-ICP-MS) to in situ (U)-Pb geochronology: Chemical Geology, v. 109, p. 1–8.
Gale, N.H., and Mussett, A.E., 1973, Episodic uranium-lead models and the interpretation of variations in the isotopic composition of lead in rocks: Reviews of Geophysics and Space Physics, v. 11, p. 37–86.
Gerling, E.K., 1942, Age of the Earth according to radioactivity data (in Russian): Comptes Rendus de l'Academie Scientifique, U.R.S.S., v. 34, p. 259–261.
Geyh, M.A., and Schleicher, H., 1990, Absolute age determination: Berlin, Springer-Verlag, 503 p.
Giletti, B.J., Moorbath, S., and Lambert, R. St J., 1961, A geochronological study of the metamorphic complexes of the Scottish Highlands: Quarterly Journal of the Geological Society of London, v. 117, p. 233–272.
Gilg, H.A., and Frei, R., 1994, Geochronology of magmatism and mineralization in the Kassandra mining area, Greece: The potentials and limitations of dating hydrothermal illites: Geochimica et Cosmochimica Acta, v. 58, p. 2107–2122.
Goldhaber, M.B., Church, S.E., Doe, B.R., Aleinikoff, J.N., Brannon, J.C., Podosek, F.A., Mosier, E.L., Taylor, C.D., and Gent, C.A., 1995, Lead and sulfur isotope investigation of Paleozoic sedimentary rocks from the southern Midcontinent of the United States: Implications for Paleohydrology and ore genesis of the southeast Missouri Lead Belts: Economic Geology, v. 90, p. 1875–1910.
Griffin, W.L., Slack, J.F., Ramsden, A.R., Win, T.T., and Ryan, C.G., 1996, Trace elements in tourmalines from massive sulfide deposits and tourmalinites: Geochemical controls and exploration applications: Economic Geology, v. 91, p. 657–675.
Gulson, B.L., 1986, Lead isotopes in mineral exploration: New York, Elsevier, 245 p.
Gulson, B.L., Perkins, W.G., and Mizon, K.J., 1983, Lead isotope studies bearing on the genesis of copper orebodies at Mount Isa, Queensland: Economic Geology, v. 78, p. 1466–1504.
Gustafson, L.B., and Hunt, J.P., 1975, The porphyry copper deposit at El Salvador, Chile: Economic Geology, v. 70, p. 857–912.
Halliday, A.N., Shepherd, T.J., Dickin, A.P., and Chesley, J.T., 1990, Sm-Nd evidence for the age and origin of a Mississippi Valley type ore deposit: Nature, v. 344, p. 54–56.
Hamelin, B., Manhes, G., Albarède, F., and Allègre, C.J., 1985, Precise lead isotope measurements by the double spike technique: A reconsideration: Geochimica et Cosmochimica Acta, v. 49, p. 173–182.
Hamilton, E.I., 1965, Applied Geochronology: New York, Academic Press, 267 p.
Hamilton, P.J., O'Nions, R.K., and Evensen, N.M., 1977, Sm-Nd dating of Archean basic and ultrabasic volcanics: Earth and Planetary Science Letters, v. 36, p. 263–268.
Hanes, J.A., 1991, K-Ar and $^{40}Ar/^{39}Ar$ geochronology: Methods and applications: *in* Heaman, L., and Ludden, J.N., eds., Applications of radiogenic isotope systems to problems in geology: Mineralogical Association of Canada Short Course Handbook, v. 19, p. 27–57.
Hanes, J.A., Archibald, D.A., and Hodgson, C.J., 1992, Dating of Archean auriferous quartz vein deposits in the Abitibi greenstone belt, Canada: $^{40}Ar/^{39}Ar$ evidence for a 70- to 100-m.y.-time gap between plutonism-metamorphism and mineralization: Economic Geology, v. 87, p. 1849–1861.
Harrison, T.M., and McDougall, I., 1981, Excess ^{40}Ar in metamorphic rocks from Broken Hill, New South Wales: Implications for $^{40}Ar/^{39}Ar$ age spectra and the thermal history of the region: Earth and Planetary Science Letters, v. 55, p. 123–149.
Hart, S.R., and Kinloch, E.D., 1989, Osmium isotope systematics in Witswatersrand and Bushveld ore deposits: Economic Geology, v. 84, p. 1651–1655.
Hart, S.R., Shimizu, N., and Sverjensky, D.A., 1981, Lead isotope zoning in galena: An ion microprobe study of a galena crystal from the Buick mine, southeast Missouri: Economic Geology, v. 76, p. 1873–1878.
Heaman, L., and Parrish, R.R., 1991, U-Pb geochronology of accessory minerals, *in* Heaman, L., and Ludden, J.N.. eds., Applications of radiogenic isotope systems to problems in geology: Mineralogical Association of Canada Short Course Handbook, v. 19, p. 59–102.
Heyl, A.V., Delevaux, M.H., Zartman, R.E., and Brock, M.R., 1966, Isotopic study of galenas from the Upper Mississippi Valley, the Illinois–Kentucky, and some Appalachian Valley mineral districts: Economic Geology, v. 61, p. 933–961.
Heyl, A.V., Landis, G.P., and Zartman, R.E., 1974, Isotopic evidence for the origin of Mississippi Valley-type mineral deposits: A review: Economic Geology, v. 69, p. 992–1006.
Hirata, T., and Nesbitt, R.W., 1995, U-Pb isotope geochronology of zircon: Evaluation of the laser probe-inductively coupled plasma mass spectrometry technique: Geochimica et Cosmochimica Acta, v. 59, p. 2491–2500.
Hoffman, A., 1971, Fractionation corrections for mixed-isotope spikes of Sr, K, and Pb: Earth and Planetary Science Letters, v. 10, p. 397–402.
Holmes, A, 1946, An estimate of the age of the earth: Nature, v. 157, p. 680–684.
Hooker, P., O'Nions, R.K., and Pankhurst, R.J., 1975, Determination of rare-earth elements in U.S.G.S. standard rocks by mixed-solvent ion exchange and mass spectrometric isotope dilution: Chemical Geology, v. 16, p. 189–196.

Houtermans, F.G., 1946, Die Isotopenhäufigkeiten im natürlichen Blei und das Alter des Urans: Naturwissenschaften, v. 33, p. 185–186, 219.

Hu, Q., Smith, P.E., Evensen, N.M., and York, D., 1994, Lasing in the Holocene: Extending the ^{40}Ar-^{39}Ar laser probe method into the ^{14}C age range: Earth and Planetary Science Letters, v. 123, p. 331–336.

Hunziker, J.C., 1979, Potassium argon dating, *in* Jäger, E., and Hunziker, J.C., eds., Lectures in isotope geology: Berlin, Springer-Verlag, p. 52–76.

Jaffey, A.H., Flynn, K.F., Glendenin, L.E., Bentley, W.C., and Essling, A.M., 1971, Precision measurements of half-lives and specific activities of ^{235}U and ^{238}U: Physics Reviews, v. C4, p. 1889–1906.

Kalsbeek, F., 1992, The statistical distribution of the mean squared weighted deviation—Comment: Isochrons, errorchrons, and the use of MSWD-values: Chemical Geology, v. 94, p. 241–243.

Kelley, S.P., Arnaud, N.O., and Turner, S.P., 1994, High spatial resolution $^{40}Ar/^{39}Ar$ investigations using an ultra-violet laser probe extraction technique: Geochimica et Cosmochimica Acta, v. 58, p. 3519–3525.

Kerrich, R., 1991, Radiogenic isotope systems applied to mineral deposits, *in* Heaman, L., and Ludden, J.N., eds., Applications of radiogenic isotope systems to problems in geology: Mineralogical Association of Canada Short Course Handbook, v. 19, p. 365–421.

Kerrich, R., and Cassidy, K.F., 1994, Temporal relationships of lode gold mineralization to accretion, magmatism, metamorphism and deformation—Archean to present: A review: Ore Geology Reviews, v. 9, p. 263–310.

Kerrich, R., and Kyser, T.K., 1994, 100 Ma timing paradox of Archean gold, Abitibi greenstone belt (Canada): New evidence from U-Pb and Pb-Pb evaporation ages of hydrothermal zircons: Geology, v. 22, p. 1131–1134.

Kesler, S.E., Jones, L.M., and Ruiz, J., 1988, Strontium isotope geochemistry of Mississippi Valley-type deposits, East Tennessee: Implications for age and source of mineralizing brines: Geological Society of America Bulletin, v. 100, p. 1300–1307.

Kesler, S.E., Cumming, G.L., Krstic, D., and Appold, M.S., 1994, Lead isotope geochemistry of Mississippi Valley-type deposits of the southern Appalachians: Economic Geology, v. 89, p. 307–321.

Kessen, K.M., Woodruff, M.S., and Grant, N.K., 1981, Gangue mineral $^{87}Sr/^{86}Sr$ ratios and the origin of Mississippi Valley-type mineralization: Economic Geology, v. 76, p. 913–920.

King, R.W., and Kerrich, R., 1989, Strontium isotope compositions of tourmaline from lode gold deposits of the Archean Abitibi greenstone belt (Ontario–Quebec, Canada): Implications for source reservoirs: Chemical Geology, v. 79, p. 225–240.

Kober, B., 1986, Whole-grain evaporation for $^{207}Pb/^{206}Pb$-age-investigations on single zircons using a double-filament thermal ion source: Contributions to Mineralogy and Petrology, v. 93, p. 482–490.

—— 1987, Single-zircon evaporation combined with Pb^+ emitter bedding for $^{207}Pb/^{206}Pb$-age investigations using thermal ion mass spectrometry, and implications to zirconology: Contributions to Mineralogy and Petrology, v. 96, p. 63–71.

Kontak, D.J., Cumming, G.L., Krstic, D., Clark, A.H., and Farrar, E., 1990, Isotopic composition of lead in ore deposits of the Cordillera Oriental, southeastern Peru: Economic Geology, v. 85, p. 1584–1603.

Kovarik, A.F., and Adams, N.E., Jr., 1955, Redetermination of the disintegration constant of ^{238}U: Physics Reviews, v. 98, p. 46.

Krogh, T.E., 1973, A low contamination method for the hydrothermal decomposition of zircon and extraction of U and Pb for isotopic age determinations: Geochimica et Cosmochimica Acta, v. 37, p. 485–494.

—— 1982a, Improved accuracy of U-Pb zircon dating by selection of more concordant fractions using a high gradient magnetic separation technique: Geochimica et Cosmochimica Acta, v. 46, p. 631–635.

—— 1982b, Improved accuracy of U-Pb zircon ages by the creation of more concordant systems using an air abrasion technique: Geochimica et Cosmochimica Acta, v. 46, p. 637–649.

Krogh, T.E., and Davis, G.L., 1975, The production and preparation of ^{205}Pb for use as a tracer for isotope dilution analyses: Carnegie Institution of Washington Yearbook 1974, p. 416–417.

Le Roux, L.J., and Glendenin, L.E., 1963, Half-life of ^{232}Th: Pretoria, South Africa, Proceedings of the National Meeting on Nuclear Energy, April 1963, p. 83–94.

Lindner, M., Leich, D.A., Russ, G.P., Bazan, J.M., and Borg, R.J., 1989, Direct determination of the half-life of ^{187}Re: Geochimica et Cosmochimica Acta, v. 53, p. 1597–1606.

Lipson, J.I., 1956, K-A dating of sediments: Geochimica et Cosmochimica Acta, v. 10, p. 149–151.

Ludwig, K.R., 1980, Calculation of uncertainties of U-Pb isotope data: Earth and Planetary Science Letters, v. 46, p. 212–220.

—— 1989, PBDAT: a computer program for processing Pb-U-Th isotope data, version 1.20: U.S. Geological Survey Open-File Report 88-542.

Lugmair, G.W., and Marti, K., 1978, Lunar initial $^{143}Nd/^{144}Nd$: differential evolution of the lunar crust and mantle: Earth and Planetary Science Letters, v. 39, p. 349–357.

Lugmair, G.W., and Scheinin, N.B., 1975, Sm-Nd systematics of the Stannern meteorite [abs.]: Meteoritics, v. 10, p. 447–448.

Maas, R., 1989, Nd-Sr isotope constraints on the age and origin of unconformity-type uranium deposits in the Alligator Rivers uranium field, Northern Territory, Australia: Economic Geology, v. 84, p. 64–90.

Maas, R., McCulloch, M.T., Campbell, I.H., and Coad, P.R., 1986, Sm-Nd and Rb-Sr dating of an Archean massive sulfide deposit: Kidd Creek, Ontario: Geology, v. 14, p. 585–588.

Maas, R., McCulloch, M.T., Campbell, I.H., and Page, R.W., 1987, Sm-Nd isotope systematics in uranium rare-earth element mineralization in the Mary Kathleen uranium mine, Queensland: Economic Geology, v. 82, p. 1805–1826.

Maluski, H., and Schaeffer, O.A., 1982, $^{39}Ar/^{40}Ar$ laser probe dating of terrestrial rocks: Earth and Planetary Science Letters, v. 59, p. 21–27.

Marcantonio, F., Zindler, A., Reisberg, L., and Mathez, E.A., 1993, Re-Os isotopic systematics in chromitites from the Stillwater complex, Montana, USA: Geochimica et Cosmochimica Acta, v. 57, p. 4029–4037.

Martin, C.E., 1989, Re-Os isotopic investigation of the Stillwater Complex, Montana: Earth and Planetary Science Letters, v. 93, p. 336–344.

Mattinson, J.M., 1972, Preparation of hydrofluoric, hydrochloric, and nitric acids at ultralow lead levels: Analytical Chemistry, v. 44, p. 1715–1716.

—— 1987, U-Pb ages of zircons: A basic examination of error propagation: Chemical Geology, v. 66, p. 151–162.

McCandless, T.E., and Ruiz, J., 1993, Rhenium-osmium evidence for regional mineralization in southwestern North America: Science, v. 261, p. 1282–1286.

McCandless, T.E., Ruiz, J., and Campbell, A.R., 1993, Rhenium behavior in molybdenite in hypogene and near-surface environments: Implications for Re-Os geochronometry: Geochimica et Cosmochimica Acta, v. 57, p. 889–905.

McCulloch, M.T., and Woodhead, J.D., 1993, Lead isotopic evidence for deep crustal-scale fluid transport during granite petrogenesis: Geochimica et Cosmochimica Acta, v. 57, p. 659–674.

McDougall, I., and Harrison, T.M., 1988, Geochronology and thermochronology by the $^{40}Ar/^{39}Ar$ method: New York, Oxford University Press, 212 p.

McIntyre, D.B., 1963, Precision and resolution in geochronometry, *in* Albritton, C.C., ed, The fabric of geology: Stanford, California, Freeman, Cooper, and Co., p. 112–134.

McLennan, S.M., and Taylor, S.R., 1979, Rare earth element mobility associated with uranium mineralization: Nature, v. 282, p. 247–250.

McNutt, R.H., Crocket, J.H., Clark, A.H., Caelles, J.C., Farrar, E., Haynes, S.J., and Zentilli, M., 1975, Initial $^{87}Sr/^{86}Sr$ ratios of plutonic and volcanic rocks of the central Andes between latitudes 26° and 29° south: Earth and Planetary Science Letters, v. 27, p. 305-313.

McNutt, R.H., Clark, A.H., and Zentilli, M., 1979, Lead isotopic compositions of Andean igneous rocks, latitudes 26° to 29° S: Petrologic and metallogenic implications: Economic Geology, v. 74, p. 827–837.

Medford, G.A., Maxwell, R.J., and Armstrong, R.L., 1983, $^{87}Sr/^{86}Sr$ ratio measurements on sulfides, carbonates, and fluid inclusions from Pine Point, Northwest Territories, Canada: An $^{87}Sr/^{86}Sr$ ratio increase accompanying the mineralizing process: Economic Geology, v. 78, p. 1375–1378.

Merrihue, C., and Turner, G., 1966, Potassium-argon dating by activation with fast neutrons: Journal of Geophysical Research, v. 71, p. 2852–2857.

Mezger, K., Hanson, G.N., and Bohlen, S.R., 1989, High-precision U-Pb ages of metamorphic rutile: Application to the cooling history of high-grade terranes: Earth and Planetary Science Letters, v. 96, p. 106–118.

Minster, J-F., Birck, J-L., and Allègre, C.J., 1982, Absolute age of formation of chondrites studied by the ^{87}Rb-^{86}Sr method: Nature, v. 300, p. 414–419.
Moorbath, S., Allaart, J.H., Bridwater, D., and McGregor, V.R., 1977, Rb-Sr ages of early Archaean supracrustal rocks and Amîtsoq gneisses at Isua: Nature, v. 270, p. 43–45.
Moyle, A.J., Doyle, B.J., Hoogvliet, H., and Ware, A.R., 1990, Ladolam gold deposit, Lihir Island, *in* Hughes, F.E., ed., Geology of the mineral deposits of Australia and Papua New Guinea: Melbourne, Australasian Institute of Mining and Metallurgy, p. 1793–1805.
Mueller, A.G., de Laeter, J.R., and Groves, D.I., 1991, Strontium isotope systematics of hydrothermal minerals from epigenetic Archean gold deposits in the Yilgarn Block, Western Australia: Economic Geology, v. 86, p. 780–809.
Mukasa, S.B.,Vidal, C.E., and Injoque-Espinoza, J., 1990, Pb isotope bearing on the metallogenesis of sulfide ore deposits in Central and Southern Peru: Economic Geology, v. 85, p. 1438–1446.
Neumann, W., and Huster, E., 1974, The half-life of ^{87}Rb measured as a difference between the isotopes of ^{87}Rb and ^{85}Rb: Zeitschrift für Physik, v. 270, p. 121–127.
Nicolaysen, L.O., 1961, Graphic interpretation of discordant age measurements of metamorphic rocks: Annals of the New York Academy of Science, v. 92, p. 198–206.
Nier, A.O., 1935, Evidence for the existence of an isotope of potassium with mass 40: Physical Review, v. 48, p. 283–284.
—— 1938, Variations in the relative abundances of the isotopes of common lead from various sources: Journal of the American Chemical Society, v. 60, p. 1571–1576.
—— 1939, The isotopic constitution of radiogenic leads and the measurement of geologic time II: Physics Reviews, v. 55, p. 153–163.
—— 1940, A mass spectrometer for routine isotope abundance measurements: Reviews of Scientific Instrumentation, v. 11, p. 212–216.
Nier, A.O., Thompson, R.W., and Murphey, B.F., 1941, The isotopic constitution of lead and the measurement of geologic time III: Physics Reviews, v. 60, p. 112–116.
Noble, S.R., and Searle, M.P., 1995, Age of crustal melting and leucogranite formation from U-Pb zircon and monazite dating in the western Himalaya, Zanskar, India: Geology, v. 23, p. 1135–1138.
Noble, S.R., Lightfoot, P.C., and Schärer, U., 1989, A method for single-filament isotopic analysis of Nd using in situ reduction: Chemical Geology (Isotope Geosciences Section), v. 79, p. 15–19.
Noble, S.R., Aspden, J.A., and Jemielita, R., 1997, Northern Andean crustal evolution: New U-Pb geochronological constraints from Ecuador: Bulletin of the Geological Society of America, v. 109, p. 789–798.
Norman, D.I., and Landis, G.P., 1983, Source of mineralizing components in hydrothermal ore fluids as evidenced by $^{87}Sr/^{86}Sr$ and stable isotope data from the Pasto Bueno deposit, Peru: Economic Geology, v. 78, p. 451–465.
Nowell, G.M., Kempton, P.D., Noble, S.R. Filton, J.G., Sauders, A.D., Mahoney, J.J., and Taylor, R.N.,1998, High precision Hf isotope measurements of MORB and OIB by thermal ionisation mass spectrometry: Insights to depleted mantle: Chemical Geology, in press.
Ohmoto H., Hart, S.R., and Holland, H.D., 1966, Studies in the Providencia area, Mexico, II, K-Ar and Rb-Sr ages of intrusive rocks and hydrothermal minerals: Economic Geology, v. 61, p. 1205–1213.
Page, R.W., and McDougall, I., 1972, Geochronology of the Panguna porphyry copper deposit, Bougainville Island, New Guinea: Economic Geology, v. 67, p. 1065–1074.
Papanastassiou, D.A., and Wasserburg, G.J., 1969, Initial strontium isotopic abundances and the resolution of small time differences in the formation of planetary objects: Earth and Planetary Science Letters, v. 5, p. 361–376.
—— 1971, Lunar chronology and evolution from Rb-Sr studies of Apollo 11 and 12 samples: Earth and Planetary Science Letters, v. 11, p. 37–62.
Parrish, R.R., 1990, U-Pb dating of monazite and its application to geological problems: Canadian Journal of Earth Sciences, v. 27, p. 1431–1450.
Parrish, R.R., and Krogh, T.E., 1987, Synthesis and purification of ^{205}Pb for U-Pb geochronology: Chemical Geology, v. 66, p. 103–110.
Parrish, R.R., and Tirrul, R., 1989, U-Pb age of the Baltoro granite, northwest Himalaya, and implications for monazite U-Pb systematics: Geology, v. 17, p. 1076–1079.
Patterson, C.C., 1956, Age of meteorites and the Earth: Geochimica et Cosmochimica Acta, v. 10, p. 230–237.
Pettke, T., and Diamond, L., 1996, Rb-Sr dating of sphalerite based on fluid inclusion–host mineral isochrons: a clarification of why it works: Economic Geology, v. 91, p. 951–956.
Piasecki, M.A.J., and van Breemen, O., 1983, Field and isotopic evidence for a c. 750 Ma tectonothermal event in the Moine rocks of the Central Highlands region of the Scottish Caledonides: Transactions of the Royal Society of Edinburgh, Earth Sciences, v. 73, p. 119–113.
Picciotto, E., and Wilgain, S., 1956, Confirmation of the period of thorium-232: Nuovo Cimento, v. 4, p. 1525.
Puig, A., 1988, Geologic and metallogenic significance of the isotopic composition of lead in galenas of the Chilean Andes: Economic Geology, v. 83, p. 843–858.
Quirt, S., Clark, A.H., Farrar, E., and Sillitoe, R.H., 1971, Potassium-argon ages of porphyry copper deposits in northern and central Chile [abs.]: Geological Society of America Abstracts with Programs, v. 3, p. 676-677.
Richard, P., Shimizu, N., and Allègre, C.J., 1976, $^{143}Nd/^{146}Nd$, a natural tracer: An application to oceanic basalts: Earth and Planetary Science Letters, v. 31, p. 269–278.
Richards, J.P., and McDougall, I., 1990, Geochronology of the Porgera gold deposit, Papua New Guinea: Resolving the effects of excess argon on K-Ar and $^{40}Ar/^{39}Ar$ age estimates for magmatism and mineralization: Geochimica et Cosmochimica Acta, v. 54, p. 1397–1415.
Richards, J.P., and Wagner, P.A., 1997, Mono-sample Pb-Pb dating of pyrrhotite and tourmaline: Proterozoic vs. Archean intracratonic gold mineralization: Comment: Geology, v. 25, p. 669–670.
Richards, J.P., Cumming, G.L., Krstic, D., Wagner, P.A., and Spooner, E.T.C., 1988a, Pb isotopic constraints on the age of sulfide ore deposition and U-Pb age of late uraninite veining at the Musoshi stratiform copper deposit, Central African Copperbelt, Zaire: Economic Geology, v. 83, p. 724–741.
Richards, J.P., Krogh, T.E., and Spooner, E.T.C., 1988b, Fluid inclusion characteristics and U-Pb rutile age of late hydrothermal alteration and veining at the Musoshi stratiform copper deposit, Central African Copperbelt, Zaire: Economic Geology, v. 83, p. 118–139.
Richards, J.P., McCulloch, M.T., Chappell, B.W., and Kerrich, R., 1991, Sources of metals in the Porgera gold deposit, Papua New Guinea: Evidence from alteration, isotope, and noble metal geochemistry: Geochimica et Cosmochimica Acta, v. 55, p. 565–580.
Roddick, J.C., 1983, High precision intercalibration of ^{40}Ar-^{39}Ar standards: Geochimica et Cosmochimica Acta, v. 47, p. 887–898.
—— 1987, Generalized numerical error analysis with applications to geochronology and thermodynamics: Geochimica et Cosmochimica Acta, v. 51, p. 2129–2135.
Roddick, J.C., and Bevier, M.L., 1995, U-Pb dating of granites with inherited zircon: Conventional and ion microprobe results from two Paleozoic plutons, Canadian Appalachians: Chemical Geology, v. 119, p 307–329.
Ruiz, J., Jones, L.M., and Kelly, W.C., 1984, Rubidium-strontium dating of ore deposits hosted by Rb-rich rocks, using calcite and other common Sr-bearing minerals: Geology, v. 12, p. 259–262.
Ruiz, J., Freydier, C., McCandless, T., Chesley, J., and Munizaga, F., 1997, Re-Os-isotope systematics of sulfides from base-metal porphyry and manto-type mineralization in Chile: International Geology Review, v. 39, p. 317–324.
Schaeffer, O.A., and Zähringer, J., eds., 1966, Potassium argon dating: Berlin, Springer-Verlag, 234 p.
Shepherd, T.J., and Darbyshire, D.P.F., 1981, Fluid inclusion Rb-Sr isochrons for dating mineral deposits: Nature, v. 290, p. 578–579.
Shirey, S.B., 1991, The Rb-Sr, Sm-Nd and Re-Os isotopic systems: A summary and comparison of their applications to the cosmochronology and geochronology of igneous rocks, *in* Heaman, L., and Ludden, J.N., eds., Applications of radiogenic isotope systems to problems in geology: Mineralogical Association of Canada Short Course Handbook, v. 19, p. 103–166.
Sillitoe, R.H., and Hart, S.R., 1984, Lead-isotope signatures of porphyry copper deposits in oceanic and continental settings, Colombian Andes: Geochimica et Cosmochimica Acta, v. 48, p. 2135–2142.
Silver, L.T., 1963, The use of cogenetic uranium-lead isotope systems in zircons in geochronology: Radioactive Dating, International Atomic Energy Agency: Athens Symposium Proceedings, p. 279–287.

Silver, L.T., and Deutsch, S., 1963, Uranium-lead isotopic variations in zircons: a case study: Journal of Geology, v. 71, p. 721–758.

Smith, P.E., and Farquhar, R.M., 1989, Direct dating of Phanerozoic sediments by the ^{238}U-^{206}Pb method: Nature, v. 341, p. 518–521.

Smoliar, M.I., Walker, R.J., and Morgan, J.W., 1996, Re-Os ages of group IIA, IIIA, IVA, and IVB iron meteorites: Science, v. 271, p. 1099–1102.

Staatz, M.H., Conklin, N.M., and Brownfield, I.K., 1977, Rare earths, thorium, and other minor elements in sphene from some plutonic rocks in west-central Alaska: Journal of Research, U.S. Geological Survey, v. 5, p. 623–628.

Stacey, J.S., and Kramers, J.D., 1975, Approximation of terrestrial lead isotope evolution by a two-stage model: Earth and Planetary Science Letters, v. 26, p. 207–221.

Steiger, R.H., and Jäger, E., 1977, Subcommission on geochronology: Convention on the use of decay constants in geo- and cosmochronology: Earth and Planetary Science Letters, v. 36, p. 359–362.

Stein, H.J., 1988, Genetic traits of Climax-type granites and molybdenum mineralization, Colorado Mineral Belt, *in* Taylor, R.P., and Strong, D.F., eds., Recent advances in the geology of granite-related mineral deposits: Canadian Institute of Mining and Metallurgy, Special Volume 39, p. 394–401.

Stein, H.J., and Crock, J.L., 1990, Late Cretaceous–Tertiary magmatism in the Colorado Mineral Belt; rare earth element and samarium-neodymium isotopic studies: Geological Society of America, Memoir 174, p. 195–223.

Stein, H.J., and Hannah, J.L., 1985, Movement and origin of ore fluids in Climax-type systems: Geology, v. 13, p. 469–474.

Stein, H.J., Morgan, J.W., Walker, R.J., and Horan, M.F., 1993, A mantle component for Climax-type granite-molybdenum systems or our first glimpse at Re-Os in the lower continental crust: EOS, Transactions, American Geophysical Union, v. 74, p. 121.

Stein, H.J., Markey, R.J., Morgan, J.W., Du, A., and Sun, Y., 1997, Highly precise and accurate Re-Os ages for molybdenite from the East Qinling molybdenum belt, Shaanxi Province, China: Economic Geology, v. 92, p. 827–835.

Stein, H.J., Morgan, J.W., Markey, R.J., and Hannah, J.L., 1998a, An introduction to Re-Os: What's in it for the mineral industry?: Society of Economic Geologists Newsletter, no. 32, p. 1, 8–15.

Stein, H.J., Sundblad, K., Markey, R.J., Morgan, J.W., and Motuza, G., 1998b, Re-Os ages for Archaean molybdenite and pyrite, Kuittila-Kivisuo, Finland and Proterozoic molybdenite, Kabeliai, Lithuania: testing the chronometer in a metamorphic and metasomatic setting: Mineralium Deposita, v. 33, p. 329–345.

Sutter, J.F., and Hartung, J.B., 1984, Laser microprobe $^{40}Ar/^{39}Ar$ dating of mineral grains in situ: Scanning electron microscopy, v. 4, p. 1525–1529.

Suzuki, K., Qi-Lu, Shimizu, H., and Masuda, A., 1993, Reliable Re-Os ages for molybdenite: Geochimica et Cosmochimica Acta, v. 57, p. 1625–1628.

Suzuki, K., Shimizu, H., and Masuda, A., 1996, Re-Os dating of molybdenites from ore deposits in Japan: Implication for the closure temperature of the Re-Os system for molybdenite and the cooling history of molybdenum ore deposits: Geochimica et Cosmochimica Acta, v. 60, p. 3151–3159.

Taylor, J.R., 1997, An introduction to error analysis, 2nd ed.: Sausalito, California, University Science Books, 327 p.

Tera, F., and Wasserburg, G.J., 1972, U-Th-Pb systematics in three Apollo 14 basalts and the problem of initial Pb in lunar rocks: Earth and Planetary Science Letters, v. 17, p. 281–304.

Thirlwall, M.F., 1991a, High-precision multicollector isotopic analysis of low levels of Nd as oxide: Chemical Geology (Isotope Geosciences Section), v. 94, p. 13–22.

—— 1991b, Long-term reproducibility of multicollector Sr and Nd isotope ratio analysis: Chemical Geology, v. 94, p. 85–104.

Thompson, F.C., and Rowlands, S., 1943, Dual decay of potassium: Nature, v. 152, p. 103.

Tilton, G.R., 1960, Volume diffusion as a mechanism for discordant lead ages: Journal of Geophysical Research, v. 65, p. 2933–2945.

Tilton, G.R., Pollak, R.J., Clark, A.H., and Robertson, R.C.R., 1981, Isotopic composition of Pb in Central Andean ore deposits: Geological Society of America, Memoir 154, p. 791–816.

Todt, W., Cliff, R.A., Hanser, A., and Hofmann, A.W., 1993, Re-calibration of NBS lead standards using a $^{202}Pb+^{205}Pb$ double spike: Terra Abstracts, v. 5, p. 396.

Tucker, R.D., Raheim, A., Krogh, T.E., and Corfu, F., 1987, Uranium-lead zircon and titanite ages from the northern portion of the Western Gneiss Region, south-central Norway: Earth and Planetary Science Letters, v. 81, p. 203–211.

Turner, G., 1966, The thermal history of the Bruderheim meteorite: Earth and Planetary Science Letters, v. 1, p. 155–157.

—— 1970, Argon-40/argon-39 dating of lunar rock samples: Science, v. 167, p. 466–468.

Turner, G., and Cadogan, P.H., 1974, Possible effects of ^{39}Ar recoil in ^{40}Ar-^{39}Ar dating: Geochimica et Cosmochimica Acta, v. 2, p. 1601–1615.

Vasconcelos, P.M., Renne, P.R., Brimhall, G.H., and Becker, T.A., 1994, Direct dating of weathering phenomena by $^{40}Ar/^{39}Ar$ and K-Ar analysis of supergene K-Mn oxides: Geochimica et Cosmochimica Acta, v. 58, p. 1635–1665.

Volkening, J., Walczyk, T., and Heumann, K.G., 1991, Osmium isotope ratio determinations by negative thermal ion mass spectrometry: International Journal of Mass Spectrometry Ion Processes, v. 105, p. 147–159.

Wager, L.R., and Brown, G.M., 1960, Collection and preparation of material for analysis, *in* Smales, A.A., and Wager, L.R., eds., Methods in geochemistry: Interscience, p. 4–32.

Walker, R.J., Morgan, J.W., Horan, M.F., Czamanske, G.K., Krogstad, E.J., Fedorenko, V.A., and Kunilov, V.E., 1994, Re-Os isotopic evidence for an enriched-mantle source for the Noril'sk-type, ore-bearing intrusions, Siberia: Geochimica et Cosmochimica Acta, v. 58, p. 4179–4197.

Wasserburg, G.J., 1963, Diffusion processes in lead-uranium systems: Journal of Geophysical Research, v. 68, p. 4823–4846.

Wasserburg, G.J., and Hayden, R.J., 1955, A^{40}-K^{40} dating: Geochimica et Cosmochimica Acta, v. 7, p. 51–60.

Wasserburg, G.J., Hayden, R.J., and Jensen, K.J., 1956, A^{40}-K^{40} dating of igneous rocks and sediments: Geochimica et Cosmochimica Acta, v. 10, p. 153–165.

Wedepohl, K.H., ed., 1969–1978, Handbook of geochemistry: Berlin, Springer-Verlag.

Wendt, I., and Carl, C., 1991, The statistical distribution of the mean squared weighted deviation: Chemical Geology, v. 86, p. 275–285.

Wetherill, G.W., 1956, Discordant uranium-lead ages: Transactions of the American Geophysical Union, v. 37, p. 320–326.

—— 1966, Radioactive decay constants and energies, *in* Clark, S.P., Jr., ed., Handbook of physical constants: Geological Society of America Memoir 97, p. 513–519.

Whitford, D.J., Korsch, M.J., and Solomon, M., 1992, Strontium isotope studies of barites: Implications for the origin of base metal mineralization in Tasmania: Economic Geology, v. 87, p. 953–959.

York, D., Hall, C.M., Yanase, Y., Hanes, J.A., and Kenyon, W.J., 1981, $^{40}Ar/^{39}Ar$ dating of terrestrial minerals with a continuous laser: Geophysical Research Letters, v. 8, p. 1136–1138.

York, D., Masliwec, A., Kuybida, P., Hanes, J.A., Hall, C.M., Kenyon, W.J., Spooner, E.T.C., and Scott, S.D., 1982, $^{40}Ar/^{39}Ar$ dating of pyrite: Nature, v. 300, p. 52–53.

Zartman, R.E., and Haines, S.M., 1988, The plumbotectonic model for Pb isotopic systematics among major terrestrial reservoirs—A case for bi-directional transport: Geochimica et Cosmochimica Acta, v. 52, p. 1327–1339.

Zentilli, M., Doe, B.R., Hedge, C.E., Alvarez, O., Tidy, E., and Daroca, J.A., 1988, Lead isotopes in porphyry copper type deposits compared with other types of metal deposits in the Andes of northern Chile and Argentina: Santiago, 8–12 August 1988, V Congreso Geologico Chileno, Tomo I, B., p. 331-369.

Chapter 10

The Influence of Geochemical Techniques on the Development of Genetic Models for Porphyry Copper Deposits

JEFFREY W. HEDENQUIST

Mineral and Fuel Resources Department, Geological Survey of Japan, 1-1-3 Higashi, Tsukuba, Japan 305-8567

AND JEREMY P. RICHARDS

Department of Earth and Atmospheric Sciences, University of Alberta, Edmonton, Alberta, Canada T6G 2E3

Introduction

In the previous chapters, we have seen how a variety of theories and geochemical techniques can be applied in practice to real geological situations. In isolation, these techniques may provide important constraints on variables such as temperature, fluid composition, or age of ore deposition. But their real strength is realized when data from a number of different lines of investigation are combined and their interpretations are integrated, each providing independent constraints on a model. This integrated approach represents a huge advance on the isolated knowledge obtained from individual techniques, and provides information of fundamental and practical value.

We aim in this chapter to illustrate the value of such a multidisciplinary approach by using as an example the development of ideas concerning the genesis of porphyry Cu deposits, which have provided over 50 percent of the world's Cu production this century. The fundamental constraints on the genesis of porphyry deposits are based on geological observations. Nevertheless, geochemical studies have helped to refine our understanding of the hydrothermal processes that lead to the formation of these deposits.

Porphyry Copper Deposits

Introduction

There is a wide diversity among porphyry Cu deposits, and thus each deposit must be considered on a case by case basis (Hunt, 1991). At the same time, there are many themes that are common among porphyry Cu systems, and this has led to a variety of generalizations and the construction of empirical models (e.g., Lowell and Guilbert, 1970). Porphyry Cu (Mo, Au) deposits worldwide are centered on porphyritic stocks with diameters of 100 m to several kilometers, which are now known to be cupolas above deeper intermediate to felsic plutons (Sillitoe, 1996). Within porphyry Cu systems there are typically several phases of intrusion, with the earliest commonly hosting the highest grade ore. Wall rocks also host ore in some deposits, although intrusions host an average of 70 percent of porphyry ore in the deposits considered by Lowell and Guilbert (1970). Cu-Fe-sulfide ore minerals occur in quartz stockwork veins and disseminations that are associated with an early stage of K-silicate ("potassic") alteration (Meyer and Hemley, 1967), consisting of biotite, magnetite, and variable K-feldspar. In some deposits, a portion of ore is also formed during later quartz-sericite-pyrite veining associated with sericitic ("phyllic") alteration, although some argue that this mineralization-type may simply constitute a remobilization of earlier-deposited metals (e.g., Brimhall, 1980). "Argillic" alteration forms outward from veins with sericitic halos; kaolinite and smectite may be accompanied by sericite and chlorite. Hypogene "advanced argillic" alteration assemblages of quartz, kaolinite, pyrophyllite, and diaspore, sometimes with andalusite or alunite (Meyer and Hemley, 1967), are temporally and genetically related to the porphyry deposit but form at shallower depths than do potassic and phyllic alteration, and may continue to develop until relatively late stages, overprinting underlying alteration styles (Sillitoe, 1993). "Propylitic" alteration, characterized by epidote, chlorite, and calcite, forms as a halo, commonly several kilometers in radius, which fades outward to unaltered or regionally altered country rocks.

Early studies of porphyry deposits were concerned with the relationship between the intrusions and the hypogene ore that they host, with geological observations focusing attention on the intimate magmatic affiliation of the deposits, and their magmatic origin. This broad view was questioned from the early 1970s, when stable isotopic data indicated a major involvement of meteoric water over the life of porphyry hydrothermal systems. However, more recent studies have swung the pendulum of opinion from the Neptunists back in the direction of the Plutonists. These investigations reveal the complexity of the magmatic-meteoric hydrothermal systems that cause porphyry Cu mineralization, and help resolve some of the ambiguities apparent in the earlier, necessarily more simplistic, studies.

The purpose of this chapter is not to provide an exhaustive review of the porphyry literature, a gargantuan task and inappropriate to this volume. Rather, we attempt to highlight some of the contributions that made critical and perceptive observations, particularly those that provided new geochemical data relating to the origin of these deposits.

Readers interested in the details of porphyry Cu deposits should refer to the various volumes that have been published over the past three decades on the geology, alteration, and mineralization of individual deposits, including Titley and Hicks (1966), Sutherland Brown

(1976), Gustafson and Titley (1978), Titley (1982), Schroeter (1995), and Pierce and Bolm (1995). Some of the many review papers that have discussed the characteristics of a variety of porphyry Cu deposits include Creasey (1966), Lowell and Guilbert (1970), Sillitoe (1973), Kesler (1973), Nielson (1976), Gustafson (1978), Titley and Beane (1981), Beane and Titley (1981), Einaudi (1982), Sillitoe and Gappe (1984), Sillitoe (1991, 1993), Titley (1994), Thompson (1995), Kirkham and Sinclair (1996), and Sillitoe (1996). The frequency of deposit-specific publications peaked in the mid-1970s, reflecting exploration activity, although the 1990s has seen a revival in exploration, and thus research interest, particularly for porphyry Cu-Au deposits. An address by Hunt (1991) also deals with the history of porphyry Cu exploration and study, particularly from the geological perspective. In contrast, porphyry Mo and Sn-W deposits have many distinct characteristics, and the deposits and their origin are discussed separately by Westra and Keith (1981) and Carten et al. (1993), and Taylor (1979), Ishihara (1981), Eugster (1985), and Heinrich (1990), respectively.

Early Observations and Interpretations

"Even partial answers may be of service, if reasonable inductions from observed facts be kept distinct from more or less speculative hypotheses." (Ransome, 1904, p. 151, commenting on his study of the Bisbee porphyry Cu deposit, southwestern United States.)

The earliest studies of porphyry ore bodies, known as "disseminated Cu" deposits at the time, were conducted in the southwestern United States, and consisted for the most part of insightful field observations. All of the deposits in this region were affected to various degrees by supergene alteration and enrichment. Despite the post-hydrothermal overprint, Ransome (1904) noted the spatial relation of the Bisbee, Arizona, disseminated Cu ore to the porphyry stock, and proposed some genetic connection. He concluded that the principal function of the porphyritic intrusion was to supply heat to deeply-circulating aqueous solutions, thus determining the locus of chemical activity. The metal source was thought to have been limestone, with fluid rising from depth along a major fault in the district.

In contrast, based on study of the Morenci disseminated Cu deposit, also in Arizona, Lindgren (1905) concluded that the hydrothermal solutions and metals were derived from the porphyry magma. He based this conclusion on geologic relationships, noting that the only common factor was an association between ore and the quartz porphyry intrusion. Among other supporting evidence was his observation of fluid inclusions in both igneous quartz phenocrysts and hydrothermal quartz veins that contained daughter minerals of halite and an opaque phase. He argued that such hot and saline liquid (estimated to be at least 45 wt % NaCl) could be derived only from magma. This may have been the first use of fluid inclusions to support interpretations concerning the genesis of porphyry deposits.

Later, Ransome (1919) suggested that the now-visible parts of the porphyry intrusions at Ray and Miami, Arizona, did not contribute in an active way to ore deposition, but had been altered together with the surrounding host rocks. In contrast to his earlier conclusions of 1904, he believed that a far larger intrusive mass was present at depth, supplying heat and "at least a part of the materials" to form ore (p. 166). Erosion from the paleosurface was believed to be at least 150 m, to several times this thickness.

Emmons (1927) reviewed the geology of a dozen porphyry districts in the southwestern United States and Mexico. He concluded that all the known Cu ores in porphyry deposits form in or near the tops of quartz monzonite or similar composition cupolas above large intrusive bodies, from which the mineralizing fluids were also derived; these conclusions were in close agreement with those of Ransome (1919). Emmons believed that fluid ascent was controlled by fractures, in which protore of pyrite and chalcopyrite was deposited along with sericite. This paper was very influential at the time, and pioneered the concept of zoning in intrusion-centered ore districts.

Locke (1926) clarified the nature of supergene oxidation and enrichment, and their products, helping to distinguish hypogene alteration and mineralization from the products of supergene processes. The mining of porphyry deposits was then, and indeed continues to be, largely feasible economically only because of the occurrence of supergene remobilization which locally generates thick blankets of chalcocite-enriched supergene ore.

Lindgren (1933) synthesized ore deposit types in the fourth edition of his classic textbook. He interpreted the disseminated Cu deposits, then being referred to as "chalcocite blankets or porphyry ores" (p. 628), to be mesothermal replacements of monzonite to quartz diorite intrusions and adjacent wall rock. However, the replacement process was recognized only to generate "prot-ore" (Ransome, 1914), with the primary grades of 0.5 to 1.0 wt percent Cu being insufficient for economic mining. Because all of the economic deposits were enriched by supergene processes, Lindgren (1933) discussed them under his supergene category, although he stressed their primary magmatic affiliation.

Ore deposits of Lindgren's broad mesothermal class, in which he placed the porphyry ores, were deduced to have formed over a temperature range of 175° to 300°C and at depths of 1,200 to 3,600 m, based on the stabilities of minerals associated with what we now recognize as phyllic alteration. He assumed the prevalence of hydrostatic pressure conditions, but acknowledged that fluid pressures may have been higher adjacent to the intrusion. Although these depth and pressure estimates were reasonably accurate, the temperature estimates did not take into account the role of the earlier higher temperature potassic alteration.

In addition to the disseminated porphyry ores, Lindgren (1933) also classified pyrite-enargite veins, commonly associated with these deposits worldwide, as mesothermal Cu veins (in fact, they are high-sulfidation epithermal ores formed over the porphyry), whereas Cu-tourmaline breccias were termed hypothermal breccia replacements. Limestone altered to calc-silicate mineral assemblages, with associated Cu ore (skarn) adjacent to the intrusions, was classified as pyrometasomatic or contact metamorphic ore. Lindgren also noted that as distance from the intrusive center increased, the ore changed style to hypothermal and then mesothermal replacement types.

Thus, all the fundamental geologic elements and ore environments now known to occur in porphyry systems (cf. Sillitoe, 1991, 1993, 1996) were identified by the early 1930s, although their interrelations were not appreciated fully at that time. Furthermore, most of these deductions were made purely from field and petrographic observations, without the luxury of modern analytical techniques. What, then, have we learned about porphyries from application of the numerous techniques described in this volume? In the following sections, we will consider various aspects of the porphyry model, and trace how our level of understanding changed with the advent of various new methodologies.

Alteration and Mineralization

The first detailed studies of wall-rock alteration in porphyry systems were conducted at Cerro de Pasco, Peru (Graton and Bowditch, 1936), and at Butte, Montana (Sales and Meyer, 1948, 1949). Sales and Meyer concluded that alteration was progressive, caused by the continual interaction of the same solution with wall rock. Sales (1913) had already noted clear zoning in sulfide minerals at Butte, from Cu minerals outward to sphalerite and galena, both vertically and laterally. Butte became a classic example of hydrothermal mineral zonation in an ore deposit (Park, 1955). A sequence of advanced argillic, to sericitic, to intermediate argillic alteration (Meyer and Hemley, 1967) was recognized with increasing distance from the veins. These observations served as the basis of subsequent experimental work by Hemley (Hemley, 1959; Hemley and Jones, 1964). In early surface mapping of alteration zoning at Ajo, Arizona, Gilluly (1946) also recognized a core of orthoclase-quartz-magnetite-biotite-(chlorite)-altered rock associated with pegmatite. This pegmatite is, in turn, spatially associated with high-grade hypogene Cu ore, surrounded by a halo of sericite and pyrite (Gilluly, 1946, plate 27).

The next year, Schwartz (1947) outlined the broad details of porphyry alteration, recognizing assemblages consisting of biotite, quartz-orthoclase, quartz-sericite-pyrite, and sericite plus clay minerals. He concluded that the introduction of chalcopyrite was coeval with sericitic alteration, whereas biotitic alteration was thought to be early or marginal to ore, and of minor extent and significance; orthoclase was noted to be common but typically overprinted by phyllic or argillic alteration. Schwartz recognized that local occurrences of hypogene advanced argillic alteration occurred close to but not associated with ore in porphyry systems, and that the hypogene variety of advanced argillic alteration can be difficult to distinguish from supergene acid alteration.

Creasey (1966) made one of the first attempts to establish the general types of porphyry alteration, and at the same time integrated a variety of experimental data. He proposed the use of the general terms propylitic, argillic, and potassic to denote specific mineral assemblages typical of porphyry deposits. This lumping of assemblages is useful from a genetic perspective, and allows intercomparison between deposits, particularly in developing a picture of alteration zonation. Nevertheless, elaboration of the minerals in each assemblage is also essential, because different authors still tend to use these general terms differently.

Potassic (or K-silicate) alteration consists of secondary biotite, magnetite, and K-feldspar, and occurs in a proximal position to the central intrusion. Creasey (1966) argued that this assemblage formed at a relatively high temperature (>400°C) because clay minerals are not observed. Argillic alteration is distinguished by the presence of clay minerals, including kaolinite and montmorillonite, and Creasey noted that this alteration style would have formed if the system had been at lower temperature. An assemblage of quartz-sericite-pyrite (sericitic or phyllic alteration) was also noted as being intermediate between the potassic and argillic zones (Fig. 1A), whereas propylitic alteration occurred marginal to the porphyry system, and was characterized by various combinations of chlorite, calcite, epidote, and kaolinite, with hydration and CO_2 metasomatism being the principal agents of alteration.

Meyer and Hemley (1967) added to this list the advanced argillic assemblage produced by extreme hydrolytic base leaching. This assemblage is characterized by dickite, kaolinite, and/or pyrophyllite, and can also include quartz, alunite, sericite, topaz, and zunyite. Somewhat surprisingly, however, subsequent studies of porphyry deposits in the United States (cf. Lowell and Guilbert, 1970) passed over the significance of hypogene advanced argillic alteration, perhaps because its shallow depth of formation meant that much of the rock affected by this process had been eroded away.

Jerome (1966) noted the zonation of alteration and sulfide minerals in porphyry deposits, and used these relationships to suggest exploration guidelines. Rose (1970) studied Santa Rita and other porphyry deposits of the southwestern United States, and was the first to stress the importance of the early-stage potassic alteration. At the same time, Lowell and Guilbert (1970) used the case study of the fault-separated San Manuel-Kalamazoo system in Arizona to highlight the vertical and horizontal zoning relationships. Based on this insight, they compiled data on 27 other porphyry deposits from around the world to establish a model for alteration zoning (Fig. 1A), which has been used for over two decades. This paper was a landmark effort for the minerals industry, in that it led to a predictive model for exploration that was in part responsible for the huge success in discovery of porphyry Cu deposits from the 1970s onward. Contributing to the successful application of this deposit model to exploration was the recognition of direct relationships between parts of the zoned system and distinct geophysical responses (e.g., ground magnetic anomalies caused by magnetite in the potassic zone; Jerome, 1966; Sillitoe, 1993). Also of critical importance to exploration was the establishment of a firm understanding of supergene processes (Anderson, 1982, and references therein). Coupled with empirical observation (Ransome, 1919; Locke, 1926), this understanding allowed the weathering products of eroded porphyry ore bodies ("leached capping") to be correlated with the original sulfide mineralization (Anderson, 1982).

At the same time, Noble (1970) suggested that metallogenic provinces are controlled by vertical metal zonation in the mantle. He argued that an intrusion was simply a structural control rather than a source of mineralizing fluids, and to support this viewpoint he noted the poor correlation between the size of the host intrusions and metal inventory, and the fact that some intrusions are barren (cf. Emmons, 1927). This argument of course ignored the idea that, although much of porphyry ore is hosted by shallow-level intrusive rocks (typically 70%; Lowell and Guilbert, 1970), the metals were likely derived from more than just these exposed intrusions, possibly distilled from extensive underlying plutonic masses (e.g., Dilles and Proffett, 1995).

Sillitoe (1973), in another landmark paper on the hottest ore deposit type of the time, discussed the nature of the tops and bottoms of porphyry Cu deposits based on observations of relatively well-preserved porphyry systems in the Andes. He argued that porphyry deposits form typically in a subvolcanic setting, with the volcanic edifice in some deposits being a stratovolcano, while post-ore magmatism may form domes and maars (Sillitoe, 1993). Regardless of the nature of the volcanic edifice, given the appreciable size of the parent intrusion (Cline and Bodnar, 1991; Dilles and Proffett, 1995) and the amount of hydrothermal fluid required to form a deposit (Hedenquist et al., 1998), it seems inescapable that there must be both a volcanologic and hydrothermal expression at the surface over a forming porphyry Cu deposit.

Sillitoe (1983) postulated an intimate relationship between enargite-bearing massive sulfide bodies, now recognized as high-sulfidation epithermal deposits, and porphyry Cu deposits, based on his observations of a common geological association. Shortly afterwards, he reviewed the variety of breccia types found in porphyry Cu deposits (Sillitoe, 1985), many related to multiple phases of intrusion during hydrothermal alteration and mineralization. Such multiplicity typically results in a highly complex series of events, and in most cases, the intrusive history can be determined only by mapping the truncations of vein sets, as emphasized by Kirkham (1971). Sillitoe (1975, 1991, 1993) further recognized the presence of an advanced argillic "lithocap" (Sillitoe, 1995) to many porphyry Cu deposits in the southeastern and southwestern

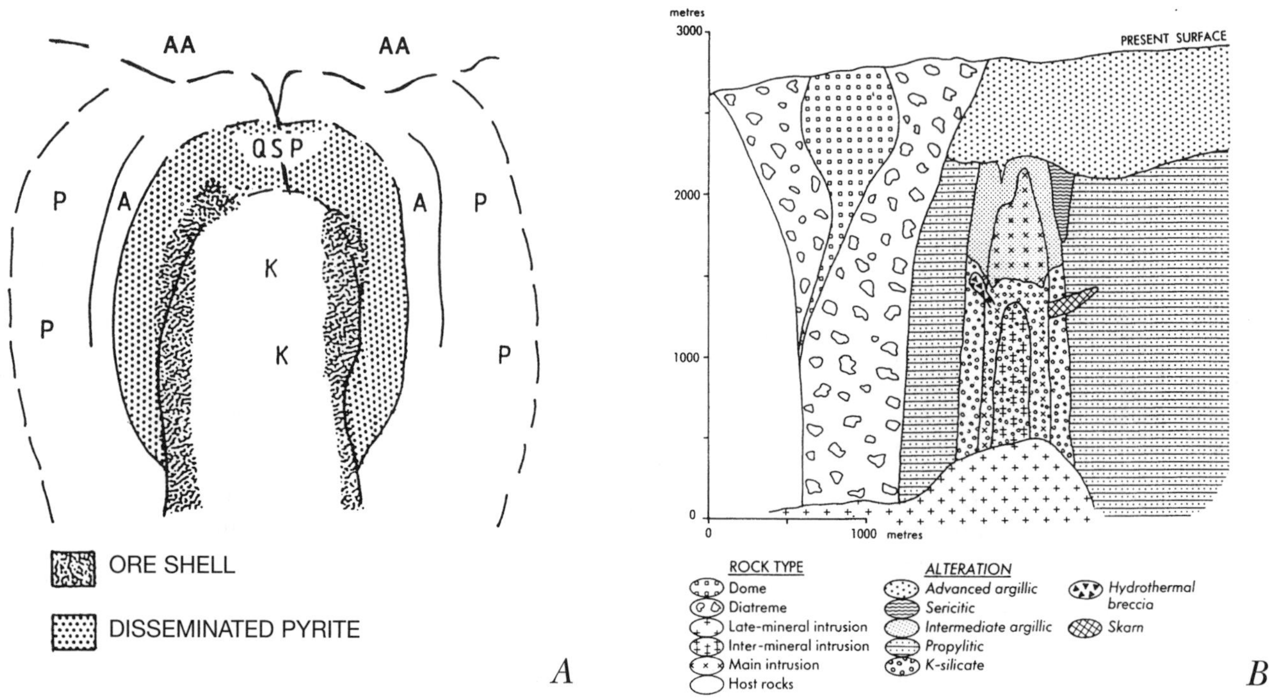

FIG. 1. (A) Zonation of hydrothermal alteration in a typical porphyry Cu deposit, as summarized by Lowell and Guilbert (1970); compilation was based largely on examples in the southwestern United States. Slightly modified from Lowell and Guilbert (1970), adding a shallow zone of advanced argillic (AA) alteration. Other abbreviations: K = potassic; A = argillic; QSP = quartz-sericite-pyrite; P = propylitic.

(B) Alteration zoning in porphyry Cu deposits, showing the relation of post-ore volcanic domes or diatreme complexes to the ore zone, incorporating observations from South America, the southwestern Pacific, and elsewhere (from Sillitoe, 1993; used with permission). The "lithocap" of advanced argillic alteration is typical over porphyry deposits (Sillitoe, 1995), because its formation is coupled to that of potassic alteration (see text); however, much or all of this shallow alteration is commonly eroded away.

Pacific regions (Fig. 1B). This alteration feature is now argued to be an essential attribute of porphyry Cu systems, because it forms at shallow depth by groundwater absorption of the vapor that separates from the hypersaline liquid associated with potassic alteration at depth (Hedenquist et al., 1998). Advanced argillic alteration may overprint deeper alteration assemblages during telescoping of the ore body, perhaps in response to sector collapse of the volcanic edifice (Sillitoe, 1994).

One of the most detailed studies of a porphyry Cu deposit was conducted by the Anaconda Company at El Salvador, Chile (Gustafson and Hunt, 1975). Multiple intrusions of early- to late-mineral stocks, recognized in other districts as well (Kirkham, 1971), created a complex series of events that was understood only after careful documentation of crosscutting relationships. About three-quarters of the Cu ore was deposited from magma-derived fluid as chalcopyrite or bornite in association with potassic alteration and early A veins; these veins comprise anhedral quartz, and are discontinuous and irregular. Intrusion of the L porphyry modified the early patterns of mineralization, and was followed by planar B quartz veins containing molybdenite. Late, through-going D veins contain sulfides, quartz, and anhydrite with halos of sericite and chlorite. These veins, radial at El Salvador, cut late-mineral intrusions, and the contained bornite, chalcopyrite, and enargite account for the balance of the Cu mineralization. A veins were interpreted to have formed in a quasi-ductile regime, B veins in a transitional, and D veins in a brittle regime, reflecting a change from lithostatic to hydrostatic pressure, from the potassic to phyllic alteration stages. Thus, porphyry studies began to offer insight into magmatic processes and their coupling to features of the hydrothermal system (Fournier, 1991).

More recent studies by Proffett and Dilles (1984), Dilles (1987), Dilles and Proffett (1995), and their Anaconda colleagues on the well-exposed Yerington district, Nevada, have revealed the nature of the magmatic roots of the porphyry system. Post-mineral faulting and rotation exposed portions of the system over a >6 km vertical interval. Dikes associated with mineralization can be traced to the Luhr Hill Granite (~65 km^3) at 6 to 9 km paleodepth, emplaced into the center of a much larger batholith from which it differentiated. The unaltered Luhr Hill Granite contains only ~10 ppm Cu with Cu/Zn ≈ 0.25, in contrast to ~60 ppm Cu and Cu/Zn ≈ 1 in the earlier batholith. Magmatic fluid exsolved relatively late in the crystallization of the Luhr Hill Granite and ascended along cogenetic dikes to result in porphyry mineralization of the Ann Mason deposit at <4 km paleodepth. The low Cu content of the progenitor Luhr Hill Granite indicates that much of the Cu was lost during crystallization of this intrusion. By contrast, the earlier, more Cu-rich parts of the batholith are not known to be associated with economic mineralization (Dilles and Proffett, 1995).

Geochemical Studies

Early Studies of Magmatic Hydrothermal Fluid

Lindgren (1933) synthesized what was then known about the nature and interrelations of various crustal fluids, and the relation of different ore types to magmatic processes. His magmatist viewpoint was based largely on geological observation, and integration with relatively limited experimental constraints. For example, he appreciated that the volatile compositions of solidified igneous rocks are different from those of the original magmas because the rock compositions do not reflect the volatiles that were lost on crystallization (p. 104). The significance of volatile-loss was missed by many later workers, who incorrectly deduced the composition of magmatic fluid from the residue fixed by hydroxyl-bearing igneous minerals (see Chap. 8).

Many of the early experiments on hydrothermal fluids were influenced by the concept of a "mother liquor" having a plutonic origin. Bowen (1933) concluded that volatiles in igneous systems are concentrated into a residual fluid during crystallization, and that this fluid is acidic on discharge but becomes alkaline on ascent and reaction with wall rock. Fenner (1933) conducted field work on hot springs at Yellowstone and concluded that gaseous emanations from magmas mix with descending hydrothermal waters, becoming less acidic, before rising to the surface.

Graton and Bowditch (1936) noted evidence that advanced argillic alteration decreases downward, leading them to conclude that deep solutions are alkaline and become acidic near the surface ($S + H_2O$ reacting to form $H_2SO_4 + H_2S$, as proposed by Allen and Day, 1935). However, Lindgren (1937) was strongly influenced by Bowen and Fenner in concluding that a magmatic ore solution starts out acidic and becomes alkaline. Lindgren believed that reactions with wall rock were the cause of ore and gangue mineral deposition, although he also noted the geologic and mineralogic evidence for shallow entrainment by, and reactions with, meteoric water. He further argued for the colloidal transport of metals, an idea that has received support from more recent studies of high-grade epithermal Au veins (e.g., Saunders, 1994).

Based on detailed field work at the Ajo porphyry Cu deposit in 1934 to 1936, Gilluly (1946) integrated his observations with experimental constraints (Goranson, 1931; Gilluly, 1937), and comparisons with volcanic emanations (Fenner, 1933). Gilluly concluded that after the Ajo quartz monzonite intruded and crystallized, it was "shattered and cracked," and altered "by solutions of magmatic derivation" (p. 73). Several previous authors had speculated that the paleosurface was 100 to 300 m above exposures of porphyry deposits. By contrast, Gilluly used experimental constraints to estimate a paleodepth of 1,000 to 3,000 m (average 2,000 m or 0.5 kbar at lithostatic pressure), consistent with solidus temperatures of ~900°C for granite containing 4 wt percent water (p. 78). He recognized that the source magma contained water, sulfur, and halogens, and that the ligands would complex with metals to produce an aqueous fluid with concentrations higher than those in the analyzed pluton. Gilluly also noted that other volatiles would decrease the solubility of water in a melt, and that the vapor pressure of exsolved fluid would "split apart" the wedge-shaped cupola of host rocks and solidified magma (p. 79; after Goranson,

1938). He concluded by stressing that the discharge of magmatic fluid was a continual process, and would lead to ponding in cupolas and intermittent fracturing (cf. Burnham, 1967, 1979). Thus, experimental results for realistic systems were now starting to play a significant role in constraining geological interpretations.

Graton (1940) refuted early ideas that there was a gaseous transfer of metals from magma, and argued that the magmatic aqueous phase was liquid (i.e., was relatively dense); he also argued for the fluid to start out alkaline, i.e., in equilibrium with the host rock at depth. Although low-density magmatic vapors can transport metals, the concentrations are typically very low, based on analyses of high-temperature volcanic vapors (Hedenquist, 1995). Rather, most metals are now believed to partition into a dense liquid at depth (see below), supporting Graton's conclusion. Neumann (1948) argued from experimental observations that fractionation of water and other components between crystals, melt, and exsolved aqueous fluid is a function of relative solubilities, with ore metals being fractionated continuously from magma to fluid (cf. Whitney, 1975; Candela, 1989).

By the end of the first half of the century, Bateman (1950, Chap. 4) was adamant in his textbook that "Magmas are the source of essentially all the ingredients of ore deposits." He concluded that the mineralizing fluids were exsolved in the final stages of magma crystallization as a residual aqueous solution.

Nature of the Ore Fluid

Kennedy (1950) established the physical properties of water in a landmark paper that allowed the calculation of many parameters of magmatic-hydrothermal fluids. The Economic Geology 50th Anniversary Volume followed soon after, and in it Ingerson (1955) made an extensive compilation of the indicators of paleotemperature known at that time, including mineral assemblages and mineral chemistry, fluid inclusions (building on Kennedy's results), and isotopic fractionation. For example, he summarized the exsolution temperatures of mineral pairs, including bornite-chalcopyrite (300°–475°C) and sphalerite-chalcopyrite (400°–650°C). Early experimental studies in the system Cu-Fe-S (Roseboom and Kullerud, 1957) suggested that chalcopyrite-pyrite, a common sulfide assemblage in porphyry deposits, was stable at temperatures up to 600° to 700°C. However, Creasey (1966) noted that these values seemed too high because they overlapped the minimum melting temperature of wet granite.

Smith (1954) concluded from early fluid inclusion studies that two principal solutions were present in porphyry systems: a saline aqueous liquid and a hydrous silicate melt. The aqueous liquid was found to have a salinity of 5 to 20 wt percent NaCl equivalent, although salt crystals in some inclusions indicated salinities in excess of 30 wt percent NaCl equivalent. Subsequent studies by Roedder (1971) and a host of other workers (compiled by Roedder, 1984) determined that in most porphyry deposits there is an early period of hypersaline liquid (>500°–700°C, and 40–60 wt % NaCl equiv.) commonly coexisting with a low-density vapor. By contrast, later in the evolution of most porphyry systems, a lower temperature (<350°C), lower salinity (5–20 wt % NaCl equiv.) liquid caused the common phyllic alteration overprint (Beane, 1983; Reynolds and Beane, 1985).

Studies of active thermal features, fluid inclusions, and phase relations of ore and alteration minerals provided much of the early information on the nature of porphyry ore fluids (Barton, 1959). For example, Holland (1956) argued that metals in hydrothermal fluids are transported as sulfide and metal chloride complexes, noting from fluid inclusion studies that solutions are rich in Na and K chlorides. White (1957) concluded that the magmatic component of hydrothermal fluids discharging from hot springs is small (<5%, based on preliminary isotopic studies by Craig et al., 1956), but that the character of the spring water is determined by the nature of the magmatic-volatile component. Although the relationship between porphyry systems and active thermal features at the surface was not discussed at this time, various authors argued that low-sulfidation epithermal veins formed in an environment beneath geothermal hot springs (Lindgren, 1933; White, 1957). Also, the origin of acidic waters forming high-sulfidation epithermal alteration as condensates of volcanic fumaroles had long been recognized (Ransome, 1907).

Following a 1964 meeting on ore fluids, Roedder (1965) noted that H. Helgeson favored chloride complexing of metals in hydrothermal solutions. This conclusion was based on the sulfur-poor solutions of the Salton Sea geothermal system, although the fluid in this system is now thought to be non-magmatic in origin (McKibben and Hardie, 1997). By contrast, H. Barnes argued for sulfide complexing of metals. Subsequent studies have shown that both Helgeson and Barnes were correct but under different circumstances, with the dominant ligand depending on many factors, including the salinity and total S concentration, pH and redox state, and the metal of interest (see Chap. 2; Seward, 1981; Henley, 1990).

Fluid Properties and the Relationship to Magmas

The properties of the H_2O-NaCl system were established experimentally in a classic study by Sourirajan and Kennedy (1962), allowing a more complete interpretation of fluid inclusion data, and particularly those for hypersaline liquids. They showed that the two-phase (liquid-vapor) univariant curve of the pure H_2O system becomes a divariant field when NaCl is added, and that the invariant H_2O critical point defines a univariant curve that rises to higher temperatures and pressures with increase in salinity (Fig. 2, and Chap. 7). Subsequent experimental studies by Pitzer and Pabalan (1986) in the low salinity range, and Bodnar et al. (1985) in the high salinity range modified the position of the isochores and, at low pressures, the topology of this system (Fig. 2). The increased reliability of experimental results in the latter study was made possible by the use of synthetic fluid inclusions trapped under controlled P-T-X conditions (Bodnar and Sterner, 1987).

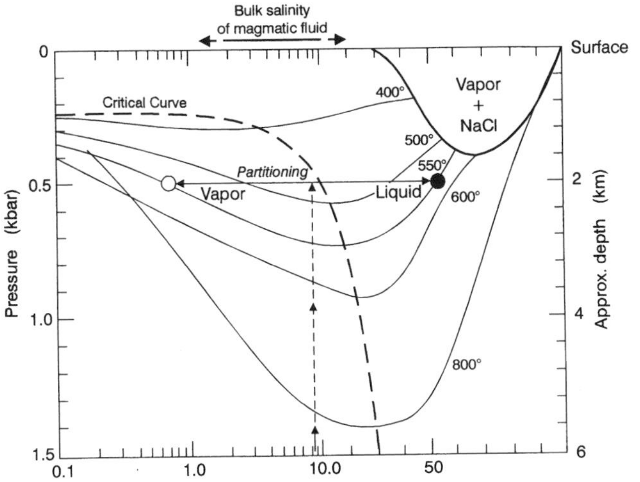

FIG. 2. System H_2O-NaCl (after Sourirajan and Kennedy, 1962, modified with data from Bodnar et al., 1985, and Pitzer and Pabalan, 1986). Ascent of a magmatic fluid with a bulk salinity of about 8.5 wt percent NaCl equivalent at a temperature of 800°C will intersect its solvus at about 1.4 kbar. If the fluid cools to, say, 550°C before ascending to this depth and pressure, it can rise to about 2 km depth and 500 bar lithostatic pressure before separating to form a hypersaline liquid of about 55 wt percent NaCl and a vapor of about 0.7 wt percent NaCl (in a mass proportion of about 1:9, respectively). Note logarithmic to linear scale change at 10 wt percent NaCl.

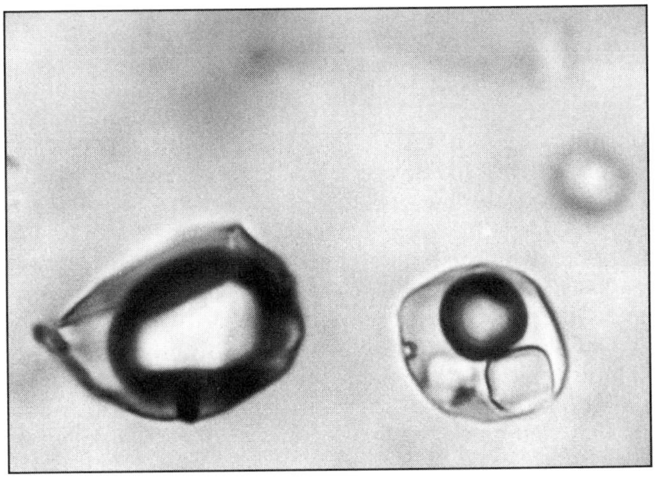

FIG. 3. Hypersaline liquid-rich and vapor-rich fluid inclusions from the Bingham porphyry Cu deposit (the vapor-rich inclusion is 20 μm-long). These coexisting phases formed when a high-temperature magmatic fluid ascended and intersected its solvus (Fig. 2). Continued ascent and depressurization causes more hypersaline liquid to condense from the vapor, until the vapor either is adsorbed by groundwater (to form acidic water and advanced argillic alteration) or discharges from high-temperature (700°–900°C) volcanic fumaroles; the latter typically contain 0.01 wt percent NaCl (Hedenquist, 1995), as expected for the atmospheric pressure solubility of NaCl in vapor at 800°C.

Roedder's (1971) work at Bingham was the first detailed study of fluid inclusions associated with porphyry mineralization. However, despite being familiar with the experimental data for the H_2O-NaCl system (Sourirajan and Kennedy, 1962), and the immiscibility relationships between a hypersaline liquid and vapor, Roedder concluded that the hypersaline liquid he observed at Bingham may have originated directly from exsolution from a melt (cf. Cline and Vanko, 1995). Eastoe (1978) obtained similar data from the Panguna deposit, Papua New Guinea, in which coexisting high-temperature vapor and hypersaline liquid inclusions are associated with potassic alteration, and low salinity (<5 wt % NaCl equivalent), lower temperature (<350°C) liquid inclusions are associated with later phyllic alteration. Eastoe concluded that this pattern was consistent with the presence of early magmatic water followed by later meteoric water.

Henley and McNabb (1978) were probably the first to argue that in most cases the hypersaline liquid observed to coexist with vapor in porphyry Cu fluid inclusions originated as a homogeneous, moderate-salinity, relatively low-density plume of magmatic fluid that separated to hypersaline liquid and low-salinity vapor during ascent and depressurization, once the fluid intersected its solvus (Fig. 2).

The common observation of coexisting hypersaline-liquid- and vapor-rich fluid inclusions in porphyry deposits (Fig. 3) is thus explained in terms of unmixing of an originally homogeneous (supercritical; Shinohara, 1994) aqueous fluid, exsolved from the magma with salinities typically in the range of 2 to 10 wt percent NaCl equivalent (Burnham, 1979; Hedenquist et al., 1998), and at pressures of 1 to 1.5 kbar, equivalent to depths of 4 to 6 km at lithostatic pressure. During ascent from its point of exsolution from the parent magmatic pluton to the depth of porphyry stock emplacement and ore formation (typically 2–3 km depth at a pressure of about 0.5 kbar), the magmatic fluid intersects its solvus, forming immiscible liquid and vapor phases of hugely contrasting density. Only in rare cases are the original supercritical fluids, with salinities of about 10 wt percent NaCl equivalent, trapped in fluid inclusions near the base of the porphyry deposit itself (Bodnar, 1995).

In experimental studies complementary to the analytical data on the hydrothermal systems, Burnham and Jahns (1962) showed that the solubility of water in silicate melts is sufficiently high that large volumes of hydrothermal fluid can be exsolved prior to complete solidification of the magma. Burnham (1967, 1979) subsequently reviewed the constraints that experimental studies provide on magma-water systems. For example, the solubility of water in a magma is pressure dependent, and partition coefficients indicate that early-exsolved fluid may be more saline than later fluid (cf. Cline and Bodnar, 1991; Cline, 1995).

Following the early flurry of experimental studies (many of which were reviewed by Burnham, 1967, and discussed in Barnes, 1967), Ridge (1967, p. 1807) commented on ore-deposit research of the previous 25 years: "An old hand cannot but think wistfully of the days when all that was needed to supply the metals and sulfur in low-T ore deposits was an unknown igneous mass at great depth" (cf. the mag[mat]ic fluid arrows of Giggenbach, 1992a).

Mineral Stabilities and Wall-Rock Alteration

Hemley (1959) and Hemley and Jones (1964) conducted experimental studies on mineral equilibria in the system K_2O-Na_2O-Al_2O_3-SiO_2-H_2O, with constraints from porphyry alteration assemblages recognized by Sales and Meyer (1948) at Butte. Hemley found that it is the cation/H^+ ratio that determines mineral stability, and not solely pH, and he was able to establish relative stabilities of minerals as a function of temperature and the ratio of KCl or NaCl to HCl (Fig. 4; the basis of alkali geothermometry in geothermal systems; see also Chap. 3). Although minor details have been refined subsequently, the geological validity of these and later studies by Hemley and his coworkers have stood the test of time, with little fundamental change to their applicability (cf. Sverjensky et al., 1991).

Hemley's results, coupled with the use of Eh–pH diagrams to represent mineral stabilities (Garrels and Christ, 1965), allowed mineral assemblages to be interpreted in terms of redox state and acidity, thus enabling the observations of variable spatial and temporal relationships between deposits to be better understood. Hemley and Jones (1964) established the fundamentals of and framework for interpreting hydrolytic alteration, and this framework was extended to specific systems by Hemley et al. (1969, 1980, 1992). These studies provided data for the interpretation of alteration assemblages in most ore-bearing hydrothermal environments, thus allowing mineral assemblages to be identified that reflected the reactivity of the fluid (Meyer and Hemley, 1967).

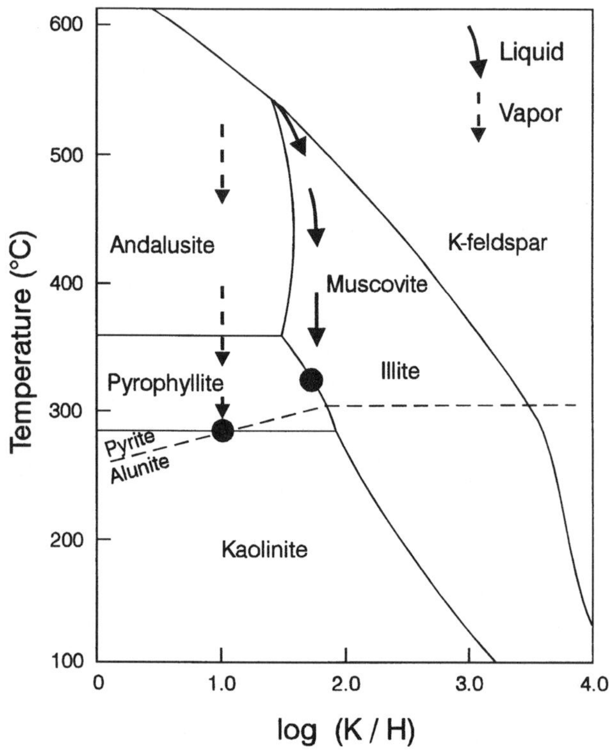

FIG. 4. Stability of alteration minerals characteristic of porphyry Cu deposits as a function of the molar ratio (K^+/H^+) and temperature (modified from Hemley and Jones, 1964; Sverjensky et al., 1991); the pyrite-alunite schematic curve is added from Giggenbach (1992a). Advanced argillic alteration assemblages may form through absorption of acidic vapor by groundwaters (dashed line), or by cooling of the liquid phase during ascent (Hemley and Hunt, 1992).

Giggenbach (1984) used a geothermal framework to highlight the fact that Na-Ca and K metasomatism are largely functions of heating and cooling of hydrothermal solutions, respectively. This can explain to a degree the common occurrence of Na-Ca alteration on the deep margins of porphyry systems (e.g., Dilles and Proffett, 1995), although saline waters of non-magmatic origin may also be a factor. By contrast, potassic, phyllic, and argillic alteration form in or above the cores of such systems, where fluid ascent is associated with progressive cooling and acidification. The extreme case of leaching and associated advanced argillic alteration is most typically caused by the direct transfer of magmatic volatiles to near-surface, low-temperature environments: dissociation of HCl and the disproportionation of SO_2 to form H_2SO_4 and H_2S generate highly reactive waters. However, simple cooling may also produce this style of alteration in an upward gradation from phyllic (or argillic) alteration (cf. Hemley and Hunt, 1992).

These studies have more recently been coupled with an improved understanding of the nature of magmatic fluid, the latter coming from the study of volcanic discharges (Giggenbach, 1992a). The chloride fluid that exsolves from a magma is in chemical equilibrium with its source rock (i.e., the crystallizing magma), and wall-rock alteration is initially restricted to subsolidus growth of "magmatic" minerals such as K-feldspar or biotite (potassic alteration). However, with continued cooling, the fluid becomes reactive, causing hydrolysis reactions that lead to the breakdown of feldspar and other silicate minerals to form sericite (phyllic alteration), or even clays (argillic alteration) at sufficiently low K/H ratios (e.g., Burnham and Ohmoto, 1980; Giggenbach, 1992a, 1997; Hemley and Hunt, 1992; see also Chap. 3). Such reactions are highly dependent on the path of fluid ascent (i.e., temperature, pressure, and water/rock ratio, etc.). Decreasing temperature affects the dissociation constant of HCl and other components (Montoya and Hemley, 1975), but is not the sole cause of the increase in reactivity.

Thus, returning to the debate about the acidity of magmatic-hydrothermal fluids, do they become acidic or alkaline on cooling? This "can now be answered unambiguously: both!" (Giggenbach, 1997, p. 789). They start out neutral with respect to reaction with the parent magma; cooling then turns them acidic, but water-rock interaction acts to neutralize the Cl- and S-based acids. Below 300°C, CO_2 becomes reactive, and the cycle of alteration begins again. "To a large degree, the problem reduces to defining 'acidity' in a meaningful way" (Giggenbach, 1997, p. 789). The problem is further compounded when H_2S oxidizes in the vadose zone to form steam-heated acid sulfate waters at the surface.

We can continue to discuss the reactivity of the fluid with respect to the host rock by examining the redox state. Meyer and Hemley (1967) were among the first to interpret sulfide mineral zoning in terms of quantifiable reactions between the hydrothermal fluid and wallrock. At the same time, Barton and Skinner (1967, 1979) calculated the relative stabilities and sulfidation state of sulfide minerals from a compilation of a large variety of thermodynamic data, and noted the continuum across ore environments. These approaches were coupled subsequently with data from active hydrothermal systems to help link the redox state of a fluid to specific ore environments (Fig. 5; Giggenbach, 1992a), and indeed to the fundamental character of the parent magma (Burnham and Ohmoto, 1980; see below). Burnham and Ohmoto (1980), Giggenbach (1992a, 1997), and others argued that the end-member redox controls in hydrothermal systems include the sulfur gas buffer, which is oxidized relative to wall rocks at submagmatic temperatures, and the rock buffer, in which the ferrous/ferric iron content of the wall-rock maintains a relatively reduced redox state. These end-member redox controls operate in fluid- and rock-dominated systems, respectively.

Stable Isotopic Studies: Sources of Water

The sources of water comprising hydrothermal systems has been a matter of debate since the 16th and 17th centuries. Agricola argued that meteoric water leaches metals from rocks and transports the metals to the sites of deposition, whereas a century later Descartes proposed that

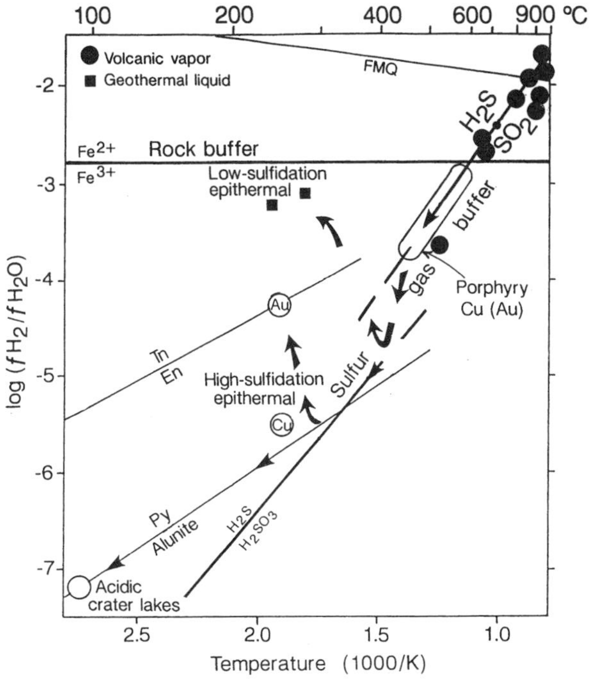

FIG. 5. Redox relationships as a function of temperature, showing a variety of igneous and alteration mineral assemblage buffers (Barton and Skinner, 1979), the sulfur gas buffer curve and the rock buffer range (Fe^{2+}/Fe^{3+}; both from Giggenbach, 1992a), the composition of high-temperature volcanic gases and acid crater lakes (Giggenbach, 1992a; Hedenquist, 1995), and the general redox environment of porphyry Cu deposits affiliated with oxidized I-type intrusions (Burnham and Ohmoto, 1980); compare with Fig. 10. Abbreviations: FMQ = fayalite-magnetite-quartz; Tn = tennantite; En = enargite; Py = pyrite.

vapors released from the cooling and crystallization of the Earth's interior are responsible for forming ore deposits. This controversy continues, despite our ability now to determine the isotopic composition of hydroxyl-bearing minerals and thus determine the isotopic value of the hydrothermal fluid responsible for forming a variety of ore types.

Giggenbach (1992b) summarized the range of isotopic compositions observed for magmatic vapors discharged from active volcanic arcs (Fig. 6). These data, coupled with the summary by Taylor (1992) of the isotopic composition of water dissolved in silicic magma prior to fluid exsolution (cf. Taylor et al., 1983; Dobson et al., 1989), allow us to estimate the isotopic composition of bulk magmatic fluid after exsolution, and its separated hypersaline component. A simple mass balance, coupled with knowledge of the D/H fractionation between hypersaline liquid and vapor (Horita et al., 1995), explains why low-salinity volcanic vapor is about 20 per mil heavier than water dissolved in silicic magmas.

In the first instance, the δD composition of the water exsolving from a melt will be on average about 20 per mil heavier than the residue still dissolved in the melt (Suzuoki and Epstein, 1976), although this will increase as the melt becomes depleted in water and the hydroxyl-to-molecular water proportion increases (Dobson et al., 1989). The bulk salinity of this exsolved fluid may vary widely, although for much of the exsolution history the salinity ranges only from 2 to 10 wt percent NaCl equivalent (Burnham, 1979; Hedenquist et al., 1998). If this exsolved fluid intersects its solvus on ascent (Fig. 2; Bodnar et al., 1985), the vapor that forms will be about 20 per mil heavier (δD) than the hypersaline liquid (Horita et al., 1995). Despite the hypersaline liquid comprising only about 10 percent by mass of the total exsolved fluid, this brine will contain the bulk of the chloride-complexed metals (Chap. 4). Mass balance constraints therefore require that the vapor will have an isotopic composition close to that of the bulk exsolved fluid (Figs. 7, inset, and 8).

These considerations illustrate the fact that mineralogically bound water remaining in the pluton after crystallization is most appropriately termed "residual magmatic water." Thus, igneous phenocrysts do not provide direct information on the composition of "primary magmatic water," as was concluded in earlier studies (e.g., Sheppard et al., 1969, 1971; Taylor, 1974).

Early studies of the O- and H-isotope compositions of porphyry-related hydrothermal alteration by Sheppard and colleagues (Sheppard et al., 1969, 1971; Sheppard and Taylor, 1974; Sheppard and Gustafson, 1976) clearly established that (1) the early, high-temperature potassic alteration is associated dominantly with magmatic fluid, whereas (2) subsequent overprinting by lower temperature alteration assemblages commonly involves a component of meteoric water circulation (Fig. 7).

The ranges in isotopic composition of the magmatic water responsible for potassic alteration in several porphyry deposits are summarized in Figure 7, with calculated water

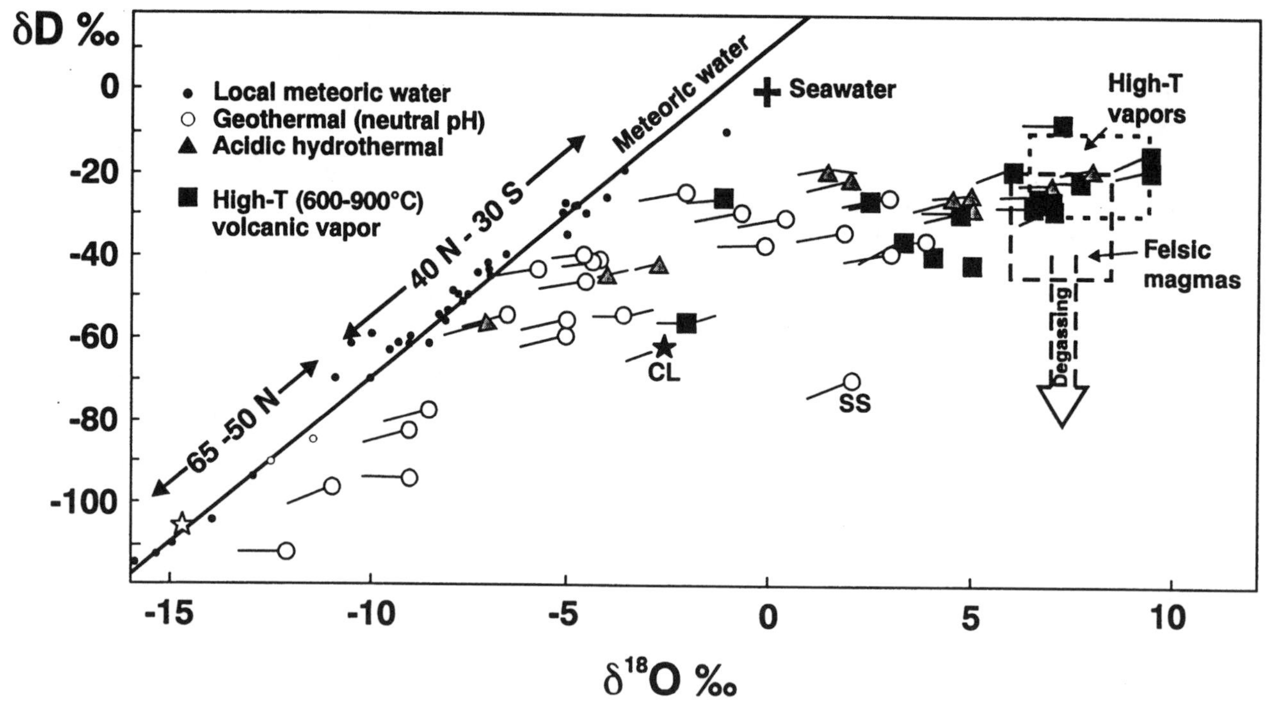

FIG. 6. Oxygen and hydrogen isotope composition of water dissolved in felsic magmas (Taylor, 1992), and that of a variety of high-temperature volcanic vapors (Giggenbach, 1992b), acidic and neutral pH hot springs, and associated local meteoric waters (the typical compositional ranges for high- and low-latitude meteoric waters are also shown). Acidic hydrothermal hot springs owe their hyperacidity to the absorption of volcanic vapors by groundwater, consistent with their isotopic composition intermediate between that of volcanic vapor and local meteoric water. These are the acidic waters that cause advanced argillically altered caps over porphyry Cu deposits. The composition of various neutral-pH geothermal waters are also shown, typically with a smaller magmatic component. The "tails" from the data symbols point to local meteoric water. Abbreviations: CL = Comstock Lode epithermal vein water; SS = Salton Sea brine (McKibben and Hardie, 1997).

values taken from the original papers. Water from El Salvador and other deposits in Chile (Sheppard and Gustafson, 1976; Kusakabe et al., 1990), plus that in equilibrium with biotites from Far Southeast, Philippines (Hedenquist et al., 1998), plot over a narrow range. Samples from Ely, Bingham, and Santa Rita (Sheppard et al., 1971) have a similarly narrow range of compositions, although δD is about 10 per mil lower, and $\delta^{18}O$ is slightly more variable than the first group, possibly reflecting a different tectonic setting and magma composition. The total range in δD from individual deposits in these areas is <15 per mil. A different pattern is shown by waters associated with potassic alteration at Yerington (Dilles et al., 1992) and at deposits in British Columbia (Zaluski et al., 1994), where δD can vary over a range of 50 per mil for a single deposit, although the $\delta^{18}O$ values have a narrow range, typical of magmatic compositions (5–9‰; Taylor, 1974, 1979).

What can be the cause of widely different δD values for potassic alteration (1) from different deposits (e.g., El Salvador vs. Butte), and (2) within the same deposit (e.g., Yerington)? Taylor (1988) stressed that such variations in the isotopic signature of potassic alteration provide information on the evolution (e.g., crystallization history) of the parent magma, because of the hydrogen isotope fractionation between melt and an aqueous fluid. Potassic alteration may be associated with the early degassing of an underlying pluton, in which intermittent (closed system) fluid exsolution results in only a small δD variation (Fig. 8), as observed in the southwestern Pacific and southwestern United States deposits (Fig. 7; see also Chap. 8). In other deposits, potassic alteration may have been formed during open-system degassing, leading to a large variation in δD, as perhaps observed at Yerington and in the British Columbia deposits (cf. Taylor, 1988). And finally, if the fluid that forms a particular mineral assemblage has exsolved from a highly degassed magma (i.e., at a late stage), then a large but uniform D-depletion relative to the early stage hydrothermal alteration may be observed (e.g., Butte). For example, potassic alteration at Butte is apparently quite depleted (δD = –120‰), although ongoing studies are reexamining this large deposit. Igneous biotite samples from the fresh Boulder Batholith rocks preserve isotopic evidence for extensive degassing elsewhere in the district (Fig. 8; Sheppard and Taylor, 1974).

In addition to the early work by Sheppard and his colleagues, subsequent detailed studies (e.g., Bowman et al., 1987; Zaluski et al., 1994; Hedenquist et al., 1998) have confirmed that magmatic water is responsible for the formation of hydrothermal biotite, whereas later sericite typically forms from a fluid containing at least a 75 percent magmatic water component (Fig. 7). Meteoric water is dominant in only rare cases of sericitic alteration (e.g., at Yerington; Dilles et al., 1992), and during late argillic alteration. Despite this finding of magmatic-water dominance even during sericite formation, the meteoric-water

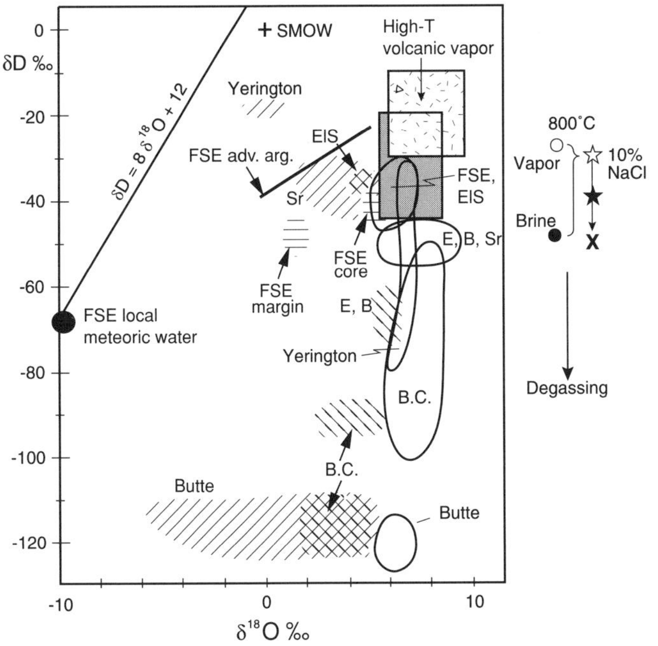

FIG. 7. Oxygen and hydrogen isotope compositions of waters from a variety of crustal environments and porphyry Cu deposits, including the composition of water dissolved in felsic magmas prior to degassing (dark-shaded box; Taylor, 1992). The sketch to the right shows the behavior of the hydrogen isotope composition of water dissolved in a melt (solid star), the composition of the bulk exsolved fluid (open star), and the residual water dissolved in the melt (X) after exsolution of 50 percent of the water dissolved in the melt. Separation of the magmatic fluid to hypersaline brine (closed circle) and vapor (open circle) also results in a hydrogen isotopic fractionation, with the vapor being heavier by about 20 per mil (Horita et al., 1995). Because of mass balance constraints and the size of the fractionation factors, the hypersaline liquid may have a hydrogen isotopic composition fortuitously similar to that of the water remaining in the melt. Much of the water exsolved from the magma discharges from volcanoes as high-temperature vapor (Giggenbach, 1992b), completing the mass balance and largely accounting for the D-depleted compositions of crystallized plutons (see text).

The composition of water that formed potassic alteration from a variety of porphyry Cu deposits is shown as open fields encircled by solid lines. In some cases (Yerington and deposits in British Columbia [B.C.]), magmatic degassing may be recorded by low δD values (Taylor, 1988). Later sericitic alteration forms from lower salinity waters (ruled fields) that have variable isotopic signatures ranging from >90 percent end-member magmatic (e.g., Far Southeast core [FSE] and El Salvador [ElS]) to about 3:1 magmatic/meteoric water mixtures (FSE margin; Santa Rita [Sr]; Ely [E]; Bingham [B]). Other deposits show evidence for larger meteoric water components responsible for late sericitic alteration (e.g., Yerington and Butte). The composition of water that formed advanced argillic (alunite) alteration at the FSE deposit (shown by the heavy line) lies between that of volcanic vapor and local meteoric water. The end-member vapor is heavier in D by about 20 per mil compared with the composition of water that formed potassic (and sericite) alteration. This is consistent with δD fractionation between vapor and brine.

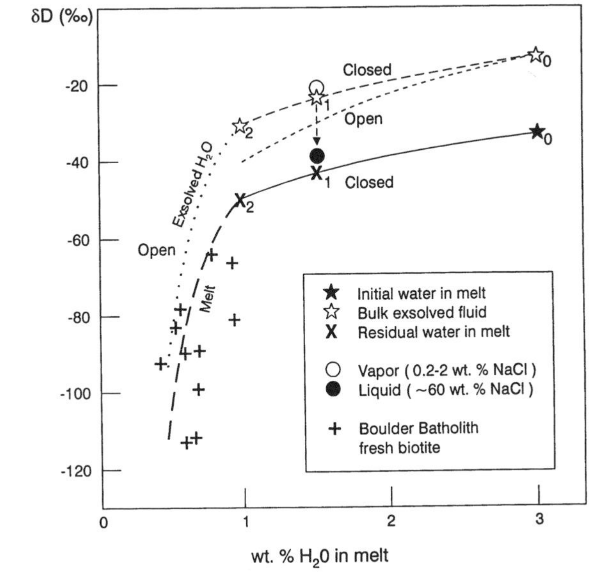

FIG. 8. Evolution of the hydrogen isotope compositions of water remaining dissolved in a melt and the exsolved supercritical fluid (Taylor, 1986; Dobson et al., 1989), and of the vapor and liquid phases after phase separation (Horita et al., 1995). The δD values of igneous phenocrysts commonly reflect the last stage of (open system) degassing of an intrusion (Dobson et al., 1989). For example, the distribution of δD values of fresh igneous biotite from the Boulder Batholith (Montana; Sheppard and Taylor, 1974) when plotted against the water content of the host rock (R.I. Tilling, pers. commun., 1996), likely reflects degassing, and not the initial composition of the water dissolved in the melt (Taylor, 1986).

component recorded by the sericite, coupled to the observation of a close spatial association of this alteration style with pyrite and chalcopyrite mineralization in some deposits (Beane, 1983), was interpreted by some to indicate that meteoric water is somehow essential for porphyry ore formation.

The results of isotopic studies in the 1970s led to the recognition that meteoric water plays a large role in the integrated history of porphyry deposits. Taylor (1974, reiterated in 1997) stressed that the dominance of meteoric convection around intrusions must in some way control ore formation. This was supported by the calculations of Norton (1982) and coworkers, who focused on the huge meteoric water convection cells that develop as a result of shallow intrusion of magmas. In conjunction with the stable isotopic data, Beane (1983) and his coworkers (Bodnar and Beane, 1980; Reynolds and Beane, 1985) integrated fluid inclusion data with their observations that higher-grade ore is typically not associated with early saline fluids ("magmatic"), but with the later lower salinity solutions (then thought to be "meteoric" in origin). Henley and McNabb (1978) recognized that the hypersaline liquid and vapor in porphyry deposits have a coupled origin, deriving from a supercritical magmatic fluid. However, even they argued that it was the interaction between the magmatic plume and meteoric water that was the primary cause of Cu mineralization.

Thus, the 1980s began and ended with the strong belief among many workers that, despite an early magmatic fluid being present in porphyry systems, and possibly associated with mineralization where ore occurred with potassic alteration, much of the ore in porphyry deposits was remobilized by, or at least precipitated through, interaction with meteoric water. The dominant thinking was summarized by Taylor (1974), who considered the intrusion to be a "heat engine," with a "negligible" amount of magmatic fluid relative to convected meteoric water. Although the volume consideration is true—intrusions can circulate 20 times more meteoric water than they can possibly exsolve as magmatic fluid (Norton, 1982)—the fundamental question is whether or not the negligible magmatic water component is in fact responsible for introducing most of the metals into the hydrothermal system.

Hedenquist et al. (1998) studied the Far Southeast (FSE) porphyry and associated Lepanto high-sulfidation epithermal system in the Philippines. The single intrusive event resulted in a lack of complicated overprinting relationships. Based on identical radiometric ages (Arribas et al., 1995; see below) and stable isotope constraints, formation of the potassic and advanced argillic alteration appears to be coupled, and related to the unmixed hypersaline liquid and vapor phases, respectively. The magmatic end-members of the two fluids responsible for the biotite (potassic) and alunite (advanced argillic) alteration have similar $\delta^{18}O$ values (5–6‰), but the latter fluid is about 20 per mil higher in δD (Fig. 7). This is consistent with the 20 per mil hydrogen isotope fractionation expected between vapor and hypersaline liquid (Horita et al., 1995), whereas the $\delta^{18}O$ difference is at most 1 per mil.

As with the deposits reviewed by Bodnar (1995), little Cu occurs with early potassic alteration at FSE, but instead mostly accompanies later euhedral quartz veins (D-type veins) with halos of sericitic alteration. The isotopic composition of the water that formed the sericite in the core of the FSE deposit (Fig. 7) indicates that this low-salinity fluid (~5 wt % NaCl equiv.) was dominantly magmatic in origin; meteoric water was restricted to the margins of the system, and to the latest, argillic stage of alteration (Hedenquist et al., 1998). And as noted above, sericitic alteration in many other porphyry deposits forms from fluids with a magmatic component typically exceeding 75 percent (Fig. 7). Earlier interpretations of a large meteoric component during the later stages of porphyry ore formation may have been influenced by the meteoric dominance during late argillic overprinting on the margins of the systems, and also to the argument that local meteoric water typically undergoes a large O-isotope shift to heavier values (Sheppard et al., 1971).

One argument for this late water being largely meteoric in origin hinged on its low salinity, with the assumption that a magmatic fluid must be hypersaline. However, Shinohara and Hedenquist (1997) considered this late fluid component to be important to the mineralization of the system, and therefore modeled the compositional evolution of a magmatic fluid during crystallization of a magma chamber. They found that a magmatic fluid will exsolve from convecting magma (beneath FSE at 6 km paleodepth, 1.5 kbar) and will advect in a high-temperature plume during the first 10 to 20 percent of magma crystallization after volatile saturation (<3,000 years). The initial plume of fluid separates to hypersaline liquid and vapor (Fig. 9), forming potassic and advanced argillic alteration, respectively. Subsequently, the magma chamber becomes stagnant and crystallizes within 30,000 years, during which time the magmatic fluid discharges at a lower flux. This lower flux results in the ascending fluid cooling to lower temperatures along a P-T path that never intersects its solvus (Fig. 9), and thus retains the low bulk salinity of the original magmatic fluid. Such a model allows for the late, low-salinity fluid associated with sericitic alteration to be magmatic in origin, consistent with the isotopic data. This fluid will also cause strong K-metasomatism as it cools, with the result being the pervasive sericitic alteration seen in many porphyry deposits. Being a bulk magmatic fluid, it is also likely to carry a significant concentration of metals. Thus, where mineralization is observed to be associated with sericitic alteration (Beane, 1983), the fluid (and metal) source may yet have been magmatic(Hedenquist and Shinohara, 1997), as argued for other magmatic hydrothermal systems such as skarns (e.g., Meinert et al., 1997).

The involvement of magmatic water in the alteration and mineralization of high-sulfidation epithermal deposits has been emphasized in reviews by Rye et al. (1992) and Arribas (1995). The leached host rock that is typical of high-sulfidation epithermal deposits shares the same geochemical environment with that of the advanced argillically altered lithocaps of porphyry Cu deposits. Not surprisingly, the mineralogic and isotopic characteristics of alteration in high-sulfidation ore deposits (with or without an associated porphyry ore deposit) and porphyry

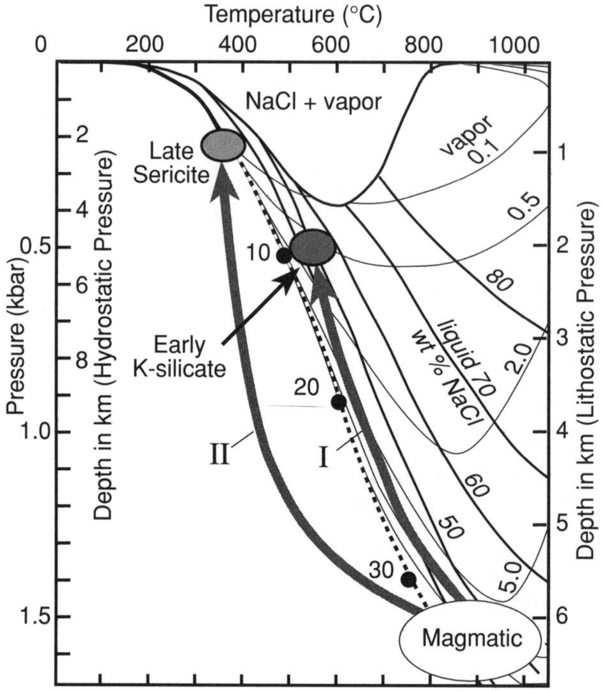

FIG. 9. P-T-X diagram for the system water-NaCl (modified from Fournier, 1987), showing two possible pathways of ascent of magmatic fluid. Soon after saturation of a melt, rapid ascent of fluid along path I results in intersection of the solvus and separation into hypersaline liquid and low-salinity vapor. Later fluids may be exsolved at a slower rate, such that they cool more extensively during ascent and do not intersect the solvus, as shown in path II (Shinohara and Hedenquist, 1997). In this way, water responsible for sericite alteration may have a relatively low salinity yet still be magmatic in origin (i.e., it reflects the bulk composition of exsolved fluid; Hedenquist et al., 1998).

lithocaps is similar. For this reason, Hedenquist et al. (1998) argued that the spatial and temporal association between the FSE porphyry and the Lepanto high-sulfidation epithermal ore deposits reflects a genetic association (cf. Sillitoe, 1983).

Radiogenic and Other Isotopic Studies: Sources of Solutes

Despite the clear spatial relationship between mineralization and porphyritic intrusive rocks, and the evidence presented above for the involvement of at least a component of magmatic-hydrothermal fluid in ore deposition, debates raged throughout the 1970s and into the 1980s regarding the source of metals in these deposits (Titley and Beane, 1981). Two strongly opposed camps were established, one favoring derivation of the major ore-forming components from the magmas themselves, and the other seeing the intrusions simply as a heat source, with convectively circulating, externally derived fluids leaching metals from the country rocks. In order to address this question, detailed studies of the isotopic compositions of S, Pb, Sr, Nd, and more recently, Os, have been conducted with a view to identifying the sources of these components, and by inference, the sources of Cu and other ore metals.

Sources of Sulfur

Porphyry Cu deposits, more than anything else, are giant S anomalies, and the source of this S should therefore tell us much about the overall mass balance and behavior of the system. Sulfur isotopes also have the potential to provide information about the oxidation state of the system, because the transition between the stable S^{6+} (sulfate) and S^{2-} (sulfide) states occurs under conditions common to many hydrothermal ore deposits.

Early studies of the S isotope compositions of ore and gangue minerals from porphyry deposits revealed quite homogeneous values, near 0 per mil for sulfides (e.g., Bingham sulfides: $\delta^{34}S = -0.6 \pm 1.5‰$), and higher values for sulfate minerals (Jensen, 1967). These data were interpreted to reflect a mantle source for the sulfur, with deposition from a well-mixed magmatic-hydrothermal fluid.

Sakai (1968), Ohmoto (1972, 1986), and Ohmoto and Rye (1979) provided a rigorous theoretical basis for the interpretation of sulfur isotope fractionation under conditions in which temperature, pH, and redox state could be variables. Because of this relatively large number of independent variables that can affect fractionation, a corresponding number of constraints must be known before unique interpretations of sulfur isotope data can be formulated.

Ohmoto and Rye (1979) showed that the average S isotope composition of primary magmatic sulfides in mantle-derived igneous rocks was 0 ± 3 per mil, thus providing a useful initial constraint. The compositions of sulfur species separating from magmas in a hydrothermal fluid can deviate significantly from this value, however, depending on the oxidation state (SO_2/H_2S ratio), temperature, and fluid/magma ratio. Fluids separating from basaltic magmas tend to be H_2S-rich, whereas those from granites can be either H_2S- or SO_2-rich, depending on their oxidation state (Fig. 10). The general association of porphyry Cu deposits with relatively oxidized magnetite-series (I-type) granitoids means that the derived fluids will tend to be enriched in ^{34}S, leading to $\delta^{34}S$ values up to 4 per mil higher than the source magma (e.g., compositions up to 7‰; Fig. 10). Note, however, that this is the bulk composition of S in the fluid; because of the relatively oxidizing conditions, much of this sulfur will be present as sulfate, with an isotopic composition close to this bulk value. In contrast, any sulfide minerals deposited from this fluid will have lower $\delta^{34}S$ values because of the fractionation between sulfide and sulfate S. Thus, Ohmoto and Rye (1979) deduced from S isotope compositions of sulfides (–3 to +1‰) and sulfates (8–15‰) in porphyry Cu deposits from the American Cordillera that these minerals were deposited from fluids carrying S of predominantly magmatic origin with compositions between –3 and +9 per mil.

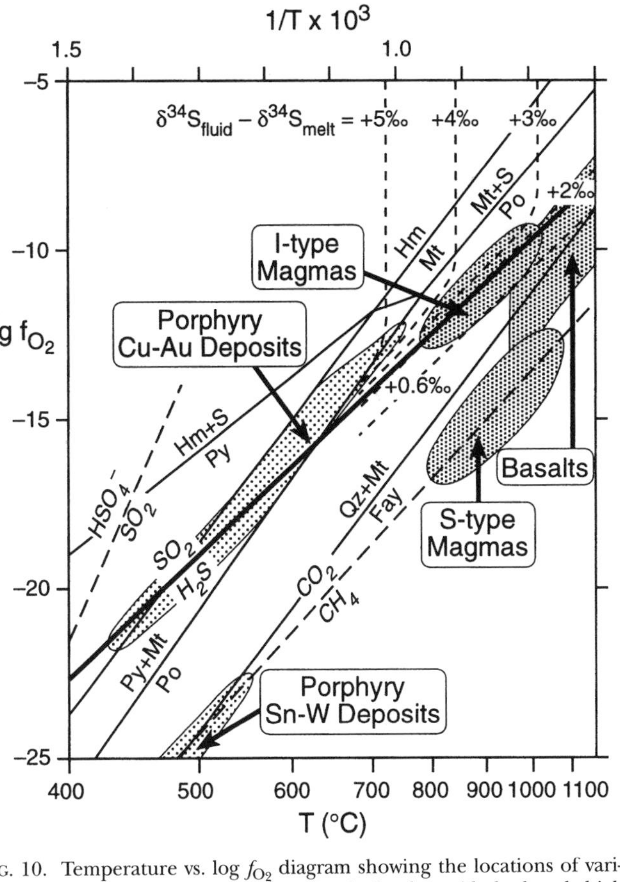

FIG. 10. Temperature vs. log f_{O_2} diagram showing the locations of various solid-phase (thin solid lines) and volatile-phase (dashed and thick solid lines) buffer reactions relative to the fields of formation of various magmas and magmatic-hydrothermal ore deposits. Also shown are contours for the fractionation of sulfur between a magmatic-hydrothermal fluid and its source magma (thin dashed lines). In oxidized systems near the wet granite solidus, total sulfur in the fluid phase can be 4 to 5‰ enriched relative to the magma. Modified after Ohmoto and Rye (1979) and Ohmoto (1986). Abbreviations: Fay = fayalite; Hm = hematite; Mt = magnetite; Po = pyrrhotite; Py = pyrite; Qz = quartz.

Sasaki et al. (1984) and Ishihara and Sasaki (1989) reported sulfur isotope compositions of sulfides from porphyry Cu deposits and whole-rocks from magnetite-series granitoids from Chile, the Philippines, and the Sierra Nevada Batholith that support Ohmoto and Rye's (1979) interpretations. Sasaki et al. (1984) expected that the whole rock sulfur would approximate the total magmatic sulfur. Based on this assumption, they found that the magmatic sulfur was consistently enriched in ^{34}S (Chile: $\delta^{34}S$ = 2.2–9.1‰; Philippines: $\delta^{34}S$ = 8.2–9.5‰; Sierra Nevada Batholith: $\delta^{34}S$ = 1.6–4.0‰), whereas associated sulfide ores were depleted (Chile: $\delta^{34}S$ = –4.7 to –1.3‰; Philippines: $\delta^{34}S$ = –3.7 to +5.0‰). Furthermore, Ishihara and Sasaki (1989) showed that magmatic sulfur in reduced ilmenite-series (S-type) granitoids was uniformly depleted ($\delta^{34}S$ = –5.3 to –3.7‰), suggesting a sedimentary sulfide component in the source region of these magmas.

Thus, magnetite-bearing magmas associated with Cu porphyries have mineral assemblages indicating redox conditions close to those of the SO_2-H_2S buffer, whereas Sn-W deposits and their associated ilmenite-bearing magmas are more reduced (Fig. 10). This contrast between oxidized and reduced magmas, their interaction with crustal rocks, and the distinctly different mineralization that they form, highlights a fundamental problem in metallogenesis and magmatism, and the need for integrated studies to determine the crustal-scale processes that can produce such an outwardly simple but nevertheless important and not fully understood metallogenic differentiation (cf. Barton, 1996).

Sources of Sr and Nd

Radiogenic isotopes have been used for many decades to identify the sources of igneous rocks, and these tracers have also been applied to the host intrusions of porphyry Cu deposits in order to see if such magmas were in some way compositionally distinct (see Chap. 9). Kesler et al. (1975) and Titley and Beane (1981) studied the initial Sr isotope compositions of island arc and continental arc porphyry Cu systems, and found that the island arc rocks displayed consistently low ratios ($^{87}Sr/^{86}Sr < 0.705$) whereas the continental rocks ranged up to 0.709. Kesler et al. (1975) interpreted these data as indicating a depleted mantle source for the island arc magmas, with little upper crustal involvement. Moreover, they argued that these data precluded an essential crustal source for Cu in porphyry deposits in general, because no crustal component was detectable in the island arc systems.

Nevertheless, many continental porphyry systems display isotopic evidence for extensive involvement of crustal materials in magma genesis, and a crustal source for metals continued, and continues in some quarters today, to be argued (e.g., Titley, 1987; Anthony and Titley, 1988). Farmer and DePaolo (1984) investigated the initial Sr and Nd isotope compositions of metaluminous intrusions in southwestern United States, and found no systematic differences between barren and mineralized systems, suggesting that the magma source region was not a control on the formation of ore deposits. The isotopic compositions of the intrusions were dominated by the basement, but a small mantle component was also recognized. Farmer and DePaolo (1984) suggested that the Cu in these systems might be related to this mantle component, whereas a crustal source for Mo was suggested for the more felsic granitoids hosting Climax-type porphyry Mo deposits. Barton (1996) and Lang and Titley (1998) have recently revisited the question of the origin of ore-forming Laramide intrusions. Barton argued that in fact most of the Laramide intrusions in Arizona are related to porphyry-type mineralization, and that depth of erosion is the main factor controlling their barren or economic appearance. Lang and Titley concluded from Sr and Nd isotope data that Proterozoic lower crustal materials may have constituted an important source reservoir for magmagenesis, through assimilation and metasomatism. They noted little evidence for a major role for upper crustal materials, but due to the isotopic variability and heterogeneity of the rocks could not rule out a more primitive contribution, presumably from the mantle.

Sources of Pb

Lead isotopes have long been used as tracers in hydrothermal ore deposits because of the close chemical similarity between Pb and other ore metals such as Cu and Zn. The behavior of Pb in hydrothermal solutions closely mirrors that of the other base metals, preferentially dissolving as chloride complexes (see Chap. 2); thus, the source of Pb and its transport and depositional history should match these metals unless the hydrothermal fluids have encountered anomalously Pb-rich country rocks, or rocks from which Pb can be easily leached. A number of studies of Pb isotopes in porphyry Cu deposits are reviewed in Chapter 9, but despite the promise of the method, no unequivocal interpretation has been forthcoming. Several studies indicate a contribution from subducted pelagic sediment (e.g., McNutt et al., 1979; Sillitoe and Hart, 1984; Mukasa et al., 1990), but the overall isotopic compositions suggest a mixture of sources including subducted MORB and lower continental crust (e.g., Doe and Zartman, 1979), the proportions of components in the mix varying broadly with geographic location.

These studies are unanimous, however, in their conclusions that (1) upper crustal materials have contributed little to the isotopic make-up of porphyry systems, and (2) the isotopic compositions of ore leads are identical to those of the host intrusions (see also Hollister, 1975). If Pb can indeed be used as an analog for the behavior of Cu, then these conclusions place the source of the Cu in the lower continental crust or below, and argue against its derivation from externally circulating hydrothermal fluids in the upper crust.

A notable feature of the Pb isotope compositions of porphyry Cu deposits is their uniformity across a given district, a feature shared by many batholithic rocks. McCulloch and Woodhead (1993) concluded that the highly uniform Pb isotope compositions characteristic of the Bega and Berridale batholiths of southeastern Australia were generated by widespread isotopic homogenization prior to melting in the lower crust, through the deep circulation of chloride brines. This may not be a necessary process in the formation of porphyry Cu deposits, particularly in island arc environments, but it may help to explain the ambiguous, mixed isotopic signatures of many continental porphyry systems. This observation also supports the concept that porphyry systems developed in established continental arc settings are the products of a protracted history of magmatic refluxing and lower crustal interaction.

Sources of Os

Recent advances in the application of the Re-Os radiogenic isotope system (Stein et al., 1998) have enabled its use as a source tracer of metals in ore-forming systems (see Chap. 9). Freydier et al. (1997) applied this technique to the Andacollo and El Teniente porphyry Cu deposits in Chile and found that initial Os isotope compositions were homogeneous within the deposits and were relatively non-radiogenic (except for one very late stage pyrite sample). Re and Os fractionate in the same sense as Rb and Sr during magmatism, with Re and Rb becoming enriched in differentiated melts; aged crustal materials thus tend to display more radiogenic Os isotope compositions than the mantle. The data from the Chilean porphyries were therefore interpreted to indicate that (1) Os, and by analogy Cu, were derived from the host intrusions and not from local upper crustal country rocks, and (2) these intrusions were derived largely from the mantle (i.e., through subduction zone magmatism). These conclusions are in broad agreement with those obtained from studies of Sr, Nd, and Pb isotopes, noted above.

Geochronologic Studies: Timing of Ore Formation

Advances in the understanding of porphyry Cu formation have closely followed the availability of increasingly more accurate geochronologic methods. Key questions that were answered early were the broad temporal relationships between porphyry ores and the host intrusions, and the relationships between porphyry magmatism and regional plate tectonic processes. For example, Quirt et al. (1971) and Sillitoe (1977, 1981) used K-Ar dating to reveal the existence of several trench-parallel linear belts of coeval magmatism and porphyry mineralization in the Chilean and Argentine Andes. These observations were combined with a developing understanding of South American plate tectonic history to formulate a comprehensive metallogenic model, which is routinely used as a baseline for exploration work in this premier porphyry region (Sillitoe, 1988, 1992). Similarly, McDougall and colleagues systematically dated many of the large porphyry systems in the southwestern Pacific region, and showed that, although a protracted history of intrusive activity spanning up to 4 m.y. could be recognized in some systems (e.g., Frieda River, Papua New Guinea), hydrothermal alteration generally occurred within 0.3 m.y. of the age of the most closely associated intrusive phase (Page and McDougall, 1972a, b; Chivas and McDougall, 1978; Whalen et al., 1982). Similar work by Silberman (1983) established that most porphyry ore-forming systems have a lifetime of <1 m.y. Regardless of how short such a time span appears relative to the age of volcanic activity in an arc, effective ore-formation may nevertheless require multiple intrusive or magma-chamber recharge events, because a single unreplenished intrusion will typically crystallize and cool in <0.1 m.y. (Cathles, 1977).

The K-Ar and related $^{40}Ar/^{39}Ar$ methods are particularly well-suited to age studies in porphyry systems because of the common presence of K-rich primary igneous minerals (K-feldspar, biotite, and hornblende), and the high mobility of K during ore formation (manifested in the potassic, phyllic, and advanced argillic alteration zones). Thus, the same method can be used to date both the intrusive and hydrothermal events. A problem arises, however, in the high susceptibility of the K-Ar system to overprinting. More recent studies using the $^{40}Ar/^{39}Ar$ or U-Pb methods have shown that many of the earlier K-Ar dates need revision because of unrecognized Ar-loss or the presence of excess-^{40}Ar (e.g., Maksaev et al., 1988; see Chap. 9). These methods also offer the potential to resolve in fine detail the ages of individual intrusive or fluid events, although to date there are few examples where this has been achieved (e.g., Arribas et al., 1995; Cornejo et al., 1997; Marsh et al., 1997; Clark et al., 1998).

This failing is not so much a function of the methodology as of the inescapable fact that porphyries are large-scale evolving systems, in which fluid circulation and chemical and isotopic overprinting are inherent features, and which operated over a geologically significant time interval as a result of multiple intrusive phases. Precise temporal information relating to the coupled magmatic and hydrothermal evolution of porphyry systems might best be obtained, therefore, from smaller, perhaps subeconomic systems, where multiple stages of overprinting are less well developed.

One exception was a recent study at the Far Southeast (FSE) deposit in Luzon, Philippines (Arribas et al., 1995), the world's second highest grade porphyry Cu-Au deposit. Its young age (hosted by rocks with a 2 Ma age) and apparently simple intrusive history resulted in a simple chronologic development of alteration. The young age also means that careful K-Ar dating of pure mineral separates (biotite, alunite, and illite) resulted in typical 2σ errors of ±40,000 to 60,000 years (biotite, illite) to 60,000 to 100,000 years (alunite). Both the potassic and advanced argillic alteration events formed coevally, at 1.41 ±0.05 Ma (biotite; n = 6) and 1.42 ± 0.08 Ma (alunite; n = 5). Sericitic alteration halos around later, crosscutting quartz-sulfide veins associated with mineralization were dated at 1.30 ± 0.07 Ma (illite; n = 10). The stable isotopic composition of the sericitic alteration (Fig. 7) indicates that it formed from a magmatic fluid that was potentially derived from the same intrusion as that which formed the potassic and advanced argillic alteration. These results indicate a potassic-to-sericitic lifespan on the order of 0.1 m.y., consistent with the period required to crystallize a 100 km^3 parent intrusion (Shinohara and Hedenquist, 1997). This volume is comparable to the minimum volume of magma necessary to supply the total contained Cu to the ore deposit (Dilles and Proffett, 1995; Cline, 1995).

An alternative approach to dating the lifespan of hydrothermal alteration in porphyry deposits might be the use of robust geochronometers that date the age of ore minerals directly. McCandless and Ruiz (1993) demonstrated the effectiveness of the Re-Os method in the dating of molybdenite in porphyry deposits from the southwestern United States, and Freydier et al. (1997) used a Re-Os isochron method to obtain a very broad estimate for the age of pyrite from the Andacollo porphyry Cu deposit, Chile. Clearly, the full potential of this method has yet to be realized (see Chap. 9).

Physical and Chemical Modeling

Magmatic versus Meteoric Water, and the Sources of Metals: Swings of the Pendulum

Cathles (1977) modeled hydrothermal convection around an essentially "dry" intrusion, i.e., one that contributed no fluid to the hydrothermal system. This constraint reflected the belief at that time in the dominant role of meteoric water in the porphyry environment with respect to mineralization. Cathles noted that meteoric convection would take 5,000 years to become established around a moderate-size (~1 km half-thickness) intrusion, and would continue for ~50,000 years.

The commonly observed stable isotopic evidence for large amounts of meteoric water circulation in porphyry systems is the result of the collapse of the magmatic-hydrothermal system. For example, in considering the thermal history of a saturated pluton, Norton (1982) demonstrated that 95 percent of the fluid circulated in a typical intrusion-centered hydrothermal system over its lifetime will consist of meteoric (and/or formation) water, whereas <5 percent will be magmatic water. The latter exsolves during the early stage of hydrothermal activity, prior to complete crystallization of the intrusion (e.g., from a quartz monzonite with initially 4 wt % water in the melt). By contrast, meteoric water continues to circulate around the heat anomaly for a much longer period, thus resulting in widespread overprinting of magmatic isotopic and mineralogic signatures. Although Norton (1982) did not explicitly state that all metals in porphyry deposits are derived from wall-rock leaching (cf. Bodnar, 1995), the results of his modeling strongly implied this. As a consequence, this study influenced the development of several exploration models that acknowledged the existence but discounted the importance of a magmatic fluid plume during the first 10 to 20,000 years of the life of the hydrothermal system. Instead, they predicted that the focus of ore-forming activity should be on the much longer-lived meteoric convection cell.

Burnham (1967, 1979) concluded that once a shallow magmatic intrusion reached saturation by crystallization, the exsolving fluid would generate a pressure sufficient to cause fracturing. Similarly, Fournier (1991) noted that rocks at >400°C are quasi-ductile, and will fracture only at high strain rates (e.g., during fluid exsolution, when wavy discontinuous A veins may form and trap early hypersaline liquid plus vapor). The fractures will not stay open to allow incursion of meteoric water at this early stage (cf. Norton, 1982, who argued for brittleness and meteoric water penetration to 700°C). Fournier (1983, 1987) believed that mixing between hypersaline brine and meteoric water is unlikely, due to density differences, and this is supported by the bimodal distribution of salinities in porphyry systems (>40 wt % and <10 wt % NaCl equiv.; Beane, 1983). The high salinity fluid in porphyry deposits is invariably associated with the early potassic alteration, whereas the lower salinity fluid is responsible for the later, lower-temperature phyllic alteration.

Bodnar (1995) summarized in a short, elegant paper the fluid inclusion evidence for a magmatic source of metals in porphyry deposits. He noted evidence for high metal concentrations in hypersaline liquids associated with barren potassic alteration, concluding that the high metal solubility in these fluids was not conducive to ore deposition. But we are left with the question about where this early hypersaline liquid goes, and what happens to its metal content. Conversely, in the same deposits, synchrotron XRF data indicated low metal concentrations in lower temperature, lower salinity fluid inclusions associated with sericitic alteration and chalcopyrite deposition. Bodnar concluded that the metal concentrations were low because the metal complement had precipitated during mixing between the saline ore fluid and meteoric waters to form this lower salinity, low-metal-content hybrid fluid. It is logical that the residual fluid, after mineralization, should have a low metal content. However, the process of metal deposition is still in question. Hedenquist et al. (1998) argued that the late, low-salinity liquid reflects the bulk magmatic fluid composition, and is not a product of dilution. If so, processes other than dilution must be invoked to account for mineralization (e.g., boiling).

Recently, new microanalytical techniques (PIXE and synchrotron XRF analysis) have provided evidence that significant concentrations of metals, including Cu, are present in vapor-rich fluid inclusions accompanying early hypersaline liquid inclusions from porphyry deposits. Heinrich et al. (1992) found high Cu in vapor-rich inclusions from Sn-W granites in Australia, and Bodnar (1996) reported preliminary data indicating high Cu in similar inclusions in porphyry Cu deposits. If these findings are confirmed, then we need to reexamine our assumptions about Cu complexes in the porphyry environment, because it is clear that Cu can be transported by the high-pressure, low salinity vapor. This indication is consistent with Cu concentrations of 50 mg/kg or more in vapor associated with quiescent eruption of volcanoes (Hedenquist, 1995), vapor that contains at most a few tenths of a percent of NaCl (see below).

Experimental Constraints

Cline and Bodnar (1991), updated by Shinohara (1994) and Cline (1995), extended the earlier advances by Burnham (1967, 1979) and coworkers on volatile saturation in magmas, the nature of the exsolved fluid, and its effects on the physical properties of the system. Lowenstern (1995) summarized data on the melt and fluid compositions of water-saturated magmas, and showed that the melts typically contain 5 wt percent water or more at saturation, consistent with Burnham's (1979) conclusion that there is typically up to 5 wt percent water in silicic magmas (cf. 1960s papers that refer to dry systems, with estimates of only 1–2 wt % water in magmas). The bulk salinity of the exsolved fluid can range widely depending on a variety of factors, particularly pressure; available data suggest a range of 2 to 10 wt percent NaCl equivalent (Hedenquist et al., 1998). Although lower and higher salinities are possible, Burnham's estimate of about 6 wt percent NaCl appears typical, if it is possible to typify such a complex environment.

Initial work on metal partitioning in magmatic systems (Whitney, 1975) has been greatly extended by Candela (1989) and his colleagues (Chap. 4). For example, Williams et al. (1995) provided experimental data on metal partitioning from silicate melt to brine and vapor, the type of system that likely approaches reality in at least part of the lifespan of porphyry deposits. They showed that fractionation of metals from melt to aqueous fluid is a strong function of pressure, with partitioning being 20 times more favorable at 1 kbar than at 0.5 kbar. Pressure can have a similarly important, but opposite, effect in determining metal solubilities in aqueous fluid at high temperatures: for example, rock-buffered metal solubilities tend to increase with decreasing pressure (Hemley et al., 1992).

The experimental results concerning melt–fluid and vapor–brine fractionation of metals are supported by observations on the metal concentrations associated with low- and high-pressure volcanic discharges (Hedenquist, 1995). Samples of low-pressure volcanic vapors are greatly depleted in NaCl and metals compared with fluid exsolved at high pressure from a magma (Fig. 2), indicating that as the pressure decreases, NaCl and metals are sequestered in condensed brines beneath active volcanoes, and typically do not reach the surface.

As noted above, the redox state of hydrothermal systems deduced for porphyry Cu-Au deposits (Burnham and Ohmoto, 1980; Figs. 5 and 10) corresponds to that of the relatively oxidized SO_2-H_2S gas buffer, which is also the buffer that controls the redox state of high-temperature volcanic vapors and acidic crater lakes. There thus appears to be a geochemical continuum in fluid compositions controlled by this buffer, albeit stepped in some cases, from magmatic emanations right through to surface discharges, with porphyry (and some epithermal) deposits forming along this pathway (Fig. 5).

Summary

Not all porphyry Cu deposits are the same, and no single model of a typical deposit, or of a magma associated with ore, is generally applicable. The porphyry deposits of southwestern United States, Canada, South America, southwestern Pacific, eastern Europe, and central Asia record variations in tectonic and structural setting, magma chemistry, intrusive depth and timing of saturation, hydrologic setting, etc. The effects of most of these variations on the nature of the resulting porphyry deposits are subtle, however, and even the variations in metal inventory (e.g., Cu/Au) that are so important to mineral economics are merely fluctuations within a geochemical range. Thus, there do appear to be some strong, repeatable themes within this spectrum of deposits.

The timing of metal deposition with respect to hydrothermal evolution varies amongst porphyry deposits. For example, it is early at Bingham and Yerington, associated with high-temperature potassic alteration and A-type veins; intermediate at El Salvador; and largely late at Santa Rita, Morenci, and FSE, associated with phyllic alteration and D-type veins with sericitic halos. This variation in timing of mineralization may be controlled by processes acting within the hydrothermal environment (Bodnar, 1995), and/or it may be a function of magma composition and the timing of metal exsolution, the latter also a function of pressure and depth of magma emplacement (Cline, 1995). Meteoric water is the major source of fluid integrated over the life of the hydrothermal system, and it interacts with magmatic fluid to varying degrees at the margins of the magmatic plume during the later phyllic stage. Meteoric water subsequently overprints the system after the collapse of the magmatic plume, contributing to the formation of argillic alteration. Later advanced argillic alteration can also be generated by steam-heated waters in the vadose zone, distinct from hypogene advanced argillic alteration that starts to form at the same time as potassic alteration. Thus, the meteoric-water convection cell is intimately coupled to the behavior of the magmatic-hydrothermal system, but our present understanding suggests that the role of meteoric water in the ore-forming process is largely passive rather than active.

Despite the analytical advances in the past three to four decades, and our improved understanding of some of the details regarding the origin of porphyry Cu deposits, it is likely that in just another decade or so we will look back at our late 1990s knowledge as being somewhat limited—assuming, of course, that field studies of porphyry deposits continue, hand-in-hand with analytical advances and experimental studies.

Future Directions

Hunt (1991, p. 202) lamented what he termed the present "box of rocks" approach to conducting research on ore deposits, bereft of detailed mapping and field constraints. He noted that one cause of this situation is the lack of funding for basic mapping and field-related study, and he encouraged broad-based cooperative efforts by industry, universities, and government agencies.

Within the framework of detailed field studies, there are a variety of geochemical projects that have the potential to improve our understanding of how and why porphyry deposits form, and in particular, the relationship of mineralization to magmatic evolution.

Continued detailed field studies of porphyry deposits and barren intrusive systems are essential, including careful paragenetic determinations of alteration and mineralization events in the ore deposits and petrologic study of ore-related and barren intrusions. Advances in radiometric dating now provide the opportunity to determine the ages of individual magmatic and ore-forming events within larger systems. Despite the many published studies of porphyry deposits, there is a surprising lack of critical observations on the timing of sulfide mineralization during porphyry evolution.

Collaborative efforts may be necessary to secure funding, and to undertake multidisciplinary studies. A downside to large projects, however, may be the tendency to omit detailed mapping and other fieldwork, due to time constraints and the pressure to publish to satisfy funding organizations, and also the inertia that does not allow new, unexpected results to be followed up on a tangent from the original project design.

Advances in microanalytical technology now mean that the evolution of hydrothermal systems can be traced by studying the detailed chemical and isotopic zonation of minerals and their fluid inclusions. Laser probe and ion probe study of isotopic and chemical variations throughout the history of porphyry systems will continue to strengthen our understanding of how these systems evolve and perhaps cycle (i.e., are magmatic fluids contributed in pulses?). Microbeam studies of the volatile and metal contents of melt inclusions, coupled with geological study of intrusive events in mineralized and barren systems, will help to link evolution of the magmatic system to the generation of a hydrothermal fluid. In turn, ICP-MS and synchrotron XRF study of metals in inclusion fluids, combined with the other microbeam approaches mentioned above, will allow the metal evolution of the system to be traced, albeit in some cases after a fluid has precipitated much of its metal content.

Experimental studies of melt-fluid fractionation (e.g., Williams et al., 1995) will provide modelers with the ability to predict under what conditions a magma will sequester, or exsolve, metals. Modeling of the crystallization history of magmas and associated magmatic-hydrothermal systems will help to identify questions that can be answered through the integration of geologic context with details of advanced analytical and experimental constraints. Perhaps surprisingly, the solubility behavior of Cu-chloride complexes is still not well understood (Chap. 2), and further solubility and speciation experiments are required before this important variable can be properly constrained in hydrothermal models (e.g., Hemley et al., 1992). Such information will assist in determining the transport and depositional controls for ore metals (Hemley and Hunt, 1992), and will eventually lead to the ability to model such results in terms of, for example, the role of metal concentration, total sulfur activity and the effects of oxidation state, the evolution of pH and its effects on mineral stability, etc. (Woitsekhowskaya and Hemley, 1995). Nevertheless, the results of analytical, experimental, and modeling studies will only be as good as the basic geological mapping and field constraints that underpin them (Shinohara, 1998).

"These questions can be answered only in part, for of what is sometimes referred to as our 'knowledge' of ore deposition a much larger proportion than some geologists seem willing to admit is more safely to be regarded as speculation than as established truth." (Ransome, 1919, p. 166)

Epilogue: Ore Deposits, Fluids, and Crustal Processes

Porphyry deposits form in volcanic arcs related to subduction. Many petrological studies (e.g., Plank and Langmuir, 1993; Ishikawa and Nakamura, 1994; Stolper and Newman, 1994; Noll et al., 1996) indicate a complex recycling of components, including volatiles and metals, from subducted oceanic crust and sediments back to the surface in association with arc magmas. Similar findings were made from the study of porphyry deposits beginning over a decade earlier (Doe and Zartman, 1979; McNutt et al., 1979; Sillitoe and Hart, 1984; Mukasa et al., 1990), and these deposits provide some of the best examples of this recycling. The combination of basic field observations and geochemical techniques applied to this major ore-deposit type thus helps to elucidate the crustal and deeper processes that control the distribution of elements in the Earth.

"In one aspect the science of mineral deposits is frankly utilitarian, but from the viewpoint of pure knowledge it records the principles governing the cycles of concentrations of the elements. It traces the processes by which the primeval gases and magmas have become differentiated into the manifold complexity of the earth's crust." (Lindgren, 1933, p. 894.)

Acknowledgments

We thank Julian Hemley and Dick Sillitoe for comments on an early outline of this paper, Bob Tilling for use of his unpublished Boulder Batholith data plotted in Figure 8, Shinohara H. for discussions, and Antonio Arribas, Jr., Mark Barton, and Dick Sillitoe for helpful reviews of the manuscript. This review is dedicated to all the geologists and geochemists who have made observations and measurements crucial to elucidating the genesis of porphyry Cu deposits.

REFERENCES

Allen, E.T., and Day, A.L., 1935, Hot springs of the Yellowstone National Park: Washington, D.C., Carnegie Institute, 525 p.

Anderson, J.A., 1982, Characteristics of leached capping and techniques of appraisal, *in* Titley, S.R., ed., Advances in geology of porphyry copper deposits of southwestern North America: Tucson, University of Arizona Press, p. 275–295.

Anthony, E.Y., and Titley, S.R., 1988, Progressive mixing of isotopic reservoirs during magma genesis at the Sierrita porphyry copper deposit, Arizona: Inverse solutions: Geochimica et Cosmochimica Acta, v. 52, p. 2235–2249.

Arribas, A., Jr., 1995, Characteristics of high-sulfidation epithermal deposits, and their relation to magmatic fluid, *in* Thompson, J.F.H., ed., Magmas, fluids, and ore deposits: Mineralogical Association of Canada Short Course, v. 23, p. 419–454.

Arribas, A., Jr., Hedenquist, J.W., Itaya, T., Okada, T., Concepción, R.A., and Garcia, J.S., Jr., 1995, Contemporaneous formation of adjacent porphyry and epithermal Cu-Au deposits over 300 ka in northern Luzon, Philippines: Geology, v. 23, p. 337–340.

Barnes, H.L., ed., 1967, Geochemistry of hydrothermal ore deposits: New York, Holt, Rinehart and Winston, 670 p.

Barton, M.D., 1996, Granitic magmatism and metallogeny of southwestern North America: Geological Society of America, Special Paper 315, p. 261–280.

Barton, P.B., Jr., 1959, The chemical environment of ore deposition and the problem of low-temperature ore transport, *in* Abelson, P.H., ed., Researches in geochemistry: New York, Wiley, p. 279–300.

Barton, P.B., Jr., and Skinner, B.J., 1967, Sulfide mineral stabilities, *in* Barnes, H.L., ed., Geochemistry of hydrothermal ore deposits: New York, Holt, Rinehart and Winston, p. 236–333.

—— 1979, Sulfide mineral stabilities, *in* Barnes, H.L., ed., Geochemistry of hydrothermal ore deposits, 2nd edition: New York, John Wiley, p. 278–403.

Bateman, A.M., 1950, Economic mineral deposits: New York, John Wiley, 916 p.

Beane, R.E., 1983, The magmatic–meteoric transition: Geothermal Resources Council, Special Report 13, p. 245–253.

Beane, R.E., and Titley, S.R., 1981, Porphyry copper deposits. Part II. Hydrothermal alteration and mineralization: Economic Geology, 75th Anniversary Volume, p. 235–263.

Bodnar, R.J., 1995, Fluid-inclusion evidence for a magmatic source of metals in porphyry copper deposit, *in* Thompson, J.F.H., ed., Magmas, fluids, and ore deposits: Mineralogical Association of Canada Short Course, v. 23, p. 139–152.

—— 1996, Fluid inclusion evidence for the source of metals in porphyry deposits and epithermal precious metal systems [abs.]: Geological Society of America, Abstracts with Programs, v. 28, A–402.

Bodnar, R.J., and Beane, R.E., 1980, Temporal and spatial variations in hydrothermal fluid characteristics during vein filling in preore cover overlying deeply buried porphyry copper-type mineralization at Red Mountain, Arizona: Economic Geology, v. 75, p. 876–893.

Bodnar, R.J., and Sterner, S.M., 1987, Synthetic fluid inclusions, *in* Ulmer, G.C., and Barnes, H.L., eds., Hydrothermal experimental techniques: New York, Wiley Interscience, p. 423–457.

Bodnar, R.J., Burnham, C.W., and Sterner, S.M., 1985, Synthetic fluid inclusions in natural quartz. III. Determination of phase equilibrium properties in the system H_2O-NaCl to 1000°C and 1500 bars: Geochimica et Cosmochimica Acta, v. 49, p. 1861–1873.

Bowen, N.L., 1933, The broader story of magmatic differentiation, briefly told, *in* Ore deposits of the Western States (Lindgren volume): American Institute of Mining and Metallurgical Engineers, p. 106–128.

Bowman, J.R., Parry, W.T., Kropp, W.P., and Kruer, S.A., 1987, Chemical and isotopic evolution of hydrothermal solutions at Bingham, Utah: Economic Geology, v. 82, p. 395–428.

Brimhall, G. H, Jr., 1980, Deep hypogene oxidation of porphyry copper potassium-silicate protore at Butte, Montana, a theoretical evaluation of the copper remobilization hypothesis: Economic Geology, v. 75, p. 384–409.

Burnham, C.W., 1967, Hydrothermal fluids at the magmatic stage, *in* Barnes, H.L., ed., Geochemistry of hydrothermal ore deposits: New York, Holt, Rinehart and Winston, p. 34–76.

—— 1979, Magmas and hydrothermal fluids, *in* Barnes, H.L., ed., Geochemistry of hydrothermal ore deposits, 2nd edition: New York, John Wiley, p. 71–136.

Burnham, C.W., and Jahns, R.H., 1962, A method for determining the solubility of water in silicate melts: American Journal of Science, v. 260, p. 721–745.

Burnham, C.W., and Ohmoto, H., 1980, Late-stage processes in felsic magmatism: Mining Geology Special Issue, No. 8, p. 1–11.

Candela, P.A., 1989, Magmatic ore-forming fluids: thermodynamic and mass transfer calculations of metal concentrations: Reviews in Economic Geology, v. 4, p. 223–233.

Carten, R.B., White, W.H., and Stein, H.J., 1993, High-grade granite-related molybdenum systems: Geological Association of Canada, Special Paper 40, p. 521–554.

Cathles, L.M., II, 1977, An analysis of the cooling of intrusives by groundwater convection that includes boiling: Economic Geology, v. 72, p. 804–826.

Chivas, A.R., and McDougall, I., 1978, Geochronology of the Koloula porphyry copper prospect, Guadalcanal, Solomon Islands: Economic Geology, v. 73, p. 678–679.

Clark, A.H., Archibald, D.A., Lee, A.W., Farrar, E., and Hodgson, C.J., 1998, Laser-probe ^{40}Ar-^{39}Ar ages of early- and late-stage alteration assemblages, Rosario porphyry copper-molybdenum deposit, Collahuasi district, I Region, Chile: Economic Geology, v. 93, in press.

Cline, J.S., 1995, Genesis of porphyry copper deposits: the behavior of water, chloride, and copper in crystallizing melts, *in* Pierce, F.W., and Bolm, J.G., eds., Porphyry copper deposits of the American Cordillera: Arizona Geological Society Digest, v. 20, p. 69–82.

Cline, J.S., and Bodnar, R.J., 1991, Can economic porphyry copper mineralization be generated by a typical calc-alkaline melt?: Journal of Geophysical Research, v. 96, p. 8113–8126.

Cline, J.S., and Vanko, D.A., 1995, Magmatically generated saline brines related to molybdenum at Questa, New Mexico, *in* Thompson, J.F.H., ed., Magmas, fluids, and ore deposits: Mineralogical Association of Canada Short Course, v. 23, p. 153–174.

Cornejo, P., Tosdal, R.M., Mpodozis, C., Tomlinson, A.J., Rivera, O., and Fanning, C.M., 1997, El Salvador, Chile porphyry copper deposit revisited: geologic and geochronologic framework: International Geology Review, v. 39, p. 22–54.

Craig, H., Boato, G., and White, D.E., 1956, The isotopic geochemistry of thermal waters: National Research Council Nuclear Sciences Series, Report 19, p. 29–44.

Creasey, S.C., 1966, Hydrothermal alteration, *in* Titley, S.R., and Hicks, C.L., eds., Geology of the porphyry copper deposits—southwestern North America: Tucson, University of Arizona Press, p. 51–74.

Dilles, J.H., 1987, Petrology of the Yerington batholith, Nevada: Evidence for evolution of porphyry copper ore fluids: Economic Geology, v. 82, p. 1750–1789.

Dilles, J.H., and Proffett, J.M, 1995, Metallogenesis of the Yerington batholith, Nevada, *in* Pierce, F.W., and Bolm, J.G., eds., Porphyry copper deposits of the American Cordillera: Arizona Geological Society Digest, v. 20, p. 306–315.

Dilles, J.H., Solomon, G.C., Taylor, H.P., Jr., and Einaudi, M.T., 1992, Oxygen and hydrogen isotope characteristics of hydrothermal alteration at the Ann-Mason porphyry copper deposit, Yerington, Nevada: Economic Geology, v. 87, p. 44–63.

Dobson, P.F., Epstein, S. and Stolper, E.M., 1989, Hydrogen isotope fractionation between coexisting vapor and silicate glasses and melts at low pressure: Geochimica et Cosmochimica Acta, v. 53, p. 2723–2730.

Doe, B.R., and Zartman, R.E., 1979, Plumbotectonics, the Phanerozoic, *in* Barnes, H.L., ed., Geochemistry of hydrothermal ore deposits, 2nd edition: New York, John Wiley, p. 22–70.

Eastoe, C.J., 1978, A fluid inclusion study of the Panguna porphyry copper deposit, Bougainville, Papua New Guinea: Economic Geology, v. 73, p. 721–748.

Einaudi, M.T., 1982, Description of skarns associated with porphyry copper plutons—southwestern North America, *in* Titley, S.R., ed., Advances in geology of the porphyry copper deposits—southwestern North America: Tucson, University of Arizona Press, p. 139–184.

Emmons, W.H., 1927, Relations of disseminated copper ores in porphyry to igneous intrusions: American Institute of Mining and Metallurgical Engineers, Transactions, v. 75, p. 797–809.

Eugster, H.P., 1985, Granites and hydrothermal ore deposits: A geochemical framework: Mineralogical Magazine, v. 49, p. 7–23.

Farmer, G.L., and DePaolo, D.J., 1984, Origin of Mesozoic and Tertiary granite in the western United States and implications for pre-Mesozoic crustal structure, 2. Nd and Sr isotopic studies of unmineralized and Cu- and Mo-mineralized granite in the Precambrian craton: Journal of Geophysical Research, v. 89, p. 10141–10160.

Fenner, C.N., 1933, Pneumatolytic processes in the formation of minerals and ores: Ore deposits of the Western States (Lindgren volume): American Institute of Mining and Metallurgical Engineers, p. 58–106.

Fournier, R.O., 1983, Active hydrothermal systems as analogues of fossil systems: Geothermal Resources Council, Special Report 13, p. 263–284.

—— 1987, Conceptual models of brine evolution in magmatic-hydrothermal systems, *in* Decker, R.W., Wright, T.L., and Stauffer, P.H., eds., Volcanism in Hawaii: U.S. Geological Survey Professional Paper 1350, p. 1487–1506.

—— 1991, Transition from hydrostatic to greater than hydrostatic fluid pressure in presently active hydrothermal systems in crystalline rocks: Geophysical Research Letters, v. 18, p. 955–958.

Freydier, C., Ruiz, J., Chesley, J., McCandless, T., and Munizaga, F., 1997. Re-Os isotope systematics of sulfides from felsic igneous rocks: Application to base metal porphyry mineralization in Chile: Geology, v. 25, p. 775–778.

Garrels, R.M., and Christ, C.L., 1965, Solutions, minerals and equilibria: New York, Harper and Row, 450 p.

Giggenbach, W.F., 1984, Mass transfer in hydrothermal alteration systems: Geochimica et Cosmochimica Acta, v. 48, p. 2693–2711.

—— 1992a, Magma degassing and mineral deposition in hydrothermal systems along convergent plate boundaries: Economic Geology, v. 87, p. 1927–1944.

—— 1992b, Isotopic shifts in waters from geothermal and volcanic systems along convergent plate boundaries and their origin: Earth and Planetary Science Letters, v. 113, p. 495–510.

—— 1997, The origin and evolution of fluids in magmatic-hydrothermal systems, *in* Barnes, H.L., ed., Geochemistry of hydrothermal ore deposits, 3rd edition: New York, John Wiley, p. 737–796.

Gilluly, J., 1937, The water content of magmas: American Journal of Science, v. 33, p. 430–441.

—— 1946, The Ajo mining district: U.S. Geological Survey Professional Paper 209, 112 p.

Goranson, R.W., 1931, The solubility of water in granite magmas: American Journal of Science, v. 22, p. 481–502.

—— 1938, Silicate–water systems: phase equilibria in the $NaAlSi_3O_8$-H_2O and $KAlSi_3O_8$-H_2O systems at high temperatures and pressures: American Journal of Science, v. 35-A, p. 71–91.

Graton, L.C., 1940, Nature of the ore-forming fluid: Economic Geology, v. 35, supplement to no. 2, p. 197–358.

Graton, L.C., and Bowditch, S.I., 1936, Alkaline and acid solutions in hypogene zoning at Cerro de Pasco, Peru: Economic Geology, v. 31, p. 651–698.

Gustafson, L.B., 1978, Some major factors of porphyry copper genesis: Economic Geology, v. 73, p. 600–607.

Gustafson, L.B., and Hunt, J.P., 1975, The porphyry copper deposit at El Salvador, Chile: Economic Geology, v. 70, p. 857–912.

Gustafson, L.B., and Titley, S.R., 1978, Porphyry copper deposits of the southwestern Pacific islands and Australia: Preface: Economic Geology, v. 73, p. 597–599.

Hedenquist, J.W., 1995, The ascent of magmatic fluid: discharge versus mineralization, *in* Thompson, J.F.H., ed., Magmas, fluids, and ore deposits: Mineralogical Association of Canada Short Course, v. 23, p. 263–289.

Hedenquist J.W., and Shinohara, H., 1997, K-silicate to sericite-stage transition in porphyry Cu deposits: Collapse of magmatic plume, or overprint by meteoric water? [abs.]: Geological Society of America, Abstracts with Programs, v. 29, A–359.

Hedenquist, J.W., Arribas, A., Jr., and Reynolds, J.R., 1998, Evolution of an intrusion-centered hydrothermal system: Far Southeast–Lepanto porphyry and epithermal Cu-Au deposits, Philippines: Economic Geology, v. 93, p. 373–404.

Heinrich, C.A., 1990, The chemistry of tin (-tungsten) ore deposition: Economic Geology, v. 85, p. 457–481.

Heinrich, C.A., Ryan, G.G., Mernagh, T.P, and Eadington, P.J., 1992, Segregation of ore metals between magmatic brine and vapor—A fluid inclusion study using PIXE microanalysis: Economic Geology, v. 87, p. 1566–1583.

Hemley, J.J., 1959, Some mineralogical equilibria in the system K_2O-Al_2O_3-SiO_2-H_2O: American Journal of Science, v. 257, p. 241–270.

Hemley, J.J., and Hunt, J.P., 1992, Hydrothermal ore-forming processes in the light of studies in rock-buffered systems: II. Some general geologic applications: Economic Geology, v. 87, p. 23–43.

Hemley, J.J., and Jones, W.R., 1964, Chemical aspects of hydrothermal alteration with emphasis on hydrogen metasomatism: Economic Geology, v. 59, p. 538–569.

Hemley, J.J., Hostetler, P.B., Gude, A.J., and Mountjoy, W.T., 1969, Some stability relations of alunite: Economic Geology, v. 64, p. 599–612.

Hemley, J.J., Montoya, J.W., Marinenko, J.W., and Luce, R.W., 1980, Equilibria in the system Al_2O_3-SiO_2-H_2O and some general implications for alteration-mineralization processes: Economic Geology, v. 75, p. 210–218.

Hemley, J.J., Cygan, G.L., Fein, J.B., Robinson, G.R., and D'Angelo, W.M., 1992, Hydrothermal ore-forming processes in the light of studies in rock-buffered systems: I. Iron-copper-zinc-lead sulfide solubility relations: Economic Geology, v. 87, p. 1–22.

Henley, R.W., 1990, Ore transport and deposition in epithermal ore environments, *in* Herbert, H.K., and Ho, S.E., eds., Stable isotopes and fluid processes in mineralization: Perth, University of Western Australia, Geology Department Publication 23, p. 51–69.

Henley, R.W., and McNabb, A., 1978, Magmatic vapor plumes and ground-water interaction in porphyry copper emplacement: Economic Geology, v. 73, p. 1–20.

Holland, H.D., 1956, The chemical composition of vein minerals and the nature of ore forming fluids: Economic Geology, v. 51, p. 781–797.

Hollister, V.F., 1975, An appraisal of the nature and source of porphyry copper deposits: Minerals Science and Engineering, v. 7, p. 225–233.

Horita, J., Cole, D.R., and Weslowski, D.J., 1995, The activity-composition relationship of oxygen and hydrogen isotopes in aqueous salt solutions: III. Vapor-liquid water equilibration of NaCl solutions to 350°C: Geochimica et Cosmochimica Acta, v. 59, p. 1139–1151.

Hunt, J.P., 1991, Porphyry copper deposits: Economic Geology Monograph 8, p. 192–206.

Ingerson, E., 1955, Methods and problems of geologic thermometry: Economic Geology 50th Anniversary Volume, part I, p. 341–410.

Ishihara, S., 1981, The granitoid series and mineralization: Economic Geology 75th Anniversary Volume, p. 458–484.

Ishihara, S., and Sasaki, A., 1989, Sulfur isotopic ratios of the magnetite-series and ilmenite-series granitoids of the Sierra Nevada batholith—a reconnaissance study: Geology, v. 17, p. 788–791.

Ishikawa, T., and Nakamura, E., 1994, Origin of the slab component in arc lavas from across-arc variation of B and Pb isotopes: Nature, v. 370, p. 205–208.

Jensen, M.L., 1967, Sulfur isotopes and mineral genesis, *in* Barnes, H.L., ed., Geochemistry of hydrothermal ore deposits: New York, Holt, Rinehart and Winston, p. 143–165.

Jerome, S.E., 1966, Some features pertinent in exploration of porphyry copper deposits, *in* Titley, S.R., and Hicks, C.L., eds., Geology of the porphyry copper deposits, southwestern North America: Tucson, University of Arizona Press, p. 75–86.

Kennedy, G.C., 1950, Pressure-volume-temperature relations in water at elevated temperatures and pressures: American Journal of Science, v. 248, p. 540–564.

Kesler, S.E., 1973, Copper, molybdenum and gold abundances in porphyry copper deposits: Economic Geology, v. 68, p. 106–112.

Kesler, S.E., Jones, L.M., and Walker, R.L., 1975, Intrusive rocks associated with porphyry copper mineralization in island arc areas: Economic Geology, v. 70, p. 515–526.

Kirkham, R.V., 1971, Intermineral intrusions and their bearing on the origin of porphyry copper and molybdenum deposits: Economic Geology, v. 66, p. 1244–1249.

Kirkham, R.V., and Sinclair, W.D., 1996, Porphyry copper, gold, molybdenum, tungsten, tin, silver, *in* Eckstrand, O.R., Sinclair, W.D., and Thorpe, R.I., eds., Geology of Canadian mineral deposits: Geological Survey of Canada, Geology of Canada, no. 8, p. 421–446.

Kusakabe, M., Hori, M., and Matsuhisa, Y., 1990, Primary mineralization of the El Teniente and Rio Blanco porphyry copper deposits, Chile: Stable isotopes, fluid inclusions, and $Mg^{2+}/Fe^{2+}/Fe^{3+}$ ratios of hydrothermal biotite, *in* Herbert, H.K., and Ho, S.E., eds., Stable isotopes and fluid processes in mineralization: Perth, University of Western Australia, Geology Department Publication 23, p. 244–259.

Lang, J.R. and Titley, S.R., 1998, Isotopic and geochemical characteristics of Laramide magmatic systems in Arizona and implications for the genesis of porphyry copper deposits: Economic Geology, v. 93, p. 138–170.

Lindgren, W., 1905, The copper deposits of the Clifton-Morenci district, Arizona: U.S. Geological Survey Professional Paper 43, 375 p.

—— 1933, Mineral deposits, 4th edition: New York, McGraw-Hill, 930 p.

—— 1937, Succession of minerals and temperatures of formation in ore deposits of magmatic affiliation: American Institute of Mining and Metallurgical Engineers, Transactions, v. 126, p. 356–376.

Locke, A., 1926, Leached outcrops as guides to copper ore: Baltimore, Williams, Wilkins Co., 175 p.

Lowell, J.D., and Guilbert, J.M., 1970, Lateral and vertical alteration-mineralization zoning in porphyry copper ore deposits: Economic Geology, v. 65, p. 373–408.

Lowenstern, J.B., 1995, Applications of silicate-melt inclusions to the study of magmatic volatiles, *in* Thompson, J.F.H., ed., Magmas, fluids, and ore deposits: Mineralogical Association of Canada Short Course, v. 23, p. 71–99.

Maksaev, V., Zentilli, M., and Reynolds, P.H., 1988, Geochronológia $^{40}Ar/^{39}Ar$ de depósitos de tipo pórfido cuprífero del Norte Grande de Chile: V Congreso Geologico Chileno, Santiago, 8–12 August 1988, v. I, p. 109–133.

Marsh, T.M., Einaudi, M.T., and McWilliams, M., 1997, $^{40}Ar/^{39}Ar$ geochronology of Cu-Au and Au-Ag mineralization in the Potrerillos district, Chile: Economic Geology, v. 92, p. 784–806.

McCandless, T.E., and Ruiz, J., 1993, Rhenium-osmium evidence for regional mineralization in southwestern North America: Science, v. 261, p. 1282–1286.

McCulloch, M.T., and Woodhead, J.D., 1993, Lead isotopic evidence for deep crustal-scale fluid transport during granite petrogenesis: Geochimica et Cosmochimica Acta, v. 57, p. 659–674.

McKibben, M.A., and Hardie, L.A., 1997, Ore-forming brines in active continental rifts, *in* Barnes, H.L., ed., Geochemistry of hydrothermal ore deposits, 3rd edition: New York, John Wiley, p. 877–935.

McNutt, R.H., Clark, A.H., and Zentilli, M., 1979, Lead isotopic compositions of Andean igneous rocks, Latitudes 26° to 29° S: Petrologic and metallogenic implications: Economic Geology, v. 74, p. 827–837.

Meinert, L.D., Hefton, K.K., Mayes, D., and Tasiran, I., 1997, Geology, zonation, and fluid evolution of the Big Gossan Cu-Au skarn deposit, Ertsberg district, Irian Jaya: Economic Geology, v. 92, p. 509–534.

Meyer, C., and Hemley, J.J., 1967, Wall rock alteration, *in* Barnes, H.L., ed., Geochemistry of hydrothermal ore deposits: New York, Holt, Rinehart, and Winston, p. 166–232.

Montoya, J.W., and Hemley, J.J., 1975, Activity relations and stabilities in alkali feldspar and mica alteration reactions: Economic Geology, v. 70, p. 577–594.

Mukasa, S.B., Vidal, C.E., and Injoque-Espinoza, J., 1990, Pb isotope bearing on the metallogenesis of sulfide ore deposits in central and southern Peru: Economic Geology, v. 85, p. 1438–1446.

Neumann, H., 1948, On hydrothermal differentiation: Economic Geology, v. 43, p. 77–83.

Nielson, R.L., 1976, Recent developments in the study of porphyry copper geology—a review: Canadian Institute of Mining and Metallurgy, Special Volume 15, p. 487–500.

Noble, J.A., 1970, Metal provinces of the western United States: Geological Society of America, Bulletin, v. 81, p. 1607–1624.

Noll, P.D., Jr., Newsom, H.E., Leeman, W.P., and Ryan, J.G, 1996, The role of hydrothermal fluids in the production of subduction zone magmas: Evidence from siderophile and chalcophile trace elements and boron: Geochimica et Cosmochimica Acta, v. 60, p. 587–611.

Norton, D.L., 1982, Fluid and heat transport phenomena typical of copper-bearing pluton environments, *in* Titley, S.R., ed., Advances in geology of porphyry copper deposits of southwestern North America: Tucson, University of Arizona Press, p. 59–72.

Ohmoto, H., 1972, Systematics of sulfur and carbon isotopes in hydrothermal ore deposits: Economic Geology, v. 67, p. 551–578.

—— 1986, Stable isotope geochemistry of ore deposits, *in* Valley, J.W., Taylor, H.P., and O'Neil, J.R., eds., Stable isotopes in high temperature geological processes: Mineralogical Society of America, Reviews in Mineralogy, v. 16, p. 491–599.

Ohmoto, H., and Rye, R.O., 1979, Isotopes of sulfur and carbon, *in* Barnes, H.L., ed., Geochemistry of hydrothermal ore deposits, 2nd edition: New York, John Wiley, p. 509–567.

Page, R.W., and McDougall, I., 1972a, Ages of mineralization of gold and porphyry copper deposits in the New Guinea Highlands: Economic Geology, v. 67, p. 1034–1048.

—— 1972b, Geochronology of the Panguna porphyry copper deposit, Bougainville Island, New Guinea: Economic Geology, v. 67, p. 1065–1074.

Park, C.F., Jr., 1955, Zonal theory of ore deposits: Economic Geology, 50th Anniversary Volume, part I, p. 226–248.

Pierce, F.W., and Bolm, J.G., eds., 1995, Porphyry copper deposits of the American Cordillera: Arizona Geological Society Digest, v. 20, 656 p.

Pitzer, K.S., and Pabalan, R.T., 1986, Thermodynamics of NaCl in steam: Geochimica et Cosmochimica Acta, v. 50, p. 1445–1454.

Plank, T., and Langmuir, C.H., 1993, Tracing trace elements from sediment input to volcanic output at subduction zones: Nature, v. 362, p. 739–743.

Proffett, J.M., Jr., and Dilles, J.H., 1984, Geologic map of the Yerington district, Nevada: Nevada Bureau of Mines and Geology, Map 77, scale, 1:24,000.

Quirt, S., Clark, A.H., Farrar, E., and Sillitoe, R.H., 1971, Potassium-argon ages of porphyry copper deposits in northern and central Chile [abs.]: Geological Society of America Abstracts with Programs, v. 3, p. 676–677.

Ransome, F.L., 1904, Geology and ore deposits of the Bisbee Quadrangle, Arizona: U.S. Geological Survey Professional Paper 21, 168 p.

—— 1907, The association of alunite with gold in the Goldfield district, Nevada: Economic Geology, v. 2, p. 667–692.

—— 1914, Copper deposits near Superior, Arizona: U.S. Geological Survey, Bulletin 540, p.139–158.

—— 1919, The copper deposits of Ray and Miami, Arizona: U.S. Geological Survey Professional Paper 115, 192 p.

Reynolds, T.J., and Beane, R.E., 1985, Evolution of hydrothermal fluid characteristics at the Santa Rita, New Mexico, porphyry copper deposit: Economic Geology, v. 80, p. 1328–1347.

Ridge, J.D., 1967, Changes and developments in the concepts of ore genesis—1933–1967, *in* Ridge, J.D., ed., Ore deposits of the United States, 1933–1967, The Graton-Sales volume: New York, American Institute of Mining, Metallurgical and Petroleum Engineers, v. II, p. 1713–1834.

Roedder, E., 1965, Report on S.E.G. Symposium on the chemistry of ore-forming fluids: Economic Geology, v. 60, p. 1380–1403.

—— 1971, Fluid inclusion studies on the porphyry-type ore deposits at Bingham, Utah, Butte, Montana, and Climax, Colorado: Economic Geology, v. 66, p. 98–120.

—— 1984, Fluid inclusions: Reviews in Mineralogy, v. 12, 644 p.

Rose, A.W., 1970, Zonal relations of wallrock alteration and sulfide distribution at porphyry copper deposits: Economic Geology, v. 65, p. 920–936.

Roseboom, E.H., Jr., and Kullerud, G., 1957, The solidus in the system Cu-Fe-S between 400° and 800°C: Washington, D.C., Carnegie Institute, Geophysical Laboratory Annual Report of the Director, 1957–1958, p. 222–227.

Rye, R.O., Bethke, P.M., and Wasserman, M.D., 1992, The stable isotope geochemistry of acid-sulfate alteration: Economic Geology, v. 87, p. 225–262.

Sakai, H., 1968, Isotopic properties of sulfur compounds in hydrothermal processes: Geochemical Journal, v. 2, p. 29–49.

Sales, R.H., 1913, Ore deposits of Butte, Montana: American Institute of Mining and Metallurgical Engineers, Transactions, v. 46, p. 1–109.

Sales, R.H., and Meyer, C., 1948, Wall rock alteration, Butte, Montana: American Institute of Mining Engineers, Transactions, v. 178, p. 9–35.

—— 1949, Results from preliminary studies of vein formation at Butte, Montana: Economic Geology, v. 44, p. 465–484.

Sasaki, A., Ulriksen, C.E., Sato, K., and Ishihara, S., 1984, Sulfur isotope reconnaissance of porphyry copper and manto-type deposits in Chile and the Philippines: Geological Survey of Japan, Bulletin, v. 35, p. 615–622.

Saunders, J.A., 1994, Silica and gold textures in bonanza ores of the Sleeper deposit, Humboldt County, Nevada: Evidence for colloids and implications for epithermal ore-forming processes: Economic Geology, v. 89, p. 628–638.

Schroeter, T.G., ed., 1995, Porphyry deposits of the northwestern Cordillera of North America: Canadian Institute of Mining, Metallurgy and Petroleum, Special Volume 46, 888 p.

Schwartz, G.M., 1947, Hydrothermal alteration in the "porphyry copper" deposits: Economic Geology, v. 42, p. 319–352.

Seward, T.M., 1981, Metal complex formation in aqueous solutions at elevated temperatures and pressures, *in* Wickman, F., and Rickard, D., eds., Physics and chemistry of the Earth: v. 13–14, p. 113–129.

Sheppard, S.M.F., and Gustafson, L.B., 1976, Oxygen and hydrogen isotopes in the porphyry copper deposit at El Salvador, Chile: Economic Geology, v. 71, p. 1549–1559.

Sheppard, S.M.F., and Taylor, H.P., Jr., 1974, Hydrogen and oxygen isotope evidence for the origins of water in the Boulder batholith and the Butte ore deposits: Economic Geology, v. 69, p. 926–946.

Sheppard, S.M.F., Nielsen, R.L., and Taylor, H.P., Jr., 1969, Oxygen and hydrogen isotope ratios of clay minerals from porphyry copper deposits: Economic Geology, v. 64, p. 755–777.
—— 1971, Hydrogen and oxygen isotope ratios in minerals from porphyry copper deposits: Economic Geology, v. 66, p. 515–542.
Shinohara, H., 1994, Exsolution of immiscible vapor and liquid phases from a crystallizing silicate melt: Implications for chlorine and metal transport: Geochimica et Cosmochimica Acta, v. 58, p. 5215–5221.
—— 1998, Acceptance speech for the 1997 Lindgren award: Economic Geology, v. 93, p. 121–122.
Shinohara, H., and Hedenquist, J.W., 1997, Constraints on magma degassing beneath the Far Southeast porphyry Cu-Au deposit, Philippines: Journal of Petrology, v. 38, p. 1741–1752.
Silberman, M.L., 1983, Geochronology of hydrothermal alteration and mineralization: Geothermal Resources Council, Special Report 13, p. 287–303.
Sillitoe, R.H., 1973, The tops and bottoms of porphyry copper deposits: Economic Geology, v. 68, p. 799–815.
—— 1975, Lead-silver, manganese, and native sulfur mineralization within a stratovolcano, El Queva, northwest Argentina: Economic Geology, v. 70, p. 1190–1201.
—— 1977, Permo-Carboniferous, Upper Cretaceous, and Miocene porphyry copper-type mineralization in the Argentinian Andes: Economic Geology, v. 72, p. 99–109.
—— 1981, Regional aspects of the Andean porphyry copper belt in Chile and Argentina: Institution of Mining and Metallurgy, Transactions, section B, v. 90, B15–B36.
—— 1983, Enargite-bearing massive sulfide deposits high in porphyry copper systems: Economic Geology, v. 78, p. 348–352.
—— 1985, Ore-related breccias in volcanoplutonic arcs: Economic Geology, v. 80, p. 1467–1514.
—— 1988, Epochs of intrusion-related copper mineralization in the Andes: Journal of South American Earth Sciences, v. 1, p. 89–108.
—— 1991, Gold metallogeny of Chile—an introduction: Economic Geology, v. 86, p. 1187–1205.
—— 1992, Gold and copper metallogeny of the central Andes—Past, present, and future exploration objectives: Economic Geology, v. 87, p. 2205–2216.
—— 1993, Gold-rich porphyry copper deposits: Geological model and exploration implications, *in* Kirkham, R.V., Sinclair, W.D., Thorpe, R.I., and Duke, J.M., eds., Mineral deposit modeling: Geological Association of Canada, Special Paper 40, p. 465–478.
—— 1994, Erosion and collapse of volcanoes: Causes of telescoping in intrusion-centered ore deposits: Geology, v. 22, p. 945–948.
—— 1995, Exploration of porphyry copper lithocaps, *in* Mauk, J.L., and St. George, J.D., eds., Proceedings Pan American Conference on Research on Fluid Inclusions Congress 1995: Australasian Institute of Mining and Metallurgy, Publication Series No. 9/95, p. 527–532.
—— 1996, Granites and metal deposits: Episodes, v. 19, p. 126–133.
Sillitoe, R.H., and Gappe, I.M. Jr., 1984, Philippine porphyry copper deposits: Geologic setting and characteristics: Bangkok, United Nations ESCAP, CCOP Technical Publication 14, 89 p.
Sillitoe, R.H., and Hart, S.R., 1984, Lead-isotope signatures of porphyry copper deposits in oceanic and continental settings, Colombian Andes: Geochimica et Cosmochimica Acta, v. 48, p. 2135–2142.
Smith, F.G., 1954, Composition of vein-forming fluids from inclusion data: Economic Geology, v. 49, p. 205–210.
Sourirajan, S., and Kennedy, G.C., 1962, The system H_2O-NaCl at elevated temperatures and pressures: American Journal of Science, v. 260, p. 115–141.
Stein, H.J., Morgan, J.W., Markey, R.J., and Hannah, J.L., 1998, An introduction to Re-Os: what's in it for the mineral industry?: Society of Economic Geologists Newsletter, No. 32, p. 1, 8–15.
Stolper, E., and Newman, S., 1994, The role of water in the petrogenesis of Mariana trough magmas: Earth and Planetary Science Letters, v. 121, p. 293–325.
Sutherland Brown, A., ed., 1976, Porphyry deposits of the Canadian Cordillera: Canadian Institute of Mining and Metallurgy, Special Volume 15, 510 p.
Suzuoki, T., and Epstein, S., 1976, Hydrogen isotope fractionation between OH-bearing minerals and water: Geochimica et Cosmochimica Acta, v. 40, p. 1229–1240.
Sverjensky, D.A., Hemley, J.J., and D'Angelo, W.M., 1991, Thermodynamic assessment of hydrothermal alkali feldspar-mica-aluminosilicate equilibria: Geochimica et Cosmochimica Acta, v. 55, p. 989–1004.
Taylor, B.E., 1986, Magmatic volatiles: Isotopic variation of C, H, and S: Reviews in Mineralogy, v. 16, p. 185–226.
—— 1988, Degassing of rhyolitic magmas: hydrogen isotope evidence and implications for magmatic-hydrothermal ore deposits, *in* Taylor, R.P., and Strong, D.F., eds., Recent advances in the geology of granite-related mineral deposits: Canadian Institute of Mining and Metallurgy, Special Volume 39, p. 33–49.
—— 1992, Degassing of H_2O from rhyolite magma during eruption and shallow intrusion, and the isotopic composition of magmatic water in hydrothermal systems, *in* Hedenquist, J.W., ed., Magmatic contributions to hydrothermal systems: Geological Survey of Japan, Report 279, p. 190–194.
Taylor, B.E., Eichelberger, J.C., and Westrich, H.R., 1983, Hydrogen isotopic evidence of rhyolitic magma degassing during shallow intrusion and eruption: Nature, v. 306, p. 541–545.
Taylor, H.P., Jr., 1974, The application of oxygen and hydrogen isotope studies to problems of hydrothermal alteration and ore deposition: Economic Geology, v. 69, p. 843–883.
—— 1979, Oxygen and hydrogen isotope relationships in hydrothermal mineral deposits, *in* Barnes, H.L., ed., Geochemistry of hydrothermal ore deposits, 2nd edition: New York, John Wiley, p. 236–277.
—— 1997, Oxygen and hydrogen isotope relationships in hydrothermal mineral deposits, *in* Barnes, H.L., ed., Geochemistry of hydrothermal ore deposits, 3rd edition: New York, John Wiley, p. 229–302.
Thompson, J.F.H., 1995, Exploration and research related to porphyry deposits, *in* Schroeter, T.G., ed., Porphyry deposits of the northwestern Cordillera of North America: Canadian Institute of Mining, Metallurgy and Petroleum, Special Volume 46, p. 857–870.
Titley, S.R., ed., 1982, Advances in geology of the porphyry copper deposits, southwestern North America: Tucson, University of Arizona Press, 560 p.
Titley, S.R., 1987, The crustal heritage of silver and gold ratios in Arizona ores: Geological Society of America, Bulletin, v. 99, p. 814–826.
—— 1994, Evolutionary habits of hydrothermal and supergene alteration in intrusion-centered ore systems, southwestern North America, *in* Lentz, D.R., ed., Alteration and alteration processes associated with ore-forming systems: Geological Association of Canada, Short Course Notes, v. 11, p. 237–260.
Titley, S.R., and Beane, R.E., 1981, Porphyry copper deposits, Part 1. Geologic settings, petrology, and tectogenesis: Economic Geology, 75th Anniversary Volume, p. 214–235.
Titley, S.R., and Hicks, C.L., eds., 1966, Geology of the porphyry copper deposits, southwestern North America: Tucson, University of Arizona Press, 287 p.
Westra, G., and Keith, S.B., 1981, Classification and genesis of stockwork molybdenum deposits: Economic Geology, v. 76, p. 844–873.
Whalen, J.B., Britten, R.M., and McDougall, I., 1982, Geochronology and geochemistry of the Frieda River prospect area, Papua New Guinea: Economic Geology, v. 77, p. 592–616.
White, D.E., 1957, Thermal waters of volcanic origin: Geological Society of America, Bulletin, v. 68, p. 1637–1657.
Whitney, J.A., 1975, Vapor generation in a quartz monzonite magma, a synthetic model with application to porphyry ore deposits: Economic Geology, v. 70, p. 346–358.
Williams, T.J., Candela, P.A., and Piccoli, P.M., 1995, The partitioning of copper between silicate melts and two-phase aqueous fluids: An experimental investigation at 1 kbar, 800°C and 0.5 kbar, 850°C: Contributions to Mineralogy and Petrology, v. 121, p. 388–399.
Woitsekhowskaya, M.B., and Hemley, J.J., 1995, Modeling metal transport and deposition in Butte-type hydrothermal systems: Economic Geology, v. 90, p. 1329–1337.
Zaluski, G., Nesbitt, B.E., and Muehlenbachs, K., 1994, Hydrothermal alteration and stable isotope systematics of the Babine porphyry Cu deposits, British Columbia: Implications for fluid evolution of porphyry systems: Economic Geology, v. 89, p. 1518–1541.